Periodic Table of the Elements

Main groups

Transition metals

Main groups

1 / 1A	2 / 2A	3 / 3B	4 / 4B	5 / 5B	6 / 6B	7 / 7B	8 / 8B	9 / 8B	10	11 / 1B	12 / 2B	13 / 3A	14 / 4A	15 / 5A	16 / 6A	17 / 7A	18 / 8A
1 H 1.00794																	2 He 4.002602
3 Li 6.941	4 Be 9.012182											5 B 10.811	6 C 12.0107	7 N 14.0067	8 O 15.9994	9 F 18.998403	10 Ne 20.1797
11 Na 22.989770	12 Mg 24.3050											13 Al 26.981538	14 Si 28.0855	15 P 30.973761	16 S 32.065	17 Cl 35.453	18 Ar 39.948
19 K 39.0983	20 Ca 40.078	21 Sc 44.955910	22 Ti 47.867	23 V 50.9415	24 Cr 51.9961	25 Mn 54.938049	26 Fe 55.845	27 Co 58.933200	28 Ni 58.6934	29 Cu 63.546	30 Zn 65.38	31 Ga 69.723	32 Ge 72.64	33 As 74.92160	34 Se 78.96	35 Br 79.904	36 Kr 83.798
37 Rb 85.4678	38 Sr 87.62	39 Y 88.90585	40 Zr 91.224	41 Nb 92.90638	42 Mo 95.94	43 Tc (98)	44 Ru 101.07	45 Rh 102.90550	46 Pd 106.42	47 Ag 107.8682	48 Cd 112.411	49 In 114.818	50 Sn 118.710	51 Sb 121.760	52 Te 127.60	53 I 126.90447	54 Xe 131.293
55 Cs 132.90545	56 Ba 137.327	71 Lu 174.9668	72 Hf 178.49	73 Ta 180.9479	74 W 183.84	75 Re 186.207	76 Os 190.23	77 Ir 192.217	78 Pt 195.078	79 Au 196.96655	80 Hg 200.59	81 Tl 204.3833	82 Pb 207.2	83 Bi 208.98038	84 Po (209)	85 At (210)	86 Rn (222)
87 Fr (223)	88 Ra (226)	103 Lr (262)	104 Rf (267)	105 Db (268)	106 Sg (271)	107 Bh (272)	108 Hs (270)	109 Mt (276)	110 Ds (281)	111 Rg (280)	112 Cn (285)	113 (284)	114 (289)	115 (288)	116 (293)	117 (293)	118 (294)

*Lanthanide series

57 La 138.9055	58 Ce 140.116	59 Pr 140.90765	60 Nd 144.24	61 Pm (145)	62 Sm 150.36	63 Eu 151.964	64 Gd 157.25	65 Tb 158.92534	66 Dy 162.500	67 Ho 164.93032	68 Er 167.259	69 Tm 168.93421	70 Yb 173.054

†Actinide series

89 Ac (227)	90 Th 232.0381	91 Pa 231.03588	92 U 238.02891	93 Np (237)	94 Pu (244)	95 Am (243)	96 Cm (247)	97 Bk (247)	98 Cf (251)	99 Es (252)	100 Fm (257)	101 Md (258)	102 No (259)

John E. McMurry • Robert C. Fay

Chemistry
CHEM 121

Custom First-semester Edition for the University of North Dakota

Taken from:
Chemistry, Sixth Edition
by John E. McMurry and Robert C. Fay

Cover Art: Courtesy of Photodisc/Getty Images.

Taken from:

Chemistry, Sixth Edition
by John E. McMurry and Robert C. Fay
Copyright © 2012, 2008, 2004, 2001 by Pearson Education, Inc.
Published by Prentice Hall
Upper Saddle River, New Jersey 07458

This special edition published in cooperation with Pearson Learning Solutions.

All trademarks, service marks, registered trademarks, and registered service marks are the property of their respective owners and are used herein for identification purposes only.

Pearson Learning Solutions, 501 Boylston Street, Suite 900, Boston, MA 02116
A Pearson Education Company
www.pearsoned.com

Printed in the United States of America

3 4 5 6 7 8 9 10 VOCR 17 16 15 14 13 12

000200010271646714

JHA

ISBN 10: 1-256-72888-8
ISBN 13: 978-1-256-72888-7

Brief Contents

Contents

8 Thermochemistry: Chemical Energy   266

9 Gases: Their Properties and Behavior   308

10 Liquids, Solids, and Phase Changes   346

Inquiries

Applications

Preface

Francie came away from her first chemistry lecture in a glow. In one hour she found out that everything was made up of atoms which were in continual motion. She grasped the idea that nothing was ever lost or destroyed. Even if something was burned up or rotted away, it did not disappear from the face of the earth; it changed into something else—gases, liquids, and powders. Everything, decided Francie after that first lecture, was vibrant with life and there was no death in chemistry. She was puzzled as to why learned people didn't adopt chemistry as a religion.

—Betty Smith, *A Tree Grows in Brooklyn*

OK, not everyone has such a breathless response to their chemistry lectures, and few would mistake chemistry for a religion, yet chemistry *is* a subject with great logical beauty. Moreover, chemistry is the fundamental, enabling science that underlies many of the great advances of the last century that have so lengthened and enriched our lives. It's study truly can be a fascinating experience.

ABOUT THIS BOOK

Our primary purpose in writing this book has been to fashion a clear and cohesive introduction to chemistry, covering both important principles and important facts. We write to explain chemistry to students today the way we wish it had been explained to us years ago when we were students ourselves. We can't claim that learning chemistry will always be easy, but we *can* promise that we have done our best in planning, writing, and illustrating this book to make the learning process as smooth as possible.

Beginning with atomic structure, the book proceeds to bonding, molecules, and bulk physical properties of substances, and then continues with all the topics necessary for a study of chemical transformations—kinetics, equilibrium, thermodynamics, and electrochemistry. The concepts described in earlier chapters are then applied to discussing more specialized topics, including the chemistry of main-group and transition elements, metals, and modern solid-state materials. Finally, the book concludes with a brief look at organic and biological chemistry.

To help students succeed in learning chemistry, we have put extraordinary effort into this book. Transitions between topics are smooth, explanations are lucid, and reminders of earlier material are frequent. Insofar as possible, distractions within the text are minimized. Each chapter is broken into numerous sections to provide frequent breathers, and each section has a consistent format. Sections generally begin with an explanation of their subject, move to a Worked Example that shows how to solve problems, and end with one or more Problems for the reader to work through. Each chapter concludes with a brief Inquiry that describes an interesting application or extension of the chapter topic. Throughout the book, every attempt has been made to explain chemistry in a visual, intuitive way so that it can be understood by all who give it an honest effort.

NEW TO THE 6th EDITION

In preparing this 6th edition, we have reworked the entire book at the sentence level and made many hundreds of alterations, updates, and small reorganizations to make it as easy as possible for our readers to understand and learn chemistry. In addition, a number of more substantial changes, reorganizations, and rewrites have been made. Among them are the following:

- The text is now shorter than the previous edition by 60 pages.

- Chapter 18 (*Hydrogen, Oxygen and Water*) has been streamlined throughout, and the former Section 18.14 on reactivity of water has been deleted.
- Chapter 19 (*Main-Group Elements*) has been shortened by removing the former Section 19.8 on germanium, tin, and lead, eliminating the coverage of polyphosphoric acids, and integrating the former material on the Haber ammonia synthesis into earlier chapters. Brief discussions of aluminum (Section 19.5) and graphene (Section 19.7) have been added.
- Chapter 22 (*Nuclear Chemistry*) has been shortened and reorganized to focus on the energy changes that take place during nuclear reactions and on fission, fusion, nuclear transmutation, and applications of nuclear chemistry. The former introductory material on nuclear reactions has been moved into Chapter 2 (*Atoms, Molecules, and Ions*), and the coverage of radioactive decay rates has been moved into Chapter 12 (*Chemical Kinetics*).
- The former Chapters 23 and 24 (*Organic Chemistry* and *Biochemistry*) have been shortened and integrated into a new Chapter 23 (*Organic and Biological Chemistry.*)
- Energy and its measurement have moved from Chapter 8 to Chapter 1, and the mole concept has moved from Chapter 3 to Chapter 2 to introduce these important topics earlier.
- Problems and problem solving have also received attention, and more than 300 new problems have been added. The 1st edition of this book pioneered the use of visual, non-numerical, Conceptual Problems, which test the understanding of principles rather than the ability to put numbers into a formula. Every subsequent edition has expanded their use. Don't make the mistake of thinking that these Conceptual Problems are simple just because they don't have numbers. Many are real challenges that will test the ability of any student.
- The art in this new edition has been improved in many ways to make the numbered figures more self-contained, informative, and easily read:
  - The boundaries of numbered figures are more clearly distinguished.
  - The figure numbers are called out in bold red print in the text so that it's easy to find the text corresponding to a given figure.
  - Internal art captions are set off in a different font from art labels so that students can more readily grasp the main points of each illustration.
  - Numerous small explanations are placed directly on the relevant parts of the figures themselves instead of having long captions beneath figures. The effect is to make the text flow naturally into the figures and thereby entice readers to spend more time understanding those figures.
  - Important text within the illustrations is color-coded to focus attention on it.
- The best features of previous editions have been retained:
  - The design remains spacious, readable, and unintimidating.
  - The writing style remains clear and concise.
  - Remember... notes to help students connect concepts from previous chapters to new contexts in subsequent chapters.
  - Worked problems are identified by subject and are immediately followed by a similar problem for students to solve.
  - Each chapter ends with a summary, a list of key words with accompanying page references, and a large set of end-of-chapter problems.
  - Most end-of-chapter problems are classified by text section and paired by topic. These are followed by a group of unclassified Chapter Problems and a final set of Multiconcept Problems, which draw on and connect concepts from several chapters.

We sincerely hope that this new edition will meet the goals we have set for it and that both students and faculty will find it to be friendly, accessible, and above all effective in teaching chemistry.

ACKNOWLEDGEMENTS

Our thanks go to our families and to the many talented people who helped bring this new edition into being. Foremost is Jordan Fantini of Denison University, who joined us as a contributing author for this edition. Jordan offered valuable input on every chapter, wrote many new end-of chapter problems, and wrote several new *INQUIRY* essays. In addition, we are grateful to Terry Haugen, Acquisitions Editor, and Carol DuPont, Assistant Editor, for their insights and suggestions that improved the book, to Erin Gardner, Marketing Manager, who brought new energy to marketing the sixth edition, to Carol Pritchard-Martinez for her work in improving the art program and manuscript development, to Wendy Perez and Gina Cheselka for their production efforts, and to Eric Schrader for his photo research.

We are particularly pleased to acknowledge the outstanding contributions of several colleagues who created the many important supplements that turn a textbook into a complete package:

- Robert Pribush at Butler University, who prepared the accompanying Test Bank and created the Instructor Resource Manual.
- Joseph Topich at Virginia Commonwealth University, who prepared both the full and partial solutions manuals
- Alan Earhart at Southeast Community College and Bradley J. Sieve at Northern Kentucky University, who contributed valuable content for the Instructor Resource DVD.
- Julie Klare at Gwinnett Technical College, who prepared the Student Study Guide to accompany this sixth edition.

In addition, we are grateful to Mingming Xu of West Virginia University and Matt Wise of the University of Colorado at Boulder for error checking the entire text.

Finally, we want to thank our colleagues at so many other institutions who read, criticized, and improved our work.

John McMurry
Robert C. Fay

REVIEWERS OF THE SIXTH EDITION OF *CHEMISTRY*

Tabitha Ruvarashe Chigwada, *West Virginia University*
Claire Cohen-Schmidt, *University of Toledo*
Kyle Wesley Felling, *University of Central Arkansas*
Milton D. Johnston, Jr., *University of South Florida*
Jerome B. Keister, *State University of New York–Buffalo*

Angela J. Nealy, M.S., *MedTech College*
Jennifer Robertson-Honecker, *West Virginia University*
Robert L. Swofford, *Wake Forest University*
Mingming Xu, *West Virginia University*
James Zubricky, *University of Toledo*

REVIEWERS OF THE PREVIOUS EDITIONS OF *CHEMISTRY*

Laura Andersson, *Big Bend Community College*
David Atwood, *University of Kentucky*
Mufeed Basti, *North Carolina A&T State University*
David S. Ballantine, *Northern Illinois University*
Debbie Beard, *Mississippi State University*
Ronald Bost, *North Central Texas University*
Danielle Brabazon, *Loyola College*
Robert Burk, *Carleton University*
Myron Cherry, *Northeastern State University*
Allen Clabo, *Francis Marion University*
Paul Cohen, *University of New Jersey*
Katherine Covert, *West Virginia University*
David De Haan, *University of San Diego*
Nordulf W. G. Debye, *Towson University*
Dean Dickerhoof, *Colorado School of Mines*
Kenneth Dorris, *Lamar University*
Jon A. Draeger, *University of Pittsburgh at Bradford*
Brian Earle, *Cedar Valley College*
Amina El- Ashmawy, *Collin County Community College*
Joseph W. Ellison, *United States Military Academy at West Point*
Erik Eriksson, *College of the Canyons*
Peter M. Fichte, *Coker College*
Kathy Flynn, *College of the Canyons*
Joanne Follweiler, *Lafayette College*
Ted Foster, *Folsom Lake College*
Cheryl Frech, *University of Central Oklahoma*
Mark Freilich, *University of Memphis*
Mark Freitag, *Creighton University*
Travis Fridgen, *Memorial University of Newfoundland*
Jack Goldsmith, *University of South Carolina Aiken*
Thomas Grow, *Pensacola Junior College*
Katherine Geiser-Bush, *Durham Technical Community College*
Mildred Hall, *Clark State University*
Tracy A. Halmi, *Pennsylvania State University Erie*
Keith Hansen, *Lamar University*
Lois Hansen-Polcar, *Cuyahoga Community College*
Wesley Hanson, *John Brown University*
Michael Hauser, *St. Louis Community College–Meramec*
M. Dale Hawley, *Kansas State University*
Patricia Heiden, *Michigan Tech University*
Thomas Hermann, *University of California–San Diego*
Thomas Herrington, *University of San Diego*
Margaret E. Holzer, *California State University–Northridge*
Todd Hopkins, *Baylor University*
Narayan S. Hosmane, *Northern Illinois University*
Jeff Joens, *Florida International University*
Jerry Keister, *University of Buffalo*
Chulsung Kim, *University of Dubuque*
Ranjit Koodali, *University of South Dakota*

Valerie Land, *University of Arkansas Community College*
John Landrum, *Florida International University*
Leroy Laverman, *University of California–Santa Barbara*
Celestia Lau, *Lorain County Community College*
Stephen S. Lawrence, *Saginaw Valley State University*
David Leddy, *Michigan Technological University*
Shannon Lieb, *Butler University*
Karen Linscott, *Tri-County Technical College*
Irving Lipschitz, *University of Massachusetts–Lowell*
Rudy Luck, *Michigan Technological University*
Ashley Mahoney, *Bethel College*
Jack F. McKenna, *St. Cloud State University*
Iain McNab, *University of Toronto*
Christina Mewhinney, *Eastfield College*
David Miller, *California State University–Northridge*
Rebecca S. Miller, *Texas Tech University*
Abdul Mohammed, *North Carolina A&T State University*
Linda Mona, *United States Naval Academy*
Edward Mottell, *Rose-Hulman Institute*
Gayle Nicoll, *Texas Technological University*
Allyn Ontko, *University of Wyoming*
Robert H. Paine, *Rochester Institute of Technology*
Cynthia N. Peck, *Delta College*
Eileen Pérez, *University of South Florida*
Michael R. Ross, *College of St. Benedict/St. John's University*
Lev Ryzhkov, *Towson University*
Svein Saebo, *Mississippi State University*
John Schreifels, *George Mason University*
Patricia Schroeder, *Johnson County Community College*
David Shoop, *John Brown University*
Penny Snetsinger, *Sacred Heart University*
Robert L. Snipp, *Creighton University*
Steven M. Socol, *McHenry County College*
Thomas E. Sorensen, *University of Wisconsin–Milwaukee*
L. Sreerama, *St. Cloud State University*
Keith Stein, *University of Missouri–St. Louis*
Beth Steiner, *University of Akron*
Kelly Sullivan, *Creighton University*
Susan Sutheimer, *Green Mountain College*
Andrew Sykes, *University of South Dakota*
Erach Talaty, *Wichita State University*
Edwin Thall, *Florida Community College at Jacksonville*
Donald Van Derveer, *Georgia Institute of Technology*
John B. Vincent, *University of Alabama*
Steve Watton, *Virginia Commonwealth University*
Marcy Whitney, *University of Alabama*
James Wu, *Tarrant County Community College*
Crystal Lin Yau, *Towson University*

Supplements

FOR THE STUDENT

MasteringChemistry® **(http://www.masteringchemistry.com)** is the most effective, widely used online tutorial, homework and assessment system for chemistry. It helps instructors maximize class time with customizable, easy-to-assign, and automatically graded assessments that motivate students to learn outside of class and arrive prepared for lecture. These assessments can easily be customized and personalized by instructors to suit their individual teaching style. The powerful gradebook provides unique insight into student and class performance even before the first test. As a result, instructors can spend class time where students need it most.

Pearson eText. Pearson eText gives students access to the text whenever and wherever they have access to the Internet. The Pearson eText pages look exactly like the printed text, and include powerful interactive and customization functions. Users can create notes, highlight text, create book marks, zoom, view in single-page or two-page format, and so forth.

Selected Solutions Manual (0-321-72726-6) by Joseph Topich, Virginia Commonwealth University. This manual contains solutions to all in-chapter problems and even-numbered end-of-chapter problems.

Study Guide (0-321-72724-X) by Julie Klare at Gwinnett Technical College. For each chapter, the Study Guide includes learning goals, an overview, progressive review section with worked examples, and self-tests with answers.

Laboratory Manual (0-321-72720-7) by Stephanie Dillon at Florida State University. This manual contains 27 experiments. that focus on real-world applications. Each experiment is specifically referenced to the sixth edition of Chemistry and corresponds with one or more topics covered in each chapter.

FOR THE INSTRUCTOR

Instructor Resource Center on DVD (0-321-72341-4) This DVD provides an integrated collection of resources designed to enhance your classroom lectures. This DVD features all art from the sixth edition in JPG and PDF format for high resolution printing as well as four pre-built PowerPoint presentations. The first presentation contains all images, figures and tables; the second includes a completely modifiable lecture outline; the third contains worked in chapter sample exercises; and the fourth contains "Clicker" questions to be used with the Classroom Response System. Also included are movies and animations, which can be easily inserted into your lecture presentations. For test preparation, this DVD also contains both the Word and Test-Gen versions of the Printed Test Bank designed to accompany the sixth edition which allows you to create and tailor exams to your students' needs. Finally, the Instructor Resource Manual is also included.

Solutions Manual (0-321-72336-8) by Joseph Topich, Virginia Commonwealth University. This solutions manual provides worked-out solutions to all in-chapter, conceptual, and end-of-chapter questions and problems. With instructor's permission, this manual may be made available to students.

Printed Test Bank (0-321-72723-1) by Robert A. Pribush, Butler University. The printed Test Bank contains nearly 4,400 multiple-choice questions.

Instructor Resource Manual (0-321-72339-2) by Robert A. Pribush, Butler University. This manual contains teaching tips, common misconceptions, lecture outlines, and suggested chapter learning goals for students, as well as lecture/laboratory demonstrations and literature references. It also describes the various resources, such as printed test bank questions, animations, and movies that are available to instructors.

BlackBoard Test Bank (0-321-72721-5) Available for download on the Instructor Resource Center.

WebCT Test Bank (0-321-72340-6) Available for download on the Instructor Resource Center.

About the Authors

John McMurry (*left*), educated at Harvard and Columbia, has taught more than 20,000 students in general and organic chemistry over a 40-year period. An emeritus Professor of Chemistry at Cornell University, Dr. McMurry previously spent 13 years on the faculty at the University of California at Santa Cruz. He has received numerous awards, including the Alfred P. Sloan Fellowship (1969–71), the National Institute of Health Career Development Award (1975–80), the Alexander von Humboldt Senior Scientist Award (1986–87), and the Max Planck Research Award (1991). With the publication of this new edition, he has now authored or coauthored 34 textbooks in various fields of chemistry.

Robert C. Fay (*right*), Professor Emeritus at Cornell University, taught general and inorganic chemistry at Cornell for 45 years beginning in 1962. Known for his clear, well-organized lectures, Dr. Fay was the 1980 recipient of the Clark Distinguished Teaching Award. He has also taught as a visiting professor at Harvard University and the University of Bologna (Italy). A Phi Beta Kappa graduate of Oberlin College, Dr. Fay received his Ph.D. from the University of Illinois. He has been an NSF Science Faculty Fellow at the University of East Anglia and the University of Sussex (England) and a NATO/Heineman Senior Fellow at Oxford University.

CHAPTER 1

Chemistry: Matter and Measurement

Instruments for scientific measurements have changed greatly over the centuries. In the 18th century, latitude was determined using this astrolabe.

CONTENTS

Life has changed more in the past two centuries than in all the previously recorded span of human history. Earth's population has increased more than fivefold since 1800 and life expectancy has nearly doubled because of our ability to synthesize medicines, control diseases, and increase crop yields. Methods of transportation have changed from horses and buggies to automobiles and airplanes because of our ability to harness the energy in petroleum. Many goods are now made of polymers and ceramics instead of wood and metal because of our ability to manufacture materials with properties unlike any found in nature.

In one way or another, all these changes involve **chemistry**, the study of the composition, properties, and transformations of matter. Chemistry is deeply involved in both the changes that take place in nature and the profound social changes of the past two centuries. In addition, chemistry is central to the current revolution in molecular biology that is revealing the details of how life is genetically controlled. No educated person today can understand the modern world without a basic knowledge of chemistry.

▲ The sequence of the approximately 5.8 billion nucleic acid units, or *nucleotides*, present in the human genome has been determined using instruments like this.

1.1 APPROACHING CHEMISTRY: EXPERIMENTATION

By opening this book, you have already decided that you need to know more about chemistry. Perhaps you want to learn how medicines are made, how genes can be sequenced and manipulated, how fertilizers and pesticides work, how living organisms function, how new high-temperature ceramics are used in space vehicles, or how microelectronic circuits are etched onto silicon chips. How do you approach chemistry?

One way to approach chemistry or any other science is to look around you and try to think of logical explanations for what you see. You would certainly observe, for instance, that different substances have different forms and appearances. Some substances are gases, some are liquids, and some are solids; some are hard and shiny, but others are soft and dull. You'd also observe that different substances behave differently. Iron rusts but gold does not; copper conducts electricity but sulfur doesn't. How can these and a vast number of other observations be explained?

▲ Gold, one of the most valuable of elements, has been prized since antiquity for its beauty and resistance to corrosion.

▲ Iron, although widely used as a structural and building material, corrodes easily.

In fact, the natural world is far too complex to be understood by looking and thinking alone, so a more active approach is needed. Specific questions must be asked, and experiments must be carried out to find their answers. Only when the results of many experiments are known can we devise an interpretation, or *hypothesis*, that explains the results. The hypothesis, in turn, can be used to make more predictions and to suggest more experiments until a consistent explanation, or **theory**, is finally arrived at.

It's important to keep in mind as you study chemistry or any other science that scientific theories are not laws of nature and can never be absolutely proven. There's always the chance that a new experiment might give results that can't be explained by present theory. All a theory can do is to represent the best explanation that we can come up with at the present time. If new experiments uncover results that present theories can't explain, the theories will have to be modified or perhaps even replaced.

1.2 CHEMISTRY AND THE ELEMENTS

Everything you see around you is formed from one or more of 118 presently known *elements*. An **element** is a fundamental substance that can't be chemically changed or broken down into anything simpler. Mercury, silver, and sulfur are common examples, as listed in Table 1.1.

▲ Samples of mercury, silver, and sulfur (clockwise from top left).

TABLE 1.1   Names and Symbols of Some Common Elements. Latin names from which the symbols of some elements are derived are shown in parentheses.

Aluminum	Al	Chlorine	Cl	Manganese	Mn	Copper (*cuprum*)	Cu
Argon	Ar	Fluorine	F	Nitrogen	N	Iron (*ferrum*)	Fe
Barium	Ba	Helium	He	Oxygen	O	Lead (*plumbum*)	Pb
Boron	B	Hydrogen	H	Phosphorus	P	Mercury (*hydrargyrum*)	Hg
Bromine	Br	Iodine	I	Silicon	Si	Potassium (*kalium*)	K
Calcium	Ca	Lithium	Li	Sulfur	S	Silver (*argentum*)	Ag
Carbon	C	Magnesium	Mg	Zinc	Zn	Sodium (*natrium*)	Na

Actually, the previous statement about everything being made of one or more of 118 elements is an exaggeration because only about 90 of the 118 occur naturally. The remaining 28 have been produced artificially by nuclear chemists using high-energy particle accelerators.

Furthermore, only 83 of the 90 or so naturally occurring elements are found in any appreciable abundance. Hydrogen is thought to account for approximately 75% of the observed mass in the universe; oxygen and silicon together account for 75% of the mass of the Earth's crust; and oxygen, carbon, and hydrogen make up more than 90% of the mass of the human body (**Figure 1.1**). By contrast, there is probably less than 20 grams of the element francium (Fr) dispersed over the entire Earth at any one time. Francium is an unstable radioactive element, atoms of which are continually being formed and destroyed. We'll discuss radioactivity in Chapter 2.

For simplicity, chemists refer to specific elements using one- or two-letter symbols. As shown by the examples in Table 1.1, the first letter of an element's symbol is always capitalized and the second letter, if any, is lowercase. Many of the symbols are just the first one or two letters of the element's English name: H = hydrogen, C = carbon, Al = aluminum, and so forth. Other symbols derive from Latin or other languages: Na = sodium (Latin, *natrium*), Pb = lead (Latin, *plumbum*), W = tungsten (German, *wolfram*). The names, symbols, and other information about all 118 known elements are given inside the front cover of this book, organized in a format you've undoubtedly seen before called the **periodic table**.

(a) Relative abundance on Earth

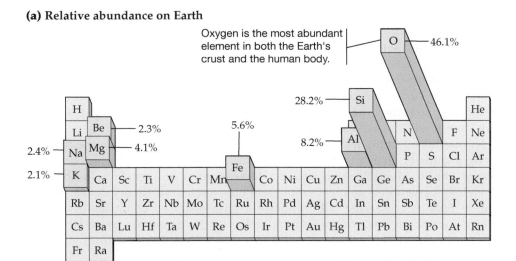

Oxygen is the most abundant element in both the Earth's crust and the human body.

Figure 1.1
Estimated elemental composition by mass percent of (a) the Earth's crust and (b) the human body. Only the major constituents are shown in each case; small amounts of many other elements are also present.

(b) Relative abundance in the human body

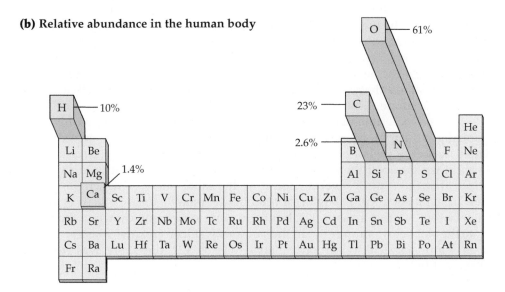

▶ **PROBLEM 1.1** Look at the alphabetical list of elements inside the front cover, and find the symbols for the following elements:

  (a) Cadmium (used in batteries)

  (b) Antimony (used in alloys with other metals)

  (c) Americium (used in smoke detectors)

▶ **PROBLEM 1.2** Look at the alphabetical list of elements inside the front cover, and tell what elements the following symbols represent:

  (a) Ag   **(b)** Rh   **(c)** Re   **(d)** Cs   **(e)** Ar   **(f)** As

1.3 ELEMENTS AND THE PERIODIC TABLE

Ten elements have been known since the beginning of recorded history: antimony (Sb), carbon (C), copper (Cu), gold (Au), iron (Fe), lead (Pb), mercury (Hg), silver (Ag), sulfur (S), and tin (Sn). The first "new" element to be found in several thousand years was arsenic (As), discovered in about 1250. In fact, only 24 elements were known when the United States was founded in 1776.

▲ Left to right, samples of chlorine, bromine, and iodine, one of Döbereiner's triads of elements with similar chemical properties.

As the pace of scientific discovery quickened in the late 1700s and early 1800s, chemists began to look for similarities among elements that might allow general conclusions to be drawn. Particularly important among the early successes was Johann Döbereiner's observation in 1829 that there were several *triads*, or groups of three elements, that appeared to behave similarly. Calcium (Ca), strontium (Sr), and barium (Ba) form one such triad; chlorine (Cl), bromine (Br), and iodine (I) form another; and lithium (Li), sodium (Na), and potassium (K) form a third. By 1843, 16 such triads were known and chemists were searching for an explanation.

Numerous attempts were made in the mid-1800s to account for the similarities among groups of elements, but the breakthrough came in 1869 when the Russian chemist Dmitri Mendeleev created the forerunner of the modern periodic table. Mendeleev's creation is an ideal example of how a scientific theory develops. At first there is only disconnected information—a large number of elements and many observations about their properties and behavior. As more and more facts become known, people try to organize the data in ways that make sense until ultimately a consistent hypothesis emerges.

A good hypothesis must do two things: It must explain known facts, and it must make predictions about phenomena yet unknown. If the predictions are tested and found true, then the hypothesis is a good one and will stand until additional facts are discovered that require it to be modified or discarded. Mendeleev's hypothesis about how known chemical information could be organized passed all tests. Not only did the periodic table arrange data in a useful and consistent way to explain known facts about chemical reactivity, it also led to several remarkable predictions that were later found to be accurate.

Using the experimentally observed chemistry of the elements as his primary organizing principle, Mendeleev arranged the known elements in order of the relative masses of their atoms with hydrogen = 1 (called their *atomic masses*, Section 2.6) and then grouped them according to their chemical reactivity. On so doing, he realized that there were several "holes" in the table, some of which are shown in **Figure 1.2**. The chemical behavior of aluminum (relative mass ≈ 27.3) is similar to that of boron (relative mass ≈ 11), but there was no element known at the time that fit into the slot below aluminum. In the same way, silicon (relative mass ≈ 28) is similar in many respects to carbon (relative mass ≈ 12), but there was no element known that fit below silicon.

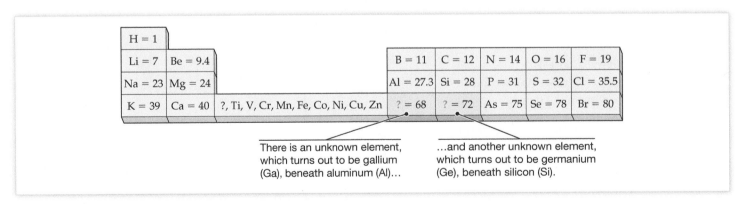

There is an unknown element, which turns out to be gallium (Ga), beneath aluminum (Al)…

…and another unknown element, which turns out to be germanium (Ge), beneath silicon (Si).

Figure 1.2
A portion of Mendeleev's periodic table. The table shows the relative masses of atoms as known at the time and some of the holes representing unknown elements.

Looking at the holes in the table, Mendeleev predicted that two then-unknown elements existed and might be found at some future time. Furthermore, he predicted with remarkable accuracy what the properties of these unknown elements would be. The element immediately below aluminum, which he called *eka*-aluminum from a Sanskrit word meaning "first," should have a relative mass near 68 and should have a low melting point. Gallium, discovered in 1875, has exactly these properties. The

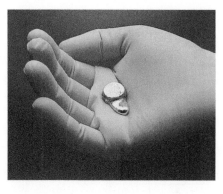

▲ Gallium is a shiny, low-melting metal.

▲ Germanium is a hard, gray semimetal.

element below silicon, which Mendeleev called *eka*-silicon, should have a relative mass near 72 and should be dark gray in color. Germanium, discovered in 1886, fits the description perfectly (Table 1.2).

TABLE 1.2   A Comparison of Predicted and Observed Properties for Gallium (*eka*-Aluminum) and Germanium (*eka*-Silicon)

Element	Property	Mendeleev's Prediction	Observed Property
Gallium	Relative mass	68	69.7
	Density	5.9 g/cm^3	5.91 g/cm^3
	Melting point	Low	29.8 °C
Germanium	Relative mass	72	72.6
	Density	5.5 g/cm^3	5.35 g/cm^3
	Color	Dark gray	Light gray

In the modern periodic table, shown in Figure 1.3, elements are placed on a grid with 7 horizontal rows, called **periods**, and 18 vertical columns, called **groups**. When organized in this way, *the elements in a given group have similar chemical properties.* Lithium, sodium, potassium, and the other metallic elements in group 1A behave similarly. Beryllium, magnesium, calcium, and the other elements in group 2A behave similarly. Fluorine, chlorine, bromine, and the other elements in group 7A behave similarly, and so on throughout the table. (Mendeleev, by the way, was completely unaware of the existence of the group 8A elements—He, Ne, Ar, Kr, Xe, and Rn—because none were known when he constructed his table. All are colorless, odorless gases with little or no chemical reactivity, and none were discovered until 1894, when argon was first isolated.)

The overall form of the periodic table is well accepted, but chemists in different countries have historically used different conventions for labeling the groups. To resolve these difficulties, an international standard calls for numbering the groups from 1 to 18 going left to right. This standard has not yet found complete acceptance, however, and we'll continue to use the U.S. system of numbers and capital letters— group 3B instead of group 3 and group 7A instead of group 17, for example. Labels for the newer system are also shown in Figure 1.3.

One further note: There are actually 32 groups in the periodic table rather than 18, but to make the table fit manageably on a page, the 14 elements beginning with lanthanum (the *lanthanides*) and the 14 beginning with actinium (the *actinides*) are pulled out and shown below the others. These groups are not numbered.

We'll see repeatedly throughout this book that the periodic table of the elements is the most important organizing principle in chemistry. The time you take now to

Atomic Number
Chemical symbol

1 H																	2 He
3 Li	4 Be											5 B	6 C	7 N	8 O	9 F	10 Ne
11 Na	12 Mg											13 Al	14 Si	15 P	16 S	17 Cl	18 Ar
19 K	20 Ca	21 Sc	22 Ti	23 V	24 Cr	25 Mn	26 Fe	27 Co	28 Ni	29 Cu	30 Zn	31 Ga	32 Ge	33 As	34 Se	35 Br	36 Kr
37 Rb	38 Sr	39 Y	40 Zr	41 Nb	42 Mo	43 Tc	44 Ru	45 Rh	46 Pd	47 Ag	48 Cd	49 In	50 Sn	51 Sb	52 Te	53 I	54 Xe
55 Cs	56 Ba	71 Lu	72 Hf	73 Ta	74 W	75 Re	76 Os	77 Ir	78 Pt	79 Au	80 Hg	81 Tl	82 Pb	83 Bi	84 Po	85 At	86 Rn
87 Fr	88 Ra	103 Lr	104 Rf	105 Db	106 Sg	107 Bh	108 Hs	109 Mt	110 Ds	111 Rg	112 Cn	113	114	115	116	117	118

57 La	58 Ce	59 Pr	60 Nd	61 Pm	62 Sm	63 Eu	64 Gd	65 Tb	66 Dy	67 Ho	68 Er	69 Tm	70 Yb
89 Ac	90 Th	91 Pa	92 U	93 Np	94 Pu	95 Am	96 Cm	97 Bk	98 Cf	99 Es	100 Fm	101 Md	102 No

Figure 1.3
The periodic table. Each element is identified by a one- or two-letter symbol and is characterized by an atomic number. The table begins with hydrogen (H, atomic number 1) in the upper left-hand corner and continues to the yet unnamed element with atomic number 118. The 14 elements beginning with lanthanum (La, atomic number 57) and the 14 elements beginning with actinium (Ac, atomic number 89) are pulled out and shown below the others.

familiarize yourself with the layout and organization of the periodic table will pay off later on. Notice in Figure 1.3, for instance, that there is a regular progression in the size of the seven periods (rows). The first period has only 2 elements, hydrogen (H) and helium (He); the second and third periods have 8 elements each; the fourth and fifth periods have 18 elements each; and the sixth and seventh periods, which include the lanthanides and actinides, have 32 elements each. We'll see in Chapter 5 that this regular progression in the periodic table reflects a similar regularity in the structure of atoms.

Notice also that not all groups in the periodic table have the same number of elements. The two larger groups on the left and the six larger groups on the right are called the **main groups**. Most of the elements on which life is based—carbon, hydrogen, nitrogen, oxygen, and phosphorus, for instance—are main-group elements. The 10 smaller groups in the middle of the table are called the **transition metal groups**. Most of the metals you're probably familiar with—iron, copper, zinc, and gold, for instance—are transition metals. And the 14 groups shown separately at the bottom of the table are called the **inner transition metal groups**.

1.4 SOME CHEMICAL PROPERTIES OF THE ELEMENTS

Any characteristic that can be used to describe or identify matter is called a **property**. Examples include volume, amount, odor, color, and temperature. Still other properties include such characteristics as melting point, solubility, and chemical behavior. For example, we might list some properties of sodium chloride (table salt) by saying that it melts at 1474 °F (or 801 °C), dissolves in water, and undergoes a chemical reaction when it comes into contact with a silver nitrate solution.

Properties can be classified as either *intensive* or *extensive*, depending on whether the value of the property changes with the amount of the sample. **Intensive properties**, like temperature and melting point, have values that do not depend on the amount of sample: a small ice cube might have the same temperature as a massive iceberg. **Extensive properties**, like length and volume, have values that *do* depend on the sample size: an ice cube is much smaller than an iceberg.

Properties can also be classified as either *physical* or *chemical*, depending on whether the property involves a change in the chemical makeup of a substance. **Physical properties** are characteristics that do not involve a change in a sample's chemical makeup, whereas **chemical properties** are characteristics that *do* involve a change in chemical makeup. The melting point of ice, for instance, is a physical property because melting causes the water to change only in form, from solid to liquid, but not in chemical makeup. The rusting of an iron bicycle left in the rain is a chemical property, however, because iron combines with oxygen and moisture from the air to give the new substance, rust. Table 1.3 lists other examples of both physical and chemical properties.

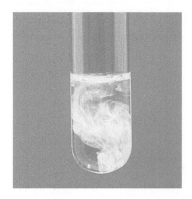

▲ Addition of a solution of silver nitrate to a solution of sodium chloride yields a white precipitate of solid silver chloride.

TABLE 1.3   Some Examples of Physical and Chemical Properties

Physical Properties		Chemical Properties
Temperature	Amount	Rusting (of iron)
Color	Odor	Combustion (of gasoline)
Melting point	Solubility	Tarnishing (of silver)
Electrical conductivity	Hardness	Hardening (of cement)

As noted previously, the elements in a group of the periodic table often show remarkable similarities in their chemical properties. Look at the following groups, for instance, to see some examples:

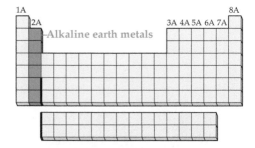

- **Group 1A—Alkali metals** Lithium (Li), sodium (Na), potassium (K), rubidium (Rb), and cesium (Cs) are soft, silvery metals. All react rapidly, often violently, with water to form products that are highly alkaline, or basic—hence the name *alkali metals*. Because of their high reactivity, the alkali metals are never found in nature in the pure state but only in combination with other elements. Francium (Fr) is also an alkali metal but, as noted previously, it is so rare that little is known about it.

  Note that group 1A also contains hydrogen (H) even though, as a colorless gas, it is completely different in appearance and behavior from the alkali metals. We'll see the reason for this classification in Section 5.13.

- **Group 2A—Alkaline earth metals** Beryllium (Be), magnesium (Mg), calcium (Ca), strontium (Sr), barium (Ba), and radium (Ra) are also lustrous, silvery metals but are less reactive than their neighbors in group 1A. Like the alkali metals, the alkaline earths are never found in nature in the pure state.

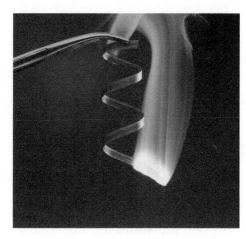

▲ Sodium, one of the alkali metals, reacts violently with water to yield hydrogen gas and an alkaline (basic) solution.

▲ Magnesium, one of the alkaline earth metals, burns in air.

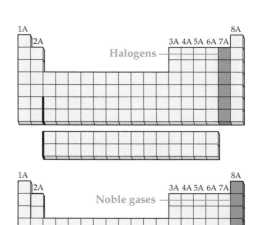

- **Group 7A—Halogens** Fluorine (F), chlorine (Cl), bromine (Br), and iodine (I), are colorful, corrosive nonmetals. They are found in nature only in combination with other elements, such as with sodium in table salt (sodium chloride, NaCl). In fact, the group name *halogen* is taken from the Greek word *hals*, meaning "salt." Astatine (At) is also a halogen, but it exists in such tiny amounts that little is known about it.

- **Group 8A—Noble gases** Helium (He), neon (Ne), argon (Ar), krypton (Kr), xenon (Xe), and radon (Rn) are colorless gases with very low chemical reactivity. Helium and neon don't combine with any other element; argon, krypton, and xenon combine with very few.

As indicated in Figure 1.3, the elements of the periodic table are often divided into three major categories: metals, nonmetals, and semimetals.

◀ Bromine, a halogen, is a corrosive dark red liquid at room temperature.

◀ Neon, one of the noble gases, is used in neon lights and signs.

- **Metals** Metals, the largest category of elements, are found on the left side of the periodic table, bounded on the right by a zigzag line running from boron (B) at the top to astatine (At) at the bottom. The metals are easy to characterize by their appearance. All except mercury are solid at room temperature, and most have the silvery shine we normally associate with metals. In addition, metals are generally malleable rather than brittle, can be twisted and drawn into wires without breaking, and are good conductors of heat and electricity.

- **Nonmetals** Except for hydrogen, nonmetals are found on the right side of the periodic table and, like metals, are easy to characterize by their appearance. Eleven of the seventeen nonmetals are gases, one is a liquid (bromine), and only five are solids at room temperature (carbon, phosphorus, sulfur, selenium, and iodine). None are silvery in appearance, and several are brightly colored. The solid nonmetals are brittle rather than malleable and are poor conductors of heat and electricity.

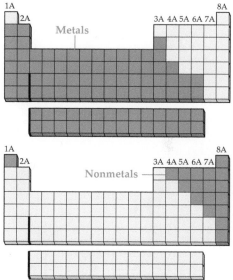

▲ Lead, aluminum, copper, gold, iron, and silver (clockwise from left) are typical metals. All conduct electricity and can be drawn into wires.

▲ Bromine, carbon, phosphorus, and sulfur (clockwise from top left) are typical nonmetals. None conduct electricity or can be made into wires.

- **Semimetals** Seven of the nine elements adjacent to the zigzag boundary between metals and nonmetals—boron, silicon, germanium, arsenic, antimony, tellurium, and astatine—are called semimetals because their properties are intermediate between those of their metallic and nonmetallic neighbors. Although most are silvery in appearance and all are solid at room temperature, semimetals are brittle rather than malleable and tend to be poor conductors of heat and electricity. Silicon, for example, is a widely used *semiconductor*, a substance whose electrical conductivity is intermediate between that of a metal and an insulator.

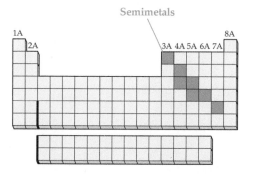

▶ **PROBLEM 1.3** Identify the following elements as metals, nonmetals, or semimetals:

(a) Ti **(b)** Te **(c)** Se **(d)** Sc **(e)** At **(f)** Ar

CONCEPTUAL PROBLEM 1.4 The three so-called coinage metals are located near the middle of the periodic table. Identify them.

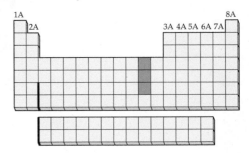

1.5 EXPERIMENTATION AND MEASUREMENT

Chemistry is an experimental science. But if our experiments are to be reproducible, we must be able to describe fully the substances we're working with—their amounts, volumes, temperatures, and so forth. Thus, one of the most important requirements in chemistry is that we have a way to measure things.

Under an international agreement concluded in 1960, scientists throughout the world now use the International System of Units for measurement, abbreviated **SI** for the French *Système Internationale d'Unités*. Based on the metric system, which is used in all industrialized countries of the world except the United States, the SI system has seven fundamental units (Table 1.4). These seven fundamental units, along with others derived from them, suffice for all scientific measurements. We'll look at three of the most common units in this chapter—those for mass, length, and temperature—and will discuss others as the need arises in later chapters.

TABLE 1.4 The Seven Fundamental SI Units of Measure

Physical Quantity	Name of Unit	Abbreviation
Mass	kilogram	kg
Length	meter	m
Temperature	kelvin	K
Amount of substance	mole	mol
Time	second	s
Electric current	ampere	A
Luminous intensity	candela	cd

One problem with any system of measurement is that the sizes of the units often turn out to be inconveniently large or small. For example, a chemist describing the diameter of a sodium atom (0.000 000 000 372 m) would find the meter (m) to be inconveniently large, but an astronomer describing the average distance from the Earth to the Sun (150,000,000,000 m) would find the meter to be inconveniently small. For this reason, SI units are modified through the use of prefixes when they refer to either smaller or larger quantities. Thus, the prefix *milli*- means one-thousandth, and a *milli*meter (mm) is 1/1000 of 1 meter. Similarly, the prefix *kilo*- means one thousand, and a *kilo*meter (km) is 1000 meters. [Note that the SI unit for mass (kilogram) already contains the *kilo*- prefix.] A list of prefixes is shown in Table 1.5, with the most commonly used ones in red.

Notice how numbers that are either very large or very small are indicated in Table 1.5 using an exponential format called **scientific notation**. For example, the

TABLE 1.5 Some Prefixes for Multiples of SI Units. The most commonly used prefixes are shown in red.

Factor	Prefix	Symbol	Example
$1{,}000{,}000{,}000{,}000 = 10^{12}$	tera	T	1 teragram (Tg) = 10^{12} g
$1{,}000{,}000{,}000 = 10^{9}$	giga	G	1 gigameter (Gm) = 10^{9} m
$1{,}000{,}000 = 10^{6}$	mega	M	1 megameter (Mm) = 10^{6} m
$1000 = 10^{3}$	kilo	k	1 kilogram (kg) = 10^{3} g
$100 = 10^{2}$	hecto	h	1 hectogram (hg) = 100 g
$10 = 10^{1}$	deka	da	1 dekagram (dag) = 10 g
$0.1 = 10^{-1}$	deci	d	1 decimeter (dm) = 0.1 m
$0.01 = 10^{-2}$	centi	c	1 centimeter (cm) = 0.01 m
$0.001 = 10^{-3}$	milli	m	1 milligram (mg) = 0.001 g
$*0.000\ 001 = 10^{-6}$	micro	μ	1 micrometer (μm) = 10^{-6} m
$*0.000\ 000\ 001 = 10^{-9}$	nano	n	1 nanosecond (ns) = 10^{-9} s
$*0.000\ 000\ 000\ 001 = 10^{-12}$	pico	p	1 picosecond (ps) = 10^{-12} s
$*0.000\ 000\ 000\ 000\ 001 = 10^{-15}$	femto	f	1 femtomole (fmol) = 10^{-15} mol

*For very small numbers, it is becoming common in scientific work to leave a thin space every three digits to the right of the decimal point, analogous to the comma placed every three digits to the left of the decimal point in large numbers.

number 55,000 is written in scientific notation as 5.5×10^4, and the number 0.003 20 as 3.20×10^{-3}. Review Appendix A if you are uncomfortable with scientific notation or if you need to brush up on how to do mathematical manipulations on numbers with exponents.

Notice also that all measurements contain both a number and a unit label. A number alone is not much good without a unit to define it. If you asked a friend how far it was to the nearest tennis court, the answer "3" alone wouldn't tell you much. 3 blocks? 3 kilometers? 3 miles?

▶ **PROBLEM 1.5** Express the following quantities in scientific notation:
(a) The diameter of a sodium atom, 0.000 000 000 372 m
(b) The distance from the Earth to the Sun, 150,000,000,000 m

▶ **PROBLEM 1.6** What units do the following abbreviations represent?
(a) μg   (b) dm   (c) ps   (d) kA   (e) mmol

1.6 MASS AND ITS MEASUREMENT

Mass is defined as the amount of *matter* in an object. **Matter,** in turn, is a catchall term used to describe anything with a physical presence—anything you can touch, taste, or smell. (Stated more scientifically, matter is anything that has mass.) Mass is measured in SI units by the **kilogram** (**kg**; 1 kg = 2.205 U.S. lb). Because the kilogram is too large for many purposes in chemistry, the metric **gram** (**g**; 1 g = 0.001 kg), the **milligram** (**mg**; 1 mg = 0.001 g = 10^{-6} kg), and the **microgram** (μ**g**; 1 μg = 0.001 mg = 10^{-6} g = 10^{-9} kg) are more commonly used. (The symbol μ is the lowercase Greek letter mu.) One gram is a bit less than half the mass of a new U.S. dime.

$$1\ \text{kg} = 1000\ \text{g} = 1{,}000{,}000\ \text{mg} = 1{,}000{,}000{,}000\ \mu\text{g} \quad (2.205\ \text{lb})$$
$$1\ \text{g} = 1000\ \text{mg} = 1{,}000{,}000\ \mu\text{g} \quad (0.035\ 27\ \text{oz})$$
$$1\ \text{mg} = 1000\ \mu\text{g}$$

▲ The mass of a U.S. dime is approximately 2.27 g.

The standard kilogram is set as the mass of a cylindrical bar of platinum–iridium alloy stored in a vault in a suburb of Paris, France. There are 40 copies of this bar distributed throughout the world, with two (Numbers 4 and 20) stored at the U.S. National Institute of Standards and Technology near Washington, D.C.

The terms "mass" and "weight," although often used interchangeably, have quite different meanings. *Mass* is a physical property that measures the amount of matter in an object, whereas *weight* measures the force with which gravity pulls on an object. Mass is independent of an object's location: your body has the same amount of matter whether you're on Earth or on the moon. Weight, however, *does* depend on an object's location. If you weigh 140 lb on Earth, you would weigh only about 23 lb on the moon, which has a lower gravity than the Earth.

At the same location on Earth, two objects with identical masses experience an identical pull of the Earth's gravity and have identical weights. Thus, the mass of an object can be measured by comparing its weight to the weight of a reference standard of known mass. Much of the confusion between mass and weight is simply due to a language problem. We speak of "weighing" when we really mean that we are measuring mass by comparing two weights. Figure 1.4 shows balances typically used for measuring mass in the laboratory.

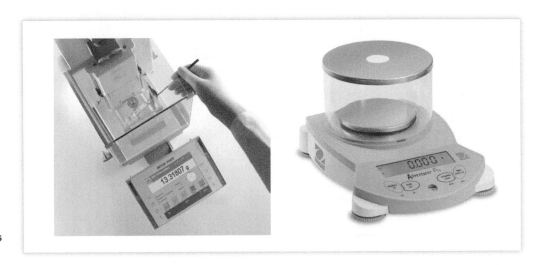

Figure 1.4
Some balances used for measuring mass in the laboratory.

1.7 LENGTH AND ITS MEASUREMENT

The **meter (m)** is the standard unit of length in the SI system. Although originally defined in 1790 as being 1 ten-millionth of the distance from the equator to the North Pole, the meter was redefined in 1889 as the distance between two thin lines on a bar of platinum–iridium alloy stored near Paris, France. To accommodate an increasing need for precision, the meter was redefined again in 1983 as equal to the distance traveled by light through a vacuum in 1/299,792,458 second. Although this new definition isn't as easy to grasp as the distance between two scratches on a bar, it has the great advantage that it can't be lost or damaged.

One meter is 39.37 inches, about 10% longer than an English yard and much too large for most measurements in chemistry. Other more commonly used measures of length are the **centimeter** (cm; 1 cm = 0.01 m, a bit less than half an inch), the **millimeter** (mm; 1 mm = 0.001 m, about the thickness of a U.S. dime), the **micrometer** (μm; 1 μm = 10^{-6} m), the **nanometer** (nm; 1 nm = 10^{-9} m), and the **picometer** (pm; 1 pm = 10^{-12} m). Thus, a chemist might refer to the diameter of a sodium atom as 372 pm (3.72×10^{-10} m).

$$1\ m = 100\ cm = 1000\ mm = 1{,}000{,}000\ \mu m = 1{,}000{,}000{,}000\ nm \qquad (1.0936\ yd)$$

$$1\ cm = 10\ mm = 10{,}000\ \mu m = 10{,}000{,}000\ nm \qquad (0.3937\ in.)$$

$$1\ mm = 1000\ \mu m = 1{,}000{,}000\ nm$$

▲ The length of the bacteria on the tip of this pin is about 5×10^{-7} m

1.8 TEMPERATURE AND ITS MEASUREMENT

Just as the kilogram and the meter are slowly replacing the pound and the yard as common units for mass and length measurement in the United States, the **degree Celsius (°C)** is slowly replacing the degree Fahrenheit (°F) as the common unit for temperature measurement. In scientific work, however, the **kelvin (K)** has replaced both. (Note that we say only "kelvin," not "kelvin degree.")

For all practical purposes, the kelvin and the degree Celsius are the same—both are one-hundredth of the interval between the freezing point of water and the boiling point of water at standard atmospheric pressure. The only real difference between the two units is that the numbers assigned to various points on the scales differ. Whereas the Celsius scale assigns a value of 0 °C to the freezing point of water and 100 °C to the boiling point of water, the Kelvin scale assigns a value of 0 K to the coldest possible temperature, −273.15 °C, sometimes called *absolute zero.* Thus, 0 K = −273.15 °C and 273.15 K = 0 °C. For example, a warm spring day with a Celsius temperature of 25 °C has a Kelvin temperature of 25 + 273.15 = 298 K.

$$\text{Temperature in K} = \text{Temperature in °C} + 273.15$$

$$\text{Temperature in °C} = \text{Temperature in K} - 273.15$$

In contrast to the Kelvin and Celsius scales, the common Fahrenheit scale specifies an interval of 180° between the freezing point (32 °F) and the boiling point (212 °F) of water. Thus, it takes 180 degrees Fahrenheit to cover the same range as 100 degrees Celsius (or kelvins), and a degree Fahrenheit is therefore only 100/180 = 5/9 as large as a degree Celsius. **Figure 1.5** compares the Fahrenheit, Celsius, and Kelvin scales.

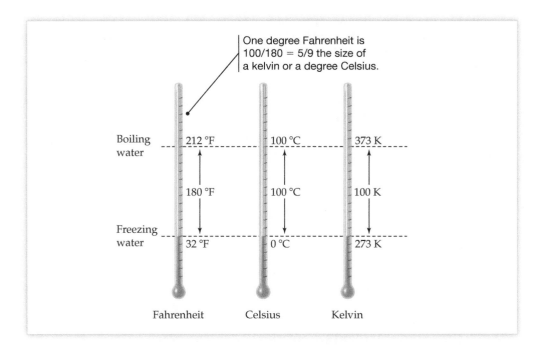

One degree Fahrenheit is 100/180 = 5/9 the size of a kelvin or a degree Celsius.

Boiling water — 212 °F — 100 °C — 373 K

180 °F   100 °C   100 K

Freezing water — 32 °F   0 °C   273 K

Fahrenheit   Celsius   Kelvin

Figure 1.5
A comparison of the Fahrenheit, Celsius, and Kelvin temperature scales.

Two adjustments are needed to convert between Fahrenheit and Celsius scales—one to adjust for the difference in degree size and one to adjust for the difference in zero points. The size adjustment is made using the relationships 1 °C = (9/5) °F and 1 °F = (5/9) °C. The zero-point adjustment is made by remembering that the freezing point of water is higher by 32 on the Fahrenheit scale than on the Celsius scale. Thus, if you want to convert from Celsius to Fahrenheit, you do a size adjustment (multiply °C by 9/5) and then a zero-point adjustment (add 32). If you want to convert from Fahrenheit to Celsius, you find out how many Fahrenheit degrees there are above freezing (by subtracting 32) and then do a size adjustment (multiply by 5/9). The following formulas describe the conversions, and Worked Example 1.1 shows how to do a calculation.

CELSIUS TO FAHRENHEIT

$$°F = \left(\frac{9\ °F}{5\ °C} \times °C\right) + 32\ °F$$

FAHRENHEIT TO CELSIUS

$$°C = \frac{5\ °C}{9\ °F} \times (°F - 32\ °F)$$

WORKED EXAMPLE 1.1

CONVERTING FROM FAHRENHEIT TO CELSIUS

The melting point of table salt is 1474 °F. What temperature is this on the Celsius and Kelvin scales?

SOLUTION

There are two ways to do this and every other problem in chemistry. One is to think things through to be sure you understand what's going on; the other is to plug numbers into a formula and hope for the best. The thinking approach always works; the formula approach works only if you use the right equation. Let's try both ways.

The thinking approach: We're given a temperature in degrees Fahrenheit, and we need to convert to degrees Celsius. A temperature of 1474 °F corresponds to 1474 °F − 32 °F = 1442 °F above the freezing point of water. Because a degree Fahrenheit is only 5/9 as large as a degree Celsius, 1442 degrees Fahrenheit above freezing equals 1442 × 5/9 = 801 degrees Celsius above freezing (0 °C), or 801 °C. The same number of degrees above freezing on the Kelvin scale (273.15 K) corresponds to a temperature of 273.15 + 801 = 1074 K.

The formula approach: Set up an equation using the temperature conversion formula for changing from Fahrenheit to Celsius:

$$°C = \left(\frac{5\ °C}{9\ °F}\right)(1474\ °F - 32\ °F) = 801\ °C$$

Converting to kelvins gives a temperature of 801° + 273.15° = 1074 K.

Because the answers obtained by the two approaches agree, we can feel fairly confident that our thinking is on track and that we understand the subject. (If the answers did *not* agree, we'd be alerted to a misunderstanding somewhere.)

▲ The melting point of sodium chloride is 1474 °F, or 801 °C.

▶ **PROBLEM 1.7**   The normal body temperature of a healthy adult is 98.6 °F. What is this value on both Celsius and Kelvin scales?

▶ **PROBLEM 1.8**   Carry out the indicated temperature conversions.
(a) −78 °C = ? K   (b) 158 °C = ? °F   (c) 375 K = ? °F

1.9 DERIVED UNITS: VOLUME AND ITS MEASUREMENT

Look back at the seven fundamental SI units given in Table 1.4 and you'll find that measures for such familiar quantities as area, volume, density, speed, and pressure are missing. All are examples of *derived* quantities rather than fundamental quantities because they can be expressed using one or more of the seven base units (Table 1.6).

TABLE 1.6   Some Derived Quantities

Quantity	Definition	Derived Unit (Name)
Area	Length times length	m^2
Volume	Area times length	m^3
Density	Mass per unit volume	kg/m^3
Speed	Distance per unit time	m/s
Acceleration	Change in speed per unit time	m/s^2
Force	Mass times acceleration	$(kg \cdot m)/s^2$ (newton, N)
Pressure	Force per unit area	$kg/(m \cdot s^2)$ (pascal, Pa)
Energy	Force times distance	$(kg \cdot m^2)/s^2$ (joule, J)

Volume, the amount of space occupied by an object, is measured in SI units by the **cubic meter (m³)**, defined as the amount of space occupied by a cube 1 meter on edge (Figure 1.6).

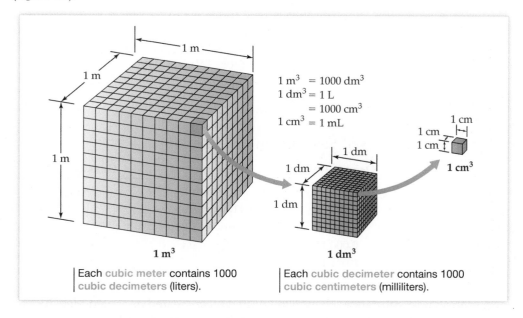

$$1\ m^3 = 1000\ dm^3$$
$$1\ dm^3 = 1\ L$$
$$= 1000\ cm^3$$
$$1\ cm^3 = 1\ mL$$

Each cubic meter contains 1000 cubic decimeters (liters).

Each cubic decimeter contains 1000 cubic centimeters (milliliters).

Figure 1.6
Units for measuring volume. A cubic meter is the volume of a cube 1 meter along each edge.

A cubic meter equals 264.2 U.S. gallons, much too large a quantity for normal use in chemistry. As a result, smaller, more convenient measures are commonly employed. Both the **cubic decimeter** ($1\ dm^3 = 0.001\ m^3$), equal in size to the more familiar metric **liter (L)**, and the **cubic centimeter** ($1\ cm^3 = 0.001\ dm^3 = 10^{-6}\ m^3$), equal in size to the metric **milliliter (mL)**, are particularly convenient. Slightly larger than 1 U.S. quart, a liter has the volume of a cube 1 dm on edge. Similarly, a milliliter has the volume of a cube 1 cm on edge (Figure 1.6).

$$1\ m^3 = 1000\ dm^3 = 1{,}000{,}000\ cm^3 \qquad (264.2\ gal)$$

$$1\ dm^3 = 1L = 1000\ mL \qquad (1.057\ qt)$$

Figure 1.7 shows some of the equipment frequently used in the laboratory for measuring liquid volume.

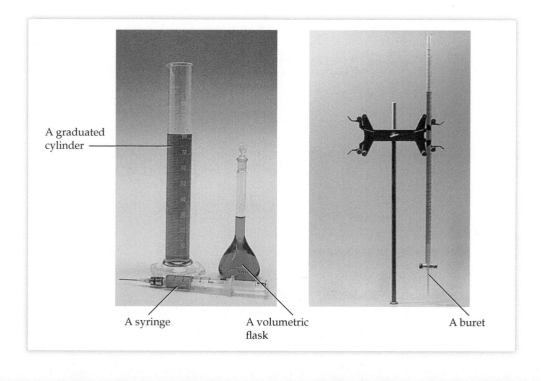

A graduated cylinder

A syringe

A volumetric flask

A buret

Figure 1.7
Common items of laboratory equipment used for measuring liquid volume.

▲ Which weighs more, the brass weight or the pillow? Actually, both have identical masses and weights, but the brass has a higher density because its volume is smaller.

1.10 DERIVED UNITS: DENSITY AND ITS MEASUREMENT

The intensive physical property that relates the mass of an object to its volume is called *density*. **Density**, which is simply the mass of an object divided by its volume, is expressed in the SI derived unit g/mL for a liquid or g/cm^3 for a solid. The densities of some common materials are given in Table 1.7.

$$\text{Density} = \frac{\text{Mass (g)}}{\text{Volume (mL or cm}^3)}$$

TABLE 1.7   Densities of Some Common Materials

Substance	Density (g/cm³)	Substance	Density (g/cm³)
Ice (0 °C)	0.917	Human fat	0.94
Water (3.98 °C)	1.0000	Human muscle	1.06
Gold	19.31	Cork	0.22–0.26
Helium (25 °C)	0.000 164	Balsa wood	0.12
Air (25 °C)	0.001 185	Earth	5.54

Because most substances change in volume when heated or cooled, densities are temperature-dependent. At 3.98 °C, for example, a 1.0000 mL container holds exactly 1.0000 g of water (density = 1.0000 g/mL). As the temperature is raised, however, the volume occupied by the water expands so that only 0.9584 g fits in the 1.0000 mL container at 100 °C (density = 0.9584 g/mL). When reporting a density, the temperature must also be specified.

Although most substances expand when heated and contract when cooled, water behaves differently. Water contracts when cooled from 100 °C to 3.98 °C, but below this temperature it begins to expand again. Thus, the density of liquid water is at its maximum of 1.0000 g/mL at 3.98 °C but decreases to 0.999 87 g/mL at 0 °C (Figure 1.8). When freezing occurs, the density drops still further to a value of 0.917 g/cm^3 for ice at 0 °C. Ice and any other substance with a density less than that of water will float, but any substance with a density greater than that of water will sink.

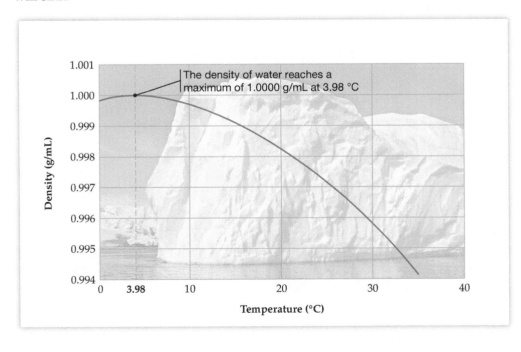

The density of water reaches a maximum of 1.0000 g/mL at 3.98 °C

Figure 1.8
The density of water at different temperatures.

Knowing the density of a substance, particularly a liquid, can be very useful because it's often easier to measure a liquid by volume than by mass. Suppose, for example, that you needed 1.55 g of ethyl alcohol. Rather than trying to weigh exactly the right amount, it would be much easier to look up the density of ethyl alcohol (0.7893 g/mL at 20 °C) and measure the correct volume with a syringe.

$$\text{Density} = \frac{\text{Mass}}{\text{Volume}} \quad \text{so} \quad \text{Volume} = \frac{\text{Mass}}{\text{Density}}$$

$$\text{Volume} = \frac{1.55 \ \cancel{g} \ \text{ethyl alcohol}}{0.7893 \ \dfrac{\cancel{g}}{\text{mL}}} = 1.96 \ \text{mL ethyl alcohol}$$

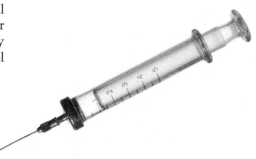

▲ The precise mass of a liquid is easily measured with a syringe if the density of the liquid is known.

WORKED EXAMPLE 1.2

CALCULATING A DENSITY

What is the density of the element copper in g/cm^3 if a sample weighing 324.5 g has a volume of 36.2 cm^3?

SOLUTION

Density is mass divided by volume:

$$\text{Density} = \frac{\text{Mass}}{\text{Volume}} = \frac{324.5 \ \text{g}}{36.2 \ \text{cm}^3} = 8.96 \ \text{g/cm}^3$$

WORKED EXAMPLE 1.3

USING DENSITY TO CALCULATE A VOLUME

What is the volume in cm^3 of 454 g of gold? (See Table 1.7.)

SOLUTION

Because density is defined as mass divided by volume, volume is mass divided by density:

$$\text{Volume} = \frac{454 \ \cancel{g} \ \text{gold}}{19.31 \ \cancel{g}/\text{cm}^3} = 23.5 \ \text{cm}^3 \ \text{gold}$$

▶ **PROBLEM 1.9**   What is the density of glass in g/cm^3 if a sample weighing 27.43 g has a volume of 12.40 cm^3?

▶ **PROBLEM 1.10**   Chloroform, a substance once used as an anesthetic, has a density of 1.483 g/mL at 20 °C. How many milliliters would you use if you needed 9.37 g?

1.11 DERIVED UNITS: ENERGY AND ITS MEASUREMENT

The word *energy* is familiar to everyone but is hard to define in simple, nontechnical terms. A good working definition, however, is to say that **energy** is the capacity to supply heat or do work. The water falling over a dam, for instance, contains energy that can be used to turn a turbine and generate electricity. A tank of propane gas contains energy that, when released in the chemical process of combustion, can heat a house or barbecue a hamburger.

Energy is classified as either *kinetic* or *potential*. **Kinetic energy (E_K)** is the energy of motion. The amount of kinetic energy in a moving object with mass m and velocity v is given by the equation

$$E_K = \frac{1}{2}mv^2$$

The larger the mass of an object and the larger its velocity, the larger the amount of kinetic energy. Thus, water that has fallen over a dam from a great height has a greater velocity and more kinetic energy than the same amount of water that has fallen only a short distance.

Potential energy (E_p), by contrast, is stored energy—perhaps stored in an object because of its height or in a molecule because of chemical reactions it can undergo. The water sitting in a reservoir behind the dam contains potential energy because of its height above the stream at the bottom of the dam. When the water is allowed to fall, its potential energy is converted into kinetic energy. Propane and other substances used as fuels contain potential energy because they can undergo a combustion reaction with oxygen that releases heat. (We'll look at energy in more detail in Chapter 8.)

The units for energy, $(kg \cdot m^2)/s^2$, follow from the expression for kinetic energy, $E_K = 1/2 \, mv^2$. If, for instance, your body has a mass of 50.0 kg (about 110 lb) and you are riding on a bicycle at a velocity of 10.0 m/s (about 22 mi/h), your kinetic energy is 2500 $(kg \cdot m^2)/s^2$.

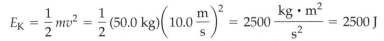

$$E_K = \frac{1}{2} mv^2 = \frac{1}{2} (50.0 \text{ kg}) \left(10.0 \, \frac{m}{s}\right)^2 = 2500 \, \frac{kg \cdot m^2}{s^2} = 2500 \text{ J}$$

The SI derived unit for energy $(kg \cdot m^2)/s^2$ is given the name **joule (J)** after the English physicist James Prescott Joule (1818–1889). The joule is a fairly small amount of energy—it takes roughly 100,000 J to heat a coffee cup full of water from room temperature to boiling—so kilojoules (kJ) are more frequently used in chemistry.

In addition to the SI energy unit joule, some chemists and biochemists still use the unit calorie (cal, with a lowercase c). Originally defined as the amount of energy necessary to raise the temperature of 1 g of water by 1 °C (specifically, from 14.5 °C to 15.5 °C), one calorie is now defined as exactly 4.184 J.

▲ The 75 watt incandescent bulb in this lamp uses energy at the rate of 75 J/s. Only about 5% of that energy appears as light, however; the remaining 95% is given off as heat.

$$1 \text{ cal} = 4.184 \text{ J (exactly)}$$

Nutritionists use the somewhat confusing unit Calorie (Cal, with a capital C), which is equal to 1000 calories, or 1 kilocalorie (kcal).

$$1 \text{ Cal} = 1000 \text{ cal} = 1 \text{ kcal} = 4.184 \text{ kJ}$$

The energy value, or caloric content, of food is measured in Calories. Thus, the statement that a banana contains 70 Calories means that 70 Cal (70 kcal, or 290 kJ) of energy is released when the banana is used by the body for fuel.

▶ **PROBLEM 1.11** What is the kinetic energy in kilojoules of a 2360 lb (1070 kg) car moving at 63.3 mi/h (28.3 m/s)?

▶ **PROBLEM 1.12** A Big Mac hamburger from McDonald's contains 540 Calories.
(a) How many kilojoules does a Big Mac contain?
(b) For how many hours could the amount of energy in a Big Mac light a 100 watt light-bulb? (1 watt = 1 J/s)

1.12 ACCURACY, PRECISION, AND SIGNIFICANT FIGURES IN MEASUREMENT

Measuring things, whether in cooking, construction, or chemistry, is something that most of us do every day. But how good are those measurements? Any measurement is only as good as the skill of the person doing the work and the reliability of the equipment being used. You've probably noticed, for instance, that you often get slightly different readings when you weigh yourself on a bathroom scale and on a scale at the doctor's office, so there's always some uncertainty about your real weight. The same is true in chemistry—there is always some uncertainty in the value of a measurement.

In talking about the degree of uncertainty in a measurement, we use the words *accuracy* and *precision*. Although most of us use the words interchangeably in daily life, there's actually an important distinction between them. **Accuracy** refers to how close to the true value a given measurement is, whereas **precision** refers to how well a number of independent measurements agree with one another. To see the difference, imagine that you weigh a tennis ball whose true mass is 54.441 778 g. Assume that you take three independent measurements on each of three different types of balance to obtain the data shown in the following table.

▲ This tennis ball has a mass of about 54 g.

Measurement #	Bathroom Scale	Lab Balance	Analytical Balance
1	0.1 kg	54.4 g	54.4418 g
2	0.0 kg	54.5 g	54.4417 g
3	0.1 kg	54.3 g	54.4418 g
(average)	(0.07 kg)	(54.4 g)	(54.4418 g)

If you use a bathroom scale, your measurement (average = 0.07 kg) is neither accurate nor precise. Its accuracy is poor because it measures to only one digit that is far from the true value, and its precision is poor because any two measurements may differ substantially. If you now weigh the ball on an inexpensive laboratory balance, the value you get (average = 54.4 g) has three digits and is fairly accurate, but it is still not very precise because the three readings vary from 54.3 g to 54.5 g, perhaps due to air movements in the room or to a sticky mechanism. Finally, if you weigh the ball on an expensive analytical balance like those found in research laboratories, your measurement (average = 54.4418 g) is both precise and accurate. It's accurate because the measurement is very close to the true value, and it's precise because it has six digits that vary little from one reading to another.

To indicate the uncertainty in a measurement, the value you record should use all the digits you are sure of plus one additional digit that you estimate. In reading a thermometer that has a mark for each degree, for example, you could be certain about the digits of the nearest mark—say 25 °C—but you would have to estimate between two marks—say between 25 °C and 26 °C—to obtain a value of 25.3 °C.

The total number of digits recorded for a measurement is called the measurement's number of **significant figures**. For example, the mass of the tennis ball as determined on the single-pan balance (54.4 g) has three significant figures, whereas the mass determined on the analytical balance (54.4418 g) has six significant figures. All digits but the last are certain; the final digit is an estimate, which we generally assume to have an error of plus or minus one (± 1).

Finding the number of significant figures in a measurement is usually easy but can be troublesome if zeros are present. Look at the following four quantities:

4.803 cm	Four significant figures: 4, 8, 0, 3
0.006 61 g	Three significant figures: 6, 6, 1
55.220 K	Five significant figures: 5, 5, 2, 2, 0
34,200 m	Anywhere from three (3, 4, 2) to five (3, 4, 2, 0, 0) significant figures

The following rules cover the different situations that arise:

1. *Zeros in the middle of a number are like any other digit; they are always significant.* Thus, 4.803 cm has four significant figures.

2. *Zeros at the beginning of a number are not significant*; they act only to locate the decimal point. Thus, 0.006 61 g has three significant figures. (Note that 0.006 61 g can be rewritten as 6.61×10^{-3} g or as 6.61 mg.)

3. *Zeros at the end of a number and after the decimal point are always significant.* The assumption is that these zeros would not be shown unless they were significant.

Thus, 55.220 K has five significant figures. (If the value were known to only four significant figures, we would write 55.22 K.)

4. *Zeros at the end of a number and before the decimal point may or may not be significant.* We can't tell whether they are part of the measurement or whether they just locate the decimal point. Thus, 34,200 m may have three, four, or five significant figures. Often, however, a little common sense is helpful. A temperature reading of 20 °C probably has two significant figures rather than one, since one significant figure would imply a temperature anywhere from 10 °C to 30 °C and would be of little use. Similarly, a volume given as 300 mL probably has three significant figures. On the other hand, a figure of 93,000,000 mi for the distance between the Earth and the Sun probably has only two or three significant figures.

The fourth rule shows why it's helpful to write numbers in scientific notation rather than ordinary notation. Doing so makes it possible to indicate the number of significant figures. Thus, writing the number 34,200 as 3.42×10^4 indicates three significant figures but writing it as 3.4200×10^4 indicates five significant figures.

One further point about significant figures: certain numbers, such as those obtained when counting objects, are exact and have an effectively infinite number of significant figures. A week has exactly 7 days, for instance, not 6.9 or 7.0 or 7.1, and a foot has exactly 12 inches, not 11.9 or 12.0 or 12.1. In addition, the power of 10 used in scientific notation is an exact number. That is, the number 10^3 is exactly 1000, but the number 1×10^3 has one significant figure.

WORKED EXAMPLE 1.4

SIGNIFICANT FIGURES

How many significant figures does each of the following measurements have?

(a) 0.036 653 m   (b) 7.2100×10^{-3} g   (c) 72,100 km   (d) $25.03

SOLUTION

(a) 5 (by rule 2)   (b) 5 (by rule 3)
(c) 3, 4, or 5 (by rule 4)   (d) $25.03 is an exact number

▶ **PROBLEM 1.13** A 1.000 mL sample of acetone, a common solvent used as a paint remover, was placed in a small bottle whose mass was known to be 38.0015 g. The following values were obtained when the acetone-filled bottle was weighed: 38.7798 g, 38.7795 g, and 38.7801 g. How would you characterize the precision and accuracy of these measurements if the true mass of the acetone was 0.7791 g?

▶ **PROBLEM 1.14** How many significant figures does each of the following quantities have? Explain your answers.

(a) 76.600 kJ   (b) $4.502\,00 \times 10^3$ g   (c) 3000 nm   (d) 0.003 00 mL
(e) 18 students   (f) 3×10^{-5} g   (g) 47.60 mL   (h) 2070 mi

1.13 ROUNDING NUMBERS

It often happens, particularly when doing arithmetic on a calculator, that a quantity appears to have more significant figures than are really justified. You might calculate the gas mileage of your car, for instance, by finding that it takes 11.70 gallons of gasoline to drive 278 miles:

$$\text{Mileage} = \frac{\text{Miles}}{\text{Gallons}} = \frac{278 \text{ mi}}{11.70 \text{ gal}} = 23.760\,684 \text{ mi/gal (mpg)}$$

Although the answer on the calculator has eight digits, your measurement is really not as precise as it appears. In fact, your answer is precise to only three significant figures and should be **rounded off** to 23.8 mi/gal by removing all nonsignificant figures.

How do you decide how many figures to keep and how many to ignore? For most purposes, a simple procedure using just two rules is sufficient.

1. *In carrying out a multiplication or division, the answer can't have more significant figures than either of the original numbers.* If you think about it, this rule is just common sense. If you don't know the number of miles you drove to better than three significant figures (278 could mean 277, 278, or 279), you certainly can't calculate your mileage to more than the same number of significant figures.

▲ Calculators often display more figures than are justified by the precision of the data.

Three significant figures

Three significant figures

$$\frac{278 \text{ mi}}{11.70 \text{ gal}} = 23.8 \text{ mi/gal}$$

Four significant figures

2. *In carrying out an addition or subtraction, the answer can't have more digits to the right of the decimal point than either of the original numbers.* For example, if you have 3.18 L of water and you add 0.013 15 L more, you now have 3.19 L. Again, this rule is just common sense. If you don't know the volume you started with past the second decimal place (it could be 3.17, 3.18, or 3.19), you can't know the total of the combined volumes past the same decimal place.

$$
\begin{array}{r}
3.18?\ ?? \\
+\ 0.013\ 15 \\
\hline
3.19?\ ??
\end{array}
$$

Ends two places past decimal point

← Ends five places past decimal point

Ends two places past decimal point

Once you decide how many digits to retain for your answer, the rules for rounding off numbers are as follows:

1. *If the first digit you remove is less than 5, round down by dropping it and all following digits.* Thus, 5.664 525 becomes 5.66 when rounded to three significant figures because the first of the dropped digits (4) is less than 5.

2. *If the first digit you remove is 6 or greater, round up by adding 1 to the digit on the left.* Thus, 5.664 525 becomes 5.7 when rounded to two significant figures because the first of the dropped digits (6) is greater than 5.

3. *If the first digit you remove is 5 and there are more nonzero digits following, round up.* Thus, 5.664 525 becomes 5.665 when rounded to four significant figures because there are nonzero digits (2, 5) after the 5.

4. *If the digit you remove is a 5 with nothing following, round down.* Thus, 5.664 525 becomes 5.664 52 when rounded to six significant figures because there is nothing after the 5.

WORKED EXAMPLE 1.5

A CALCULATION USING SIGNIFICANT FIGURES

It takes 9.25 hours to fly from London, England, to Chicago, Illinois, a distance of 3952 miles. What is the average speed of the airplane in miles per hour?

SOLUTION

First, set up an equation dividing the number of miles flown by the number of hours:

$$\text{Average speed} = \frac{3952 \text{ mi}}{9.25 \text{ h}} = 427.243\ 24 \text{ mi/h}$$

continued on next page

Next, decide how many significant figures should be in your answer. Because the problem involves a division, and because one of the quantities you started with (9.25 h) has only three significant figures, the answer must also have three significant figures. Finally, round off your answer. The first digit to be dropped (2) is less than 5, so the answer 427.243 24 must be rounded off to 427 mi/h.

In doing this or any other problem, use all figures, significant or not, for the calculation and then round off the final answer. Don't round off at any intermediate step.

▸ **PROBLEM 1.15**   Round off each of the following quantities to the number of significant figures indicated in parentheses:
   (a) 3.774 499 L (4)   **(b)** 255.0974 K (3)   **(c)** 55.265 kg (4)   **(d)** 906.401 kJ (5)

▸ **PROBLEM 1.16**   Carry out the following calculations, expressing each result with the correct number of significant figures:
   (a) 24.567 g + 0.044 78 g = ? g
   (b) 4.6742 g ÷ 0.003 71 L = ? g/L
   (c) 0.378 mL + 42.3 mL − 1.5833 mL = ? mL

CONCEPTUAL PROBLEM 1.17   What is the temperature reading on the following Celsius thermometer? How many significant figures do you have in your answer?

1.14 CALCULATIONS: CONVERTING FROM ONE UNIT TO ANOTHER

Because so many scientific activities involve numerical calculations—measuring, weighing, preparing solutions, and so forth—it's often necessary to convert a quantity from one unit to another. Converting between units isn't difficult; we all do it every day. If you run 7.5 laps around a 200 meter track, for instance, you have to convert between the distance unit *lap* and the distance unit *meter* to find that you have run 1500 m (7.5 laps times 200 meters/lap). Converting from one scientific unit to another is just as easy.

$$7.5 \text{ laps} \times \frac{200 \text{ meters}}{1 \text{ lap}} = 1500 \text{ meters}$$

The simplest way to carry out calculations that involve different units is to use the **dimensional-analysis method**. In this method, a quantity described in one unit is converted into an equivalent quantity with a different unit by multiplying with a **conversion factor** that expresses the relationship between units.

Original quantity × Conversion factor = Equivalent quantity

As an example, we know from Section 1.7 that 1 meter equals 39.37 inches. Writing this relationship as a ratio restates it in the form of a conversion factor, either meters per inch or inches per meter.

Conversion factors between meters and inches $\dfrac{1 \text{ m}}{39.37 \text{ in.}}$ equals $\dfrac{39.37 \text{ in.}}{1 \text{ m}}$ equals 1

▲ Runners have to convert from laps to meters to find out how far they have run.

Note that this and all other conversion factors are effectively equal to 1 because the quantity above the division line (the numerator) is equal in value to the quantity below the division line (the denominator). Thus, multiplying by a conversion factor is equivalent to multiplying by 1 and so does not change the value of the quantity.

The key to the dimensional-analysis method of problem solving is that units are treated like numbers and can thus be multiplied and divided just as numbers can. The idea when solving a problem is to set up an equation so that unwanted units cancel, leaving only the desired units. Usually it's best to start by writing what you know and then manipulating that known quantity. For example, say you know your height is 69.5 inches and you want to find it in meters. Begin by writing your height in inches and then set up an equation multiplying your height by the conversion factor meters per inch:

$$69.5 \text{ in.} \times \frac{1 \text{ m}}{39.37 \text{ in.}} = 1.77 \text{ m}$$

Starting quantity

Conversion factor

Equivalent quantity

The unit "in." cancels because it appears both above and below the division line, so the only unit that remains is "m."

The dimensional-analysis method gives the right answer only if the conversion factor is arranged so that the unwanted units cancel. If the equation is set up in any other way, the units won't cancel properly and you won't get the right answer. Thus, if you were to multiply your height in inches by an inverted conversion factor of inches per meter rather than meters per inch, you would end up with an incorrect answer expressed in meaningless units.

$$69.5 \text{ in} \times \frac{39.37 \text{ in.}}{1 \text{ m}} = 2740 \text{ in.}^2/\text{m} \quad ??$$

The main drawback to using the dimensional-analysis method is that it's easy to get the right answer without really understanding what you're doing. It's therefore best after solving a problem to think through a rough estimate, or "ballpark" solution, as a check on your work. If your ballpark check isn't close to the answer you get from the detailed solution, there's a misunderstanding somewhere and you should think through the problem again.

Even if you don't make an estimate, it's important to be sure that your calculated answer makes sense. If, for example, you were trying to calculate the volume of a human cell and you came up with the answer 5.3 cm^3, you should realize that such an answer couldn't possibly be right. Cells are too tiny to be distinguished with the naked eye, but a volume of 5.3 cm^3 is about the size of a walnut.

The dimensional-analysis method and the use of ballpark checks are techniques that will help you solve problems of many kinds, not just unit conversions. Problems sometimes seem complicated, but you can usually sort out the complications by analyzing the problem properly.

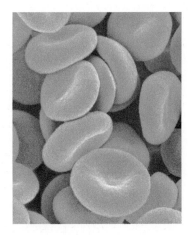

▲ What is the volume of a red blood cell?

- Identify the information given, including units.
- Identify the information needed in the answer, including units.
- Find a relationship between the known information and unknown answer, and plan a strategy for getting from one to the other.
- Solve the problem.
- Make a rough estimate to be sure your calculated answer is reasonable.

Examples 1.6–1.8 show how to devise strategies and estimate answers. To conserve space, we'll use this approach routinely in only the next few chapters, but you should make it a standard part of your problem solving.

▲ This Koenigsegg CCXR has a top speed of 265 mph.

WORKED EXAMPLE 1.6

UNIT CONVERSION USING SIGNIFICANT FIGURES

The Koenigsegg CCXR is the fastest sports car in the world, with a top speed of 265 miles per hour. What is this speed in kilometers per hour?

STRATEGY

The known information is the speed in mi/h; the unknown is the speed in km/h. Find the appropriate conversion factor inside the back cover of this book, and use the dimensional-analysis method to set up an equation so the "mi" units cancel.

SOLUTION

$$\frac{265 \text{ mi}}{1 \text{ h}} \times \frac{1.609 \text{ km}}{1 \text{ mi}} = 426 \frac{\text{km}}{\text{h}}$$

A very fast car!

BALLPARK CHECK

The answer is certainly large, perhaps several hundred km/h. A better estimate is to realize that, because 1 mi = 1.609 km, it takes about 1 1/2 times as many kilometers as miles to measure the same distance. Thus, 265 mi is about 400 km, and 265 mi/h is about 400 km/h. The estimate agrees with the detailed solution.

WORKED EXAMPLE 1.7

COMPLEX UNIT CONVERSIONS AND SIGNIFICANT FIGURES

A large sport utility vehicle moving at a speed of 125 km/h might use gasoline at a rate of 16 L per 100 km. What does this correspond to in mi/gal?

STRATEGY

We are given a gasoline mileage in L/km (or km/L), and we need to find the mileage in mi/gal. Thus, two conversions are necessary, one from kilometers to miles and one from liters to gallons. It's best to do multiple conversions one step at a time until you get used to them. First, convert the distance from kilometers to miles and the amount of fuel from liters to gallons, and then divide the distance by the amount of fuel to find the mileage.

SOLUTION

$$100 \text{ km} \times \frac{0.6214 \text{ mi}}{1 \text{ km}} = 62.14 \text{ mi} \qquad 16 \text{ L} \times \frac{1 \text{ gal}}{3.79 \text{ L}} = 4.22 \text{ gal}$$

$$\frac{62.14 \text{ mi}}{4.22 \text{ gal}} = 14.73 \frac{\text{mi}}{\text{gal}} \qquad \text{Round off to 15 mi/gal}$$

Note that extra digits are carried through the intermediate calculations and only the final answer is rounded off.

When you become more confident in working multiple conversion problems, you can set up one large equation in which all unwanted units cancel.

$$\frac{100 \text{ km}}{16 \text{ L}} \times \frac{3.79 \text{ L}}{1 \text{ gal}} \times \frac{0.6214 \text{ mi}}{1 \text{ km}} = 14.73 \frac{\text{mi}}{\text{gal}} \qquad \text{Round off to 15 mi/gal}$$

BALLPARK CHECK

The mileage is probably low, perhaps in the range of 10 to 15 mi/gal. This is a difficult problem to estimate, however, because it requires several different conversions. It's therefore best to think the problem through one step at a time, writing down the intermediate estimates:

• A distance of 100 km per 16 L is approximately 6 km/L.
• Because 1 km is about 0.6 mi, 6 km/L is about 4 mi/L.
• Because 1 L is approximately 1 qt, or 1/4 gal, 4 mi/L is about 16 mi/gal.

This estimate agrees with the detailed solution.

WORKED EXAMPLE 1.8

COMPLEX UNIT CONVERSIONS AND SIGNIFICANT FIGURES

The volcanic explosion that destroyed the Indonesian island of Krakatau on August 27, 1883, released an estimated 4.3 cubic miles (mi^3) of debris into the atmosphere and affected global weather for years. In SI units, how many cubic meters (m^3) of debris were released?

STRATEGY

We are given a volume in cubic miles and need to convert to cubic meters. It's probably simplest to convert first from mi^3 to km^3 and then convert km^3 to m^3.

SOLUTION

$$4.3 \text{ mi}^3 \times \left(\frac{1 \text{ km}}{0.6214 \text{ mi}}\right)^3 = 17.92 \text{ km}^3$$

$$17.92 \text{ km}^3 \times \left(\frac{1000 \text{ m}}{1 \text{ km}}\right)^3 = 1.792 \times 10^{10} \text{ m}^3$$

$$= 1.8 \times 10^{10} \text{ m}^3 \quad \text{Rounded off}$$

BALLPARK CHECK

One meter is much less than 1 mile, so it takes a large number of cubic meters to equal 1 mi^3, and the answer is going to be very large. Because 1 km is about 0.6 mi, 1 km^3 is about $(0.6)^3 = 0.2$ times as large as 1 mi^3. Thus, each mi^3 contains about 5 km^3, and 4.3 mi^3 contains about 20 km^3. Each km^3, in turn, contains $(1000 \text{ m})^3 = 10^9 \text{ m}^3$. Thus, the volume of debris from the Krakatau explosion was about $20 \times 10^9 \text{ m}^3$, or $2 \times 10^{10} \text{ m}^3$. The estimate agrees with the detailed solution.

▶ **PROBLEM 1.18** Calculate answers to the following problems, and check your solutions by making ballpark estimates.
  (a) The melting point of gold is 1064 °C. What is this temperature in degrees Fahrenheit?
  (b) How large, in cubic centimeters, is the volume of a red blood cell if the cell has a cylindrical shape with a diameter of 6×10^{-6} m and a height of 2×10^{-6} m?

▶ **PROBLEM 1.19** Gemstones are weighed in *carats*, with 1 carat = 200 mg (exactly). What is the mass in grams of the Hope Diamond, the world's largest blue diamond at 44.4 carats? What is this mass in ounces?

▶ **PROBLEM 1.20** A pure diamond with a mass of 0.1000 g contains 5.014×10^{21} carbon atoms and has a density of 3.52 g/cm^3. What is the volume of the Hope Diamond (Problem 1.19), and how many carbon atoms does it contain?

INQUIRY WHAT ARE THE RISKS AND BENEFITS OF CHEMICALS?

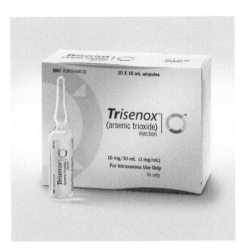

▲ Is this a poison or a treatment for leukemia?

Life is not risk-free—we all take many risks each day, often without even thinking about it. We may decide to ride a bike rather than drive, even though the likelihood per mile of being killed on a bicycle is 10 times greater than in a car. We may decide to smoke cigarettes, even though smoking kills more than 170,000 people each year in the United States.

What about risks from "chemicals"? News reports sometimes make it seem that our food is covered with pesticides and filled with dangerous additives, that our land is polluted by toxic waste dumps, and that our medicines are unsafe. How bad are the risks from chemicals, and how are the risks evaluated?

First, it's important to realize that *everything*, including your own body, is made of chemicals—that's what matter is. There is no such thing as a "chemical-free" food, cosmetic, cleanser, or anything else. Second, there is no meaningful distinction between a "natural" substance and a "synthetic" one; a chemical is a chemical. Many naturally occurring substances—snake venom, for example—are extraordinarily toxic, and many synthetic substances—polyethylene, for example—are harmless.

Risk evaluation of chemicals is carried out by exposing test animals, usually mice or rats, to a chemical and then monitoring for signs of harm. To limit the expense and time needed for testing, the amounts administered are often hundreds or thousands of times larger than those a person might normally encounter. The *acute chemical toxicity* (as opposed to chronic toxicity) observed in animal tests is reported as an LD_{50} *value*, the amount of a substance per kilogram of body weight that is a lethal dose for 50% of the test animals. Some LD_{50} values of different substances are shown in Table 1.8. The lower the value, the more toxic the substance.

TABLE 1.8 Some LD_{50} Values in Rats

Substance	LD_{50} (g/kg)	Substance	LD_{50} (g/kg)
Strychnine	0.005	Chloroform	1.2
Arsenic trioxide	0.015	Iron(II) sulfate	1.5
DDT	0.115	Ethyl alcohol	7.1
Aspirin	1.1	Sodium cyclamate	12.8

Even with an LD_{50} value established in test animals, the risk of human exposure to a given substance is still hard to assess. If a substance is harmful to rats, is it necessarily harmful to humans? How can a large dose for a small animal be translated into a small dose for a large human? All substances are toxic to some organisms to some extent, and the difference between help and harm is often a matter of degree. Vitamin A, for example, is necessary for vision, yet it can promote cancer at high doses. Arsenic trioxide is the most classic of poisons, yet it induces remissions in some types of leukemia and is sold for drug use under the name Trisenox. Even water can be toxic if drunk in large amounts because it dilutes the salt in body fluids and causes a potentially life-threatening condition called *hyponatremia* that has resulted in the death of several marathon runners. Furthermore, how we evaluate risk is strongly influenced by familiarity. Many foods contain natural ingredients far more toxic than synthetic additives or pesticide residues, but the ingredients are ignored because the foods are familiar.

All decisions involve trade-offs. Does the benefit of a pesticide that increases food production outweigh a possible health risk to 1 person in 1 million? Do the beneficial effects of a new drug outweigh a potentially dangerous side effect in a small number of users? Different people will have different opinions, but an honest evaluation of the facts is surely better than a purely emotional response.

▶ **PROBLEM 1.21** Table salt (sodium chloride) has an LD_{50} of 4 g/kg in rats. Assuming that rats and humans have the same LD_{50}, how much salt would a 155 lb person have to consume to have a 50% chance of dying?

SUMMARY

Chemistry is the study of the composition, properties, and transformations of **matter**. It is best approached by posing questions, conducting experiments, and devising **theories** to interpret the experimental results.

All matter is formed from one or more of 118 presently known **elements**—fundamental substances that can't be chemically broken down. Elements are symbolized by one- or two-letter abbreviations and can be organized into a **periodic table** with **groups** (columns) and **periods** (rows). Elements in the same group of the periodic table show similar chemical behavior. The two larger groups on the left and the six larger groups on the right of the table are called the **main groups**, the 10 smaller ones in the middle of the table are called the **transition metal groups**, and the 14 shown separately at the bottom of the table are called the **inner transition metal groups**. Elements are classified as **metals, nonmetals**, or **semimetals**.

The characteristics, or **properties**, that are used to describe matter can be classified in several ways. **Physical properties** are those that can be determined without changing the chemical composition of the sample, whereas **chemical properties** are those that do involve a chemical change in the sample. **Intensive properties** are those whose values do not depend on the size of the sample, whereas **extensive properties** are those whose values do depend on sample size.

Accurate measurement is crucial to scientific experimentation. The units used are those of the Système Internationale (**SI units**). There are seven fundamental SI units, together with other derived units. **Mass**, the amount of matter in an object, is measured in **kilograms (kg)**; **length** is measured in **meters (m)**; **temperature** is measured in **kelvin (K)**; and **volume** is measured in **cubic meters (m^3)**. The more familiar metric **liter (L)** and **milliliter (mL)** are also still used for measuring volume, and the **Celsius degree (°C)** is still used for measuring temperature. **Density** is an intensive physical property that relates mass to volume and is measured in the derived SI unit g/cm^3 or g/mL. **Energy** is the capacity to supply heat or do work and is measured in the derived SI unit (kg · m^2/s^2), or **joule (J)**. Energy is of two kinds, potential and kinetic. **Kinetic energy (E_K)** is the energy of motion, and **potential energy (E_P)** is stored energy.

Because many experiments involve numerical calculations, it's often necessary to manipulate and convert different units of measure. The simplest way to carry out such conversions is to use the **dimensional-analysis method**, in which an equation is set up so that unwanted units cancel and only the desired units remain. It's also important when measuring physical quantities or carrying out calculations to indicate the precision of the measurement by **rounding off** the result to the correct number of **significant figures**.

KEY WORDS

CONCEPTUAL PROBLEMS

Problems at the end of each chapter begin with a section called "Conceptual Problems." The problems in this section are visual rather than numerical and are intended to probe your understanding rather than your facility with numbers and formulas. Answers to even-numbered problems (in color) can be found at the end of the book following the appendixes. Problems 1.1–1.21 appear within the chapter.

1.22 Where on the following outline of a periodic table are the indicated elements or groups of elements?

   (a) Alkali metals

   (b) Halogens

   (c) Alkaline earth metals

   (d) Transition metals

   (e) Hydrogen

   (f) Helium

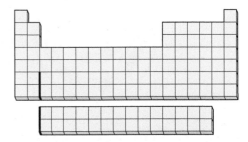

1.23 Where on the following outline of a periodic table does the dividing line between metals and nonmetals fall?

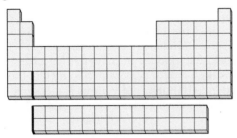

1.24 Is the red element on the following periodic table likely to be a gas, a liquid, or a solid? What is the atomic number of the blue element? Name at least one other element that is chemically similar to the green element.

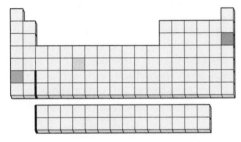

1.25 The radioactive element indicated on the following periodic table is used in smoke detectors. Identify it, give its atomic number, and tell what kind of group it's in.

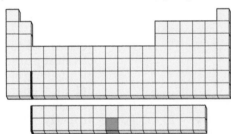

1.26 Characterize each of the following dartboards according to the accuracy and precision of the results.

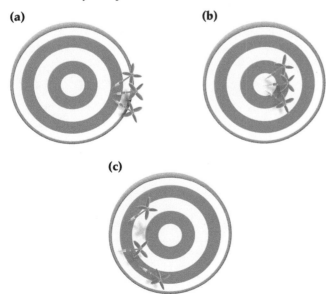

1.27 How many milliliters of water does the graduated cylinder in (a) contain, and how tall in centimeters is the paper clip in (b)? How many significant figures do you have in each answer?

(a)   **(b)**

1.28 Assume that you have two graduated cylinders, one with a capacity of 5 mL (a) and the other with a capacity of 50 mL (b). Draw a line in each, showing how much liquid you would add if you needed to measure 2.64 mL of water. Which cylinder will give the more accurate measurement? Explain.

(a)   **(b)**

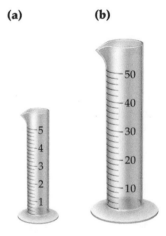

1.29 The following cylinder contains three liquids that do not mix with one another: water (density = 1.0 g/mL), vegetable oil (density = 0.93 g/mL), and mercury (density = 13.5 g/mL). Which liquid is which?

SECTION PROBLEMS

The Section Problems at the end of each chapter cover specific topics from the various sections of the chapter. These problems are presented in pairs, with each even-numbered problem followed by an odd-numbered one requiring similar skills. These paired problems are followed by unpaired Chapter Problems that draw on various parts of the chapter. Even-numbered problems (in color) are answered at the end of the book following the appendixes.

Elements and the Periodic Table (Sections 1.2–1.4)

1.30 How many elements are presently known? About how many occur naturally?

1.31 What are the rows called and what are the columns called in the periodic table?

1.32 How many groups are there in the periodic table? How are they labeled?

1.33 What common characteristics do elements within a group of the periodic table have?

1.34 Where in the periodic table are the main-group elements found? Where are the transition metal groups found?

1.35 Where in the periodic table are the metallic elements found? Where are the nonmetallic elements found?

1.36 What is a semimetal, and where in the periodic table are semimetals found?

1.37 List several general properties of the following:
(a) Alkali metals (b) Noble gases (c) Halogens

1.38 Without looking at a periodic table, list as many alkali metals as you can. (There are five common ones.)

1.39 Without looking at a periodic table, list as many alkaline earth metals as you can. (There are five common ones.)

1.40 Without looking at a periodic table, list as many halogens as you can. (There are four common ones.)

1.41 Without looking at a periodic table, list as many noble gases as you can. (There are six common ones.)

1.42 At room temperature, a certain element is found to be a soft, silver-colored solid that reacts violently with water and is a good conductor of electricity. Is the element likely to be a metal, a nonmetal, or a semimetal?

1.43 At room temperature, a certain element is found to be shiny, silver-colored solid that is a poor conductor of electricity. When a sample of the element is hit with a hammer, it shatters. Is the element likely to be a metal, a nonmetal, or a semimetal?

1.44 In which of the periodic groups 1A, 2A, 5A, and 7A is the first letter of all elements' symbol the same as the first letter of their name?

1.45 For which elements in groups 1A, 2A, 5A, and 7A of the periodic table does the first letter of their symbol differ from the first letter of their name?

1.46 What are the symbols for the following elements?
(a) Gadolinium (used in color TV screens)
(b) Germanium (used in semiconductors)
(c) Technetium (used in biomedical imaging)
(d) Arsenic (used in pesticides)

1.47 What are the symbols for the following elements?
(a) Cadmium (used in rechargeable ni-cad batteries)
(b) Iridium (used for hardening alloys)

(c) Beryllium (used in the space shuttle)
(d) Tungsten (used in lightbulbs)

1.48 Give the names corresponding to the following symbols:
(a) Te (b) Re (c) Be
(d) Ar (e) Pu

1.49 Give the names corresponding to the following symbols:
(a) B (b) Rh (c) Cf
(d) Os (e) Ga

1.50 What is wrong with each of the following statements?
(a) The symbol for tin is Ti.
(b) The symbol for manganese is Mg.
(c) The symbol for potassium is Po.
(d) The symbol for helium is HE.

1.51 What is wrong with each of the following statements?
(a) The symbol for carbon is ca.
(b) The symbol for sodium is So.
(c) The symbol for nitrogen is Ni.
(d) The symbol for chlorine is Cr.

Units and Significant Figures (Sections 1.5–1.13)

1.52 What is the difference between mass and weight?

1.53 What is the difference between a derived SI unit and a fundamental SI unit? Give an example of each.

1.54 What SI units are used for measuring the following quantities? For derived units, express your answers in terms of the six fundamental units.
(a) Mass (b) Length (c) Temperature
(d) Volume (e) Energy (f) Density

1.55 What SI prefixes correspond to the following multipliers?
(a) 10^3 (b) 10^{-6} (c) 10^9
(d) 10^{-12} (e) 10^{-2}

1.56 Which is larger, a Fahrenheit degree or a Celsius degree? By how much?

1.57 What is the difference between a kelvin and a Celsius degree?

1.58 What is the difference between a cubic decimeter (SI) and a liter (metric)?

1.59 What is the difference between a cubic centimeter (SI) and a milliliter (metric)?

1.60 Which of the following statements use exact numbers?
(a) 1 ft = 12 in.
(b) 1 cal = 4.184 J
(c) The height of Mt. Everest is 29,035 ft.
(d) The world record for the 1 mile run, set by Morocco's Hicham el Guerrouj in July, 1999, is 3 minutes, 43.13 seconds.

1.61 What is the difference in mass between a nickel that weighs 4.8 g and a nickel that weighs 4.8673 g?

1.62 Bottles of wine sometimes carry the notation "Volume = 75 cL." What does the unit cL mean?

1.63 What do the following abbreviations stand for?
(a) dL (b) dm (c) μm
(d) nL (e) MJ

1.64 Which quantity in each of the following pairs is larger?
(a) 5.63×10^6 cm or 6.02×10^1 km
(b) 46 μs or 3.2×10^{-2} ms
(c) 200,098 g or 17×10^1 kg

1.65 Which quantity in each of the following pairs is smaller?
(a) 154 pm or 7.7×10^{-9} cm
(b) 1.86×10^{11} μm or 2.02×10^2 km
(c) 2.9 GA or 3.1×10^{15} μA

1.66 How many picograms are in 1 mg? In 35 ng?

1.67 How many microliters are in 1 L? In 20 mL?

1.68 Carry out the following conversions:
(a) 5 pm = _____ cm = _____ nm
(b) 8.5 cm^3 = _____ m^3 = _____ mm^3
(c) 65.2 mg = _____ g = _____ pg

1.69 Which is larger, and by approximately how much?
(a) A liter or a quart   (b) A mile or a kilometer
(c) A gram or an ounce   (d) A centimeter or an inch

1.70 How many significant figures are in each of the following measurements?
(a) 35.0445 g   (b) 59.0001 cm   (c) 0.030 03 kg
(d) 0.004 50 m   (e) 67,000 m^2 (f) 3.8200×10^3 L

1.71 How many significant figures are in each of the following measurements?
(a) $130.95   (b) 2000.003 g   (c) 5 ft 3 in.
(d) 510 J   (e) 5.10×10^2 J   (f) 10 students

1.72 The Vehicle Assembly Building at the John F. Kennedy Space Center in Cape Canaveral, Florida, is the largest building in the world, with a volume of 3,666,500 m^3. Express this volume in scientific notation.

1.73 The diameter of the Earth at the equator is 7926.381 mi. Round off this quantity to four significant figures; to two significant figures. Express the answers in scientific notation.

1.74 Express the following measurements in scientific notation:
(a) 453.32 mg   (b) 0.000 042 1 mL   (c) 667,000 g

1.75 Convert the following measurements from scientific notation to standard notation:
(a) 3.221×10^{-3} mm   (b) 8.940×10^5 m
(c) $1.350 82 \times 10^{-12}$ m^3 (d) 6.4100×10^2 km

1.76 Round off the following quantities to the number of significant figures indicated in parentheses:
(a) 35,670.06 m (4, 6)   (b) 68.507 g (2, 3)
(c) 4.995×10^3 cm (3)   (d) $2.309 85 \times 10^{-4}$ kg (5)

1.77 Round off the following quantities to the number of significant figures indicated in parentheses:
(a) 7.0001 kg (4)   (b) 1.605 km (3)
(c) 13.2151 g/cm^3 (3)   (d) 2,300,000.1 (7)

1.78 Express the results of the following calculations with the correct number of significant figures:
(a) 4.884×2.05 (b) $94.61 \div 3.7$
(c) $3.7 \div 94.61$ (d) $5502.3 + 24 + 0.01$
(e) $86.3 + 1.42 - 0.09$ (f) 5.7×2.31

1.79 Express the results of the following calculations with the correct number of significant figures:
(a) $\dfrac{3.41 - 0.23}{5.233} \times 0.205$ (b) $\dfrac{5.556 \times 2.3}{4.223 - 0.08}$

1.80 The world record for the women's outdoor 20,000 meter run, set in 2000 by Tegla Loroupe, is 1:05:26.6 (seconds are given to the nearest tenth). What was her average speed, expressed in miles per hour with the correct number of significant figures? (Assume that the race distance is accurate to 5 significant figures.)

1.81 In the U.S., the emissions limit for carbon monoxide in motorcycle engine exhaust is 12.0 g of carbon monoxide per kilometer driven. What is this limit expressed in mg per mile with the correct number of significant figures?

Unit Conversions (Section 1.14)

1.82 Carry out the following conversions:
(a) How many grams of meat are in a quarter-pound hamburger (0.25 lb)?
(b) How tall in meters is the Willis Tower, formerly called the Sears Tower, in Chicago (1454 ft)?
(c) How large in square meters is the land area of Australia (2,941,526 mi^2)?

1.83 Convert the following quantities into SI units with the correct number of significant figures:
(a) 5.4 in.   (b) 66.31 lb   (c) 0.5521 gal
(d) 65 mi/h   (e) 978.3 yd^3 (f) 2.380 mi^2

1.84 The volume of water used for crop irrigation is measured in acre-feet, where 1 acre-foot is the amount of water needed to cover 1 acre of land to a depth of 1 ft.
(a) If there are 640 acres per square mile, how many cubic feet of water are in 1 acre-foot?
(b) How many acre-feet are in Lake Erie (total volume = 116 mi^3)?

1.85 The height of a horse is usually measured in *hands* instead of in feet, where 1 hand equals 1/3 ft (exactly).
(a) How tall in centimeters is a horse of 18.6 hands?
(b) What is the volume in cubic meters of a box measuring $6 \times 2.5 \times 15$ hands?

1.86 Concentrations of substances dissolved in solution are often expressed as mass per unit volume. For example, normal human blood has a cholesterol concentration of about 200 mg/100 mL. Express this concentration in the following units:
(a) mg/L   (b) μg/mL   (c) g/L   (d) ng/μL
(e) How much total blood cholesterol in grams does a person have if the normal blood volume in the body is 5 L?

1.87 Weights in England are commonly measured in *stones*, where 1 stone = 14 lb. What is the weight in pounds of a person who weighs 8.65 stones?

1.88 Among many alternative units that might be considered as a measure of time is the *shake* rather than the second. Based on the expression "faster than a shake of a lamb's tail," we'll define 1 shake as equal to 2.5×10^{-4} s. If a car is traveling at 55 mi/h, what is its speed in cm/shake?

1.89 Administration of digitalis, a drug used to control atrial fibrillation in heart patients, must be carefully controlled because even a modest overdosage can be fatal. To take differences between patients into account, drug dosages are prescribed in terms of mg/kg body weight. Thus, a child and an adult differ greatly in weight, but both receive the same dosage per kilogram of body weight. At a dosage of 20 μg/kg body weight, how many milligrams of digitalis should a 160 lb patient receive?

Temperature (Section 1.8)

1.90 The normal body temperature of a goat is 39.9 °C, and that of an Australian spiny anteater is 22.2 °C. Express these temperatures in degrees Fahrenheit.

1.91 Of the 90 or so naturally occurring elements, only four are liquid near room temperature: mercury (melting point = −38.87 °C), bromine (melting point = −7.2 °C), cesium (melting point = 28.40 °C), and gallium (melting point = 29.78 °C). Convert these melting points to degrees Fahrenheit.

1.92 Tungsten, the element used to make filaments in light-bulbs, has a melting point of 6192 °F. Convert this temperature to degrees Celsius and to kelvin.

1.93 Suppose that your oven is calibrated in degrees Fahrenheit but a recipe calls for you to bake at 175 °C. What oven setting should you use?

1.94 Suppose you were dissatisfied with both Celsius and Fahrenheit units and wanted to design your own temperature scale based on ethyl alcohol (ethanol). On the Celsius scale, ethanol has a melting point of −117.3 °C and a boiling point of 78.5 °C, but on your new scale calibrated in units of degrees ethanol, °E, you define ethanol to melt at 0 °E and boil at 200 °E.
   (a) How does your ethanol degree compare in size with a Celsius degree?
   (b) How does an ethanol degree compare in size with a Fahrenheit degree?
   (c) What are the melting and boiling points of water on the ethanol scale?
   (d) What is normal human body temperature (98.6 °F) on the ethanol scale?
   (e) If the outside thermometer reads 130 °E, how would you dress to go out?

1.95 Answer parts **(a)**–**(d)** of Problem 1.94 assuming that your new temperature scale is based on ammonia, NH_3. On the Celsius scale, ammonia has a melting point of −77.7 °C and a boiling point of −33.4 °C, but on your new scale calibrated in units of degrees ammonia, °A, you define ammonia to melt at 0 °A and boil at 100 °A.

Density (Section 1.10)

1.96 The density of silver is 10.5 g/cm³. What is the mass (in kilograms) of a cube of silver that measures 0.62 m on each side?

1.97 A vessel contains 4.67 L of bromine, whose density is 3.10 g/cm³. What is the mass of the bromine in the vessel (in kilograms)?

1.98 Aspirin has a density of 1.40 g/cm³. What is the volume in cubic centimeters of an aspirin tablet weighing 250 mg? Of a tablet weighing 500 lb?

1.99 Gaseous hydrogen has a density of 0.0899 g/L at 0 °C, and gaseous chlorine has a density of 3.214 g/L at the same temperature. How many liters of each would you need if you wanted 1.0078 g of hydrogen and 35.45 g of chlorine?

1.100 What is the density of lead in g/cm³ if a rectangular bar measuring 0.50 cm in height, 1.55 cm in width, and 25.00 cm in length has a mass of 220.9 g?

1.101 What is the density of lithium metal in g/cm³ if a cylindrical wire with a diameter of 2.40 mm and a length of 15.0 cm has a mass of 0.3624 g?

Energy (Section 1.11)

1.102 Which has more kinetic energy, a 1400 kg car moving at 115 km/h or a 12,000 kg truck moving at 38 km/h?

1.103 Assume that the kinetic energy of a 1400 kg car moving at 115 km/h (Problem 1.102) is converted entirely into heat. How many calories of heat are released, and what amount of water in liters could be heated from 20.0 °C to 50.0 °C by the car's energy? (One calorie raises the temperature of 1 mL of water by 1 °C.)

1.104 The combustion of 45.0 g of methane (natural gas) releases 2498 kJ of heat energy. How much energy in kilocalories (kcal) would combustion of 0.450 ounces of methane release?

1.105 Sodium (Na) metal undergoes a chemical reaction with chlorine (Cl) gas to yield sodium chloride, or common table salt. If 1.00 g of sodium reacts with 1.54 g of chlorine, 2.54 g of sodium chloride is formed and 17.9 kJ of heat is released. How much sodium and how much chlorine in grams would have to react to release 171 kcal of heat?

CHAPTER PROBLEMS

1.106 When an irregularly shaped chunk of silicon weighing 8.763 g was placed in a graduated cylinder containing 25.00 mL of water, the water level in the cylinder rose to 28.76 mL. What is the density of silicon in g/cm³?

1.107 Lignum vitae is a hard, durable, and extremely dense wood used to make ship bearings. A sphere of this wood with a diameter of 7.60 cm has a mass of 313 g.

   (a) What is the density of the lignum vitae sphere?
   (b) Will the sphere float or sink in water?
   (c) Will the sphere float or sink in chloroform? (The density of chloroform is 1.48 g/mL).

1.108 Sodium chloride has a melting point of 1074 K and a boiling point of 1686 K. Convert these temperatures to degrees Celsius and to degrees Fahrenheit.

1.109 A large tanker truck for carrying gasoline has a capacity of 3.4×10^4 L.

 (a) What is the tanker's capacity in gallons?

 (b) If the retail price of gasoline is $3.00 per gallon, what is the value of the truck's full load of gasoline?

1.110 The density of chloroform, a widely used organic solvent, is 1.4832 g/mL at 20 °C. How many milliliters would you use if you wanted 112.5 g of chloroform?

1.111 More sulfuric acid (density = 1.8302 g/cm^3) is produced than any other chemical—approximately 3.6×10^{11} lb/yr worldwide. What is the volume of this amount in liters?

1.112 Answer the following questions:

 (a) An old rule of thumb in cooking says: "A pint's a pound the world around." What is the density in g/mL of a substance for which 1 pt = 1 lb exactly?

 (b) There are exactly 640 acres in 1 square mile. How many square meters are in 1 acre?

 (c) A certain type of wood has a density of 0.40 g/cm^3. What is the mass of 1.0 cord of this wood in kg, where 1 cord is 128 cubic feet of wood?

 (d) A particular sample of crude oil has a density of 0.85 g/mL. What is the mass of 1.00 barrel of this crude oil in kg, where a barrel of oil is exactly 42 gallons?

 (e) A gallon of ice cream contains exactly 32 servings, and each serving has 165 Calories, of which 30.0% are derived from fat. How many Calories derived from fat would you consume if you ate one half-gallon of ice cream?

1.113 A 1.0 ounce piece of chocolate contains 15 mg of caffeine, and a 6.0 ounce cup of regular coffee contains 105 mg of caffeine. How much chocolate would you have to consume to get as much caffeine as you would from 2.0 cups of coffee?

1.114 A bag of Hershey's Kisses contains the following information:

 Serving size: 9 pieces = 41 grams

 Calories per serving: 230

 Total fat per serving: 13 g

 (a) The bag contains 2.0 lbs of Hershey's Kisses. How many Kisses are in the bag?

 (b) The density of a Hershey's Kiss is 1.4 g/mL. What is the volume of a single Hershey's Kiss?

 (c) How many Calories are in one Hershey's Kiss?

 (d) Each gram of fat yields 9 Calories when metabolized. What percent of the calories in Hershey's Kisses are derived from fat?

1.115 Vinaigrette salad dressing consists mainly of oil and vinegar. The density of olive oil is 0.918 g/cm^3, the density of vinegar is 1.006 g/cm^3, and the two do not mix. If a certain mixture of olive oil and vinegar has a total mass of 397.8 g and a total volume of 422.8 cm^3, what is the volume of oil and what is the volume of vinegar in the mixture?

1.116 At a certain point, the Celsius and Fahrenheit scales "cross," giving the same numerical value on both. At what temperature does this crossover occur?

1.117 Imagine that you place a cork measuring 1.30 cm × 5.50 cm × 3.00 cm in a pan of water and that on top of the cork you place a small cube of lead measuring 1.15 cm on each edge. The density of cork is 0.235 g/cm^3, and the density of lead is 11.35 g/cm^3. Will the combination of cork plus lead float or sink?

1.118 The LD$_{50}$ of aspirin in rats is given in the *Inquiry* at the end of the chapter. If a baby aspirin tablet contains 81 mg of aspirin, how many whole tablets would a 0.75 lb rat have to consume to have at least a 50% chance of dying from the dose?

1.119 An Eastern diamondback rattlesnake was milked until 0.134 g of venom was obtained. The venom was then administered subcutaneously in equal portions to 550 mice with an average weight of 0.70 oz, and exactly half the mice died. What is the LD$_{50}$ (in g/kg) for the snake venom in mice? See the *Inquiry* at the end of this chapter.

1.120 A 125 mL sample of water at 293.2 K was heated for 8 min, 25 s so as to give a constant temperature increase of 3.0 °F/min. What is the final temperature of the water in degrees Celsius?

1.121 A calibrated flask was filled to the 25.00 mL mark with ethyl alcohol. By weighing the flask before and after adding the alcohol, it was determined that the flask contained 19.7325 g of alcohol. In a second experiment, 25.0920 g of metal beads were added to the flask, and the flask was again filled to the 25.00 mL mark with ethyl alcohol. The total mass of the metal plus alcohol in the flask was determined to be 38.4704 g. What is the density of the metal in g/mL?

1.122 Brass is a copper–zinc alloy. What is the mass in grams of a brass cylinder having a length of 1.62 in. and a diameter of 0.514 in. if the composition of the brass is 67.0% copper and 33.0% zinc by mass? The density of copper is 8.92 g/cm^3, and the density of zinc is 7.14 g/cm^3. Assume that the density of the brass varies linearly with composition.

1.123 Ocean currents are measured in *Sverdrups* (sv) where 1 sv = 10^9 m^3/s. The Gulf Stream off the tip of Florida, for instance, has a flow of 35 sv.

 (a) What is the flow of the Gulf Stream in milliliters per minute?

 (b) What mass of water in the Gulf Stream flows past a given point in 24 hours? The density of seawater is 1.025 g/mL.

 (c) How much time is required for 1 petaliter (PL; 1 PL = 10^{15} L) of seawater to flow past a given point?

1.124 The element gallium (Ga) has the second largest liquid range of any element, melting at 29.78 °C and boiling at 2204 °C at atmospheric pressure.

 (a) Is gallium a metal, a nonmetal, or a semimetal?

(b) Name another element whose chemical properties might be similar to those of gallium.

(c) What is the density of gallium in g/cm^3 at 25 °C if a 1 in. cube has a mass of 0.2133 lb?

(d) Assume that you construct a thermometer using gallium as the fluid instead of mercury, and that you define the melting point of gallium as 0 °G and the boiling point of gallium as 1000 °G. What is the melting point of sodium chloride (801 °C) on the gallium scale?

1.125 Distances over land are measured in *statute miles* (5280 ft), but distances over water are measured in *nautical miles*, where 1 nautical mile was originally defined as 1 minute of arc along an Earth meridian, or 1/21,600 of the Earth's circumference through the poles. A ship's speed through the water is measured in *knots*, where 1 knot = 1 nautical mile per hour. Historically, the unit *knot* derived from the practice of measuring a ship's speed by throwing a log tied to a knotted line over the side. The line had a knot tied in it at intervals of 47 ft. 3 in., and the number of knots run out in 28 seconds was counted to determine speed.

(a) How many feet are in a nautical mile? How many meters?

(b) The northern bluefin tuna can weigh up to 1500 pounds and can swim at speeds up to 48 miles per hour. How fast is this in knots?

(c) A *league* is defined as 3 nautical miles. The Mariana Trench, with a depth of 35,798 feet, is the deepest point in the ocean. How many leagues deep is this?

(d) By international agreement, the nautical mile is now defined as exactly 1852 meters. By what percentage does this current definition differ from the original definition, and by what percentage does it differ from a statute mile?

CHAPTER 2

Atoms, Molecules, and Ions

If you could take a large piece of pure gold and cut it into ever smaller and smaller pieces, you would find that it is made of a vast number of tiny fundamental units that we call *atoms*. In fact, one pound of gold contains 1.387×10^{24} atoms!

CONTENTS

People have always been fascinated by changes, particularly by changes that are dramatic or useful. In the ancient world, the change that occurred when a stick of wood burned, gave off heat, and turned into a small pile of ash was especially important. Similarly, the change that occurred when a reddish lump of rock (iron ore) was heated with charcoal and produced a gray metal (iron) useful for making weapons, tools, and other implements was of enormous value. Observing such changes eventually caused philosophers to think about what different materials might be composed of and led to the idea of fundamental substances that we today call elements.

At the same time philosophers were pondering the question of elements, they were also thinking about related matters: What is an element made of? Is matter continuously divisible into ever smaller and smaller pieces, or is there an ultimate limit? Can you cut a piece of gold in two, take one of the pieces and cut *it* in two, and so on infinitely, or is there a point at which you must stop? Most thinkers, including Plato and Aristotle, believed that matter is continuously divisible, but the Greek philosopher Democritus (460–370 B.C.) disagreed. Democritus proposed that matter is composed of tiny, discrete particles, which we now call *atoms*, from the Greek word *atomos*, meaning "indivisible." Little else was learned about elements and atoms until the birth of modern experimental science some 2000 years later.

2.1 THE CONSERVATION OF MASS AND THE LAW OF DEFINITE PROPORTIONS

The Englishman Robert Boyle (1627–1691) is generally credited with being the first to study chemistry as a separate intellectual discipline and the first to carry out rigorous chemical experiments. Through a careful series of researches into the nature and behavior of gases, Boyle provided clear evidence for the atomic makeup of matter. In addition, Boyle was the first to clearly define an element as a substance that cannot be chemically broken down further and to suggest that a substantial number of different elements might exist. Atoms of these different elements, in turn, can join together in different ways to yield a vast number of different substances we call **chemical compounds**.

Progress in chemistry was slow in the decades following Boyle, and it was not until the work of Joseph Priestley (1733–1804) that the next great leap was made. Priestley prepared and isolated the gas oxygen in 1774 by heating the compound mercury oxide (HgO) according to the chemical equation we would now write as $2\,HgO \rightarrow 2\,Hg + O_2$.

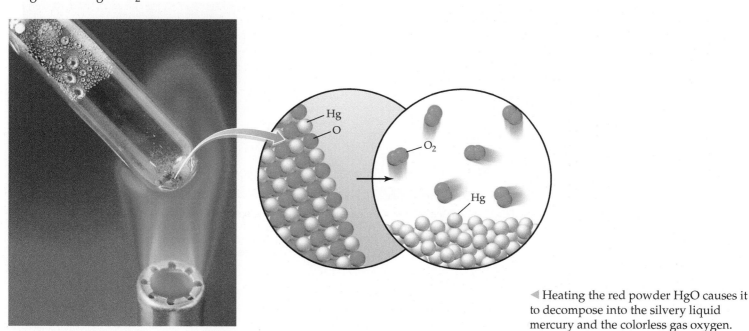

◀ Heating the red powder HgO causes it to decompose into the silvery liquid mercury and the colorless gas oxygen.

In this standard format for writing chemical transformations, each compound is described by its **chemical formula**, which lists the symbols of its constituent elements and uses subscripts to indicate the number of atoms of each. If no subscript is given, the number 1 is understood. Thus, sodium chloride (table salt) is written as NaCl, water as H_2O, and sucrose (table sugar) as $C_{12}H_{22}O_{11}$. A chemical reaction is written in a standard format called a **chemical equation**, in which the reactant substances undergoing change are written on the left, the product substances being formed are written on the right, and an arrow is drawn between them to indicate the direction of the chemical transformation.

Soon after Priestley's discovery, Antoine Lavoisier (1743–1794) showed that oxygen is the key substance involved in combustion. Furthermore, Lavoisier demonstrated with careful measurements that when combustion is carried out in a closed container, the mass of the combustion products exactly equals the mass of the starting reactants. When hydrogen gas burns and combines with oxygen to yield water (H_2O), for instance, the mass of the water formed is equal to the mass of the hydrogen and oxygen consumed. Called the **law of mass conservation**, this principle is a cornerstone of chemical science.

> **Law of Mass Conservation**   Mass is neither created nor destroyed in chemical reactions.

It's easy to demonstrate the law of mass conservation by carrying out an experiment like that shown in **Figure 2.1**. If 3.25 g of mercury nitrate [$Hg(NO_3)_2$] and 3.32 g of potassium iodide (KI) are each dissolved in water and the solutions are mixed, an immediate chemical reaction occurs leading to formation of the insoluble orange solid mercury iodide (HgI_2). Filtering the reaction mixture gives 4.55 g of mercury iodide, and evaporation of the water from the remaining solution leaves 2.02 g of potassium nitrate (KNO_3). Thus, the combined mass of the reactants (3.25 g + 3.32 g = 6.57 g) is exactly equal to the combined mass of the products (4.55 g + 2.02 g = 6.57 g).

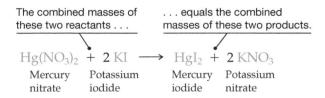

The combined masses of these two reactants . . .   . . . equals the combined masses of these two products.

$$Hg(NO_3)_2 \ + \ 2\,KI \ \longrightarrow \ HgI_2 \ + \ 2\,KNO_3$$

Mercury   Potassium   Mercury   Potassium
nitrate   iodide   iodide   nitrate

Known amounts of solid KI and solid $Hg(NO_3)_2$ are weighed and then dissolved in water.

The solutions are mixed to give solid HgI_2, which is removed by filtration.

The solution that remains is evaporated to give solid KNO_3. On weighing, the combined masses of the products equals the combined masses of the reactants.

Figure 2.1

An illustration of the law of mass conservation. In any chemical reaction, the combined mass of the final products equals the combined mass of the starting reactants.

Further investigations in the decades following Lavoisier led the French chemist Joseph Proust (1754–1826) to formulate a second fundamental chemical principle that we now call the **law of definite proportions**:

Law of Definite Proportions   Different samples of a pure chemical compound always contain the same proportion of elements by mass.

Every sample of water (H_2O) contains 1 part hydrogen and 8 parts oxygen by mass; every sample of carbon dioxide (CO_2) contains 3 parts carbon and 8 parts oxygen by mass; and so on. *Elements combine in specific proportions, not in random proportions.*

2.2 THE LAW OF MULTIPLE PROPORTIONS AND DALTON'S ATOMIC THEORY

At the same time that Proust was formulating the law of definite proportions, the English schoolteacher John Dalton (1766–1844) was exploring along similar lines. His work led him to propose what has come to be called the **law of multiple proportions**:

Law of Multiple Proportions   Elements can combine in different ways to form different chemical compounds, with mass ratios that are small whole-number multiples of each other.

The key to Dalton's proposition was his realization that the *same* elements sometimes combine in different ratios to give *different* chemical compounds. For example, nitrogen and oxygen can combine either in a $7:8$ mass ratio to make the compound we know today as nitric oxide (NO) or in a $7:16$ mass ratio to make the compound we know as nitrogen dioxide (NO_2). The second compound contains exactly twice as much oxygen as the first.

▲ Copper metal reacts with nitric acid (HNO_3) to yield the brown gas NO_2.

NO:	7 g nitrogen per 8 g oxygen	N:O mass ratio = $7:8$
NO_2:	7 g nitrogen per 16 g oxygen	N:O mass ratio = $7:16$

Comparison of N:O ratios in NO and NO_2

$$\frac{\text{N:O mass ratio in NO}}{\text{N:O mass ratio in NO}_2} = \frac{(7 \text{ g N})/(8 \text{ g O})}{(7 \text{ g N})/(16 \text{ g O})} = 2$$

This result makes sense only if we assume that matter is composed of discrete atoms that have characteristic masses and combine with one another in specific and well-defined ways (Figure 2.2).

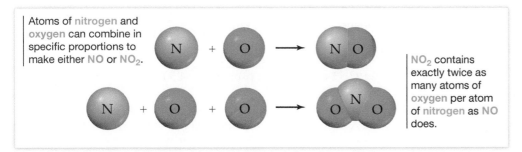

Atoms of nitrogen and oxygen can combine in specific proportions to make either NO or NO_2.

NO_2 contains exactly twice as many atoms of oxygen per atom of nitrogen as NO does.

Figure 2.2
An illustration of Dalton's law of multiple proportions.

Taking all three laws together—the law of mass conservation, the law of definite proportions, and the law of multiple proportions—ultimately led Dalton to propose a new theory of matter. He reasoned as follows:

- *Elements are made up of tiny particles called* **atoms**. Although Dalton didn't know what atoms were like, he nevertheless felt they were necessary to explain why there were so many different elements.

- *Each element is characterized by the mass of its atoms. Atoms of the same element have the same mass, but atoms of different elements have different masses.* Dalton realized that there must be some feature that distinguishes the atoms of one element from those of another. Because Proust's law of definite proportions showed that elements always combine in specific mass ratios, Dalton reasoned that the distinguishing feature among atoms of different elements must be mass.

- *The chemical combination of elements to make different chemical compounds occurs when atoms join in small whole-number ratios.* Only if whole numbers of atoms combine will different samples of a pure chemical compound always contain the same proportion of elements by mass (the law of definite proportions and the law of multiple proportions). Fractional parts of atoms are never involved in chemical reactions.

- *Chemical reactions only rearrange how atoms are combined in chemical compounds; the atoms themselves don't change.* Dalton realized that atoms must be chemically indestructible for the law of mass conservation to be valid. If the same numbers and kinds of atoms are present in both reactants and products, then the masses of reactants and products must also be the same.

Not everything that Dalton proposed was correct. He thought, for instance, that water had the formula HO rather than H_2O. Nevertheless, his atomic theory of matter was ultimately accepted and came to form a cornerstone of modern chemical science.

▲ These samples of sulfur and carbon have different masses but contain the same number of atoms.

WORKED EXAMPLE 2.1

USING THE LAW OF MULTIPLE PROPORTIONS

Methane and propane are both constituents of natural gas. A sample of methane contains 5.70 g of carbon atoms and 1.90 g of hydrogen atoms combined in a certain way, whereas a sample of propane contains 4.47 g of carbon atoms and 0.993 g of hydrogen atoms combined in a different way. Show that the two compounds obey the law of multiple proportions.

STRATEGY

Find the C:H mass ratio in each compound, and then compare the ratios to see whether they are small whole-number multiples of each other.

SOLUTION

$$\text{Methane:} \quad \text{C:H mass ratio} = \frac{5.70 \text{ g C}}{1.90 \text{ g H}} = 3.00$$

$$\text{Propane:} \quad \text{C:H mass ratio} = \frac{4.47 \text{ g C}}{0.993 \text{ g H}} = 4.50$$

$$\frac{\text{C:H mass ratio in methane}}{\text{C:H mass ratio in propane}} = \frac{3.00}{4.50} = \frac{2}{3}$$

▶ **PROBLEM 2.1** Compounds A and B are colorless gases obtained by combining sulfur with oxygen. Compound A results from combining 6.00 g of sulfur with 5.99 g of oxygen, and compound B results from combining 8.60 g of sulfur with 12.88 g of oxygen. Show that the mass ratios in the two compounds are simple multiples of each other.

▲ Sulfur burns with a bluish flame to yield colorless SO_2 gas.

2.3 ATOMIC STRUCTURE: ELECTRONS

Dalton's atomic theory is fine as far as it goes, but it leaves unanswered the obvious question: What is an atom made of? Dalton himself had no way of answering this question, and it was not until nearly a century later that experiments by the English physicist J. J. Thomson (1856–1940) provided some clues. Thomson's experiments involved the use of *cathode-ray tubes* (CRTs), early predecessors of the tubes found in older televisions and computer displays.

As shown in Figure 2.3a, a cathode-ray tube is a sealed glass vessel from which the air has been removed and in which two thin pieces of metal, called *electrodes*, have been sealed. When a sufficiently high voltage is applied across the electrodes, an electric current flows through the tube from the negatively charged electrode (the *cathode*) to the positively charged electrode (the *anode*). If the tube is not fully evacuated but still contains a small amount of air or other gas, the flowing current is visible as a glow called a *cathode ray*. Furthermore, if the anode has a hole in it and the end of the tube is coated with a phosphorescent substance such as zinc sulfide, some of the rays pass through the hole and strike the end of the tube, where they are visible as a bright spot of light—exactly what happens in a CRT television screen or computer monitor.

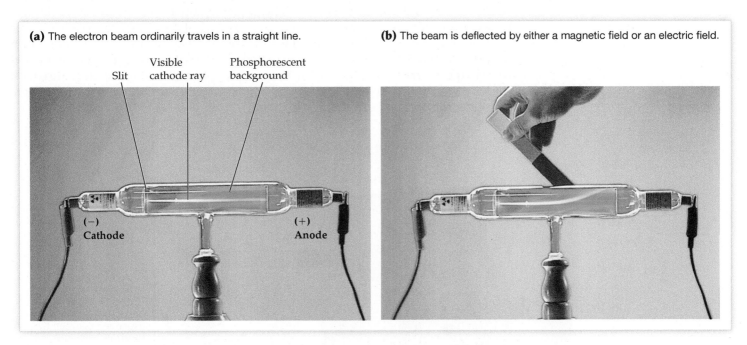

(a) The electron beam ordinarily travels in a straight line.

Slit   Visible cathode ray   Phosphorescent background

(−) Cathode   (+) Anode

(b) The beam is deflected by either a magnetic field or an electric field.

Figure 2.3

A cathode-ray tube. In a cathode-ray tube, a stream of electrons emitted from the negatively charged cathode passes through a slit, moves toward the positively charged anode, and is detected by a phosphorescent strip.

Experiments by a number of physicists in the 1890s had shown that cathode rays can be deflected by bringing either a magnet or an electrically charged plate near the tube (Figure 2.3b). Because the beam is produced at a negative electrode and is deflected toward a positive plate, Thomson proposed that cathode rays must consist of tiny, negatively charged particles, which we now call **electrons**. Furthermore, because electrons are emitted from electrodes made of many different metals, all these different metals must contain electrons.

Thomson reasoned that the amount of deflection of the electron beam in a cathode-ray tube due to a nearby magnetic or electric field should depend on three factors:

1. *The strength of the deflecting magnetic or electric field.* The stronger the magnet or the higher the voltage on the charged plate, the greater the deflection.

2. *The size of the negative charge on the electron.* The larger the charge on the particle, the greater its interaction with the magnetic or electric field and the greater the deflection.

3. *The mass of the electron.* The lighter the particle, the greater its deflection (just as a Ping-Pong ball is more easily deflected than a bowling ball).

By carefully measuring the amount of deflection caused by electric and magnetic fields of known strength, Thomson was able to calculate the ratio of the electron's electric charge to its mass: its *charge-to-mass ratio, e/m.* The modern value is

$$\frac{e}{m} = 1.758\ 820 \times 10^8\,\text{C/g}$$

where e is the magnitude of the charge on the electron in coulombs (C) and m is the mass of the electron in grams. (We'll say more about coulombs and electrical charge in Chapter 17.) Note that because e is defined as a positive quantity, the actual (negative) charge on the electron is $-e$.

Thomson was able to measure only the ratio of charge to mass, not charge or mass itself, and it was left to the American R. A. Millikan (1868–1953) to devise a method for measuring the mass of an electron (**Figure 2.4**). In Millikan's experiment, a fine mist of oil was sprayed into a chamber, and the tiny droplets were allowed to fall between two horizontal plates. Observing the spherical droplets through a telescopic eyepiece made it possible to determine how rapidly they fell through the air, which in turn allowed their masses to be calculated. The droplets were then given a negative charge by irradiating them with X rays. By applying a voltage to the plates, with the upper plate positive, it was possible to counteract the downward fall of the charged droplets and keep them suspended.

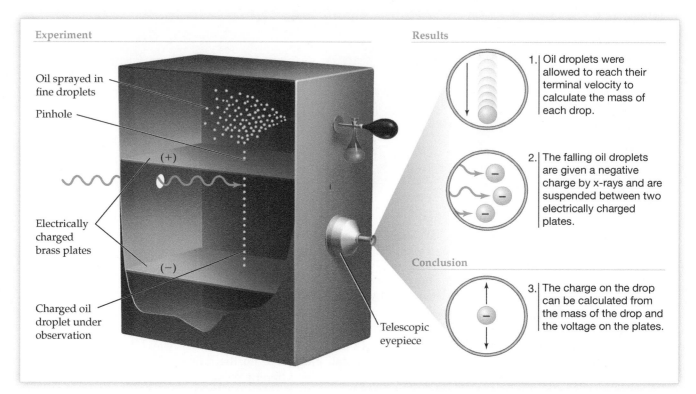

Figure 2.4
Millikan's oil drop experiment.

With the voltage on the plates and the mass of the droplets known, Millikan was able to show that the charge on a given droplet was always a small whole-number multiple of e, whose modern value is $1.602\ 176 \times 10^{-19}$ C. Substituting the value of e into Thomson's charge-to-mass ratio then gives the mass m of the electron as $9.109\,382 \times 10^{-28}$ g:

$$\text{Because} \quad \frac{e}{m} = 1.758\,820 \times 10^{8}\,\text{C/g}$$

$$\text{then} \quad m = \frac{e}{1.758\,820 \times 10^{8}\,\text{C/g}} = \frac{1.602\,176 \times 10^{-19}\,\text{C}}{1.758\,820 \times 10^{8}\,\text{C/g}}$$

$$= 9.109\,382 \times 10^{-28}\,\text{g}$$

2.4 ATOMIC STRUCTURE: PROTONS AND NEUTRONS

Think about the consequences of Thomson's cathode-ray experiments. Because matter is electrically neutral overall, the fact that the atoms in an electrode can give off negatively charged particles (electrons) must mean that those same atoms also contain positively charged particles for electrical balance. The search for those positively charged particles and for an overall picture of atomic structure led to a landmark experiment published in 1911 by the New Zealand physicist Ernest Rutherford (1871–1937).

Rutherford's work involved the use of *alpha (α) particles*, a type of emission previously found to be given off by a number of naturally occurring radioactive elements, including radium, polonium, and radon. Rutherford knew that alpha particles are about 7000 times more massive than electrons and that they have a positive charge that is twice the magnitude of the charge on an electron, but opposite in sign.

When Rutherford directed a beam of alpha particles at a thin gold foil, he found that almost all the particles passed through the foil undeflected. A very small number, however (about 1 of every 20,000), were deflected at an angle, and a few actually bounced back toward the particle source (**Figure 2.5**).

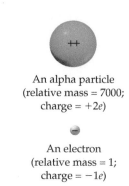

An alpha particle
(relative mass = 7000;
charge = +2e)

An electron
(relative mass = 1;
charge = −1e)

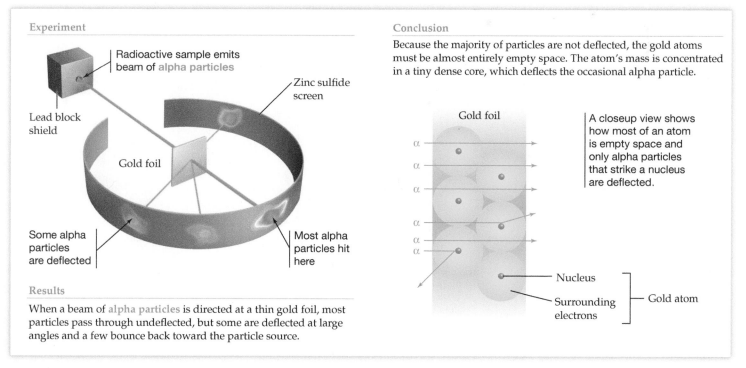

Experiment

Radioactive sample emits beam of alpha particles

Zinc sulfide screen

Lead block shield

Gold foil

Some alpha particles are deflected

Most alpha particles hit here

Results

When a beam of alpha particles is directed at a thin gold foil, most particles pass through undeflected, but some are deflected at large angles and a few bounce back toward the particle source.

Conclusion

Because the majority of particles are not deflected, the gold atoms must be almost entirely empty space. The atom's mass is concentrated in a tiny dense core, which deflects the occasional alpha particle.

Gold foil

A closeup view shows how most of an atom is empty space and only alpha particles that strike a nucleus are deflected.

Nucleus

Surrounding electrons

Gold atom

Figure 2.5
Rutherford's scattering experiment.

▲ The relative size of the nucleus in an atom is roughly the same as that of a pea in the middle of this huge stadium.

Rutherford explained his results by proposing that a metal atom must be almost entirely empty space and have its mass concentrated in a tiny central core that he called the **nucleus**. If the nucleus contains the atom's positive charges and most of its mass, and if the electrons are a relatively large distance away, then it is clear why the observed scattering results are obtained: most alpha particles encounter empty space as they fly through the foil. Only when a positive alpha particle chances to come near a small but massive positive nucleus is it repelled strongly enough to make it bounce backward.

Modern measurements show that an atom has a diameter of roughly 10^{-10} m and that a nucleus has a diameter of about 10^{-15} m. It's difficult to imagine from these numbers alone, though, just how small a nucleus really is. For comparison purposes, if an atom were the size of a large domed stadium, the nucleus would be approximately the size of a small pea in the center of the playing field.

Further experiments by Rutherford and others between 1910 and 1930 showed that a nucleus is composed of two kinds of particles, called *protons* and *neutrons*. **Protons** have a mass of $1.672\,622 \times 10^{-24}$ g (about 1836 times that of an electron) and are positively charged. Because the charge on a proton is opposite in sign but equal in size to that on an electron, the numbers of protons and electrons in a neutral atom are equal. **Neutrons** ($1.674\,927 \times 10^{-24}$ g) are almost identical in mass to protons but carry no charge, and the number of neutrons in a nucleus is not directly related to the numbers of protons and electrons. Table 2.1 compares the three fundamental subatomic particles, and Figure 2.6 gives an overall view of the atom.

TABLE 2.1   A Comparison of Subatomic Particles

Particle	Mass grams	amu*	Charge coulombs	e
Electron	$9.109\,382 \times 10^{-28}$	$5.485\,799 \times 10^{-4}$	$-1.602\,176 \times 10^{-19}$	-1
Proton	$1.672\,622 \times 10^{-24}$	$1.007\,276$	$+1.602\,176 \times 10^{-19}$	$+1$
Neutron	$1.674\,927 \times 10^{-24}$	$1.008\,665$	0	0

* The atomic mass unit (amu) is defined in Section 2.6.

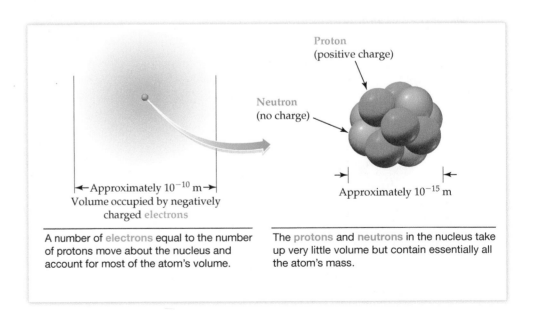

Figure 2.6
A view of the atom.

WORKED EXAMPLE 2.2

CALCULATIONS USING ATOMIC SIZE

Ordinary "lead" pencils actually are made of a form of carbon called graphite. If a pencil line is 0.35 mm wide and the diameter of a carbon atom is 1.5×10^{-10} m, how many atoms wide is the line?

STRATEGY

Begin with the known information, and set up an equation using appropriate conversion factors so that the unwanted units cancel. In this example, let's begin with the width of the pencil line in millimeters, then convert to meters, and then divide the line width in meters by the diameter of a single atom in meters.

SOLUTION

$$\text{Atoms} = 0.35 \, \text{mm} \times \frac{1 \, \text{m}}{1000 \, \text{mm}} \times \frac{1 \, \text{atom}}{1.5 \times 10^{-10} \, \text{m}} = 2.3 \times 10^6 \, \text{atoms}$$

BALLPARK CHECK

A single carbon atom is about 10^{-10} m across, so it takes 10^{10} carbon atoms placed side by side to stretch 1 m, 10^7 carbon atoms to stretch 1 mm, and about 0.3×10^7 (or 3×10^6; 3 *million*) carbon atoms to stretch 0.35 mm. The estimate agrees with the solution.

▶ **PROBLEM 2.2**   The gold foil Rutherford used in his scattering experiment had a thickness of approximately 0.005 mm. If a single gold atom has a diameter of 2.9×10^{-8} cm, how many atoms thick was Rutherford's foil?

▶ **PROBLEM 2.3**   A small speck of carbon the size of a pinhead contains about 10^{19} atoms, the diameter of a carbon atom is 1.5×10^{-10} m, and the circumference of the Earth at the equator is 40,075 km. How many times around the Earth would the atoms from this speck of carbon extend if they were laid side by side?

2.5   ATOMIC NUMBERS

Thus far, we've described atoms only in general terms and have not yet answered the most important question: What is it that makes one atom different from another? How, for example, does an atom of gold differ from an atom of carbon? The answer turns out to be quite simple. *Elements differ from one another according to the number of protons in their atoms' nuclei*, a value called the element's **atomic number (Z)**. That is, all atoms of a given element contain the same number of protons in their nuclei. All hydrogen atoms, atomic number 1, have 1 proton; all helium atoms, atomic number 2, have 2 protons; all carbon atoms, atomic number 6, have 6 protons; and so on. In addition, every neutral atom contains a number of electrons equal to its number of protons.

Atomic Number (Z) = Number of protons in an atom's nucleus
                    = Number of electrons around an atom's nucleus

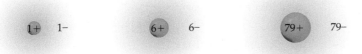

A hydrogen atom   A carbon atom   A gold atom
(1 proton; 1 electron)   (6 protons; 6 electrons)   (79 protons; 79 electrons)

In addition to protons, the nuclei of all atoms (other than hydrogen) also contain neutrons. The sum of the numbers of protons (Z) and neutrons (N) in an atom is called the atom's **mass number (A)**. That is, $A = Z + N$.

$$\text{Mass Number } (A) = \text{Number of protons } (Z) + \text{number of neutrons } (N)$$

Most hydrogen atoms have 1 proton and no neutrons, so their mass number is $A = 1 + 0 = 1$. Most helium atoms have 2 protons and 2 neutrons, so their mass number is $A = 2 + 2 = 4$. Most carbon atoms have 6 protons and 6 neutrons, so their mass number is $A = 6 + 6 = 12$; and so on. Except for hydrogen, stable atoms always contain at least as many neutrons as protons, although there is no simple way to predict how many neutrons a given atom will have.

Notice that we said *most* hydrogen atoms have mass number 1, *most* helium atoms have mass number 4, and *most* carbon atoms have mass number 12. In fact, different atoms of the same element can have different mass numbers depending on how many neutrons they have. Atoms with identical atomic numbers but different mass numbers are called **isotopes**. Hydrogen, for example, has three isotopes.

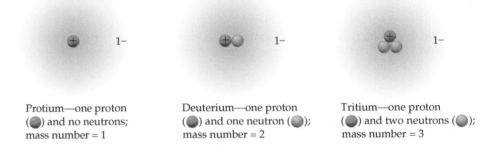

Protium—one proton (●) and no neutrons; mass number = 1

Deuterium—one proton (●) and one neutron (●); mass number = 2

Tritium—one proton (●) and two neutrons (●); mass number = 3

All hydrogen atoms have 1 proton in their nucleus (otherwise they wouldn't be hydrogen), but 99.985% of them have no neutrons. These hydrogen atoms, called *protium*, have mass number 1. In addition, 0.015% of hydrogen atoms, called *deuterium*, have 1 neutron and mass number 2. Still other hydrogen atoms, called *tritium*, have 2 neutrons and mass number 3. An unstable, radioactive isotope, tritium occurs only in trace amounts on Earth but is made artificially in nuclear reactors. As other examples, there are 15 known isotopes of nitrogen, only 2 of which occur naturally on Earth, and 25 known isotopes of uranium, only 3 of which occur naturally. In total, more than 3600 isotopes of the 118 known elements have been identified.

A specific isotope is represented by showing its element symbol, along with its mass number as a left superscript and its atomic number as a left subscript. Thus, protium is represented as $^{1}_{1}\text{H}$, deuterium as $^{2}_{1}\text{H}$, and tritium as $^{3}_{1}\text{H}$. Similarly, the two naturally occurring isotopes of nitrogen are represented as $^{14}_{7}\text{N}$ (spoken as "nitrogen-14") and $^{15}_{7}\text{N}$ (nitrogen-15). The number of neutrons in an isotope is not given explicitly but can be calculated by subtracting the atomic number (subscript) from the mass number (superscript). For example, subtracting the atomic number 7 from the mass number 14 indicates that a $^{14}_{7}\text{N}$ atom has 7 neutrons.

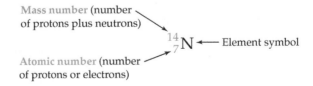

Mass number (number of protons plus neutrons)

$^{14}_{7}\text{N}$ ← Element symbol

Atomic number (number of protons or electrons)

The number of neutrons in an atom has relatively little effect on the atom's chemical properties. The chemical behavior of an element is determined almost entirely by the number of electrons it has, which in turn is determined by the number of protons in its nucleus. All three isotopes of hydrogen therefore behave similarly (although not identically) in their chemical reactions.

WORKED EXAMPLE 2.3

INTERPRETING AN ISOTOPE SYMBOL

The isotope of uranium used to generate nuclear power is $^{235}_{92}U$. How many protons, neutrons, and electrons does an atom of $^{235}_{92}U$ have?

STRATEGY

The atomic number (subscript 92) in the symbol $^{235}_{92}U$ indicates the number of protons and electrons in the atom. The number of neutrons is the difference between the mass number (superscript 235) and the atomic number (92).

SOLUTION

An atom of $^{235}_{92}U$ has 92 protons, 92 electrons, and $235 - 92 = 143$ neutrons.

▲ Uranium-235 is used as fuel in this nuclear-powered icebreaker.

WORKED EXAMPLE 2.4

WRITING AN ISOTOPE SYMBOL

Element X is toxic to humans in high concentration but is essential to life in low concentrations. Identify element X, whose atoms contain 24 protons, and write the symbol for the isotope of X that has 28 neutrons.

STRATEGY

The number of protons in an atom's nucleus is the element's atomic number. The mass number is the sum of the atomic number and the number of neutrons.

SOLUTION

According to the periodic table, the element with atomic number 24 is chromium (Cr). The particular isotope of chromium in this instance has a mass number of $24 + 28 = 52$ and is written $^{52}_{24}Cr$.

▶ **PROBLEM 2.4**   The isotope $^{75}_{34}Se$ is used medically for the diagnosis of pancreatic disorders. How many protons, neutrons, and electrons does an atom of $^{75}_{34}Se$ have?

▶ **PROBLEM 2.5**   Chlorine, one of the elements in common table salt (sodium chloride), has two main isotopes, with mass numbers 35 and 37. Look up the atomic number of chlorine, tell how many neutrons each isotope contains, and give the standard symbol for each.

▶ **PROBLEM 2.6**   An atom of element X contains 47 protons and 62 neutrons. Identify the element, and write the symbol for the isotope in the standard format.

2.6 ATOMIC MASSES AND THE MOLE

Pick up a pencil, and look at the small amount of tip visible. How many atoms (pencil lead is made of carbon) do you think are in the tip? One thing is certain: atoms are so tiny that the number needed to make a visible sample is enormous. In fact, even the smallest speck of dust visible to the naked eye contains at least 10^{17} atoms. Thus, the mass in grams of a single atom is much too small a number for convenience so chemists use a unit called an **atomic mass unit (amu)**, also called a *dalton* (Da) in biological work. One amu is defined as exactly 1/12 the mass of an atom of $^{12}_{6}C$ and is equal to $1.660\ 539 \times 10^{-24}$ g.

$$\text{Mass of one } ^{12}_{6}C \text{ atom} = 12 \text{ amu (exactly)}$$

$$1 \text{ amu} = \frac{\text{Mass of one } ^{12}_{6}C \text{ atom}}{12} = 1.660\ 539 \times 10^{-24} \text{ g}$$

Because the mass of an atom's electrons is negligible compared to the mass of its protons and neutrons, defining 1 amu as 1/12 the mass of a $^{12}_{6}C$ atom means that protons and neutrons both have a mass of almost exactly 1 amu (Table 2.1 on page 42).

Thus, the mass of a specific atom in atomic mass units—called the atom's *isotopic mass*—is numerically close to the atom's mass number. A $_1^1$H atom, for instance, has a mass of 1.007 825 amu; a $_{92}^{235}$U atom has a mass of 235.043 930 amu; and so forth.

Most elements occur naturally as a mixture of different isotopes. Thus, if you look at the periodic table inside the front cover, you'll see listed below the symbol for each element a value called the element's *atomic mass*, or *atomic weight*. The unit amu is understood but not specified.

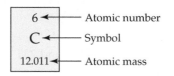

An element's **atomic mass** is the weighted average of the isotopic masses of the element's naturally occurring isotopes. Carbon, for example, occurs on Earth as a mixture of two major isotopes, $_6^{12}$C (98.89% natural abundance) and $_6^{13}$C (1.11% natural abundance). Although the isotopic mass of any individual carbon atom is either 12 amu (a carbon-12 atom) or 13.0034 amu (a carbon-13 atom), the average isotopic mass—that is, the atomic mass—of a large collection of carbon atoms is 12.011 amu. A third carbon isotope, $_6^{14}$C, also exists, but its natural abundance is so small that it can be ignored when calculating atomic mass.

$$\text{Atomic mass of C} = (\text{Mass of }_6^{12}\text{C})(\text{Abundance of }_6^{12}\text{C}) + (\text{Mass of }_6^{13}\text{C})(\text{Abundance of }_6^{13}\text{C})$$

$$= (12 \text{ amu})(0.9889) + (13.0034 \text{ amu})(0.0111)$$

$$= 11.867 \text{ amu} + 0.144 \text{ amu} = 12.011 \text{ amu}$$

A particularly useful point about atomic masses is that they act as conversion factors between numbers of atoms and masses; that is, they allow us to *count* a large number of atoms by *weighing* a sample of the substance. For instance, knowing that carbon has an atomic mass of 12.011 amu lets us calculate that a small pencil tip made of carbon and weighing 15 mg (1.5×10^{-2} g) contains 7.5×10^{20} atoms:

$$(1.5 \times 10^{-2} \text{ g})\left(\frac{1 \text{ amu}}{1.6605 \times 10^{-24} \text{ g}}\right)\left(\frac{1 \text{ C atom}}{12.011 \text{ amu}}\right) = 7.5 \times 10^{20} \text{ C atoms}$$

As another example, the fact that the atomic mass of silver is 107.868 amu means that a silver ring weighing 1.872 g contains 1.045×10^{22} silver atoms:

$$(1.872 \text{ g})\left(\frac{1 \text{ amu}}{1.6605 \times 10^{-24} \text{ g}}\right)\left(\frac{1 \text{ Ag atom}}{107.868 \text{ amu}}\right) = 1.045 \times 10^{22} \text{ Ag atoms}$$

Let's think some more about what it means to be able to count atoms using atomic masses. As we've just seen, the total mass of a given number of atoms is the atom's atomic mass times the number of atoms. Thus, if you have two samples of different elements that both contain the same number of atoms, then the ratio of masses of the two samples is the same as the ratio of their atomic masses. Take carbon and silver, for instance. The average mass ratio of one carbon atom (12.011 amu) to one silver atom (107.868 amu) is 12.011 : 107.868, so the mass ratio of any given number of C atoms to the same number of Ag atoms is always 12.011 : 107.868. Furthermore, the numerical value of the ratio is the same regardless of the mass units used. That is, 12.011 *amu* of carbon contains exactly the same number of atoms as 107.868 *amu* of silver, and 12.011 *grams* of carbon contains exactly the same number of atoms as 107.868 *grams* of silver.

$$\frac{12.011 \text{ amu}}{107.868 \text{ amu}} = \frac{12.011 \text{ mg}}{107.868 \text{ mg}} = \frac{12.011 \text{ g}}{107.868 \text{ g}} = \frac{12.011 \text{ kg}}{107.868 \text{ kg}} = 0.111 \ 35$$

When referring to the enormous numbers of atoms that make up the visible amounts we typically deal with, chemists use the fundamental SI unit for amount called a *mole*, abbreviated *mol*. One **mole** of any element is the amount whose mass in grams, called its **molar mass**, is numerically equal to its atomic mass. One mole of carbon atoms has a mass of 12.011 g, one mole of silver atoms has a mass of 107.868 g, and so on. Molar mass thus acts as a conversion factor that lets you convert between mass in grams and number of atoms. Whenever you have the same number of moles of different elements, you also have the same number of atoms.

How many atoms are there in a mole? Experiments show that one mole of any element contains $6.022\,141 \times 10^{23}$ atoms, a value called **Avogadro's number**, abbreviated N_A, after the Italian scientist who first recognized the importance of the mass/number relationship. Avogadro's number of atoms of any element—that is, one mole—has a mass in grams equal to the element's atomic mass.

It's hard to grasp the magnitude of a quantity as large as Avogadro's number, but some comparisons might give you a sense of scale: The age of the universe in seconds (13.7 billion years, or 4.32×10^{17} s) is less than a millionth the size of Avogadro's number. The number of milliliters of water in the world's oceans (1.3×10^{24} mL) is only twice the size of Avogadro's number. The mass of the Earth in kilograms (5.98×10^{24} kg) is only ten times Avogadro's number, and so on.

▲ These samples of helium, sulfur, copper, and mercury each contain 1 mole. Do they have the same mass?

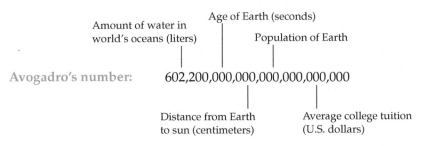

We'll return to the mole and see its uses in Section 3.3.

WORKED EXAMPLE 2.5

CALCULATING AN ATOMIC MASS

Chlorine has two naturally occurring isotopes: $^{35}_{17}\text{Cl}$, with a natural abundance of 75.76% and an isotopic mass of 34.969 amu, and $^{37}_{17}\text{Cl}$, with a natural abundance of 24.24% and an isotopic mass of 36.966 amu. What is the atomic mass of chlorine?

STRATEGY

The atomic mass of an element is the weighted average of the isotopic masses, which equals the sum of the masses of each isotope times the natural abundance of that isotope:

$$\text{Atomic mass} = \left(\text{Mass of } ^{35}_{17}\text{Cl}\right)\left(\text{Abundance of } ^{35}_{17}\text{Cl}\right)$$
$$+ \left(\text{Mass of } ^{37}_{17}\text{Cl}\right)\left(\text{Abundance of } ^{37}_{17}\text{Cl}\right)$$

SOLUTION

$$\text{Atomic mass} = (34.969\text{ amu})(0.7576) + (36.966\text{ amu})(0.2424) = 35.45\text{ amu}$$

BALLPARK CHECK

The atomic mass is somewhere between 35 amu and 37 amu, the masses of the two individual isotopes, and is closer to 35 amu, the mass of the more abundant isotope—perhaps about 35.5 amu.

WORKED EXAMPLE 2.6

CONVERTING FROM MASS TO NUMBERS OF MOLES AND ATOMS

How many moles and how many atoms of silicon are in a sample weighing 10.53 g? The atomic mass of silicon is 28.0855 amu.

STRATEGY

The fact that the atomic mass of silicon is 28.0855 amu means that 1 mol of silicon has a mass of 28.0855 g. Use this molar mass to convert between mass and number of moles, and then use Avogadro's number to find the number of atoms.

continued on the next page

SOLUTION

$$(10.53 \text{ g Si})\left(\frac{1 \text{ mol Si}}{28.0855 \text{ g Si}}\right) = 0.3749 \text{ mol Si}$$

$$(0.3749 \text{ mol Si})\left(\frac{6.022 \times 10^{23} \text{ atoms Si}}{1 \text{ mol Si}}\right) = 2.258 \times 10^{23} \text{ atoms Si}$$

BALLPARK CHECK

A mass of 10.53 g of silicon is a bit more than 1/3 the molar mass of silicon (28.0855 g/mol), so the sample contains a bit more than 0.33 mol. This number of moles, in turns, contains a bit more than 1/3 of Avogadro's number of atoms, or about 2×10^{23} atoms.

▶ **PROBLEM 2.7** Copper metal has two naturally occurring isotopes: copper-63 (69.15%; isotopic mass = 62.93 amu) and copper-65 (30.85%; isotopic mass = 64.93 amu). Calculate the atomic mass of copper, and check your answer in a periodic table.

▶ **PROBLEM 2.8** Based on your answer to Problem 2.7, how many atoms of copper are in an old penny made of pure copper and weighing 2.15 g?

▶ **PROBLEM 2.9** What is the mass in grams of each of the following samples?
(a) 1.505 mol of Ti (b) 0.337 mol of Na (c) 2.583 mol of U

▶ **PROBLEM 2.10** How many moles are in each of the following samples?
(a) 11.51 g of Ti (b) 29.127 g of Na (c) 1.477 kg of U

2.7 NUCLEAR CHEMISTRY: THE CHANGE OF ONE ELEMENT INTO ANOTHER

We saw at the beginning of this chapter, and we'll see repeatedly throughout the book, that the identities of atoms don't change when different chemical substances react with one another to give products. When natural gas (methane; CH_4) burns in oxygen, for instance, the C, H, and O atoms combine in a different way to yield carbon dioxide (CO_2) and water (H_2O), but they still remain C, H, and O atoms. When metallic sodium (Na) reacts with gaseous chlorine atoms (Cl), solid sodium chloride (NaCl) forms but the Na and Cl atoms remain the same. Yet anyone who reads a newspaper or watches television knows that atoms *can* change identity, resulting in the conversion of one element into another. Atomic weapons, nuclear energy, and radioactive radon gas in our homes are all topics of societal importance, and all involve **nuclear chemistry**—the study of the properties and changes of atomic nuclei.

Take the element carbon, for example. There are 15 known isotopes of carbon, two of which occur commonly (^{12}C and ^{13}C) and one of which (^{14}C) is produced in small amounts in the upper atmosphere by the action of cosmic rays on ^{14}N atoms. The remaining 12 carbon isotopes have been produced artificially. Only the two commonly occurring isotopes are stable; the other 13 undergo spontaneous changes to their nuclei. Carbon-14, for instance, slowly decays to give nitrogen-14 plus an electron, a process we can write as the following *nuclear equation* (as opposed to a chemical equation, described previously in Section 2.1).

$$^{14}_{6}C \rightarrow ^{14}_{7}N + ^{0}_{-1}e$$

In a **nuclear equation**, the element symbols represent only the *nuclei* of atoms rather than the entire neutral atoms, so the subscript represents only the number of nuclear charges (protons). An emitted electron is written as $^{0}_{-1}e$, where the superscript 0 indicates that the mass of an electron is essentially zero when compared to that of a proton or neutron, and the subscript indicates that the charge is −1.

Nuclear reactions, such as the spontaneous change of ^{14}C to ^{14}N, are distinguished from chemical reactions, such as that of sodium with chlorine, in several ways:

- A nuclear reaction involves a change in an atom's nucleus, usually producing a different element. A chemical reaction, by contrast, involves only a change in the way that different atoms are combined. A chemical reaction never changes the nuclei themselves or produces a different element.
- Different isotopes of an element have essentially the same behavior in chemical reactions but often have completely different behavior in nuclear reactions.
- The energy change accompanying a nuclear reaction is far greater than that accompanying a chemical reaction. The nuclear transformation of 1.0 g of uranium-235 ($^{235}_{92}U$) releases more than one *million* times as much energy as the chemical combustion of 1.0 g of methane.

2.8 RADIOACTIVITY

Scientists have known since 1896 that many nuclei are **radioactive**—they undergo a spontaneous decay and emit some form of *radiation*. Early studies of radioactive isotopes, or **radioisotopes**, by Ernest Rutherford in 1897 showed that there are three common types of radiation with markedly different properties: *alpha (α), beta (β),* and *gamma (γ) radiation*, named after the first three letters of the Greek alphabet.

Alpha (α) Radiation

Using the simple experiment shown in **Figure 2.7**, Rutherford found that **α radiation** consists of a stream of particles that are repelled by a positively charged electrode, attracted by a negatively charged electrode, and have a mass-to-charge ratio identifying them as helium nuclei, $^{4}_{2}He^{2+}$. Alpha particles thus consist of two protons and two neutrons.

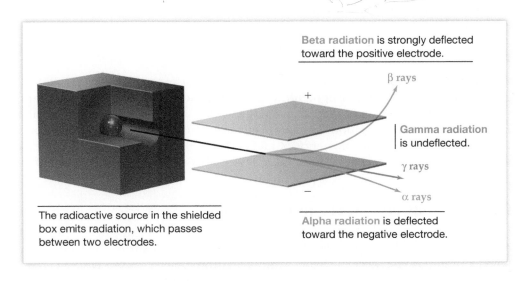

Beta radiation is strongly deflected toward the positive electrode.

β rays

Gamma radiation is undeflected.

γ rays

α rays

The radioactive source in the shielded box emits radiation, which passes between two electrodes.

Alpha radiation is deflected toward the negative electrode.

Figure 2.7
The effect of an electric field on α, β, and γ radiation.

Because the emission of an α particle from a nucleus results in a loss of two protons and two neutrons, it reduces the mass number of the nucleus by 4 and reduces the atomic number by 2. Alpha emission is particularly common for heavy radioactive isotopes. Uranium-238, for example, spontaneously emits an α particle and forms thorium-234.

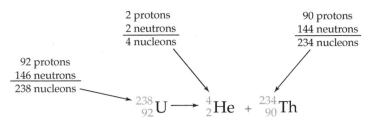

2 protons
2 neutrons
4 nucleons

90 protons
144 neutrons
234 nucleons

92 protons
146 neutrons
238 nucleons

$$^{238}_{92}U \longrightarrow {}^{4}_{2}He + {}^{234}_{90}Th$$

Note how the nuclear equation for the radioactive decay of uranium-238 is written. The equation is said to be *balanced* because the total number of neutrons and protons, collectively called **nucleons**, or nuclear particles, is the same on both sides of the equation and the number of charges on the nuclei and on any elementary particles (protons and electrons) is the same on both sides. In the decay of $^{238}_{92}\text{U}$ to give $^{4}_{2}\text{He}$ and $^{234}_{90}\text{Th}$, for instance, there are 238 nucleons and 92 nuclear charges on both sides of the equation.

Beta (β) Radiation

Further work by Rutherford in the late 1800s showed that **β radiation** consists of a stream of particles that are attracted to a positive electrode (Figure 2.7), repelled by a negative electrode, and have a mass-to-charge ratio identifying them as electrons, $^{0}_{-1}\text{e}$ or β^-. Beta emission occurs when a neutron in the nucleus spontaneously decays into a proton plus an electron, which is then ejected. The product nucleus has the same mass number as the starting nucleus because a neutron has turned into a proton, but it has a higher atomic number because it has the newly created proton. The reaction of ^{131}I to give ^{131}Xe is an example:

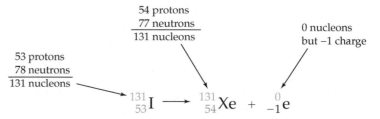

Writing the emitted β particle as $^{0}_{-1}\text{e}$ in the nuclear equation makes clear the charge balance of the nuclear reaction. The subscript in the $^{131}_{53}\text{I}$ nucleus on the left (53) is balanced by the sum of the two subscripts on the right ($54 - 1 = 53$).

Gamma (γ) Radiation

Gamma (γ) radiation is unaffected by either electric or magnetic fields (Figure 2.7) and has no mass. Like visible light, ultraviolet rays, and X rays, γ radiation is simply electromagnetic radiation of very high energy, which we'll discuss in more detail in Section 5.1. Gamma radiation almost always accompanies α and β emission as a mechanism for the release of energy, but it is often not shown when writing nuclear equations because it changes neither the mass number nor the atomic number of the product nucleus.

Positron Emission and Electron Capture

In addition to α, β, and γ radiation, two other types of radioactive decay processes also occur commonly: *positron emission* and *electron capture*. **Positron emission** occurs when a proton in the nucleus changes into a neutron plus an ejected *positron* ($^{0}_{+1}\text{e}$ or β^+), a particle that can be thought of as a positive electron. A positron has the same mass as an electron but an opposite charge.

The result of positron emission is a decrease in the atomic number of the product nucleus but no change in the mass number. Potassium-40, for example, undergoes positron emission to yield argon-40, a nuclear reaction important in geology for dating rocks. Note once again that the sum of the two subscripts on the right of the nuclear equation ($18 + 1 = 19$) is equal to the subscript in the $^{40}_{19}\text{K}$ nucleus on the left.

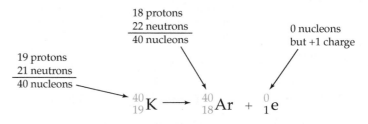

You might already know that the acronym PET used in medical imaging stands for *positron emission tomography*. A chemical compound containing a positron-emitting isotope, usually ^{18}F, is injected into the body and accumulates at a certain site, such as in a tumor. When decay occurs, the emitted positron reacts with a nearby electron and is instantly annihilated, releasing gamma rays whose position in the body can be detected.

Electron capture is a process in which the nucleus captures one of the surrounding electrons in an atom, thereby converting a proton into a neutron. The mass number of the product nucleus is unchanged, but the atomic number decreases by 1, just as in positron emission. The conversion of mercury-197 into gold-197 is an example:

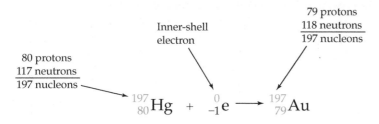

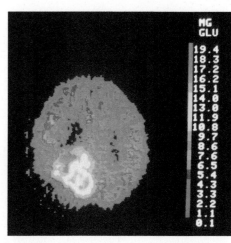

▲ A PET scan of a 62 year old man with a brain tumor, as indicated by the yellow and orange area in the lower left portion of the brain.

Characteristics of the different kinds of radioactive decay processes are summarized in Table 2.2.

TABLE 2.2 A Summary of Radioactive Decay Processes

Process	Symbol	Change in Atomic Number	Change in Mass Number	Change in Neutron Number
Alpha emission	$^4_2$He or α	−2	−4	−2
Beta emission	$^0_{-1}$e or β^-	+1	0	−1
Gamma emission	$^0_0\gamma$ or γ	0	0	0
Positron emission	$^0_1$e or β^+	−1	0	+1
Electron capture	E. C.	−1	0	+1

WORKED EXAMPLE 2.7

BALANCING NUCLEAR EQUATIONS

Write a balanced nuclear equation for each of the following processes:

(a) Alpha emission from curium-242: $^{242}_{96}$Cm → $^4_2$He + ?
(b) Beta emission from magnesium-28: $^{28}_{12}$Mg → $^0_{-1}$e + ?
(c) Positron emission from xenon-118: $^{118}_{54}$Xe → $^0_1$e + ?

STRATEGY

The key to writing nuclear equations is to make sure that the number of nucleons is the same on both sides of the equation and that the number of nuclear charges plus electron or positron charges is the same.

SOLUTION

(a) In α emission, the mass number decreases by 4 and the atomic number decreases by 2, giving plutonium-238: $^{242}_{96}$Cm → $^4_2$He + $^{238}_{94}$Pu

(b) In β emission, the mass number is unchanged and the atomic number increases by 1, giving aluminum-28: $^{28}_{12}$Mg → $^0_{-1}$e + $^{28}_{13}$Al

(c) In positron emission, the mass number is unchanged and the atomic number decreases by 1, giving iodine-118: $^{118}_{54}$Xe → $^0_1$e + $^{118}_{53}$I

▶ **PROBLEM 2.11**   Write a balanced nuclear equation for each of the following processes:

(a) Beta emission from ruthenium-106: $^{106}_{44}Ru \rightarrow {}^{0}_{-1}e + ?$

(b) Alpha emission from bismuth-189: $^{189}_{83}Bi \rightarrow {}^{4}_{2}He + ?$

(c) Electron capture by polonium-204: $^{204}_{84}Po + {}^{0}_{-1}e \rightarrow ?$

▶ **PROBLEM 2.12**   What particle is produced by decay of thorium-214 to radium-210?

$$^{214}_{90}Th \rightarrow {}^{210}_{88}Ra + ?$$

CONCEPTUAL PROBLEM 2.13   Identify the isotopes involved, and tell what type of decay process is occurring in the following nuclear reaction:

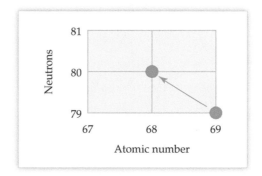

2.9   NUCLEAR STABILITY

Why do some nuclei undergo spontaneous radioactive decay while others do not? Why, for instance, does a carbon-*14* nucleus, with 6 protons and *8* neutrons, spontaneously emit a *β* particle, whereas a carbon-*13* nucleus, with 6 protons and 7 neutrons, is nonradioactive?

The answer has to do with the neutron/proton ratio in the nucleus and with the forces holding the nucleus together. To see the effect of the neutron/proton ratio on nuclear stability, look at the grid in **Figure 2.8**. Numbers on the side of the grid give the number of neutrons in different nuclei, and numbers along the bottom give the

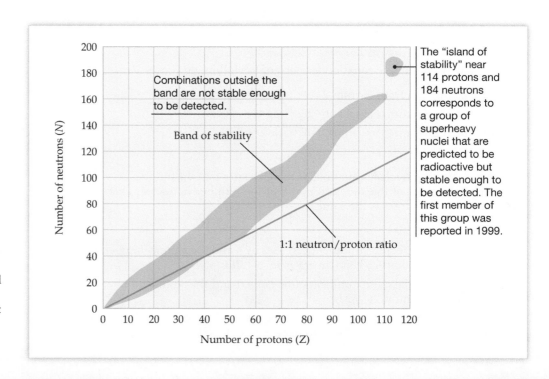

Figure 2.8
The band of nuclear stability. The band indicates various neutron/proton combinations that give rise to nuclei that are either nonradioactive or that are radioactive but decay slowly enough to exist for a measurable time.

number of protons. The first 92 elements are naturally occurring, while the remainder are the artificially produced **transuranium elements**. (Actually, only 90 of the first 92 elements occur naturally. Technetium and promethium do not occur naturally because all their isotopes are radioactive and have very short lifetimes. Francium and astatine occur on Earth only in very tiny amounts.)

When the more than 3600 known isotopes are plotted on the neutron/proton grid in Figure 2.8, they fall in a curved band sometimes called the *band of nuclear stability*. Even within the band, only 264 of the isotopes are nonradioactive. The others decay spontaneously, although their rates of decay vary enormously. On either side of the band is a so-called sea of instability representing the large number of unstable neutron–proton combinations that have never been detected. Particularly interesting is the island of stability predicted to exist for a few superheavy isotopes near 114 protons and 184 neutrons. The first members of this group—^{287}114, ^{288}114, and ^{289}114—were prepared in 1999 and do indeed seem to be stable enough to live for several seconds before they decay.

Several generalizations can be made about nuclear stability:

• Every element in the periodic table has at least one radioactive isotope.

• Hydrogen is the only element whose most abundant isotope ($^1_1$H) contains more protons (1) than neutrons (0).

• The ratio of neutrons to protons gradually increases, giving a curved appearance to the band of stability.

• All isotopes heavier than bismuth-209 are radioactive, even though they may decay slowly and be stable enough to occur naturally.

A close-up look at a segment of the band of nuclear stability (**Figure 2.9**) shows the interesting trend that radioactive nuclei with higher neutron/proton ratios (top side

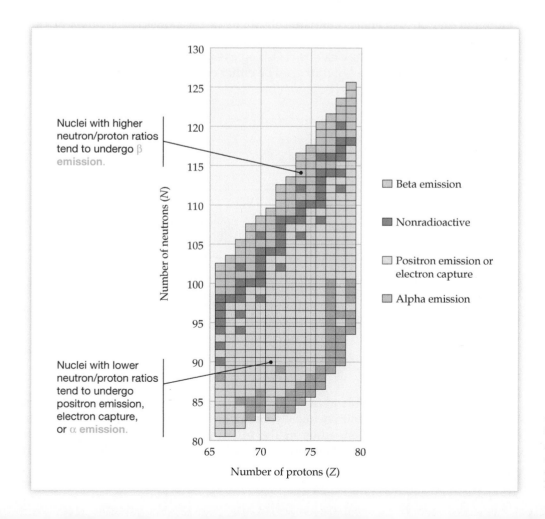

Figure 2.9
A close-up look at the band of nuclear stability. This look at the region from $Z = 66$ (dysprosium) through $Z = 79$ (gold) shows the types of radioactive processes that various radioisotopes undergo.

of the band) tend to emit β particles while nuclei with lower neutron/proton ratios (bottom side of the band) tend to undergo nuclear decay by positron emission, electron capture, or α emission.

The trend shown in Figure 2.9 makes sense if you think about it: The nuclei on the top side of the band are neutron-rich and therefore undergo a process—β emission—that *decreases* the neutron/proton ratio by converting a neutron into a proton. The nuclei on the bottom side of the band, by contrast, are neutron-poor and therefore undergo processes that *increase* the neutron/proton ratio. Take a minute to convince yourself that α emission does, in fact, increase the neutron/proton ratio for heavy nuclei in which n > p.

This process decreases the neutron/proton ratio:
$$\begin{cases} \text{Beta emission:} & \text{Neutron} \rightarrow \text{Proton} + \beta^- \end{cases}$$

These processes increase the neutron/proton ratio:
$$\begin{cases} \text{Positron emission:} & \text{Proton} \rightarrow \text{Neutron} + \beta^+ \\ \text{Electron capture:} & \text{Proton} + \text{Electron} \rightarrow \text{Neutron} \\ \text{Alpha emission:} & {}_{Z}^{A}X \rightarrow {}_{Z-2}^{A-4}Y + {}_{2}^{4}He \end{cases}$$

▶ **PROBLEM 2.14**

(a) Of the two isotopes ^{173}Au and ^{199}Au, one decays by β emission and one decays by α emission. Which does which?

(b) Of the two isotopes ^{196}Pb and ^{206}Pb, one is nonradioactive and one decays by positron emission. Which is which?

2.10   MIXTURES AND CHEMICAL COMPOUNDS; MOLECULES AND COVALENT BONDS

Although only 90 elements occur naturally, there are far more than 90 different kinds of matter on Earth. Just look around, and you'll surely find a few hundred. All the many kinds of matter you see can be classified as either mixtures or pure substances (Figure 2.10). Pure substances, in turn, can be either elements or chemical compounds.

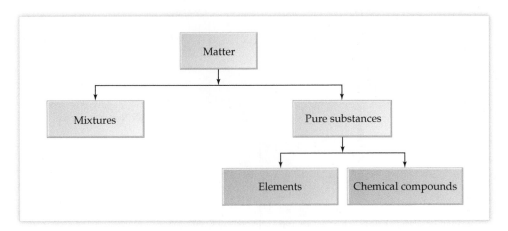

Figure 2.10
A scheme for the classification of matter.

A **mixture** is simply a blend of two or more substances added together in some arbitrary proportion without chemically changing the individual substances themselves. Thus, the constituent units in the mixture are not all the same, and the proportion of the units is variable. Hydrogen gas and oxygen gas, for instance, can be mixed in any ratio without changing them (as long as there is no flame nearby to initiate reaction), just as a spoonful of sugar and a spoonful of salt can be mixed.

A chemical compound, in contrast to a mixture, is a pure substance that is formed when atoms of different elements combine in a specific way to create a new material with properties completely unlike those of its constituent elements. A chemical compound has a constant composition throughout, and its constituent units are all identical. For example, when atoms of sodium (a soft, silvery metal) combine with atoms of chlorine (a toxic, yellow-green gas), the familiar white solid called sodium chloride (table salt) is formed. Similarly, when two atoms of hydrogen combine with one atom of oxygen, water is formed.

To see how a chemical compound is formed, imagine what must happen when two atoms approach each other at the beginning of a chemical reaction. Because the electrons of an atom occupy a much greater volume than the nucleus, it's the electrons that actually make the contact when atoms collide. Thus, it's the electrons that form the connections, or **chemical bonds**, that join atoms together in compounds. Chemical bonds between atoms are usually classified as either *covalent* or *ionic*. As a general rule, covalent bonds occur primarily between nonmetal atoms, while ionic bonds occur primarily between metal and nonmetal atoms. Let's look briefly at both kinds, beginning with covalent bonds.

A **covalent bond**, the most common kind of chemical bond, results when two atoms *share* several (usually two) electrons. A simple way to think about a covalent bond is to imagine it as a tug-of-war. If two people pull on the same rope, they are effectively joined together. Neither person can escape from the other as long as both hold on. Similarly with atoms: when two atoms both hold on to some shared electrons, the atoms are bonded together (Figure 2.11).

▲ The crystalline quartz sand on this beach is a pure compound (SiO_2), but the seawater is a liquid mixture of many compounds dissolved in water.

The two teams are joined together because both are tugging on the same rope.

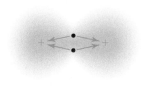

Similarly, two atoms are joined together when both nuclei (+) tug on the same electrons (dots).

Figure 2.11
A covalent bond between atoms is analogous to a tug-of-war.

The unit of matter that results when two or more atoms are joined by covalent bonds is called a **molecule**. A hydrogen chloride molecule (HCl) results when a hydrogen atom and a chlorine atom share two electrons. A water molecule (H_2O) results when each of two hydrogen atoms shares two electrons with a single oxygen atom. An ammonia molecule (NH_3) results when each of three hydrogen atoms shares two electrons with a nitrogen atom, and so on. To visualize these and other molecules, it helps to imagine the individual atoms as spheres joined together to form molecules with specific three-dimensional shapes, as shown in Figure 2.12. *Ball-and-stick* models specifically indicate the covalent bonds between atoms, while *space-filling* models accurately portray overall molecular shape but don't explicitly show covalent bonds.

Figure 2.12
Molecular models. Drawings such as these help in visualizing molecules.

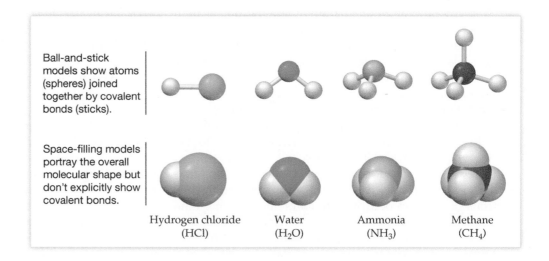

Ball-and-stick models show atoms (spheres) joined together by covalent bonds (sticks).

Space-filling models portray the overall molecular shape but don't explicitly show covalent bonds.

| Hydrogen chloride (HCl) | Water (H₂O) | Ammonia (NH₃) | Methane (CH₄) |

Chemists normally represent a molecule by giving its **structural formula**, which shows the specific connections between atoms and therefore gives much more information than the chemical formula alone. Ethyl alcohol, for example, has the chemical formula C_2H_6O and the following structural formula:

$$C_2H_6O$$

Chemical formula

Structural formula

Molecular model

Ethyl alcohol

A structural formula uses lines between atoms to indicate the covalent bonds. Thus, the two carbon atoms in ethyl alcohol are covalently bonded to each other, the oxygen atom is bonded to one of the carbon atoms, and the six hydrogen atoms are distributed three to one carbon, two to the other carbon, and one to the oxygen.

Structural formulas are particularly important in *organic chemistry*—the chemistry of carbon compounds—where the behavior of large, complex molecules is almost entirely governed by their structure. Take even a relatively simple substance like glucose, for instance. The molecular formula of glucose, $C_6H_{12}O_6$, tells nothing about how the atoms are connected. In fact, you could probably imagine a great many different ways in which the 24 atoms might be connected. The structural formula for glucose, however, shows that 5 carbons and 1 oxygen form a ring of atoms, with the remaining 5 oxygens each bonded to 1 hydrogen and distributed on different carbons.

Glucose—$C_6H_{12}O_6$

[Red = O, gray = C, ivory = H]

Even some elements exist as molecules rather than as individual atoms. Hydrogen, nitrogen, oxygen, fluorine, chlorine, bromine, and iodine all exist as diatomic (two-atom) molecules whose two atoms are held together by covalent bonds. We therefore have to write them as such—H_2, N_2, O_2, F_2, Cl_2, Br_2, and I_2—when using any of these elements in a chemical equation. Notice that all these diatomic elements except hydrogen cluster toward the far right side of the periodic table.

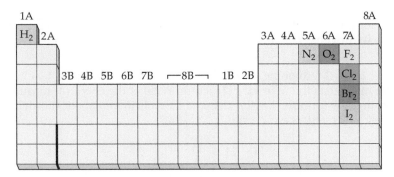

WORKED EXAMPLE 2.8

DRAWING A STRUCTURAL FORMULA

Propane, C_3H_8, has a structure in which the three carbon atoms are bonded in a row, each end carbon is bonded to three hydrogens, and the middle carbon is bonded to two hydrogens. Draw the structural formula, using lines between atoms to represent covalent bonds.

SOLUTION

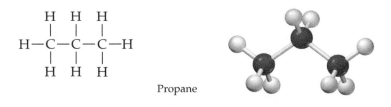

Propane

WORKED CONCEPTUAL EXAMPLE 2.9

VISUAL REPRESENTATIONS OF MIXTURES AND COMPOUNDS

Which of the following drawings represents a mixture, which a pure compound, and which an element?

(a)   **(b)**   **(c)**

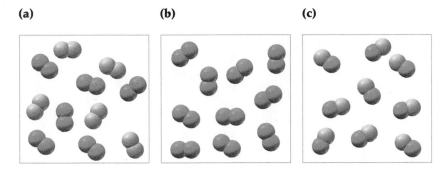

STRATEGY

Most people (professional chemists included) find chemistry easier to grasp when they can visualize the behavior of atoms, thereby turning symbols into pictures. The Conceptual Problems in this text are intended to help you do that, frequently representing atoms and molecules as collections of spheres. Don't take the pictures literally; focus instead on interpreting what they represent.

continued on the next page

SOLUTION

Drawing (a) represents a mixture of two diatomic elements, one composed of two red atoms and one composed of two blue atoms. Drawing (b) represents molecules of a pure diatomic element because all atoms are identical. Drawing (c) represents molecules of a pure compound composed of one red and one blue atom.

▶ **PROBLEM 2.15**   Draw the structural formula of methylamine, CH_5N, a substance responsible for the odor of rotting fish. The carbon atom is bonded to the nitrogen atom and to three hydrogens. The nitrogen atom is bonded to the carbon and two hydrogens.

▶ **PROBLEM 2.16**   Methionine, one of the 20 amino acid building blocks from which proteins are made, has the following structure. What is the chemical formula of methionine? In writing the formula, list the element symbols in alphabetical order and give the number of each element as a subscript.

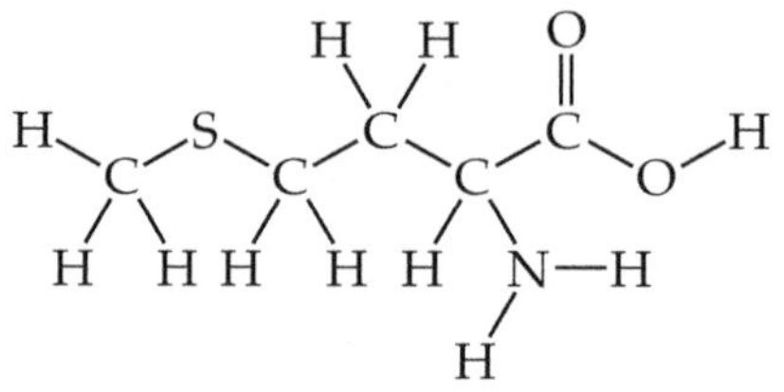

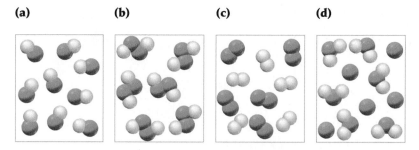

Methionine
(an amino acid)

CONCEPTUAL PROBLEM 2.17   Which of the following drawings represents a collection of hydrogen peroxide (H_2O_2) molecules? The red spheres represent oxygen atoms and the ivory spheres represent hydrogen.

(a)   (b)   (c)   (d)

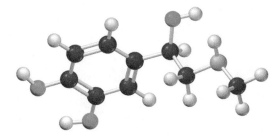

CONCEPTUAL PROBLEM 2.18   Adrenaline, the so-called "flight or fight" hormone, can be represented by the following ball-and-stick model. What is the chemical formula of adrenaline? (Gray = C, ivory = H, red = O, blue = N)

2.11 IONS AND IONIC BONDS

In contrast to a covalent bond, an **ionic bond** results not from a sharing of electrons but from a transfer of one or more electrons from one atom to another. As noted previously, ionic bonds generally form between a metal and a nonmetal. Metals, such as sodium, magnesium, and zinc, tend to give up electrons, whereas nonmetals, such as oxygen, nitrogen, and chlorine, tend to accept electrons.

For example, when sodium metal comes in contact with chlorine gas, a sodium atom gives an electron to a chlorine atom, resulting in the formation of two charged particles, called **ions**. Because a sodium atom loses one electron, it loses one negative charge and becomes an Na^+ ion with a charge of $+1$. Such positive ions are called **cations** (pronounced **cat**-ions). Conversely, because a chlorine atom gains an electron, it gains a negative charge and becomes a Cl^- ion with a charge of -1. Such negative ions are called **anions** (**an**-ions).

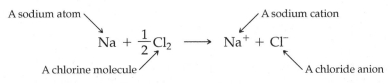

$$\text{A sodium atom} \quad \text{A sodium cation}$$
$$Na + \frac{1}{2}Cl_2 \longrightarrow Na^+ + Cl^-$$
$$\text{A chlorine molecule} \quad \text{A chloride anion}$$

A similar reaction takes place when magnesium and chlorine molecules (Cl_2) come in contact to form $MgCl_2$. A magnesium atom transfers an electron to each of two chlorine atoms, yielding the doubly charged Mg^{2+} cation and two Cl^- anions.

$$Mg + Cl_2 \rightarrow Mg^{2+} + Cl^- + Cl^- \ (MgCl_2)$$

Because opposite charges attract, positively charged cations like Na^+ and Mg^{2+} experience a strong electrical attraction to negatively charged anions like Cl^-, an attraction that we call an ionic bond. Unlike what happens when covalent bonds are formed, though, we can't really talk about discrete Na^+Cl^- *molecules* under normal conditions. We can speak only of an **ionic solid**, in which equal numbers of Na^+ and Cl^- ions are packed together in a regular way (**Figure 2.13**). In a crystal of table salt, for instance, each Na^+ ion is surrounded by six nearby Cl^- ions, and each Cl^- ion is surrounded by six nearby Na^+ ions, but we can't specify what pairs of ions "belong" to each other as we can with atoms in covalent molecules.

▲ Chlorine is a toxic green gas, sodium is a reactive metal, and sodium chloride is a harmless white solid.

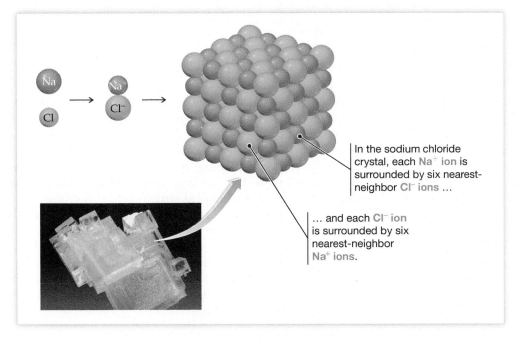

In the sodium chloride crystal, each Na^+ ion is surrounded by six nearest-neighbor Cl^- ions ...

... and each Cl^- ion is surrounded by six nearest-neighbor Na^+ ions.

Figure 2.13
The arrangement of Na^+ ions and Cl^- ions in a crystal of sodium chloride. There is no discrete "molecule" of NaCl. Instead, the entire crystal is an ionic solid.

Charged, covalently bonded groups of atoms, called **polyatomic ions**, are also common—ammonium ion (NH_4^+), hydroxide ion (OH^-), nitrate ion (NO_3^-), and the doubly charged sulfate ion (SO_4^{2-}) are examples. You can think of these polyatomic ions as charged molecules because they consist of specific numbers and kinds of atoms joined together by covalent bonds, with the overall unit having a positive or negative charge. When writing the formulas of substances that contain more than one of these ions, parentheses are placed around the entire polyatomic unit. The formula $Ba(NO_3)_2$, for instance, indicates a substance made of Ba^{2+} cations and NO_3^- polyatomic anions in a $1:2$ ratio. We'll say more about these ions in Section 2.12.

WORKED EXAMPLE 2.10

IDENTIFYING IONIC AND MOLECULAR COMPOUNDS

Which of the following compounds would you expect to be ionic and which molecular (covalent)?

(a) BaF_2 (b) SF_4 (c) PH_3 (d) CH_3OH

STRATEGY

Remember that covalent bonds generally form between nonmetal atoms, while ionic bonds form between metal and nonmetal atoms.

SOLUTION

Compound **(a)** is composed of a metal (barium) and a nonmetal (fluorine) and is likely to be ionic. Compounds **(b)–(d)** are composed entirely of nonmetals and therefore are probably molecular.

▶ **PROBLEM 2.19** Which of the following compounds would you expect to be ionic and which molecular (covalent)?

(a) LiBr   (b) $SiCl_4$ (c) BF_3 (d) CaO

CONCEPTUAL PROBLEM 2.20 Which of the following drawings is most likely to represent an ionic compound and which a molecular (covalent) compound? Explain.

(a)   (b)

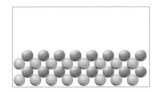 

2.12 NAMING CHEMICAL COMPOUNDS

In the early days of chemistry, when few pure substances were known, newly discovered compounds were often given fanciful names—morphine, quicklime, potash, and barbituric acid (said to be named by its discoverer in honor of his friend Barbara) to cite a few. Today, with more than 40 million pure compounds known, there would be chaos unless a systematic method for naming compounds were used. Every chemical compound must be given a name that not only defines it uniquely but also allows chemists (and computers) to know its chemical structure.

Different kinds of compounds are named by different rules. Ordinary table salt, for instance, is named *sodium chloride* because of its formula NaCl, but common table sugar ($C_{12}H_{22}O_{11}$) is named *β-D-fructofuranosyl-α-D-glucopyranoside* because of special rules for carbohydrates. (Organic compounds often have quite complex structures and correspondingly complex names, though we'll not discuss them in this text.) We'll begin by seeing how to name simple ionic compounds and then introduce additional rules in later chapters as the need arises.

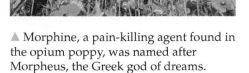

▲ Morphine, a pain-killing agent found in the opium poppy, was named after Morpheus, the Greek god of dreams.

Naming Binary Ionic Compounds

Binary ionic compounds—those made of only two elements—are named by identifying first the positive ion and then the negative ion. The positive ion takes the same name as the element, while the negative ion takes the first part of its name from the element and then adds the ending -*ide*. For example, KBr is named potassium bromide: *potassium* for the K^+ ion, and *bromide* for the negative Br^- ion derived from the element *brom*ine. Figure 2.14 shows some common main-group ions, and Figure 2.15 shows some common transition-metal ions.

LiF	$CaBr_2$	$AlCl_3$
Lithium fluoride	Calcium bromide	Aluminum chloride

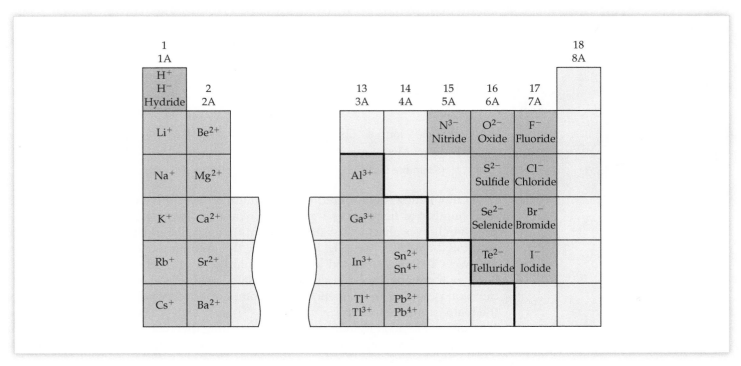

Figure 2.14
Main-group cations (blue) and anions (purple). A cation bears the same name as the element it is derived from; an anion name has an -*ide* ending.

Figure 2.14 illustrates several interesting points. Note, for instance, that metals tend to form cations and nonmetals tend to form anions, as mentioned previously in Section 2.11. Note also that elements within a given group of the periodic table form similar kinds of ions and that the charge on the ion is related to the group number. Main-group metals usually form cations whose charge is equal to the group number. Group 1A elements form singly positive ions (M^+, where M is a metal), group 2A elements form doubly positive ions (M^{2+}), and group 3A elements form triply positive ions (M^{3+}). Main-group nonmetals usually form anions whose charge is equal to the group number in the U.S. system minus eight. Thus, group 6A elements form doubly negative ions ($6 - 8 = -2$), group 7A elements form singly negative ions ($7 - 8 = -1$), and group 8A elements form no ions at all ($8 - 8 = 0$). We'll see the reason for this behavior in Chapter 6.

3 3B	4 4B	5 5B	6 6B	7 7B	8 	9 8B	10 	11 1B	12 2B	
Sc^{3+}	Ti^{3+}	V^{3+}	Cr^{2+} Cr^{3+}	Mn^{2+}	Fe^{2+} Fe^{3+}	Co^{2+}	Ni^{2+}	Cu^+ Cu^{2+}	Zn^{2+}	
Y^{3+}					Ru^{3+}	Rh^{3+}	Pd^{2+}	Ag^+	Cd^{2+}	
									Hg^{2+}	

Figure 2.15
Common transition metal ions. Only ions that exist in aqueous solution are shown.

Notice also, in both Figures 2.14 and 2.15, that some metals form more than one kind of cation. Iron, for instance, forms both the doubly charged Fe^{2+} ion and the triply charged Fe^{3+} ion. In naming these ions, we distinguish between them by using a Roman numeral in parentheses to indicate the number of charges. Thus, $FeCl_2$ is

▲ Crystals of iron(II) chloride tetrahydrate are greenish, and crystals of iron(III) chloride hexahydrate are brownish yellow.

named iron(II) chloride and $FeCl_3$ is iron(III) chloride. Alternatively, an older method distinguishes between the ions by using the Latin name of the element (*ferrum* in the case of iron) together with the ending *-ous* for the ion with lower charge and *-ic* for the ion with higher charge. Thus, $FeCl_2$ is sometimes called ferrous chloride and $FeCl_3$ is called ferric chloride. Although still in use, this older naming system is being phased out and we'll rarely use it in this book.

Fe^{2+}	Fe^{3+}	Sn^{2+}	Sn^{4+}
Iron(II) ion	Iron(III) ion	Tin(II) ion	Tin(IV) ion
Ferrous ion	Ferric ion	Stannous ion	Stannic ion
(From the Latin *ferrum* = iron)		(From the Latin *stannum* = tin)	

In any neutral compound, the total number of positive charges must equal the total number of negative charges. Thus, you can always figure out the number of positive charges on a metal cation by counting the number of negative charges on the associated anion(s). In $FeCl_2$, for example, the iron ion must be Fe(II) because there are two Cl^- ions associated with it. Similarly, in $TiCl_3$ the titanium ion is Ti(III) because there are three Cl^- anions associated with it. As a general rule, a Roman numeral is needed for transition-metal compounds to avoid ambiguity. In addition, the main-group metals tin (Sn), thallium (Tl), and lead (Pb) can form more than one kind of ion and need Roman numerals for naming their compounds. Metals in group 1A and group 2A form only one cation, however, so Roman numerals are not needed.

WORKED EXAMPLE 2.11

NAMING BINARY IONIC COMPOUNDS

Give systematic names for the following compounds:

(a) $BaCl_2$ (b) $CrCl_3$ (c) PbS   (d) Fe_2O_3

STRATEGY

Try to figure out the number of positive charges on each cation by counting the number of negative charges on the associated anion(s). Refer to Figures 2.14 and 2.15 as necessary.

SOLUTION

(a) Barium chloride	No Roman numeral is necessary because barium, a group 2A element, forms only Ba^{2+}.
(b) Chromium(III) chloride	The Roman numeral III is necessary to specify the +3 charge on chromium (a transition metal).
(c) Lead(II) sulfide	The sulfide anion (S^{2-}) has a double negative charge, so the lead cation must be doubly positive.
(d) Iron(III) oxide	The three oxide anions (O^{2-}) have a total negative charge of −6, so the two iron cations must have a total charge of +6. Thus, each is Fe(III).

WORKED EXAMPLE 2.12

CONVERTING NAMES INTO FORMULAS

Write formulas for the following compounds:

(a) Magnesium fluoride   (b) Tin(IV) oxide   (c) Iron(III) sulfide

STRATEGY

For transition metal compounds, the charge on the cation is indicated by the Roman numeral in the name. Knowing the number of positive charges, you can then figure out the number of necessary negative charges for the associated anions.

SOLUTION

(a) MgF_2 Magnesium (group 2A) forms only a 2+ cation, so there must be two fluoride ions (F^-) to balance the charge.

(b) SnO_2 Tin(IV) has a +4 charge, so there must be two oxide ions (O^{2-}) to balance the charge.

(c) Fe_2S_3 Iron(III) has a +3 charge and sulfide ion a −2 charge (S^{2-}), so there must be two irons and three sulfurs.

▶ **PROBLEM 2.21** Give systematic names for the following compounds:

(a) CsF   **(b)** K_2O **(c)** CuO   **(d)** BaS   **(e)** $BeBr_2$

▶ **PROBLEM 2.22** Write formulas for the following compounds:

(a) Vanadium(III) chloride   **(b)** Manganese(IV) oxide
(c) Copper(II) sulfide   **(d)** Aluminum oxide

CONCEPTUAL PROBLEM 2.23 Three binary ionic compounds are represented on the following periodic table: red with red, green with green, and blue with blue. Name each, and tell its likely formula.

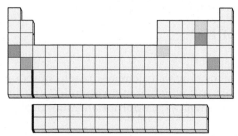

Naming Binary Molecular Compounds

Binary molecular compounds with covalent bonds are named in much the same way as binary ionic compounds by assuming that one of the elements in the compound is more cationlike and the other element is more anionlike. As with ionic compounds, the cationlike element takes the name of the element itself, and the anionlike element takes an *-ide* ending. The compound HF, for example, is called *hydrogen fluoride*.

HF   Hydrogen is more cationlike because it is farther left in the periodic table, and fluoride is more anionlike because it is farther right. The compound is therefore named *hydrogen fluoride*.

We'll see a quantitative way to decide which element is more cationlike and which is more anionlike in Section 7.4 but you might note for now that it's usually possible to decide by looking at the relative positions of the elements in the periodic table. The farther left and toward the bottom of the periodic table an element occurs, the more likely it is to be cationlike; the farther right and toward the top an element occurs (except for the noble gases), the more likely it is to be anionlike.

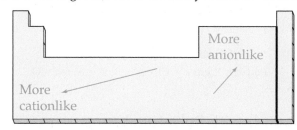

The following examples show how this generalization applies:

CO   Carbon monoxide (C is in group 4A; O is in group 6A)
CO_2 Carbon dioxide
PCl_3 Phosphorus trichloride (P is in group 5A; Cl is in group 7A)
SF_4 Sulfur tetrafluoride (S is in group 6A; F is in group 7A)
N_2O_4 Dinitrogen tetroxide (N is in group 5A; O is in group 6A)

TABLE 2.3 Numerical Prefixes for Naming Compounds

Prefix	Meaning
mono-	1
di-	2
tri-	3
tetra-	4
penta-	5
hexa-	6
hepta-	7
octa-	8
nona-	9
deca-	10

Because nonmetals often combine with one another in different proportions to form different compounds, numerical prefixes are usually included in the names of binary molecular compounds to specify the numbers of each kind of atom present. The compound CO, for example, is called carbon *mono*xide, and CO_2 is called carbon *di*oxide. Table 2.3 lists the most common numerical prefixes. Note that when the prefix ends in *a* or *o* (but not *i*) and the anion name begins with a vowel (*oxide*, for instance), the *a* or *o* on the prefix is dropped to avoid having two vowels together in the name. Thus, we write carbon *mono*xide rather than carbon *mono*oxide for CO and dinitrogen *tetr*oxide rather than dinitrogen *tetra*oxide for N_2O_4. A *mono-* prefix is not used for the atom named first: CO_2 is called carbon dioxide rather than monocarbon dioxide.

WORKED EXAMPLE 2.13

NAMING BINARY MOLECULAR COMPOUNDS

Give systematic names for the following compounds:

(a) PCl_3 (b) N_2O_3 (c) P_4O_7 (d) BrF_3

STRATEGY

Look at a periodic table to see which element in each compound is more cationlike (farther to the left or lower) and which is more anionlike (farther to the right or higher). Then name the compound using the appropriate numerical prefix.

SOLUTION

(a) Phosphorus trichloride (b) Dinitrogen trioxide
(c) Tetraphosphorus heptoxide (d) Bromine trifluoride

▶ **PROBLEM 2.24** Give systematic names for the following compounds:

(a) NCl_3 (b) P_4O_6 (c) S_2F_2 (d) SeO_2

▶ **PROBLEM 2.25** Write formulas for compounds with the following names:

(a) Disulfur dichloride (b) Iodine monochloride
(c) Nitrogen triiodide

CONCEPTUAL PROBLEM 2.26 Give systematic names for the following compounds:

(a)   (b)

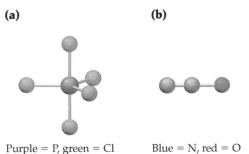

Purple = P, green = Cl   Blue = N, red = O

Naming Compounds with Polyatomic Ions

Ionic compounds that contain polyatomic ions (Section 2.11) are named in the same way as binary ionic compounds: First the cation is identified and then the anion. For example, $Ba(NO_3)_2$ is called *barium nitrate* because Ba^{2+} is the cation and the NO_3^- polyatomic anion has the name *nitrate*. Unfortunately, there is no simple systematic way of naming the polyatomic ions themselves, so it's necessary to memorize the names, formulas, and charges of the most common ones, listed in Table 2.4. The ammonium ion (NH_4^+) is the only cation on the list; all the others are anions.

TABLE 2.4   Some Common Polyatomic Ions

Formula	Name	Formula	Name
Cation		**Singly charged anions (continued)**	
NH_4^+	Ammonium	NO_2^-	Nitrite
		NO_3^-	Nitrate
Singly charged anions			
$CH_3CO_2^-$	Acetate	**Doubly charged anions**	
CN^-	Cyanide	CO_3^{2-}	Carbonate
ClO^-	Hypochlorite	CrO_4^{2-}	Chromate
ClO_2^-	Chlorite	$Cr_2O_7^{2-}$	Dichromate
ClO_3^-	Chlorate	O_2^{2-}	Peroxide
ClO_4^-	Perchlorate	HPO_4^{2-}	Hydrogen phosphate
$H_2PO_4^-$	Dihydrogen phosphate	SO_3^{2-}	Sulfite
HCO_3^-	Hydrogen carbonate (or bicarbonate)	SO_4^{2-}	Sulfate
		$S_2O_3^{2-}$	Thiosulfate
HSO_4^-	Hydrogen sulfate (or bisulfate)		
		Triply charged anion	
OH^-	Hydroxide	PO_4^{3-}	Phosphate
MnO_4^-	Permanganate		

Several points about the ions in Table 2.4 need special mention. First, note that the names of most polyatomic anions end in *-ite* or *-ate*. Only hydroxide (OH^-), cyanide (CN^-), and peroxide (O_2^{2-}) have the *-ide* ending. Second, note that several of the ions form a series of **oxoanions**, binary polyatomic anions in which an atom of a given element is combined with different numbers of oxygen atoms—hypochlorite (ClO^-), chlorite (ClO_2^-), chlorate (ClO_3^-), and perchlorate (ClO_4^-), for example. When there are only two oxoanions in a series, as with sulfite (SO_3^{2-}) and sulfate (SO_4^{2-}), the ion with fewer oxygens takes the *-ite* ending and the ion with more oxygens takes the *-ate* ending.

SO_3^{2-}	Sul*fite* ion (fewer oxygens)	SO_4^{2-}	Sul*fate* ion (more oxygens)
NO_2^-	Nit*rite* ion (fewer oxygens)	NO_3^-	Nit*rate* ion (more oxygens)

When there are more than two oxoanions in a series, the prefix *hypo-* (meaning "less than") is used for the ion with the fewest oxygens, and the prefix *per-* (meaning "more than") is used for the ion with the most oxygens.

ClO^-	*Hypo*chlorite ion (less oxygen than chlorite)
ClO_2^-	Chlorite ion
ClO_3^-	Chlorate ion
ClO_4^-	*Per*chlorate ion (more oxygen than chlorate)

Third, note that several pairs of ions are related by the presence or absence of a hydrogen. The hydrogen carbonate anion (HCO_3^-) differs from the carbonate anion (CO_3^{2-}) by the presence of H^+, and the hydrogen sulfate anion (HSO_4^-) differs from the sulfate anion (SO_4^{2-}) by the presence of H^+. The ion that has the additional hydrogen is sometimes referred to using the prefix *bi-*, although this usage is now discouraged; for example, $NaHCO_3$ is sometimes called sodium bicarbonate.

HCO_3^-	Hydrogen carbonate (*bi*carbonate) ion	CO_3^{2-}	Carbonate ion
HSO_4^-	Hydrogen sulfate (*bi*sulfate) ion	SO_4^{2-}	Sulfate ion

WORKED EXAMPLE 2.14

NAMING COMPOUNDS WITH POLYATOMIC IONS

Give systematic names for the following compounds:

(a) $LiNO_3$ (b) $KHSO_4$ (c) $CuCO_3$ (d) $Fe(ClO_4)_3$

STRATEGY

Unfortunately, there is no alternative: The names and charges of the common polyatomic ions must be memorized. Refer to Table 2.4 if you need help.

SOLUTION

(a) Lithium nitrate   Lithium (group 1A) forms only the Li^+ ion and does not need a Roman numeral.

(b) Potassium hydrogen sulfate   Potassium (group 1A) forms only the K^+ ion.

(c) Copper(II) carbonate   The carbonate ion has a −2 charge, so copper must be +2. A Roman numeral is needed because copper, a transition metal, can form more than one ion.

(d) Iron(III) perchlorate   There are three perchlorate ions, each with a −1 charge, so the iron must have a +3 charge.

WORKED EXAMPLE 2.15

WRITING FORMULAS OF COMPOUNDS WITH POLYATOMIC IONS

Write formulas for the following compounds:

(a) Potassium hypochlorite   (b) Silver(I) chromate
(c) Iron(III) carbonate

SOLUTION

(a) KClO   Potassium forms only the K^+ ion, so only one ClO^- is needed.

(b) Ag_2CrO_4 The polyatomic chromate ion has a −2 charge, so two Ag^+ ions are needed.

(c) $Fe_2(CO_3)_3$ Iron(III) has a +3 charge and the polyatomic carbonate ion has a −2 charge, so there must be two iron ions and three carbonate ions. The polyatomic carbonate ion is set off in parentheses to indicate that there are three of them.

▶ PROBLEM 2.27   Give systematic names for the following compounds:

(a) $Ca(ClO)_2$ (b) $Ag_2S_2O_3$ (c) NaH_2PO_4
(d) $Sn(NO_3)_2$ (e) $Pb(CH_3CO_2)_4$ (f) $(NH_4)_2SO_4$

▶ PROBLEM 2.28   Write formulas for the following compounds:

(a) Lithium phosphate   (b) Magnesium hydrogen sulfate
(c) Manganese(II) nitrate   (d) Chromium(III) sulfate

CONCEPTUAL PROBLEM 2.29   The following drawings are those of solid ionic compounds, with red spheres representing the cations and blue spheres representing the anions in each.

(1)   (2)

Which of the following formulas are consistent with each drawing?

(a) LiBr   (b) $NaNO_2$ (c) $CaCl_2$
(d) K_2CO_3 (e) $Fe_2(SO_4)_3$

INQUIRY WHERE DO CHEMICAL ELEMENTS COME FROM?

Cosmologists theorize that the universe began some 13.7 billion years ago in an extraordinary event they call the big bang. Initially, the temperature must have been inconceivably high, but after 1 second, the temperature had dropped to about 10^{10} K and elementary particles began to form: protons, neutrons, and electrons, as well as positrons and *neutrinos*—neutral particles with a mass much less than that of an electron. After 3 minutes, the temperature had dropped to 10^9 K, and protons began fusing with neutrons to form helium nuclei ($^4_2\text{He}^{2+}$). Matter remained in this form for many millions of years until the expanding universe had cooled to about 10,000 K. Electrons were then able to bind to protons and to helium nuclei, forming stable hydrogen and helium atoms.

The attractive force of gravity acting on regions of higher-than-average density slowly produced massive local concentrations of matter and ultimately formed billions of galaxies, each with many billions of stars. As the gas clouds of hydrogen and helium condensed under gravitational attraction and stars formed, their temperatures reached 10^7 K and their densities reached 100 g/cm^3. Protons and neutrons again fused to yield helium nuclei, generating vast amounts of heat and light.

Most of these early stars probably burned out after a few billion years, but a few were so massive that, as their nuclear fuel diminished, gravitational attraction caused a rapid contraction leading to still higher core temperatures and higher densities—up to 5×10^8 K and 5×10^5 g/cm^3. Much larger nuclei were now formed, including carbon, oxygen, silicon, magnesium, and iron. Ultimately, these massive stars underwent gravitational collapse, resulting in the synthesis of still heavier elements and explosions visible throughout the universe as *supernovas*.

Matter from exploding supernovas was blown throughout the galaxy, forming a new generation of stars and planets. Our own sun and solar system formed only about 4.5 billion years ago from matter released by former supernovas. Except for hydrogen and helium, all the atoms in our bodies, our planet, and our solar system were created more than 5 billion years ago in exploding stars. We are made of stardust.

▶ **PROBLEM 2.30** What two elements are thought to be the first ones formed in the big bang?

▲ The stars in the Milky Way galaxy condensed from gas clouds under gravitational attraction.

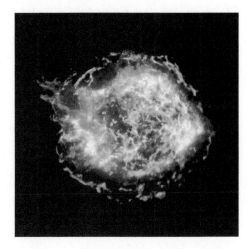

▲ In 1667, the instantaneous gravitational collapse of the massive star Cassiopeia A resulted in a supernova explosion, whose remnants are still visible.

SUMMARY

Elements are made of tiny particles called **atoms**, which can combine in simple numerical ratios according to the **law of multiple proportions**. Atoms are composed of three fundamental particles: **protons** are positively charged, **electrons** are negatively charged, and **neutrons** are neutral. According to the nuclear model of an atom proposed by Ernest Rutherford, protons and neutrons are clustered into a dense core called the **nucleus**, while electrons move around the nucleus at a relatively great distance.

Elements differ from one another according to how many protons their atoms contain, a value called the **atomic number (Z)** of the element. The sum of an atom's protons and neutrons is its **mass number (A)**. Although all atoms of a specific element have the same atomic number, different atoms of an element can have different mass numbers, depending on how many neutrons they have. Atoms with identical atomic numbers but different mass numbers are called **isotopes**. Atomic masses are measured using the **atomic mass unit (amu)**, defined as 1/12 the mass of a ^{12}C atom. Because both protons and neutrons have a mass of approximately 1 amu, the mass of an atom in atomic mass units (the isotopic mass) is numerically close to the atom's mass number. The element's **atomic mass** is a weighted mass average of its naturally occurring isotopes.

When referring to the enormous numbers of atoms that make up visible amounts of matter, the fundamental SI unit called a *mole* is used. One **mole** is the amount whose mass in grams, called its **molar mass**, is numerically equal to the atomic mass. Numerically, one mole of any element contains 6.022×10^{23} atoms, a value called **Avogadro's number (N_A)**.

Nuclear chemistry is the study of the properties and reactions of atomic nuclei. Nuclear reactions differ from chemical reactions in that they involve a change in an atom's nucleus, producing a

different element. Nuclear reactions are written using balanced **nuclear equations**, in which the element symbols represent only the nuclei rather than neutral atoms.

Radioactivity is the spontaneous emission of radiation from an unstable nucleus. **Alpha (α) radiation** consists of helium nuclei, small particles containing two protons and two neutrons ($^4_2He^{2+}$). **Beta (β) radiation** consists of electrons ($^0_{-1}e$), and **gamma (γ) radiation** consists of high-energy electromagnetic radiation that has no mass. **Positron emission** is the conversion of a proton in the nucleus into a neutron plus an ejected *positron* (^0_1e or β^+), a particle that has the same mass as an electron but a positive charge. **Electron capture** is the capture of a surrounding electron by a proton in the nucleus. The process is accompanied by the emission of γ rays and results in the conversion of a proton in the nucleus into a neutron.

Most substances are **chemical compounds**, formed when atoms of two or more elements combine in a **chemical reaction**. The atoms in a compound are held together by one of two kinds of **chemical bonds**. **Covalent bonds** form when two atoms share electrons to give a new unit of matter called a **molecule**. **Ionic bonds** form when one atom completely transfers one or more electrons to another atom, resulting in the formation of **ions**. Positively charged ions (**cations**) are strongly attracted to negatively charged ions (**anions**) by electrical forces.

Chemical compounds are named systematically by following a series of rules. Binary ionic compounds are named by identifying first the positive ion and then the negative ion. Binary molecular compounds are similarly named by identifying the cationlike and anionlike elements. Naming compounds with **polyatomic ions** involves memorizing the names and formulas of the most common ones.

KEY WORDS

alpha (α) radiation   49
anion   59
atom   38
atomic mass   46
atomic mass unit (amu)   45
atomic number (Z)   43
Avogadro's number (N_A)   47
beta (β) radiation   50
cation   59
chemical bond   55
chemical compound   35

chemical equation   36
chemical formula   36
covalent bond   55
electron   39
electron capture   51
gamma (γ) radiation   50
ion   59
ionic bond   58
ionic solid   59
isotope   44
law of definite
   proportions   37

law of mass
   conservation   36
law of multiple
   proportions   37
mass number (A)   44
mixture   54
molar mass   47
mole   46
molecule   55
neutron   42
nuclear chemistry   48
nuclear equation   48

nucleon   50
nucleus   42
oxoanion   65
polyatomic ion   59
positron emission   50
proton   42
radioactive   49
radioisotope   49
structural formula   56
transuranium element   53

CONCEPTUAL PROBLEMS

Problems 2.1–2.30 appear within the chapter.

2.31 In the following drawings, red spheres represent cations and blue spheres represent anions. Match each of the drawings **(a)–(d)** with the following ionic compounds:
   (i) $Ca_3(PO_4)_2$ **(ii)** Li_2CO_3
   (iii) $FeCl_2$ **(iv)** $MgSO_4$

(a)

(b)

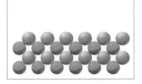

(c)   **(d)**

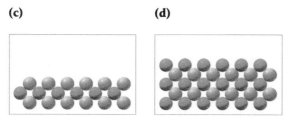

2.32 If yellow spheres represent sulfur atoms and red spheres represent oxygen atoms, which of the following drawings shows a collection of sulfur dioxide (SO_2) units?

(a)   **(b)**

(c)   **(d)**

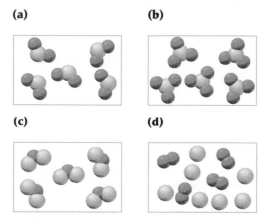

2.33 Assume that the mixture of substances in drawing **(a)** undergoes a reaction. Which of the drawings **(b)**–**(d)** represents a product mixture consistent with the law of mass conservation?

(a)

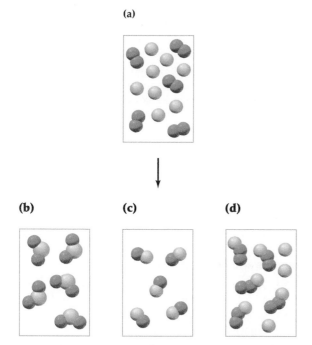

(b)   **(c)**   **(d)**

2.34 If red and blue spheres represent atoms of different elements, which two of the following drawings illustrate the law of multiple proportions?

(a)   **(b)**

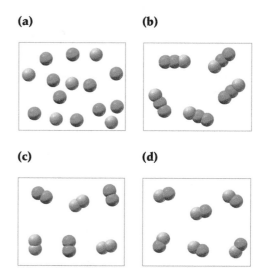

(c)   **(d)**

2.35 Which of the following three drawings represents a neutral Na atom, which represents a Ca atom with two positive electrical charges (Ca^{2+}), and which represents an F atom with one minus charge (F^-)?

(a)   **(b)**   **(c)**

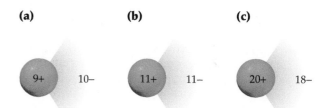

9+ 10–   11+ 11–   20+ 18–

2.36 Give molecular formulas corresponding to each of the following ball-and-stick molecular representations (red = O, gray = C, blue = N, ivory = H). In writing the formula, list the elements in alphabetical order.

(a) Alanine (an amino acid)

(b) Ethylene glycol (automobile antifreeze)

(c) Acetic acid (vinegar)

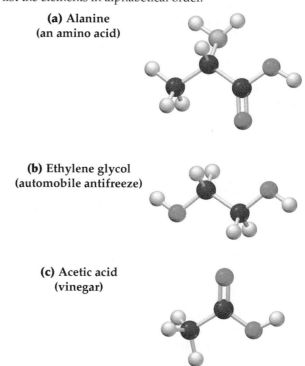

2.37 Isotope A decays to isotope E through the following series of steps, in which the products of the individual decay events are themselves radioactive and undergo further decay until a stable nucleus is ultimately reached. Two kinds of processes are represented, one by the shorter arrows pointing right and the other by the longer arrows pointing left.

(a) To what kind of nuclear decay process does each kind of arrow correspond?

(b) Identify and write the symbol $^A_Z X$ for each isotope in the series:

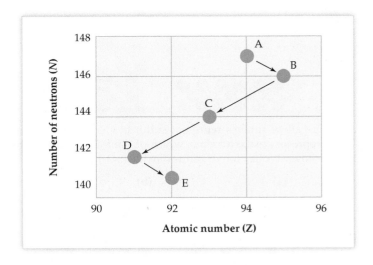

SECTION PROBLEMS

Atomic Theory (Sections 2.1 and 2.2)

2.38 How does Dalton's atomic theory account for the law of mass conservation and the law of definite proportions?

2.39 What is the law of multiple proportions, and how does Dalton's atomic theory account for it?

2.40 A sample of mercury with a mass of 114.0 g was combined with 12.8 g of oxygen gas, and the resulting reaction gave 123.1 g of mercury(II) oxide. How much oxygen was left over after the reaction was complete?

2.41 A sample of $CaCO_3$ was heated, causing it to form CaO and CO_2 gas. Solid CaO remained behind, while the CO_2 escaped to the atmosphere. If the $CaCO_3$ weighed 612 g and the CaO weighed 343 g, how many grams of CO_2 were formed in the reaction?

2.42 Benzene, ethane, and ethylene are just three of a large number of *hydrocarbons*—compounds that contain only carbon and hydrogen. Show how the following data are consistent with the law of multiple proportions.

Compound	Mass of carbon in 5.00 g sample	Mass of hydrogen in 5.00 g sample
Benzene	4.61 g	0.39 g
Ethane	4.00 g	1.00 g
Ethylene	4.29 g	0.71 g

2.43 In addition to carbon monoxide (CO) and carbon dioxide (CO_2), there is a third compound of carbon and oxygen called *carbon suboxide*. If a 2.500 g sample of carbon suboxide contains 1.32 g of C and 1.18 g of O, show that the law of multiple proportions is followed.

2.44 The atomic mass of carbon (12.011 amu) is approximately 12 times that of hydrogen (1.008 amu).

(a) Show how you can use this knowledge to calculate possible formulas for benzene, ethane, and ethylene (Problem 2.42).

(b) Show how your answer to part (a) is consistent with the actual formulas for benzene (C_6H_6), ethane (C_2H_6), and ethylene (C_2H_4).

2.45 What is a possible formula for carbon suboxide (Problem 2.43)?

2.46 If the atomic mass of an element is x, what is the mass in grams of 6.02×10^{23} atoms of the element?

2.47 If 6.02×10^{23} atoms of element Y have a mass of 83.80 g, what is the identity of Y?

2.48 If the atomic mass of an element is x, what is the mass in grams of 3.17×10^{20} atoms of the element?

2.49 If 4.61×10^{21} atoms of element Z have a mass of 0.815 g, what is the identity of Z?

2.50 A compound of zinc and sulfur contains 67.1% zinc by mass. What is the ratio of zinc and sulfur atoms in the compound?

2.51 There are two compounds of titanium and chlorine. One compound contains 31.04% titanium by mass, and the other contains 74.76% chlorine by mass. What are the ratios of titanium and chlorine atoms in the two compounds?

2.52 In methane, one part hydrogen combines with three parts carbon by mass. If a sample of a compound containing only carbon and hydrogen contains 32.0 g of carbon and 8.0 g of hydrogen, could the sample be methane? If the sample is not methane, show that the law of multiple proportions is followed for methane and this other substance.

2.53 In borane, one part hydrogen combines with 3.6 parts boron by mass. A compound containing only hydrogen and boron contains 6.0 g of hydrogen and 43.2 g of boron. Could this compound be borane? If it is not borane, show that the law of multiple proportions is followed for borane and this other substance.

Elements and Atoms (Sections 2.3–2.6)

2.54 What is the difference between an atom's atomic number and its mass number?

2.55 What is the difference between an element's atomic number and its atomic mass?

2.56 The subscript giving the atomic number of an atom is often left off when writing an isotope symbol. For example, $^{13}_6C$ is often written simply as ^{13}C. Why is this allowable?

2.57 Iodine has a *lower* atomic mass than tellurium (126.90 for iodine, 127.60 for tellurium) even though it has a *higher* atomic number (53 for iodine, 52 for tellurium). Explain.

2.58 Copper has two naturally occurring isotopes, including ^{65}Cu. Look at the periodic table and tell whether the second isotope is ^{63}Cu or ^{66}Cu.

2.59 Sulfur has four naturally occurring isotopes, including ^{33}S, ^{34}S, and ^{36}S. Look at the periodic table and tell whether the fourth isotope is ^{32}S or ^{35}S.

2.60 Give the names and symbols for the following elements:
(a) An element with atomic number 6
(b) An element with 18 protons in its nucleus
(c) An element with 23 electrons

2.61 The radioactive isotope cesium-137 was produced in large amounts in fallout from the 1985 nuclear power plant disaster at Chernobyl, Ukraine. Write the symbol for this isotope in standard format.

2.62 Write symbols for the following isotopes:
(a) Radon-220
(b) Polonium-210
(c) Gold-197

2.63 Write symbols for the following isotopes:
(a) $Z = 58$ and $A = 140$
(b) $Z = 27$ and $A = 60$

2.64 How many protons, neutrons, and electrons are in each of the following atoms?
(a) $^{15}_{7}$N (b) $^{60}_{27}$Co (c) $^{131}_{53}$I
(d) $^{142}_{58}$Ce

2.65 How many protons and neutrons are in the nucleus of the following atoms?
(a) ^{27}Al (b) ^{32}S (c) ^{64}Zn
(d) ^{207}Pb

2.66 Identify the following elements:
(a) $^{24}_{12}$X (b) $^{58}_{28}$X (c) $^{104}_{46}$X
(d) $^{183}_{74}$X

2.67 Identify the following elements:
(a) $^{202}_{80}$X (b) $^{195}_{78}$X (c) $^{184}_{76}$X
(d) $^{209}_{83}$X

2.68 Which of the following isotope symbols can't be correct?
$^{18}_{9}$F $^{12}_{5}$C $^{33}_{35}$Br $^{18}_{8}$O $^{11}_{5}$Bo

2.69 Which of the following isotope symbols can't be correct?
$^{14}_{7}$Ni $^{131}_{54}$Xe $^{54}_{26}$Fe $^{73}_{23}$Ge $^{1}_{2}$He

2.70 Naturally occurring boron consists of two isotopes: ^{10}B (19.9%) with an isotopic mass of 10.0129 amu and ^{11}B (80.1%) with an isotopic mass of 11.009 31 amu. What is the atomic mass of boron? Check your answer by looking at a periodic table.

2.71 Naturally occurring silver consists of two isotopes: ^{107}Ag (51.84%) with an isotopic mass of 106.9051 amu and ^{109}Ag (48.16%) with an isotopic mass of 108.9048 amu. What is the atomic mass of silver? Check your answer in a periodic table.

2.72 Magnesium has three naturally occurring isotopes: ^{24}Mg (23.985 amu) with 78.99% abundance, ^{25}Mg (24.986 amu) with 10.00% abundance, and a third with 11.01% abundance. Look up the atomic mass of magnesium, and then calculate the mass of the third isotope.

2.73 A sample of naturally occurring silicon consists of ^{28}Si (27.9769 amu), ^{29}Si (28.9765 amu), and ^{30}Si (29.9738 amu). If the atomic mass of silicon is 28.0855 amu and the natural abundance of ^{29}Si is 4.68%, what are the natural abundances of ^{28}Si and ^{30}Si?

Nuclear Reactions and Radioactivity (Sections 2.7–2.9)

2.74 Positron emission and electron capture both give a product nucleus whose atomic number is 1 less than the starting nucleus. Explain.

2.75 What is the difference between an α particle and a helium atom?

2.76 Why does beta emission *raise* the atomic number of the product while positron emission *lowers* the atomic number?

2.77 Why do nuclei that are neutron rich emit β particles, but nuclei that are neutron poor emit α particles or positrons or undergo electron capture?

2.78 Complete and balance the following nuclear equations:
(a) $^{126}_{50}$Sn $\rightarrow$ $^{0}_{-1}$e + ? (b) $^{210}_{88}$Ra $\rightarrow$ $^{4}_{2}$He + ?
(c) $^{77}_{37}$Rb $\rightarrow$ $^{0}_{1}$e + ? (d) $^{76}_{36}$Kr + $^{0}_{-1}$e $\rightarrow$?

2.79 Complete and balance the following nuclear equations:
(a) $^{90}_{38}$Sr $\rightarrow$ $^{0}_{-1}$e + ? (b) $^{247}_{100}$Fm $\rightarrow$ $^{4}_{2}$He + ?
(c) $^{49}_{25}$Mn $\rightarrow$ $^{0}_{1}$e + ? (d) $^{37}_{18}$Ar + $^{0}_{-1}$e $\rightarrow$?

2.80 What particle is produced in each of the following decay reactions?
(a) $^{188}_{80}$Hg $\rightarrow$ $^{188}_{79}$Au + ?
(b) $^{218}_{85}$At $\rightarrow$ $^{214}_{83}$Bi + ?
(c) $^{234}_{90}$Th $\rightarrow$ $^{234}_{91}$Pa + ?

2.81 What particle is produced in each of the following decay reactions?
(a) $^{24}_{11}$Na $\rightarrow$ $^{24}_{12}$Mg + ?
(b) $^{135}_{60}$Nd $\rightarrow$ $^{135}_{59}$Pr + ?
(c) $^{170}_{78}$Pt $\rightarrow$ $^{166}_{76}$Os + ?

2.82 Write balanced nuclear equations for the following processes:
(a) Alpha emission of ^{162}Re
(b) Electron capture of ^{138}Sm
(c) Beta emission of ^{188}W
(d) Positron emission of ^{165}Ta

2.83 Write balanced nuclear equations for the following processes:
(a) Beta emission of ^{157}Eu
(b) Electron capture of ^{126}Ba
(c) Alpha emission of ^{146}Sm
(d) Positron emission of ^{125}Ba

2.84 Of the two isotopes of tungsten, ^{160}W and ^{185}W, one decays by β emission and one decays by α emission. Which does which? Explain.

2.85 Of the two isotopes of iodine, ^{136}I and ^{122}I, one decays by β emission and one decays by positron emission. Which does which? Explain.

2.86 Americium-241, a radioisotope used in smoke detectors, decays by a series of 12 reactions involving sequential loss of α, α, β, α, α, β, α, α, α, β, α, and β particles. Identify each intermediate nucleus and the final stable product nucleus.

2.87 Radon-222 decays by a series of three α emissions and two β emissions. What is the final stable nucleus?

2.88 Thorium-232 decays by a 10-step series, ultimately yielding lead-208. How many α particles and how many β particles are emitted?

2.89 How many α particles and how many β particles are emitted in the 11-step decay of ^{235}U into ^{207}Pb?

Chemical Compounds (Sections 2.10 and 2.11)

2.90 What is the difference between a covalent bond and an ionic bond? Give an example of each.

2.91 Which of the following bonds are likely to be covalent and which ionic? Explain.
  (a) B⋯Br (b) Na⋯Br (c) Br⋯Cl (d) O⋯Br

2.92 The symbol CO stands for carbon monoxide, but the symbol Co stands for the element cobalt. Explain.

2.93 Correct the error in each of the following statements:
  (a) The formula of ammonia is NH3.
  (b) Molecules of potassium chloride have the formula KCl.
  (c) Cl^- is a cation.
  (d) CH_4 is a polyatomic ion.

2.94 How many protons and electrons are in each of the following ions?
  (a) Be^{2+} (b) Rb^+ (c) Se^{2-} (d) Au^{3+}

2.95 What is the identity of the element X in the following ions?
  (a) X^{2+}, a cation that has 36 electrons
  (b) X^-, an anion that has 36 electrons

2.96 The structural formula of isopropyl alcohol, better known as "rubbing alcohol," is shown. What is the chemical formula of isopropyl alcohol?

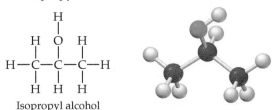

Isopropyl alcohol

2.97 Lactic acid, a compound found both in sour milk and in tired muscles, has the structure shown. What is its chemical formula?

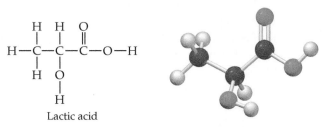

Lactic acid

2.98 Butane, the fuel used in disposable lighters, has the formula C_4H_{10}. The carbon atoms are connected in the sequence C—C—C—C, and each carbon has four covalent bonds. Draw the structural formula of butane.

2.99 Cyclohexane, C_6H_{12}, is an important starting material used in the industrial synthesis of nylon. Each carbon has four covalent bonds, two to hydrogen and two to other carbons. Draw the structural formula of cyclohexane.

2.100 Isooctane, the substance in gasoline from which the term *octane rating* derives, has the formula C_8H_{18}. Each carbon has four covalent bonds, and the atoms are connected in the sequence shown. Draw the complete structural formula of isooctane.

```
        C       C
        |       |
    C — C — C — C — C
        |
        C
```

2.101 Fructose, $C_6H_{12}O_6$, is the sweetest naturally occurring sugar and is found in many fruits and berries. Each carbon has four covalent bonds, each oxygen has two covalent bonds, each hydrogen has one covalent bond, and the atoms are connected in the sequence shown. Draw the complete structural formula of fructose.

```
  O — C        C — O
        \  O  /
         C   C
          \   \
           C — C    O
           |   |
           O   O
```

Naming Compounds (Section 2.12)

2.102 Write formulas for the following binary compounds:
  (a) Potassium chloride (b) Tin(II) bromide
  (c) Calcium oxide (d) Barium chloride
  (e) Aluminum hydride

2.103 Write formulas for the following compounds:
  (a) Calcium acetate (b) Iron(II) cyanide
  (c) Sodium dichromate (d) Chromium(III) sulfate
  (e) Mercury(II) perchlorate

2.104 Name the following ions:
  (a) Ba^{2+} (b) Cs^+ (c) V^{3+}
  (d) HCO_3^- (e) NH_4^+ (f) Ni^{2+}
  (g) NO_2^- (h) ClO_2^- (i) Mn^{2+}
  (j) ClO_4^-

2.105 Name the following binary molecular compounds:
  (a) CCl_4 (b) ClO_2
  (c) N_2O (d) N_2O_3

2.106 What are the formulas of the compounds formed from the following ions:
  (a) Ca^{2+} and Br^-
  (b) Ca^{2+} and SO_4^{2-}
  (c) Al^{3+} and SO_4^{2-}

2.107 What are the formulas of the compounds formed from the following ions:
  (a) Na^+ and NO_3^- (b) K^+ and SO_4^{2-} (c) Sr^{2+} and Cl^-

2.108 Write formulas for compounds of calcium with each of the following:
  (a) chlorine (b) oxygen (c) sulfur

2.109 Write formulas for compounds of rubidium with each of the following:
  (a) bromine (b) nitrogen (c) selenium

2.110 Give the formulas and charges of the following ions:
  (a) Sulfite ion (b) Phosphate ion
  (c) Zirconium(IV) ion (d) Chromate ion
  (e) Acetate ion (f) Thiosulfate ion

2.111 What are the charges on the positive ions in the following compounds?
  (a) $Zn(CN)_2$ (b) $Fe(NO_2)_3$
  (c) $Ti(SO_4)_2$ (d) $Sn_3(PO_4)_2$
  (e) Hg_2S (f) MnO_2
  (g) KIO_4 (h) $Cu(CH_3CO_2)_2$

2.112 Name the following binary compounds of nitrogen and oxygen:

(a) NO   (b) N_2O (c) NO_2

(d) N_2O_4 (e) N_2O_5

2.113 Name the following binary compounds of sulfur and oxygen:

(a) SO   (b) S_2O_2 (c) S_5O

(d) S_7O_2 (e) SO_3

2.114 Fill in the missing information to give formulas for the following compounds:

(a) $Na_?SO_4$ (b) $Ba_?(PO_4)_?$ (c) $Ga_?(SO_4)_?$

2.115 Write formulas for each of the following compounds:

(a) Sodium peroxide

(b) Aluminum bromide

(c) Chromium(III) sulfate

CHAPTER PROBLEMS

2.116 Germanium has five naturally occurring isotopes: ^{70}Ge, 20.5%, 69.924 amu; ^{72}Ge, 27.4%, 71.922 amu; ^{73}Ge, 7.8%, 72.923 amu; ^{74}Ge, 36.5%, 73.921 amu; and ^{76}Ge, 7.8%, 75.921 amu. What is the atomic mass of germanium?

2.117 Fluorine occurs naturally as a single isotope. How many protons, neutrons, and electrons are present in deuterium fluoride (^2HF)? (Deuterium is ^2H.)

2.118 Ammonia (NH_3) and hydrazine (N_2H_4) are both compounds of nitrogen and hydrogen. Based on the law of multiple proportions, how many grams of hydrogen would you expect 2.34 g of nitrogen to combine with to yield ammonia? To yield hydrazine?

2.119 If 3.670 g of nitrogen combines with 0.5275 g of hydrogen to yield compound X, how many grams of nitrogen would combine with 1.575 g of hydrogen to make the same compound? Is X ammonia or hydrazine (Problem 2.118)?

2.120 Identify the following atoms:

(a) A halogen with 53 electrons

(b) A noble gas with $A = 84$

2.121 Hydrogen has three isotopes (^1H, ^2H, and ^3H), and chlorine has two isotopes (^{35}Cl and ^{37}Cl). How many isotopic kinds of HCl are there? Write the formula for each, and tell how many protons, neutrons, and electrons each contains.

2.122 Prior to 1961, the atomic mass unit was defined as 1/16 the mass of the atomic mass of oxygen; that is, the atomic mass of oxygen was defined as exactly 16 amu. What was the mass of a ^{12}C atom prior to 1961 if the atomic mass of oxygen on today's scale is 15.9994 amu?

2.123 What was the mass in atomic mass units of a ^{40}Ca atom prior to 1961 if its mass on today's scale is 39.9626 amu? (See Problem 2.122)

2.124 The *molecular mass* of a compound is the sum of the atomic masses of all atoms in the molecule. What is the molecular mass of acetaminophen ($C_8H_9NO_2$), the active ingredient in Tylenol?

2.125 The *mass percent* of an element in a compound is the mass of the element (total mass of the element's atoms in the compound) divided by the mass of the compound (total mass of all atoms in the compound) times 100%. What is the mass percent of each element in acetaminophen? (See Problem 2.124.)

Acetaminophen

2.126 Radioactive ^{100}Tc decays to form ^{100}Mo. There are two possible pathways for this decay. Write balanced equations for both.

2.127 ^{226}Ac can decay by any of three different nuclear processes: α emission, β emission, or electron capture. Write a balanced nuclear equation for the decay of ^{226}Ac by each process.

2.128 Tetrahydrofuran, an organic substance used as a solvent in many pharmaceutical processes, has the formula C_4H_8O. In tetrahydrofuran, the four C atoms are bonded in a row, each C atom is bonded to two H atoms, each H atom is bonded to one C atom, and the O atom is bonded to two C atoms. Write a structural formula for tetrahydrofuran.

2.129 In an alternate universe, the smallest negatively charged particle, analogous to our electron, is called a blorvek. To determine the charge on a single blorvek, an experiment like Millikan's with charged oil droplets was carried out and the following results were recorded:

Droplet Number	Charge (C)
1	7.74×10^{-16}
2	4.42×10^{-16}
3	2.21×10^{-16}
4	4.98×10^{-16}
5	6.64×10^{-16}

(a) Based on these observations, what is the largest possible value for the charge on a blorvek?

(b) Further experiments found a droplet with a charge of 5.81×10^{-16} C. Does this new result change your answer to part (a)? If so, what is the new largest value for the blorvek's charge?

CHAPTER 3

Mass Relationships in Chemical Reactions

All chemical reactions, including those responsible for the spectacular displays of exploding fireworks, require specific mass relationships between reactants.

CONTENTS

It's sometimes easy when beginning the study of chemistry to forget that *reactions* are at the heart of the science. New words, ideas, and principles are introduced so quickly that the central concern of chemistry—the change of one substance into another—can get lost in the rush.

In this chapter, we'll begin learning about how to describe chemical reactions, starting with a look at the conventions for writing chemical equations and at the mass relationships between reactants and products. Because most chemical reactions are carried out using solutions rather than pure substances, we'll also discuss units for describing the concentration of a substance in solution. Finally, we'll see how chemical formulas are determined and how molecular masses are measured.

3.1 BALANCING CHEMICAL EQUATIONS

The previous chapters have provided several examples of reactions: hydrogen reacting with oxygen to yield water, sodium reacting with chlorine to yield sodium chloride, mercury(II) nitrate reacting with potassium iodide to yield mercury(II) iodide, and so forth.

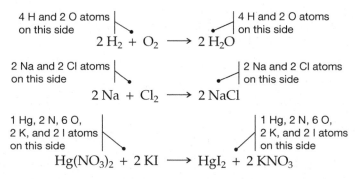

Look carefully at how these equations are written. Because hydrogen, oxygen, and chlorine exist as covalent H_2, O_2, and Cl_2 diatomic molecules rather than as isolated atoms (Section 2.10), we must write them as such in chemical equations. Now look at the atoms on each side of the reaction arrow. Although we haven't explicitly stated it yet, chemical equations are always written so that they are **balanced**; that is, so that the numbers and kinds of atoms on both sides of the reaction arrow are the same. This requirement is just a consequence of the mass conservation law (Section 2.1). Because atoms are neither created nor destroyed in chemical reactions, their numbers and kinds must remain the same in both products and reactants.

Balancing a chemical equation involves finding out how many *formula units* of each different substance take part in the reaction. A **formula unit**, as its name implies, is one unit—whether atom, ion, or molecule—corresponding to a given formula. One formula unit of NaCl is one Na^+ ion and one Cl^- ion, one formula unit of $MgBr_2$ is one Mg^{2+} ion and two Br^- ions, and one formula unit of H_2O is one H_2O molecule.

Complicated equations generally need to be balanced using a systematic method, such as we'll discuss in the next chapter, but simpler equations can often be balanced using a mixture of common sense and trial-and-error:

1. Write the unbalanced equation using the correct chemical formula for each reactant and product. In the combustion reaction of methane (CH_4; natural gas) with oxygen to yield carbon dioxide and water, for example, we begin by writing:

$$CH_4 + O_2 \longrightarrow CO_2 + H_2O \qquad \text{Unbalanced}$$

2. Find suitable **coefficients**—the numbers placed before formulas to indicate how many formula units of each substance are required to balance the equation. Only these coefficients can be changed when balancing an equation; the formulas

Remember...

According to the **law of mass conservation**, mass is neither created nor destroyed in chemical reactions.   (Section 2.1)

themselves can't be changed. Again using the reaction of methane with oxygen as an example, we can balance the equation by adding a coefficient of 2 to both O_2 and H_2O. By so doing, we now have 1 carbon atom, 4 hydrogen atoms, and 4 oxygen atoms on both sides of the equation:

Add these coefficients to balance the equation.

$$CH_4 + 2 O_2 \longrightarrow CO_2 + 2 H_2O$$

3. Reduce the coefficients to their smallest whole-number values, if necessary, by dividing them all by a common divisor.

4. Check your answer by making sure that the numbers and kinds of atoms are the same on both sides of the equation.

Let's work through some additional examples:

WORKED EXAMPLE 3.1

BALANCING A CHEMICAL EQUATION

Propane, C_3H_8, is a colorless, odorless gas often used as a heating and cooking fuel in campers and rural homes. Write a balanced equation for the combustion reaction of propane with oxygen to yield carbon dioxide and water.

STRATEGY AND SOLUTION

Follow the four steps described in the text:

Step 1. Write the unbalanced equation using correct chemical formulas for all substances:

$$C_3H_8 + O_2 \longrightarrow CO_2 + H_2O \qquad \text{Unbalanced}$$

Step 2. Find coefficients to balance the equation. It's usually best to begin with the most complex substance—in this case C_3H_8—and to deal with one element at a time. Look at the unbalanced equation, and note that there are 3 carbon atoms on the left side of the equation but only 1 on the right side. If we add a coefficient of 3 to CO_2 on the right, the carbons balance:

$$C_3H_8 + O_2 \longrightarrow 3 CO_2 + H_2O \qquad \text{Balanced for C}$$

Next, look at the number of hydrogen atoms. There are 8 hydrogens on the left but only 2 (in H_2O) on the right. By adding a coefficient of 4 to the H_2O on the right, the hydrogens balance:

$$C_3H_8 + O_2 \longrightarrow 3 CO_2 + 4 H_2O \qquad \text{Balanced for C and H}$$

Finally, look at the number of oxygen atoms. There are 2 on the left but 10 on the right. By adding a coefficient of 5 to the O_2 on the left, the oxygens balance:

$$C_3H_8 + 5 O_2 \longrightarrow 3 CO_2 + 4 H_2O \qquad \text{Balanced for C, H, and O}$$

Step 3. Make sure the coefficients are reduced to their smallest whole-number values. In fact, our answer is already correct, but we might have arrived at a different answer through trial and error:

$$2 C_3H_8 + 10 O_2 \longrightarrow 6 CO_2 + 8 H_2O$$

Although the preceding equation is balanced, the coefficients are not the smallest whole numbers. It would be necessary to divide all coefficients by 2 to reach the final equation.

Step 4. Check your answer. Count the numbers and kinds of atoms on both sides of the equation to make sure they're the same:

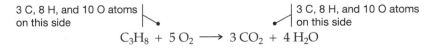

3 C, 8 H, and 10 O atoms on this side | 3 C, 8 H, and 10 O atoms on this side

$$C_3H_8 + 5 O_2 \longrightarrow 3 CO_2 + 4 H_2O$$

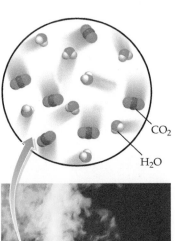

CO_2

H_2O

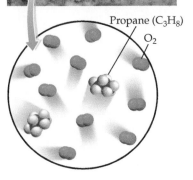

▲ Propane is used as a fuel in camp stoves and in rural homes.

Propane (C_3H_8)

O_2

BALANCING A CHEMICAL EQUATION

The major ingredient in ordinary safety matches is potassium chlorate, $KClO_3$, a substance that can act as a source of oxygen in combustion reactions. Its reaction with ordinary table sugar (sucrose, $C_{12}H_{22}O_{11}$), for example, occurs violently to yield potassium chloride, carbon dioxide, and water. Write a balanced equation for the reaction.

STRATEGY AND SOLUTION

Step 1. Write the unbalanced equation, making sure the formulas for all substances are correct:

$$KClO_3 + C_{12}H_{22}O_{11} \longrightarrow KCl + CO_2 + H_2O \qquad \text{Unbalanced}$$

Step 2. Find coefficients to balance the equation by starting with the most complex substance (sucrose) and considering one element at a time. Since there are 12 C atoms on the left and only 1 on the right, we can balance for carbon by adding a coefficient of 12 to CO_2 on the right:

$$KClO_3 + C_{12}H_{22}O_{11} \longrightarrow KCl + 12\,CO_2 + H_2O \qquad \text{Balanced for C}$$

Since there are 22 H atoms on the left and only 2 on the right, we can balance for hydrogen by adding a coefficient of 11 to H_2O on the right:

$$KClO_3 + C_{12}H_{22}O_{11} \longrightarrow KCl + 12\,CO_2 + 11\,H_2O \qquad \text{Balanced for C and H}$$

There are now 35 O atoms on the right but only 14 on the left (11 in sucrose and 3 in $KClO_3$). Thus, 21 oxygens must be added on the left. We can do this without disturbing the C and H balance by adding 7 more $KClO_3$, giving a coefficient of 8 for $KClO_3$ on the left:

$$8\,KClO_3 + C_{12}H_{22}O_{11} \longrightarrow KCl + 12\,CO_2 + 11\,H_2O \qquad \text{Balanced for C, H, and O}$$

Potassium and chlorine can both be balanced by adding a coefficient of 8 to KCl on the right:

$$8\,KClO_3 + C_{12}H_{22}O_{11} \longrightarrow 8\,KCl + 12\,CO_2 + 11\,H_2O \qquad \text{Balanced for C, H, O, K, and Cl}$$

Step 3 and 4. The coefficients in the balanced equation are already reduced to their smallest whole-number values, and a check shows that the numbers and kinds of atoms are the same on both sides of the equation.

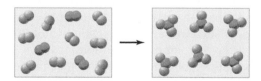

8 K, 8 Cl, 12 C, 22 H, and 35 O atoms ⟍   8 K, 8 Cl, 12 C, 22 H, and 35 O atoms ⟋

$$8\,KClO_3 + C_{12}H_{22}O_{11} \longrightarrow 8\,KCl + 12\,CO_2 + 11\,H_2O$$

▲ Safety matches contain potassium chlorate, which acts as a source of oxygen for ignition.

BALANCING A CHEMICAL EQUATION

Write a balanced equation for the reaction of element A (red spheres) with element B (blue spheres) as represented below:

STRATEGY

Balancing the reactions shown in graphic representations of this sort is just a matter of counting the numbers of reactant and product formula units. In this example, the reactant box contains three red A_2 molecules and nine blue B_2 molecules, while the product box contains six AB_3 molecules with no reactant left over.

SOLUTION

$$3\,A_2 + 9\,B_2 \longrightarrow 6\,AB_3 \quad \text{or} \quad A_2 + 3\,B_2 \longrightarrow 2\,AB_3$$

▶ **PROBLEM 3.1**   Sodium chlorate, $NaClO_3$, decomposes when heated to yield sodium chloride and oxygen, a reaction used to provide oxygen for the emergency breathing masks in many airliners. Balance the equation.

▶ **PROBLEM 3.2**   Balance the following equations:
(a) $C_6H_{12}O_6 \longrightarrow C_2H_6O + CO_2$ (fermentation of sugar to yield ethyl alcohol)
(b) $CO_2 + H_2O \longrightarrow C_6H_{12}O_6 + O_2$ (photosynthesis reaction in green plants)
(c) $NH_3 + Cl_2 \longrightarrow N_2H_4 + NH_4Cl$ (synthesis of hydrazine for rocket fuel)

CONCEPTUAL PROBLEM 3.3   Write a balanced equation for the reaction of element A (red spheres) with element B (green spheres) as represented below:

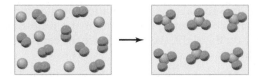

3.2   REPRESENTING CHEMISTRY ON DIFFERENT LEVELS

What does it mean when we write a chemical formula or equation? Answering this question isn't as easy as it sounds because a chemical symbol can have different meanings under different circumstances. Chemists use the same symbols to represent chemistry on both a small-scale, microscopic level and a large-scale, macroscopic level, and they tend to slip back and forth between the two levels without realizing the confusion this can cause for newcomers to the field.

On the microscopic level, chemical symbols represent the behavior of individual atoms and molecules. Atoms and molecules are much too small to be seen, but we can nevertheless describe their microscopic behavior if we read the equation $2 H_2 + O_2 \longrightarrow 2 H_2O$ to mean "Two molecules of hydrogen react with one molecule of oxygen to yield two molecules of water." It's this microscopic world that we deal with when trying to understand how reactions occur, and it's often helpful to visualize a molecule as a collection of spheres stuck together. In trying to understand how H_2 reacts with O_2, for example, you might picture H_2 and O_2 molecules as made of two spheres pressed together and a water molecule as made of three spheres.

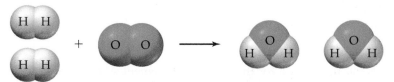

On the macroscopic level, formulas and equations represent the large-scale behaviors of atoms and molecules that give rise to visible properties. In other words, the symbols H_2, O_2, and H_2O represent not just single molecules but vast numbers of molecules that together have a set of measurable physical properties. A *single* isolated H_2O molecule is neither solid nor liquid nor gas, but a huge collection of H_2O molecules appears to us as a colorless liquid that freezes at 0 °C and boils at 100 °C. Clearly, it's this macroscopic behavior we deal with in the laboratory when we weigh specific amounts of reactants, place them in a flask, and observe visible changes.

In the same way, a single atom of copper is neither solid, liquid, nor gas, does not conduct electricity, and has no color on a microscopic level. On a macroscopic level, however, a large collection of copper atoms appears to us as a shiny, reddish-brown metal that can be drawn into electrical wires or made into coins.

What does a chemical formula or equation mean? It means different things depending on the context. The symbol H_2O can mean either one tiny, invisible molecule or a vast collection of molecules large enough to swim in.

3.3 CHEMICAL ARITHMETIC: STOICHIOMETRY

Imagine a laboratory experiment—perhaps the reaction of ethylene, C_2H_4, with hydrogen chloride, HCl, to prepare ethyl chloride, C_2H_5Cl, a colorless, low-boiling liquid that doctors and athletic trainers use as a spray-on anesthetic for minor injuries. You might note that in writing this and other equations, the designations (*g*) for gas, (*l*) for liquid, (*s*) for solid, and (*aq*) for aqueous solutions are often appended to the symbols of reactants and products to show their physical state. We'll do this frequently from now on.

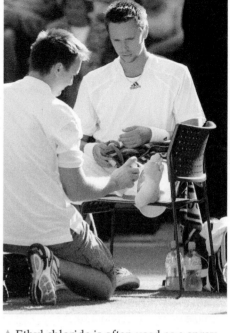

▲ Ethyl chloride is often used as a spray-on anesthetic for athletic injuries.

$$C_2H_4(g) + HCl(g) \longrightarrow C_2H_5Cl(l)$$
Ethylene   Hydrogen chloride   Ethyl chloride
                                         (an anesthetic)

How much ethylene and how much hydrogen chloride should you use for your experiment? According to the coefficients of the balanced equation, a 1:1 numerical ratio of the two reactants is needed. But because you can't count the reactant molecules, you have to weigh them. That is, you must convert a *number* ratio of reactant molecules, as given by coefficients in the balanced equation, into a *mass* ratio to be sure you are using the right amounts.

Mass ratios are determined by using the *molecular masses* (also called *molecular weights*) of the substances involved in a reaction. Just as the atomic mass of an element is the average mass of the element's *atoms* (Section 2.6), the **molecular mass** of a substance is the average mass of the substance's *molecules*. Numerically, molecular mass (or, more generally, **formula mass** to include both ionic and molecular substances) equals the sum of the atomic masses of all atoms in the molecule.

◁▭▶ **Molecular Mass**   Sum of atomic masses of all atoms in a molecule.

◁▭▶ **Formula Mass**   Sum of atomic masses of all atoms in a formula unit of any compound, molecular or ionic.

As examples, the molecular mass of ethylene is 28.0 amu, the molecular mass of hydrogen chloride is 36.5 amu, and the molecular mass of ethyl chloride is 64.5 amu. (These numbers are rounded off to one decimal place for convenience; the actual values are known more precisely.)

For ethylene, C_2H_4:

atomic mass of 2 C = (2)(12.0 amu)	= 24.0 amu
atomic mass of 4 H = (4)(1.0 amu)	= 4.0 amu
Molecular mass of C_2H_4	= 28.0 amu

For hydrogen chloride, HCl:

atomic mass of H	= 1.0 amu
atomic mass of Cl	= 35.5 amu
Molecular mass of HCl = 36.5 amu

For ethyl chloride, C_2H_5Cl:

atomic mass of 2 C = (2)(12.0 amu)	= 24.0 amu
atomic mass of 5 H = (5)(1.0 amu)	= 5.0 amu
atomic mass of Cl	= 35.5 amu
Molecular mass of C_2H_5Cl	= 64.5 amu

How do we use molecular masses? We saw in Section 2.6 that one **mole** of any element is the amount whose mass, or *molar mass*, is numerically equal to the element's atomic mass in grams. In the same way, one mole of any chemical compound is numerically equal to the compound's molecular mass (or formula mass) in grams and contains **Avogadro's number** of formula units (6.022×10^{23}). Thus, 1 mol of ethylene has a mass of 28.0 g, 1 mol of HCl has a mass of 36.5 g, 1 mol of C_2H_5Cl has a mass of 64.5 g, and so on.

Molec. mass of HCl = 36.5 amu	Molar mass of HCl = 36.5 g	1 mol of HCl = 6.022×10^{23} HCl molecules
Molec. mass of C_2H_4 = 28.0 amu	Molar mass of C_2H_4 = 28.0 g	1 mol of C_2H_4 = 6.022×10^{23} C_2H_4 molecules
Molec. mass of C_2H_5Cl = 64.5 amu	Molar mass of C_2H_5Cl = 64.5 g	1 mol of C_2H_5Cl = 6.022×10^{23} C_2H_5Cl molecules

Remember...
The **mole** is the fundamental SI unit for measuring amount of matter. One mole of any substance—atom, ion, or molecule—is the amount whose mass in grams is numerically equal to the substance's atomic or formula mass. One mole contains **Avogadro's number** (6.022×10^{23}) of formula units. (Section 2.6)

In any balanced chemical equation, the coefficients tell the number of formula units, and thus the number of moles, of each substance in the reaction. You can then use molar masses as conversion factors to calculate reactant masses. If you saw the following balanced equation for the industrial synthesis of ammonia, for instance, you would know that 3 mol of $H_2(g)$ (3 mol $\times$ 2.0 g/mol = 6.0 g) is needed for reaction with 1 mol of $N_2(g)$ (28.0 g) to yield 2 mol of $NH_3(g)$ (2 mol $\times$ 17.0 g/mol = 34.0 g).

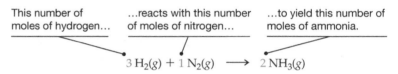

This number of moles of hydrogen... ...reacts with this number of moles of nitrogen... ...to yield this number of moles of ammonia.

$$3\,H_2(g) + 1\,N_2(g) \longrightarrow 2\,NH_3(g)$$

In referring to the chemical arithmetic needed for mole–mass conversions, we use the word **stoichiometry** (stoy-key-**ahm**-uh-tree; from the Greek *stoicheion*, "element," and *metron*, "measure"). Let's look again at the reaction of ethylene with HCl and assume that we have 15.0 g of ethylene and need to know how many grams of HCl to use in the reaction.

$$C_2H_4(g) + HCl(g) \longrightarrow C_2H_5Cl(l)$$

According to the coefficients in the balanced equation, 1 molecule of HCl reacts with 1 molecule of ethylene, so 1 mol of HCl is needed for reaction with each mole of ethylene. To find out how many grams of HCl are needed to react with 15.0 g of ethylene, we first have to find out how many moles of ethylene are in 15.0 g. We do this gram-to-mole conversion by calculating the molar mass of ethylene and using that value as a conversion factor:

Molecular mass of C_2H_4 = (2 $\times$ 12.0 amu) + (4 $\times$ 1.0 amu) = 28.0 amu

Molar mass of C_2H_4 = 28.0 g/mol

$$\text{Moles of } C_2H_4 = 15.0 \text{ g ethylene} \times \frac{1 \text{ mol ethylene}}{28.0 \text{ g ethylene}} = 0.536 \text{ mol ethylene}$$

Now that we know how many moles of ethylene we have (0.536 mol), we also know from the balanced equation how many moles of HCl we need (0.536 mol), and we have to do a mole-to-gram conversion to find the mass of HCl required. Once again, the conversion is done by calculating the molar mass of HCl and using that value as a conversion factor:

Molecular mass of HCl = 1.0 amu + 35.5 amu = 36.5 amu

Molar mass of HCl = 36.5 g/mol

$$\text{Grams of HCl} = 0.536 \text{ mol } C_2H_4 \times \frac{1 \text{ mol HCl}}{1 \text{ mol } C_2H_4} \times \frac{36.5 \text{ g HCl}}{1 \text{ mol HCl}} = 19.6 \text{ g HCl}$$

Thus, 19.6 g of HCl is needed to react with 15.0 g of ethylene.

Look carefully at the sequence of steps in the calculation just completed. *Moles* (numbers of molecules) are given by the coefficients in the balanced equation but *grams* are used to weigh reactants in the laboratory. Moles tell us *how many molecules* of each reactant are needed, while grams tell us *how much mass* of each reactant is needed.

$$\text{Moles} \longrightarrow \text{Numbers of molecules or formula units}$$
$$\text{Grams} \longrightarrow \text{Mass}$$

The flow diagram in **Figure 3.1** illustrates the necessary conversions. Note again that you can't go directly from the number of grams of one reactant to the number of grams of another reactant. You *must* first convert to moles.

For the balanced equation:
$$a\,A + b\,B \longrightarrow c\,C + d\,D$$

GIVEN → Grams of A

Use molar mass as a conversion factor. → Moles of A

Use coefficients in the balanced equation to find mole ratios. → Moles of B

Use molar mass as a conversion factor. → Grams of B

FIND

Figure 3.1

Conversions between moles and grams for a chemical reaction. The numbers of moles tell how many molecules of each reactant are needed, as given by the coefficients of the balanced equation; the numbers of grams tell what mass of each reactant is needed.

WORKED EXAMPLE 3.4

CALCULATING A MOLECULAR MASS

What is the molecular mass of table sugar (sucrose, $C_{12}H_{22}O_{11}$), and what is its molar mass in g/mol?

STRATEGY

The molecular mass of a substance is the sum of the atomic masses of the constituent atoms. List the elements present in the molecule, and look up the atomic mass of each (we'll round off to one decimal place for convenience):

C (12.0 amu); H (1.0 amu); O (16.0 amu)

Then, multiply the atomic mass of each element by the number of times that element appears in the chemical formula, and total the results.

SOLUTION

$$C_{12} \quad (12 \times 12.0 \text{ amu}) = 144.0 \text{ amu}$$
$$H_{22} \quad (22 \times 1.0 \text{ amu}) = 22.0 \text{ amu}$$
$$O_{11} \quad (11 \times 16.0 \text{ amu}) = 176.0 \text{ amu}$$
$$\overline{\text{Molecular mass of } C_{12}H_{22}O_{11} = 342.0 \text{ amu}}$$

Because one molecule of sucrose has a mass of 342.0 amu, 1 mol of sucrose has a mass of 342.0 g. Thus, the molar mass of sucrose is 342.0 g/mol.

WORKED EXAMPLE 3.5

CONVERTING MASS TO MOLES

How many moles of sucrose are in a tablespoon of sugar containing 2.85 g? (The molar mass of sucrose, $C_{12}H_{22}O_{11}$, was calculated in Worked Example 3.4.)

STRATEGY

The problem gives the mass of sucrose and asks for a mass-to-mole conversion. Use the molar mass of sucrose as a conversion factor, and set up an equation so that the unwanted unit cancels.

SOLUTION

$$2.85 \text{ g sucrose} \times \frac{1 \text{ mol sucrose}}{342.0 \text{ g sucrose}} = 0.008\,33 \text{ mol sucrose}$$
$$= 8.33 \times 10^{-3} \text{ mol sucrose}$$

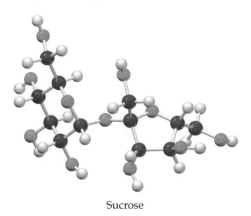

Sucrose

BALLPARK CHECK

Because the molecular mass of sucrose is 342.0 amu, 1 mol of sucrose has a mass of 342.0 g. Thus, 2.85 g of sucrose is a bit less than one-hundredth of a mole, or 0.01 mol. The estimate agrees with the detailed solution.

CONVERTING MOLES TO MASS

How many grams are in 0.0626 mol of $NaHCO_3$, the main ingredient in Alka-Seltzer tablets?

STRATEGY

The problem gives the number of moles of $NaHCO_3$ and asks for a mole-to-mass conversion. First, calculate the molar mass of $NaHCO_3$. Then use molar mass as a conversion factor, and set up an equation so that the unwanted unit cancels.

SOLUTION

$$\text{Formula mass of } NaHCO_3 = 23.0 \text{ amu} + 1.0 \text{ amu} + 12.0 \text{ amu} + (3 \times 16.0 \text{ amu})$$
$$= 84.0 \text{ amu}$$
$$\text{Molar mass of } NaHCO_3 = 84.0 \text{ g/mol}$$

$$0.0626 \text{ mol } NaHCO_3 \times \frac{84.0 \text{ g } NaHCO_3}{1 \text{ mol } NaHCO_3} = 5.26 \text{ g } NaHCO_3$$

▲ Household bleach is an aqueous solution of NaOCl, made by reaction of NaOH with Cl_2.

FINDING THE MASS OF ONE REACTANT, GIVEN THE MASS OF ANOTHER

Aqueous solutions of sodium hypochlorite (NaOCl), best known as household bleach, are prepared by reaction of sodium hydroxide with chlorine. How many grams of NaOH are needed to react with 25.0 g of Cl_2?

$$2 NaOH(aq) + Cl_2(g) \longrightarrow NaOCl(aq) + NaCl(aq) + H_2O(l)$$

STRATEGY

Finding the relationship between numbers of reactant formula units always requires working in moles, using the general strategy outlined in Figure 3.1.

SOLUTION

First, find out how many moles of Cl_2 are in 25.0 g of Cl_2. This gram-to-mole conversion is done in the usual way, using the molar mass of Cl_2 (70.9 g/mol) as the conversion factor:

$$25.0 \text{ g } Cl_2 \times \frac{1 \text{ mol } Cl_2}{70.9 \text{ g } Cl_2} = 0.353 \text{ mol } Cl_2$$

Next, look at the coefficients in the balanced equation. Each mole of Cl_2 reacts with 2 mol of NaOH, so 0.353 mol of Cl_2 reacts with $2 \times 0.353 = 0.706$ mol of NaOH. With the number of moles of NaOH known, carry out a mole-to-gram conversion using the molar mass of NaOH (40.0 g/mol) as a conversion factor to find that 28.2 g of NaOH is required for the reaction:

$$\text{Grams of NaOH} = 0.353 \text{ mol } Cl_2 \times \frac{2 \text{ mol NaOH}}{1 \text{ mol } Cl_2} \times \frac{40.0 \text{ g NaOH}}{1 \text{ mol NaOH}}$$
$$= 28.2 \text{ g NaOH}$$

The problem can also be worked by combining the steps and setting up one large equation:

$$\text{Grams of NaOH} = 25.0 \text{ g } Cl_2 \times \frac{1 \text{ mol } Cl_2}{70.9 \text{ g } Cl_2} \times \frac{2 \text{ mol NaOH}}{1 \text{ mol } Cl_2} \times \frac{40.0 \text{ g NaOH}}{1 \text{ mol NaOH}}$$
$$= 28.2 \text{ g NaOH}$$

BALLPARK CHECK

The molar mass of NaOH is about half that of Cl_2, and 2 mol of NaOH is needed per 1 mol of Cl_2. Thus, the needed mass of NaOH will be similar to that of Cl_2, or about 25 g.

▶ **PROBLEM 3.4**   Calculate the formula mass or molecular mass of the following substances:

(a) Fe_2O_3 (rust)

(b) H_2SO_4 (sulfuric acid)

(c) $C_6H_8O_7$ (citric acid)

(d) $C_{16}H_{18}N_2O_4S$ (penicillin G)

CONCEPTUAL PROBLEM 3.5   Aspirin can be represented by the adjacent ball-and-stick molecular model. Give the formula for aspirin, and calculate its molecular mass (red = O, gray = C, ivory = H). How many moles of aspirin are in a tablet weighing 500 mg? How many molecules?

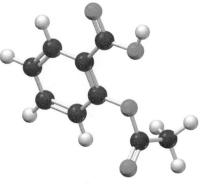

Aspirin

▶ **PROBLEM 3.6**   Aspirin is prepared by reaction of salicylic acid ($C_7H_6O_3$) with acetic anhydride ($C_4H_6O_3$) according to the following equation:

$$C_7H_6O_3 + C_4H_6O_3 \longrightarrow C_9H_8O_4 + CH_3CO_2H$$

Salicylic acid   Acetic anhydride   Aspirin   Acetic acid

(a) How many grams of acetic anhydride are needed to react with 4.50 g of salicylic acid?

(b) How many grams of aspirin will result?

(c) How many grams of acetic acid are formed as a byproduct?

3.4 YIELDS OF CHEMICAL REACTIONS

In the stoichiometry examples worked out in the preceding section, we made the unstated assumption that all reactions "go to completion." That is, we assumed that all reactant molecules are converted to products. In fact, few reactions behave so nicely. More often, a large majority of molecules react as expected, but other processes, or *side reactions*, also occur. Thus, the amount of product actually formed, called the **yield** of the reaction, is usually less than the amount predicted by calculations.

The amount of product actually formed in a reaction divided by the amount theoretically possible and multiplied by 100% is the reaction's **percent yield**. For example, if a given reaction *could* provide 6.9 g of a product according to its stoichiometry, but actually provides only 4.7 g, then its percent yield is $4.7/6.9 \times 100\% = 68\%$.

$$\text{Percent yield} = \frac{\text{Actual yield of product}}{\text{Theoretical yield of product}} \times 100\%$$

Worked Examples 3.8 and 3.9 show how to calculate and use percent yield.

WORKED EXAMPLE 3.8

CALCULATING A PERCENT YIELD

Methyl *tert*-butyl ether (MTBE, $C_5H_{12}O$), a gasoline additive now being phased out in many places because of health concerns, can be made by reaction of isobutylene (C_4H_8) with methanol (CH_4O). What is the percent yield of the reaction if 32.8 g of methyl *tert*-butyl ether is obtained from reaction of 26.3 g of isobutylene with sufficient methanol?

$$C_4H_8(g) + CH_4O(l) \longrightarrow C_5H_{12}O(l)$$

Isobutylene   Methyl *tert*-butyl ether (MTBE)

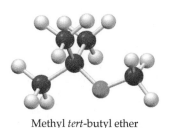

Methyl *tert*-butyl ether

STRATEGY

We need to calculate the amount of methyl *tert*-butyl ether that could be produced theoretically from 26.3 g of isobutylene and compare that theoretical amount to the

continued on next page

actual amount (32.8 g). As always, stoichiometry problems begin by calculating the molar masses of reactants and products. Coefficients of the balanced equation then tell mole ratios, and molar masses act as conversion factors between moles and masses.

SOLUTION

Isobutylene, C_4H_8: Molec. mass = $(4 \times 12.0 \text{ amu}) + (8 \times 1.0 \text{ amu}) = 56.0 \text{ amu}$

Molar mass of isobutylene = 56.0 g/mol

MTBE, $C_5H_{12}O$: Molec. mass = $(5 \times 12.0 \text{ amu}) + (12 \times 1.0 \text{ amu}) + 16.0 \text{ amu}$

= 88.0 amu

Molar mass of MTBE = 88.0 g/mol

To calculate the amount of MTBE that could theoretically be produced from 26.3 g of isobutylene, we first have to find the number of moles of reactant, using molar mass as the conversion factor:

$$26.3 \text{ g isobutylene} \times \frac{1 \text{ mol isobutylene}}{56.0 \text{ g isobutylene}} = 0.470 \text{ mol isobutylene}$$

According to the balanced equation, 1 mol of product is produced per mol of reactant, so we know that 0.470 mol of isobutylene can theoretically yield 0.470 mol of MTBE. Finding the mass of this MTBE requires a mole-to-mass conversion:

$$0.470 \text{ mol isobutylene} \times \frac{1 \text{ mol MTBE}}{1 \text{ mol isobutylene}} \times \frac{88.0 \text{ g MTBE}}{1 \text{ mol MTBE}} = 41.4 \text{ g MTBE}$$

Dividing the actual amount by the theoretical amount and multiplying by 100% gives the percent yield:

$$\frac{32.8 \text{ g MTBE}}{41.4 \text{ g MTBE}} \times 100\% = 79.2\%$$

WORKED EXAMPLE 3.9

CALCULATING A YIELD IN GRAMS, GIVEN A PERCENT YIELD

Diethyl ether ($C_4H_{10}O$), the "ether" used medically as an anesthetic, is prepared commercially by treatment of ethyl alcohol (C_2H_6O) with an acid. How many grams of diethyl ether would you obtain from 40.0 g of ethyl alcohol if the percent yield of the reaction is 87%?

$$2\,C_2H_6O(l) \xrightarrow{\text{Acid}} C_4H_{10}O(l) + H_2O(l)$$

Ethyl alcohol   Diethyl ether

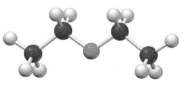

Diethyl ether

STRATEGY

Treat this as a typical stoichiometry problem to find the amount of diethyl ether that can theoretically be formed from 40.0 g of ethyl alcohol, and then multiply the answer by 87% to find the amount actually formed.

SOLUTION

First, calculate the molar masses of the reactant and product:

Ethyl alcohol, C_2H_6O: Molec. mass = $(2 \times 12.0 \text{ amu}) + (6 \times 1.0 \text{ amu}) + 16.0 \text{ amu}$

= 46.0 amu

Molar mass of ethyl alcohol = 46.0 g/mol

Diethyl ether, $C_4H_{10}O$: Molec. mass = $(4 \times 12.0 \text{ amu}) + (10 \times 1.0 \text{ amu}) + 16.0 \text{ amu}$

= 74.0 amu

Molar mass of diethyl ether = 74.0 g/mol

Next, find how many moles of ethyl alcohol are in 40.0 g by using molar mass as a conversion factor:

$$40.0 \text{ g ethyl alcohol} \times \frac{1 \text{ mol ethyl alcohol}}{46.0 \text{ g ethyl alcohol}} = 0.870 \text{ mol ethyl alcohol}$$

Because we started with 0.870 mol of ethyl alcohol, and because the balanced equation indicates that 2 mol of ethyl alcohol yield 1 mol of diethyl ether, we can theoretically obtain 0.435 mol of product:

$$0.870 \text{ mol ethyl alcohol} \times \frac{1 \text{ mol diethyl ether}}{2 \text{ mol ethyl alcohol}} = 0.435 \text{ mol diethyl ether}$$

We therefore need to find how many grams of diethyl ether are in 0.435 mol, using molar mass as the conversion factor:

$$0.435 \text{ mol diethyl ether} \times \frac{74.0 \text{ g diethyl ether}}{1 \text{ mol diethyl ether}} = 32.2 \text{ g diethyl ether}$$

Finally, we have to multiply the theoretical amount of product by the observed yield (87% = 0.87) to find how much diethyl ether is actually formed:

$$32.2 \text{ g diethyl ether} \times 0.87 = 28 \text{ g diethyl ether}$$

▶ **PROBLEM 3.7** Ethyl alcohol is prepared industrially by the reaction of ethylene, C_2H_4, with water. What is the percent yield of the reaction if 4.6 g of ethylene gives 4.7 g of ethyl alcohol?

$$C_2H_4(g) + H_2O(l) \longrightarrow C_2H_6O(l)$$

Ethylene   Ethyl alcohol

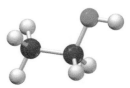

Ethyl alcohol

▶ **PROBLEM 3.8** Dichloromethane (CH_2Cl_2), used as a solvent in the decaffeination of coffee beans, is prepared by reaction of methane (CH_4) with chlorine. How many grams of dichloromethane result from reaction of 1.85 kg of methane if the yield is 43.1%?

$$CH_4(g) + 2\,Cl_2(g) \longrightarrow CH_2Cl_2(l) + 2\,HCl(g)$$

Methane   Chlorine   Dichloromethane

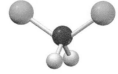

Dichloromethane

3.5 REACTIONS WITH LIMITING AMOUNTS OF REACTANTS

Because chemists usually write balanced equations, it's easy to get the impression that reactions are always carried out using exactly the right proportions of reactants. In fact, this is often not the case. Many reactions are carried out using an excess amount of one reactant—more than is actually needed according to stoichiometry. Look, for instance, at the industrial synthesis of ethylene glycol, $C_2H_6O_2$, a substance used both as automobile antifreeze and as a starting material for the preparation of polyester polymers. Approximately 18 million metric tons of ethylene glycol are prepared each year worldwide by reaction of ethylene oxide, C_2H_4O, with water at high temperature (1 metric ton = 1000 kg = 2205 lb).

C_2H_4O + H_2O $\xrightarrow{\text{Heat}}$ $C_2H_6O_2$
Ethylene oxide   Water   Ethylene glycol

Because water is so cheap and so abundant, it doesn't make sense to worry about using exactly 1 mol of water for each mole of ethylene oxide. Rather, it's much easier to use an excess of water to be certain that enough is present to consume entirely the more valuable ethylene oxide reactant. Of course, when an excess of water is present, only the amount required by stoichiometry undergoes reaction. The excess water does not react and remains unchanged.

Whenever the ratios of reactant molecules used in an experiment are different from those given by the coefficients of the balanced equation, a surplus of one reactant is left over after the reaction is finished. Thus, the extent to which a chemical reaction takes place depends on the reactant that is present in limiting amount—the **limiting reactant**. The other reactant is said to be the *excess reactant*.

The situation with excess reactants and limiting reactants is analogous to what sometimes happens with people and chairs. If there are five people in a room but only three chairs, then only three people can sit while the other two stand because the number of people sitting is limited by the number of available chairs. In the same way, if 5 moles of water come in contact with 3 moles of ethylene oxide, only 3 moles of water can undergo a reaction while the other 2 moles of water are unchanged.

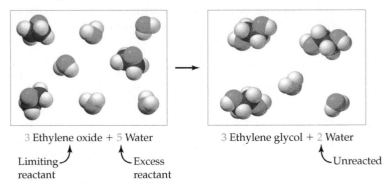

3 Ethylene oxide + 5 Water → 3 Ethylene glycol + 2 Water

Limiting reactant   Excess reactant   Unreacted

Worked Example 3.10 shows how to tell whether a limiting amount of one reactant is present and how to calculate the amounts of the excess reactant consumed and remaining.

WORKED EXAMPLE 3.10

CALCULATING THE AMOUNT OF AN EXCESS REACTANT

Cisplatin, an anticancer agent used for the treatment of solid tumors, is prepared by the reaction of ammonia with potassium tetrachloroplatinate. Assume that 10.0 g of K_2PtCl_4 and 10.0 g of NH_3 are allowed to react.

$$K_2PtCl_4(aq) + 2\ NH_3(aq) \longrightarrow Pt(NH_3)_2Cl_2(s) + 2\ KCl(aq)$$

Potassium tetrachloroplatinate   Cisplatin

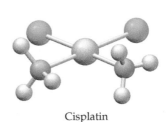

Cisplatin

(a) Which reactant is limiting, and which is in excess?
(b) How many grams of the excess reactant are consumed, and how many grams remain?
(c) How many grams of cisplatin are formed?

STRATEGY

When solving a problem that deals with limiting reactants, the idea is to find how many moles of all reactants are actually present and compare the mole ratios of those actual amounts to the mole ratios required by the balanced equation. That comparison will identify the reactant there is too much of (the excess reactant) and the reactant there is too little of (the limiting reactant).

SOLUTION

(a) Finding the molar amounts of reactants always begins by calculating formula masses and using molar masses as conversion factors:

Form. mass of K_2PtCl_4 = (2 × 39.1 amu) + 195.1 amu + (4 × 35.5 amu) = 415.3 amu

Molar mass of K_2PtCl_4 = 415.3 g/mol

Moles of K_2PtCl_4 = 10.0 g K_2PtCl_4 × $\dfrac{1 \, mol \, K_2PtCl_4}{415.3 \, g \, K_2PtCl_4}$ = 0.0241 mol K_2PtCl_4

Molec. mass of NH_3 = 14.0 amu + (3 × 1.0 amu) = 17.0 amu

Molar mass of NH_3 = 17.0 g/mol

Moles of NH_3 = 10.0 g NH_3 × $\dfrac{1 \, mol \, NH_3}{17.0 \, g \, NH_3}$ = 0.588 mol NH_3

These calculations tell us that we have 0.588 mol of ammonia and 0.0241 mol of K_2PtCl_4, or 0.588/0.0241 = 24.4 times as much ammonia as K_2PtCl_4. The coefficients in the balanced equation, however, say that only *two* times as much ammonia as K_2PtCl_4 is needed. Thus, a large excess of NH_3 is present, and K_2PtCl_4 is the limiting reactant.

(b) With the identities of the excess reactant and limiting reactant known, we now have to find how many moles of each undergo reaction and then carry out mole-to-gram conversions to find the mass of each reactant consumed. The entire amount of the limiting reactant (K_2PtCl_4) is used up, but only the amount of the excess reactant (NH_3) required by stoichiometry undergoes reaction:

Moles of K_2PtCl_4 consumed = 0.0241 mol K_2PtCl_4

Moles of NH_3 consumed = 0.0241 mol K_2PtCl_4 × $\dfrac{2 \, mol \, NH_3}{1 \, mol \, K_2PtCl_4}$ = 0.0482 mol NH_3

Grams of NH_3 consumed = 0.0482 mol NH_3 × $\dfrac{17.0 \, g \, NH_3}{1 \, mol \, NH_3}$ = 0.819 g NH_3

Grams of NH_3 not consumed = (10.0 g − 0.819 g) NH_3 = 9.2 g NH_3

(c) The balanced equation shows that 1 mol of cisplatin is formed for each mole of K_2PtCl_4 consumed. Thus, 0.0241 mol of cisplatin is formed from 0.0241 mol of K_2PtCl_4. To determine the mass of cisplatin produced, we must calculate its molar mass and then carry out a mole-to-gram conversion:

Molec. mass of $Pt(NH_3)_2Cl_2$ = 195.1 amu + (2 × 17.0 amu) + (2 × 35.5 amu) = 300.1 amu

Molar mass of $Pt(NH_3)_2Cl_2$ = 300.1 g/mol

Grams of $Pt(NH_3)_2Cl_2$ = 0.0241 mol $Pt(NH_3)_2Cl_2$ × $\dfrac{300.1 \, g \, Pt(NH_3)_2Cl_2}{1 \, mol \, Pt(NH_3)_2Cl_2}$ = 7.23 g $Pt(NH_3)_2Cl_2$

▶ **PROBLEM 3.9** Lithium oxide is used aboard the space shuttle to remove water from the air supply. If 80.0 kg of water is to be removed and 65 kg of Li_2O is available, which reactant is limiting? How many kilograms of the excess reactant remain?

$$Li_2O(s) + H_2O(g) \longrightarrow 2 \, LiOH(s)$$

▶ **PROBLEM 3.10** After lithium hydroxide is produced aboard the space shuttle by reaction of Li_2O with H_2O (Problem 3.9), it is used to remove exhaled carbon dioxide from the air supply. How many grams of CO_2 can 500.0 g of LiOH absorb?

$$LiOH(s) + CO_2(g) \longrightarrow LiHCO_3(s)$$

CONCEPTUAL PROBLEM 3.11 The following diagram represents the reaction of A (red spheres) with B_2 (blue spheres):

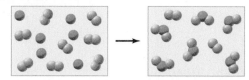

(a) Write a balanced equation for the reaction, and identify the limiting reactant.
(b) How many moles of product can be made from 1.0 mol of A and 1.0 mol of B_2?

3.6 CONCENTRATIONS OF REACTANTS IN SOLUTION: MOLARITY

For a chemical reaction to occur, the reacting molecules or ions must come into contact. This means that the reactants must be mobile, which in turn means that most chemical reactions are carried out in the liquid state or in solution rather than in the solid state. It's therefore necessary to have a standard means to describe exact quantities of substances in solution.

As we've seen, stoichiometry calculations for chemical reactions always require working in moles. Thus, the most generally useful means of expressing a solution's concentration is **molarity (M)**, the number of moles of a substance, or **solute**, dissolved in enough solvent to make one liter of solution. For example, a solution made by dissolving 1.00 mol (58.5 g) of NaCl in enough water to give 1.00 L of solution has a concentration of 1.00 mol/L, or 1.00 M. The molarity of any solution is found by dividing the number of moles of solute by the number of liters of solution:

$$\text{Molarity (M)} = \frac{\text{Moles of solute}}{\text{Liters of solution}}$$

Note that it's the final volume of the *solution* that's important, not the starting volume of the *solvent* used. The final volume of the solution might be a bit larger than the volume of the solvent because of the additional volume of the solute. In practice, a solution of known molarity is prepared by weighing an appropriate amount of solute and placing it in a container called a *volumetric flask*, as shown in Figure 3.2. Enough solvent is added to dissolve the solute, and further solvent is added until an accurately calibrated final volume is reached. The solution is then shaken until it's uniformly mixed.

Molarity can be used as a conversion factor to relate a solution's volume to the number of moles of solute. If we know the molarity and volume of a solution, we can

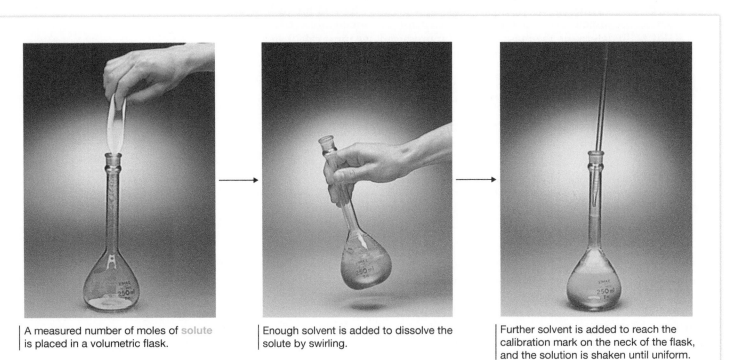

A measured number of moles of solute is placed in a volumetric flask.

Enough solvent is added to dissolve the solute by swirling.

Further solvent is added to reach the calibration mark on the neck of the flask, and the solution is shaken until uniform.

Figure 3.2
Preparing a solution of known molarity.

calculate the number of moles of solute. If we know the number of moles of solute and the molarity of the solution, we can find the solution's volume. Worked Examples 3.11 and 3.12 show how the calculations are done.

$$\text{Molarity} = \frac{\text{Moles of solute}}{\text{Volume of solution (L)}}$$

$$\begin{array}{c}\text{Moles of}\\\text{solute}\end{array} = \text{Molarity} \times \begin{array}{c}\text{Volume of}\\\text{solution}\end{array} \qquad \begin{array}{c}\text{Volume of}\\\text{solution}\end{array} = \frac{\text{Moles of solute}}{\text{Molarity}}$$

WORKED EXAMPLE 3.11

CALCULATING THE MOLARITY OF A SOLUTION

What is the molarity of a solution made by dissolving 2.355 g of sulfuric acid (H_2SO_4) in water and diluting to a final volume of 50.0 mL?

STRATEGY

Molarity is the number of moles of solute per liter of solution. Thus, it's necessary to find the number of moles of sulfuric acid in 2.355 g and then divide by the volume of the solution.

SOLUTION

Molec. mass of H_2SO_4 = (2 × 1.0 amu) + 32.1 amu + (4 × 16.0 amu) = 98.1 amu

Molar mass of H_2SO_4 = 98.1 g/mol

$$2.355 \text{ g } H_2SO_4 \times \frac{1 \text{ mol } H_2SO_4}{98.1 \text{ g } H_2SO_4} = 0.0240 \text{ mol } H_2SO_4$$

$$\frac{0.0240 \text{ mol } H_2SO_4}{0.0500 \text{ L}} = 0.480 \text{ M}$$

The solution has a sulfuric acid concentration of 0.480 M.

WORKED EXAMPLE 3.12

CALCULATING THE NUMBER OF MOLES OF SOLUTE IN A SOLUTION

Hydrochloric acid is sold commercially as a 12.0 M aqueous solution. How many moles of HCl are in 300.0 mL of 12.0 M solution?

STRATEGY

The number of moles of solute is calculated by multiplying the molarity of the solution by its volume.

SOLUTION

$$\text{Moles of HCl} = (\text{Molarity of solution}) \times (\text{Volume of solution})$$

$$= \frac{12.0 \text{ mol HCl}}{1 \text{ L}} \times 0.3000 \text{ L} = 3.60 \text{ mol HCl}$$

There are 3.60 mol of HCl in 300.0 mL of 12.0 M solution.

BALLPARK CHECK

One liter of 12.0 M HCl solution contains 12 mol of HCl, so 300 mL (0.3 L) of solution contains 0.3 × 12 = 3.6 mol.

▶ **PROBLEM 3.12** How many moles of solute are present in the following solutions?
(a) 125 mL of 0.20 M $NaHCO_3$ **(b)** 650.0 mL of 2.50 M H_2SO_4

▶ **PROBLEM 3.13** How many grams of solute would you use to prepare the following solutions?
(a) 500.0 mL of 1.25 M NaOH **(b)** 1.50 L of 0.250 M glucose ($C_6H_{12}O_6$)

▶ **PROBLEM 3.14** How many milliliters of a 0.20 M glucose ($C_6H_{12}O_6$) solution are needed to provide a total of 25.0 g of glucose?

▶ **PROBLEM 3.15** The concentration of cholesterol ($C_{27}H_{46}O$) in normal blood is approximately 0.005 M. How many grams of cholesterol are in 750 mL of blood?

Cholesterol

3.7 DILUTING CONCENTRATED SOLUTIONS

For convenience, chemicals are sometimes bought and stored as concentrated solutions, which are then diluted before use. Aqueous hydrochloric acid, for example, is sold commercially as a 12.0 M solution, yet it is most commonly used in the laboratory after dilution with water to a final concentration of either 6.0 M or 1.0 M.

Concentrated solution + Solvent ⟶ Dilute solution

The main thing to remember when diluting a concentrated solution is that the number of moles of solute is constant; only the volume of the solution is changed by adding more solvent. Because the number of moles of solute can be calculated by multiplying molarity times volume, we can set up the following equation:

$$\text{Moles of solute (constant)} = \text{Molarity} \times \text{Volume}$$
$$= M_i \times V_i = M_f \times V_f$$

▲ Just as frozen orange juice concentrate must be diluted before use by adding water, many chemical solutions must also be diluted.

where M_i is the initial molarity, V_i is the initial volume, M_f is the final molarity, and V_f is the final volume after dilution. Rearranging this equation into a more useful form shows that the molar concentration after dilution (M_f) can be found by multiplying the initial concentration (M_i) by the ratio of initial and final volumes (V_i/V_f):

$$M_f = M_i \times \frac{V_i}{V_f}$$

Suppose, for example, that we dilute 50.0 mL of a solution of 2.00 M H_2SO_4 to a volume of 200.0 mL. The solution volume *increases* by a factor of four (from 50 mL to 200 mL), so the concentration of the solution must *decrease* by a factor of four (from 2.00 M to 0.500 M):

$$M_f = 2.00 \text{ M} \times \frac{50.0 \text{ mL}}{200.0 \text{ mL}} = 0.500 \text{ M}$$

In practice, dilutions are usually carried out as shown in Figure 3.3. The volume to be diluted is withdrawn using a calibrated tube called a *pipet*, placed in an empty volumetric flask of the chosen volume, and diluted to the calibration mark on the flask. The one common exception to this order of steps is when diluting a strong acid such as H_2SO_4, where a large amount of heat is released. In such instances, it is much safer to add the acid slowly to the water rather than adding water to the acid.

WORKED EXAMPLE 3.13

DILUTING A SOLUTION

How would you prepare 500.0 mL of 0.2500 M NaOH solution starting from a concentration of 1.000 M?

STRATEGY

The problem gives initial and final concentrations (M_i and M_f) and final volume (V_f) and asks for the initial volume (V_i) that we need to dilute. Rewriting the equation $M_i \times V_i = M_f \times V_f$ as $V_i = (M_f/M_i) \times V_f$ gives the answer.

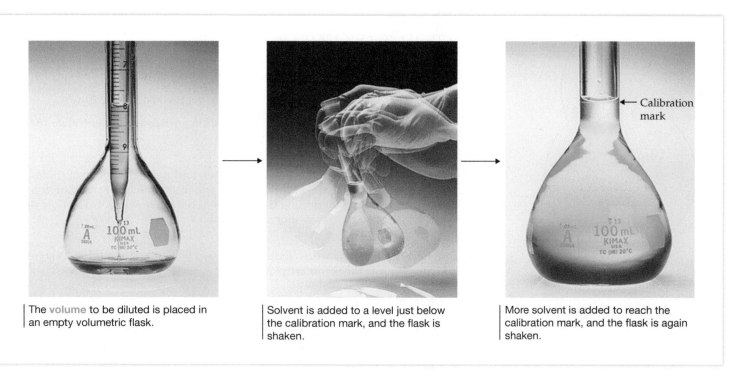

The volume to be diluted is placed in an empty volumetric flask.

Solvent is added to a level just below the calibration mark, and the flask is shaken.

More solvent is added to reach the calibration mark, and the flask is again shaken.

Calibration mark

Figure 3.3
The procedure for diluting a concentrated solution.

SOLUTION

$$V_i = \frac{M_f}{M_i} \times V_f = \frac{0.2500\ \text{M}}{1.000\ \text{M}} \times 500.0\ \text{mL} = 125.0\ \text{mL}$$

We need to place 125.0 mL of 1.000 M NaOH solution in a 500.0 mL volumetric flask and fill to the calibration mark with water.

BALLPARK CHECK

Because the concentration decreases by a factor of four after dilution (from 1.000 M to 0.2500 M), the volume must increase by a factor of four. Thus, to prepare 500.0 mL of solution, we should start with 500.0/4 = 125.0 mL.

▶ **PROBLEM 3.16** What is the final concentration if 75.0 mL of a 3.50 M glucose solution is diluted to a volume of 400.0 mL?

▶ **PROBLEM 3.17** Sulfuric acid is normally purchased at a concentration of 18.0 M. How would you prepare 250.0 mL of 0.500 M aqueous H_2SO_4? (Remember to add the acid to water rather than water to the acid.)

3.8 SOLUTION STOICHIOMETRY

We remarked in Section 3.6 that molarity is a conversion factor between numbers of moles of solute and the volume of a solution. Thus, if we know the volume and molarity of a solution, we can calculate the number of moles of solute. If we know the number of moles of solute and molarity, we can find the volume.

As indicated by the flow diagram in Figure 3.4, using molarity is critical for carrying out stoichiometry calculations on substances in solution. Molarity makes it possible to calculate the volume of one solution needed to react with a given volume of another solution. This sort of calculation is particularly important in the chemistry of acids and bases, as shown in Worked Example 3.14.

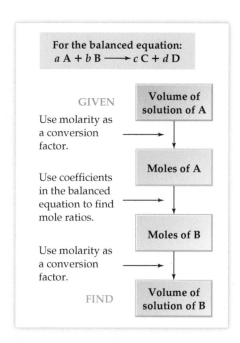

For the balanced equation:
$$a\,\text{A} + b\,\text{B} \longrightarrow c\,\text{C} + d\,\text{D}$$

GIVEN — Volume of solution of A

Use molarity as a conversion factor.

Moles of A

Use coefficients in the balanced equation to find mole ratios.

Moles of B

Use molarity as a conversion factor.

FIND — Volume of solution of B

Figure 3.4
Using molarity as a conversion factor between moles and volume in stoichiometry calculations.

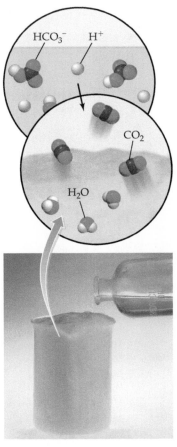

▲ Neutralization of sodium hydrogen carbonate with acid leads to release of CO_2 gas, visible in this fizzing solution.

WORKED EXAMPLE 3.14

REACTION STOICHIOMETRY IN SOLUTION

Stomach acid, a dilute solution of HCl in water, can be neutralized by reaction with sodium hydrogen carbonate, $NaHCO_3$, according to the equation

$$HCl(aq) + NaHCO_3(aq) \longrightarrow NaCl(aq) + H_2O(l) + CO_2(g)$$

How many milliliters of 0.125 M $NaHCO_3$ solution are needed to neutralize 18.0 mL of 0.100 M HCl?

STRATEGY

Solving stoichiometry problems always requires finding the number of moles of one reactant, using the coefficients of the balanced equation to find the number of moles of the other reactant, and then finding the amount of the other reactant. The flow diagram summarizing the situation was shown in Figure 3.4.

SOLUTION

We first have to find how many moles of HCl are in 18.0 mL of a 0.100 M solution by multiplying volume times molarity:

$$\text{Moles of HCl} = 18.0 \; \text{mL} \times \frac{1 \; L}{1000 \; \text{mL}} \times \frac{0.100 \; \text{mol}}{1 \; L} = 1.80 \times 10^{-3} \, \text{mol HCl}$$

Next, check the coefficients of the balanced equation to find that 1 mol of HCl reacts with 1 mol of $NaHCO_3$, and then calculate how many milliliters of a 0.125 M $NaHCO_3$ solution contains 1.80×10^{-3} mol:

$$1.80 \times 10^{-3} \; \text{mol HCl} \times \frac{1 \; \text{mol NaHCO}_3}{1 \; \text{mol HCl}} \times \frac{1 \; \text{L solution}}{0.125 \; \text{mol NaHCO}_3} = 0.0144 \; \text{L solution}$$

Thus, 14.4 mL of the 0.125 M $NaHCO_3$ solution is needed to neutralize 18.0 mL of the 0.100 M HCl solution.

BALLPARK CHECK

The balanced equation shows that HCl and $NaHCO_3$ react in a 1 : 1 molar ratio, and we are told that the concentrations of the two solutions are about the same. Thus, the volume of the $NaHCO_3$ solution must be about the same as that of the HCl solution.

▶ **PROBLEM 3.18** What volume of 0.250 M H_2SO_4 is needed to react with 50.0 mL of 0.100 M NaOH? The equation is

$$H_2SO_4(aq) + 2 \, NaOH(aq) \longrightarrow Na_2SO_4(aq) + 2 \, H_2O(l)$$

▶ **PROBLEM 3.19** What is the molarity of an HNO_3 solution if 68.5 mL is needed to react with 25.0 mL of 0.150 M KOH solution? The equation is

$$HNO_3(aq) + KOH(aq) \longrightarrow KNO_3(aq) + H_2O(l)$$

3.9 TITRATION

There are two ways to make a solution of known molarity. One way is to use the method described in Section 3.6; that is, to dissolve an accurately weighed amount of solute in enough solvent to reach an accurately calibrated volume. Often though, it's more convenient to make up a solution quickly, using an estimated amount of solute and an estimated amount of solvent, and then determine the solution's exact molarity by *titration*.

Titration is a procedure for determining the concentration of a solution by allowing a measured volume of that solution to react with a second solution of another substance (the *standard solution*) whose concentration is known. By finding the volume of the standard solution that reacts with the measured volume of the first solution, the concentration of the first solution can be calculated. (It's necessary, though, that the reaction go to completion and have a yield of 100%.)

To see how titration works, let's imagine that we have an HCl solution (an acid) whose concentration we want to find by allowing it to react with NaOH (a base) in what is called an acid–base neutralization reaction. (We'll learn more about acid–base neutralizations in the next chapter.) The balanced equation is

$$NaOH(aq) + HCl(aq) \longrightarrow NaCl(aq) + H_2O(l)$$

We'll begin the titration by measuring out a known volume of the HCl solution and adding a small amount of an *indicator*, a compound that undergoes a color change during the course of the reaction. The compound phenolphthalein, for instance, is colorless in acid solution but turns red in base solution. Next, we fill a calibrated glass tube called a *buret* with an NaOH standard solution of known concentration and slowly add the NaOH to the HCl. When the phenolphthalein just begins to turn pink, all the HCl has completely reacted and the solution now has a tiny amount of excess NaOH. By then reading from the buret to find the volume of the NaOH standard solution that has been added to react with the known volume of HCl solution, we can calculate the concentration of the HCl. The strategy is summarized in Figure 3.5, and the procedure is shown in Figure 3.6.

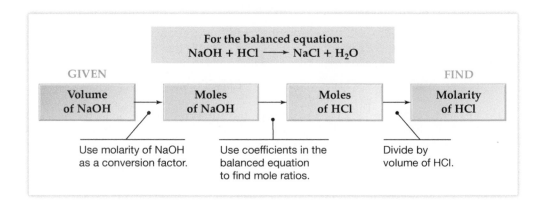

For the balanced equation:
NaOH + HCl ⟶ NaCl + H₂O

GIVEN   FIND

| Volume of NaOH | Moles of NaOH | Moles of HCl | Molarity of HCl |

Use molarity of NaOH as a conversion factor.   Use coefficients in the balanced equation to find mole ratios.   Divide by volume of HCl.

Figure 3.5
A flow diagram for an acid–base titration. The calculations needed to determine the concentration of an HCl solution by titration with an NaOH standard solution are summarized.

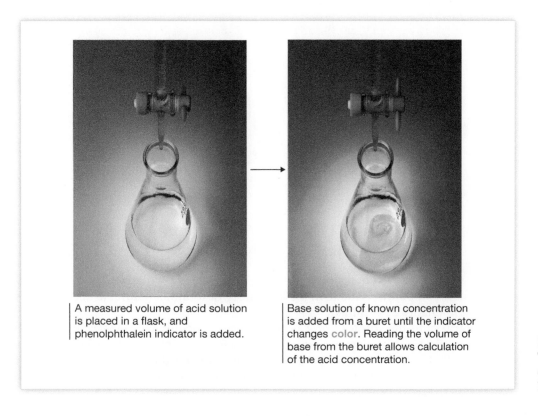

A measured volume of acid solution is placed in a flask, and phenolphthalein indicator is added.

Base solution of known concentration is added from a buret until the indicator changes color. Reading the volume of base from the buret allows calculation of the acid concentration.

Figure 3.6
Titration of an acid solution of unknown concentration with a base solution of known concentration.

Let's assume that we take 20.0 mL of the HCl solution and find that we have to add 48.6 mL of 0.100 M NaOH from a buret to obtain complete reaction. Using the molarity of the NaOH standard solution as a conversion factor, we can calculate the number of moles of NaOH undergoing reaction:

$$\text{Moles of NaOH} = 0.0486 \ \text{L NaOH} \times \frac{0.100 \ \text{mol NaOH}}{1 \ \text{L NaOH}}$$

$$= 0.004\,86 \ \text{mol NaOH}$$

According to the balanced equation, the number of moles of HCl is the same as that of NaOH:

$$\text{Moles of HCl} = 0.004\,86 \ \text{mol NaOH} \times \frac{1 \ \text{mol HCl}}{1 \ \text{mol NaOH}} = 0.004\,86 \ \text{mol HCl}$$

Dividing the number of moles of HCl by the volume then gives the molarity of the HCl:

$$\text{HCl molarity} = \frac{0.004\,86 \ \text{mol HCl}}{0.0200 \ \text{L HCl}} = 0.243 \ \text{M HCl}$$

▶ **PROBLEM 3.20** A 25.0 mL sample of vinegar (dilute acetic acid, CH_3CO_2H) is titrated and found to react with 94.7 mL of 0.200 M NaOH. What is the molarity of the acetic acid solution? The reaction is

$$NaOH(aq) + CH_3CO_2H(aq) \longrightarrow CH_3CO_2Na(aq) + H_2O(l)$$

CONCEPTUAL PROBLEM 3.21 Assume that the buret contains H^+ ions, the flask contains OH^- ions, the volumes in the buret and the flask are identical, and the concentration of the acid in the buret is 1.00 M. If the entire volume of the buret is required for titration of the base in the flask, what is the concentration of base? The equation is $H^+(aq) + OH^-(aq) \longrightarrow H_2O(l)$.

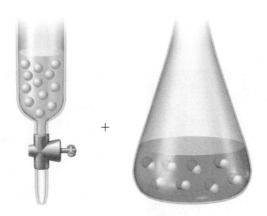

+

3.10 PERCENT COMPOSITION AND EMPIRICAL FORMULAS

All the substances we've dealt with thus far have had known formulas. When, however, a new compound is made in the laboratory or found in nature, its formula must be experimentally determined.

Determining the formula of a new compound begins with analyzing the substance to find what elements it contains and how much of each element is present—that is, to find its *composition*. The **percent composition** of a compound is expressed by identifying the elements present and giving the mass percent of each.

For example, we might express the percent composition of a certain colorless liquid found in gasoline by saying that it contains 84.1% carbon and 15.9% hydrogen by mass. In other words, a 100.0 g sample of the compound contains 84.1 g of carbon atoms and 15.9 g of hydrogen atoms.

Knowing a compound's percent composition makes it possible to calculate the compound's chemical formula. As shown in **Figure 3.7**, the strategy is to find the relative number of moles of each element in the compound and then use those numbers to establish the mole ratios of the elements. The mole ratios, in turn, correspond to the subscripts in the chemical formula.

Let's use for our example the colorless liquid whose composition is 84.1% carbon and 15.9% hydrogen by mass. Arbitrarily taking 100 g of the substance to make the calculation easier, we find by using molar masses as conversion factors that the 100 g contains:

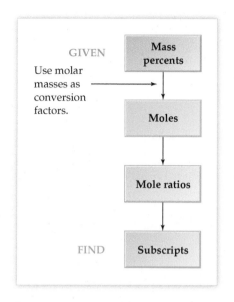

Figure 3.7
Calculating the formula of a compound from its percent composition.

$$84.1 \text{ g C} \times \frac{1 \text{ mol C}}{12.01 \text{ g C}} = 7.00 \text{ mol C}$$

$$15.9 \text{ g H} \times \frac{1 \text{ mol H}}{1.008 \text{ g H}} = 15.8 \text{ mol H}$$

With the relative numbers of moles of C and H known, we find the mole ratio by dividing both by the smaller number (7.00):

$$C_{\left(\frac{7.00}{7.00}\right)}H_{\left(\frac{15.8}{7.00}\right)} = C_1H_{2.26}$$

The C:H mole ratio of 1:2.26 means that we can write $C_1H_{2.26}$ as a temporary formula for the liquid. Multiplying the subscripts by small integers in a trial-and-error procedure until whole numbers are found then gives the **empirical formula**, which tells the smallest whole-number ratios of atoms in the compound. In the present instance, multiplication of the subscripts by 4 is needed to give the empirical formula C_4H_9. (The subscripts may not always be *exact* integers because of small errors in the data, but the discrepancies should be small.)

$$C_{(1\times4)}H_{(2.26\times4)} = C_4H_{9.04} = C_4H_9$$

An empirical formula determined from percent composition tells only the ratios of atoms in a compound. The **molecular formula**, which tells the actual numbers of atoms in a molecule, can be either the same as the empirical formula or a multiple of it. To determine the molecular formula, it's necessary to know the molecular mass of the substance. In the present instance, the molecular mass of our compound (a substance called octane) is 114.2 amu, which is a simple multiple of the empirical molecular mass for C_4H_9 (57.1 amu).

To find the multiple, divide the molecular mass by the empirical formula mass:

$$\text{Multiple} = \frac{\text{Molecular mass}}{\text{Empirical formula mass}} = \frac{114.2}{57.1} = 2.00$$

Then multiply the subscripts in the empirical formula by this multiple to obtain the molecular formula. In our example, the molecular formula of octane is $C_{(4\times2)}H_{(9\times2)}$, or C_8H_{18}.

Just as we can find the empirical formula of a substance from its percent composition, we can also find the percent composition of a substance from its empirical (or molecular) formula. The strategies for the two kinds of calculations are exactly opposite. Aspirin, for example, has the molecular formula $C_9H_8O_4$ and thus has a C:H:O mole ratio of 9:8:4. We can convert this mole ratio into a mass ratio, and thus into percent composition, by carrying out mole-to-gram conversions.

Let's assume we start with 1 mol of compound to simplify the calculation:

$$1 \text{ mol aspirin} \times \frac{9 \text{ mol C}}{1 \text{ mol aspirin}} \times \frac{12.0 \text{ g C}}{1 \text{ mol C}} = 108 \text{ g C}$$

$$1 \text{ mol aspirin} \times \frac{8 \text{ mol H}}{1 \text{ mol aspirin}} \times \frac{1.01 \text{ g H}}{1 \text{ mol H}} = 8.08 \text{ g H}$$

$$1 \text{ mol aspirin} \times \frac{4 \text{ mol O}}{1 \text{ mol aspirin}} \times \frac{16.0 \text{ g O}}{1 \text{ mol O}} = 64.0 \text{ g O}$$

Dividing the mass of each element by the total mass and multiplying by 100% then gives the percent composition:

Total mass of 1 mol aspirin = 108 g + 8.08 g + 64.0 g = 180 g

$$\% \text{ C} = \frac{108 \text{ g C}}{180 \text{ g}} \times 100\% = 60.0\%$$

$$\% \text{ H} = \frac{8.08 \text{ g H}}{180 \text{ g}} \times 100\% = 4.49\%$$

$$\% \text{ O} = \frac{64.0 \text{ g O}}{180 \text{ g}} \times 100\% = 35.6\%$$

The answer can be checked by confirming that the sum of the mass percentages is within a rounding error of 100%: 60.0% + 4.49% + 35.6% = 100.1%.

Worked Examples 3.15 and 3.16 show further conversions between percent composition and empirical formulas.

WORKED EXAMPLE 3.15

CALCULATING AN EMPIRICAL FORMULA FROM A PERCENT COMPOSITION

Vitamin C (ascorbic acid) contains 40.92% C, 4.58% H, and 54.50% O by mass. What is the empirical formula of ascorbic acid?

STRATEGY

Assume that you have 100.00 g of ascorbic acid, and then carry out the procedure outlined in Figure 3.7.

SOLUTION

First, find the number of moles of each element in the sample:

$$40.92 \text{ g C} \times \frac{1 \text{ mol C}}{12.0 \text{ g C}} = 3.41 \text{ mol C}$$

$$4.58 \text{ g H} \times \frac{1 \text{ mol H}}{1.01 \text{ g H}} = 4.53 \text{ mol H}$$

$$54.50 \text{ g O} \times \frac{1 \text{ mol O}}{16.0 \text{ g O}} = 3.41 \text{ mol O}$$

Dividing each of the three numbers by the smallest (3.41 mol) gives a C:H:O mole ratio of 1:1.33:1 and a temporary formula of $C_1H_{1.33}O_1$. Multiplying the subscripts by small integers in a trial-and-error procedure until whole numbers are found then gives the empirical formula: $C_{(3\times1)}H_{(3\times1.33)}O_{(3\times1)} = C_3H_4O_3$.

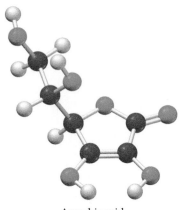

Ascorbic acid

WORKED EXAMPLE 3.16

CALCULATING A PERCENT COMPOSITION FROM A FORMULA

Glucose, or blood sugar, has the molecular formula $C_6H_{12}O_6$. What is the empirical formula, and what is the percent composition of glucose?

STRATEGY AND SOLUTION

The empirical formula is found by reducing the subscripts in the molecular formula to their smallest whole-number values. In this case, dividing the subscripts by 6 reduces $C_6H_{12}O_6$ to CH_2O.

The percent composition of glucose can be calculated either from the molecular formula or from the empirical formula. Using the molecular formula, for instance, the C:H:O mole ratio of 6:12:6 can be converted into a mass ratio by assuming that we have 1 mol of compound and carrying out mole-to-gram conversions:

$$1 \text{ mol glucose} \times \frac{6 \text{ mol C}}{1 \text{ mol glucose}} \times \frac{12.0 \text{ g C}}{1 \text{ mol C}} = 72.0 \text{ g C}$$

$$1 \text{ mol glucose} \times \frac{12 \text{ mol H}}{1 \text{ mol glucose}} \times \frac{1.01 \text{ g H}}{1 \text{ mol H}} = 12.1 \text{ g H}$$

$$1 \text{ mol glucose} \times \frac{6 \text{ mol O}}{1 \text{ mol glucose}} \times \frac{16.0 \text{ g O}}{1 \text{ mol O}} = 96.0 \text{ g O}$$

Dividing the mass of each element by the total mass, and multiplying by 100%, gives the percent composition. Note that the sum of the mass percentages is 100%.

Total mass of 1 mol glucose = 72.0 g + 12.1 g + 96.0 g = 180.1 g

$$\% \text{ C} = \frac{72.0 \text{ g C}}{180.1 \text{ g}} \times 100\% = 40.0\%$$

$$\% \text{ H} = \frac{12.1 \text{ g H}}{180.1 \text{ g}} \times 100\% = 6.72\%$$

$$\% \text{ O} = \frac{96.0 \text{ g O}}{180.1 \text{ g}} \times 100\% = 53.3\%$$

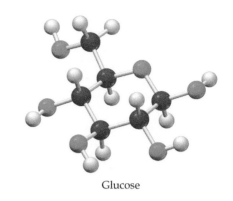

Glucose

▶ **PROBLEM 3.22** What is the empirical formula, and what is the percent composition of dimethylhydrazine, $C_2H_8N_2$, a colorless liquid used as a rocket fuel?

▶ **PROBLEM 3.23** What is the empirical formula of the ingredient in Bufferin tablets that has the percent composition C 14.25%, O 56.93%, Mg 28.83% by mass?

▶ **PROBLEM 3.24** What is the percent composition of citric acid, an organic acid, commonly found in citrus fruits, whose structure is shown in the nearby margin? (Gray = C, red = O, H = ivory.)

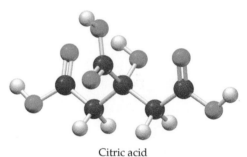

Citric acid

3.11 DETERMINING EMPIRICAL FORMULAS: ELEMENTAL ANALYSIS

One of the most common methods used to determine percent composition and empirical formulas, particularly for organic compounds containing carbon and hydrogen, is *combustion analysis*. In this method, a compound of unknown composition is burned with oxygen to produce the volatile combustion products CO_2 and H_2O, which are separated and have their amounts determined by an automated instrument. Methane (CH_4), for instance, burns according to the balanced equation

$$CH_4(g) + 2\,O_2(g) \longrightarrow CO_2(g) + 2\,H_2O(g)$$

With the amounts of the carbon-containing product (CO_2) and hydrogen-containing product (H_2O) established, the strategy is to calculate the number of moles of carbon and hydrogen in the products, from which we can find the C:H mole ratio of the starting compound. This information, in turn, provides the chemical formula, as outlined by the flow diagram in Figure 3.8.

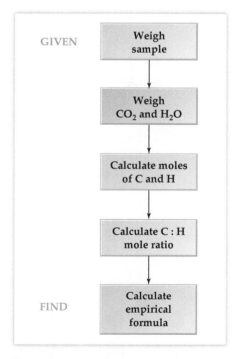

GIVEN → Weigh sample

↓

Weigh CO_2 and H_2O

↓

Calculate moles of C and H

↓

Calculate C:H mole ratio

↓

FIND → Calculate empirical formula

Figure 3.8
Determining an empirical formula from combustion analysis of a compound containing C and H.

As an example of how combustion analysis works, imagine that we have a sample of a pure substance—say, naphthalene, which is often used for household moth balls. We weigh a known amount of the sample, burn it in pure oxygen, and then analyze the products. Let's say that 0.330 g of naphthalene reacts with O_2 and that 1.133 g of CO_2 and 0.185 g of H_2O are formed. The first thing to find out is the number of moles of carbon and hydrogen in the CO_2 and H_2O products so that we can calculate the number of moles of each element originally present in the naphthalene sample.

$$\text{Moles of C in 1.133 g } CO_2 = 1.133 \text{ g } CO_2 \times \frac{1 \text{ mol } CO_2}{44.01 \text{ g } CO_2} \times \frac{1 \text{ mol C}}{1 \text{ mol } CO_2}$$

$$= 0.02574 \text{ mol C}$$

$$\text{Moles of H in 0.185 g } H_2O = 0.185 \text{ g } H_2O \times \frac{1 \text{ mol } H_2O}{18.02 \text{ g } H_2O} \times \frac{2 \text{ mol H}}{1 \text{ mol } H_2O}$$

$$= 0.0205 \text{ mol H}$$

Although it's not necessary in this instance since naphthalene contains only carbon and hydrogen, we can make sure that all the mass is accounted for and that no other elements are present. To do so, we carry out mole-to-gram conversions to find the number of grams of C and H in the starting sample:

$$\text{Mass of C} = 0.02574 \text{ mol C} \times \frac{12.01 \text{ g C}}{1 \text{ mol C}} = 0.3091 \text{ g C}$$

$$\text{Mass of H} = 0.0205 \text{ mol H} \times \frac{1.01 \text{ g H}}{1 \text{ mol H}} = 0.0207 \text{ g H}$$

$$\text{Total mass of C and H} = 0.3091 \text{ g} + 0.0207 \text{ g} = 0.3298 \text{ g}$$

Because the total mass of the C and H in the products (0.3298 g) is the same as the mass of the starting sample (0.330 g), we know that no other elements are present in naphthalene.

With the relative number of moles of C and H in naphthalene known, divide the larger number of moles by the smaller number to get the formula $C_{1.26}H_1$.

$$C_{\left(\frac{0.02574}{0.0205}\right)}H_{\left(\frac{0.0205}{0.0205}\right)} = C_{1.26}H_1$$

Then multiply the subscripts by small integers in a trial-and-error procedure until whole numbers are found to obtain the whole-number formula C_5H_4:

Multiply subscripts by 2: $C_{(1.26 \times 2)}H_{(1 \times 2)} = C_{2.52}H_2$

Multiply subscripts by 3: $C_{(1.26 \times 3)}H_{(1 \times 3)} = C_{3.78}H_3$

Multiply subscripts by 4: $C_{(1.26 \times 4)}H_{(1 \times 4)} = C_{5.04}H_4 = C_5H_4$ (Both subscripts are integers)

Elemental analysis provides only an empirical formula. To determine the molecular formula, it's also necessary to know the substance's molecular mass. In the present problem, the molecular mass of naphthalene is 128.2 amu, or twice the empirical formula mass of C_5H_4 (64.1 amu). Thus, the molecular formula of naphthalene is $C_{(2 \times 5)}H_{(2 \times 4)} = C_{10}H_8$.

Worked Example 3.17 shows a combustion analysis when the sample contains oxygen in addition to carbon and hydrogen. Because oxygen yields no combustion products, its presence in a molecule can't be directly detected by this method. Rather, the presence of oxygen must be inferred by subtracting the calculated masses of C and H from the total mass of the sample.

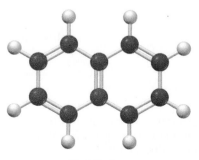

Naphthalene

WORKED EXAMPLE 3.17

CALCULATING AN EMPIRICAL FORMULA AND A MOLECULAR FORMULA FROM A COMBUSTION ANALYSIS

Caproic acid, the substance responsible for the aroma of goats, dirty socks, and old shoes, contains carbon, hydrogen, and oxygen. On combustion analysis, a 0.450 g sample of caproic acid gives 0.418 g of H_2O and 1.023 g of CO_2. What is the empirical formula of caproic acid? If the molecular mass of caproic acid is 116.2 amu, what is the molecular formula?

STRATEGY

Use the steps outlined in Figure 3.8 to find the empirical formula of caproic acid. Then calculate a formula mass and compare it to the known molecular mass.

SOLUTION

First, find the molar amounts of C and H in the sample:

$$\text{Moles of C} = 1.023 \text{ g } CO_2 \times \frac{1 \text{ mol } CO_2}{44.01 \text{ g } CO_2} \times \frac{1 \text{ mol C}}{1 \text{ mol } CO_2} = 0.023\,24 \text{ mol C}$$

$$\text{Moles of H} = 0.418 \text{ g } H_2O \times \frac{1 \text{ mol } H_2O}{18.02 \text{ g } H_2O} \times \frac{2 \text{ mol H}}{1 \text{ mol } H_2O} = 0.0464 \text{ mol H}$$

Caproic acid

Next, find the number of grams of C and H in the sample:

$$\text{Mass of C} = 0.023\,24 \text{ mol C} \times \frac{12.01 \text{ g C}}{1 \text{ mol C}} = 0.2791 \text{ g C}$$

$$\text{Mass of H} = 0.0464 \text{ mol H} \times \frac{1.01 \text{ g H}}{1 \text{ mol H}} = 0.0469 \text{ g H}$$

Subtracting the masses of C and H from the mass of the starting sample indicates that 0.124 g is unaccounted for:

$$0.450 \text{ g} - (0.2791 \text{ g} + 0.0469 \text{ g}) = 0.124 \text{ g}$$

Because we are told that oxygen is also present in the sample, the "missing" mass must be due to oxygen, which can't be detected by combustion. We therefore need to find the number of moles of oxygen in the sample:

$$\text{Moles of O} = 0.124 \text{ g O} \times \frac{1 \text{ mol O}}{16.00 \text{ g O}} = 0.007\,75 \text{ mol O}$$

Knowing the relative numbers of moles of all three elements, C, H, and O, we divide the three numbers of moles by the smallest number (0.007 75 mol of oxygen) to arrive at a C:H:O ratio of 3:6:1.

$$C_{\left(\frac{0.02324}{0.00775}\right)} H_{\left(\frac{0.0464}{0.00775}\right)} O_{\left(\frac{0.00775}{0.00775}\right)} = C_3H_6O$$

The empirical formula of caproic acid is therefore C_3H_6O, and the empirical formula mass is 58.1 amu. Because the molecular mass of caproic acid is 116.2, or twice the empirical formula mass, the molecular formula of caproic acid must be $C_{(2\times3)}H_{(2\times6)}O_{(2\times1)} = C_6H_{12}O_2$.

▶ **PROBLEM 3.25** Menthol, a flavoring agent obtained from peppermint oil, contains carbon, hydrogen, and oxygen. On combustion analysis, 1.00 g of menthol yields 1.161 g of H_2O and 2.818 g of CO_2. What is the empirical formula of menthol?

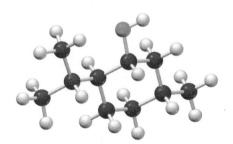

Menthol

▶ **PROBLEM 3.26** Ribose, a sugar present in the cells of all living organisms, has a molecular mass of 150 amu and the empirical formula CH_2O. What is the molecular formula of ribose?

▶ **PROBLEM 3.27** Convert the following percent compositions into molecular formulas:

(a) Diborane: H 21.86%, B 78.14%; Molec. mass = 27.7 amu
(b) Trioxan: C 40.00%, H 6.71%, O 53.28%; Molec. mass = 90.08 amu

Ribose

3.12 DETERMINING MOLECULAR MASSES: MASS SPECTROMETRY

As we saw in the previous section, determining a compound's molecular formula requires a knowledge of its molecular mass. But how is molecular mass determined?

The most common method of determining both atomic and molecular masses is with an instrument called a *mass spectrometer*. More than 20 different kinds of mass spectrometer are commercially available, depending on the intended application, but the electron-impact, magnetic-sector instrument shown in **Figure 3.9a** is particularly common. In this instrument, the sample is vaporized and injected as a dilute gas into an evacuated chamber, where it is bombarded with a beam of high-energy electrons. The electron beam knocks other electrons from the sample molecules, which become positively charged ions. Some of these ionized molecules survive, and others fragment into smaller ions. The various ions of different masses are then accelerated by an electric field and passed between the poles of a strong magnet, which deflects them through a curved, evacuated pipe.

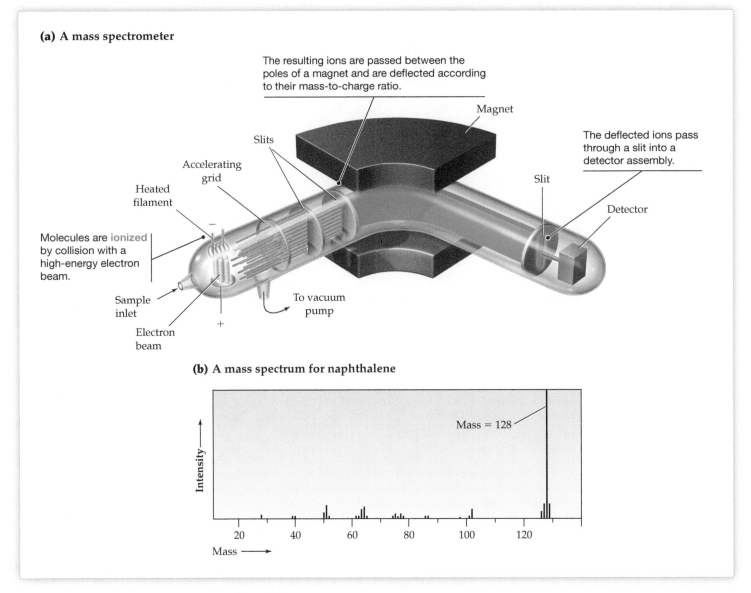

(a) A mass spectrometer

The resulting ions are passed between the poles of a magnet and are deflected according to their mass-to-charge ratio.

Magnet

Slits

Accelerating grid

Heated filament

The deflected ions pass through a slit into a detector assembly.

Slit

Detector

Molecules are ionized by collision with a high-energy electron beam.

Sample inlet

To vacuum pump

Electron beam

(b) A mass spectrum for naphthalene

Mass = 128

Intensity

Mass

Figure 3.9

Mass spectrometry. (a) Schematic illustration of an electron-impact, magnetic-sector mass spectrometer. **(b)** A mass spectrum of naphthalene, molec. mass = 128, showing peaks of different masses on the horizontal axis.

The radius of deflection of a charged ion M^+ as it passes between the magnet poles depends on its mass, with lighter ions deflected more strongly than heavier ones. By varying the strength of the magnetic field, it's possible to focus ions of different masses through a slit at the end of the curved pipe and onto a detector assembly. The mass spectrum that results is plotted as a graph of ion mass versus intensity—that is, as the molecular masses of the various ions versus the relative number of those ions produced in the instrument.

Although a typical mass spectrum contains ions of many different masses, the heaviest ion is generally due to the ionized molecule itself, the so-called molecular ion. By measuring the mass of this molecular ion, the molecular mass of the molecule can be determined. The naphthalene sample discussed in the previous section, for example, gives rise to an intense peak at mass 128 amu in its spectrum, consistent with a molecular formula of $C_{10}H_8$ (Figure 3.9b).

Modern mass spectrometers are so precise that molecular masses can often be measured to seven significant figures. A $^{12}C_{10}{}^{1}H_8$ molecule of naphthalene, for example, has a molecular mass of 128.0626 amu as measured by mass spectrometry.

▲ What did these two have in common?

INQUIRY DID BEN FRANKLIN HAVE AVOGADRO'S NUMBER?

At length being at Clapham, where there is on the common a large pond ... I fetched out a cruet of oil and dropped a little of it on the water. I saw it spread itself with surprising swiftness upon the surface. The oil, although not more than a teaspoonful, produced an instant calm over a space several yards square which spread amazingly and extended itself gradually ... making all that quarter of the pond, perhaps half an acre, as smooth as a looking glass.

Excerpt from a letter of Benjamin Franklin to William Brownrigg, 1773.

Benjamin Franklin, author and renowned statesman, was also an inventor and a scientist. Every schoolchild knows of Franklin's experiment with a kite and a key, demonstrating that lightning is electricity. Less well-known is that his measurement of the extent to which oil spreads on water makes possible a simple estimate of molecular size and Avogadro's number.

The calculation goes like this: Avogadro's number is the number of molecules in a mole. So, if we can estimate both the number of molecules and the number of moles in Franklin's teaspoon of oil, we can calculate Avogadro's number. Let's start by calculating the number of molecules in the oil.

1. The volume (V) of oil Franklin used was 1 tsp = 4.9 cm^3, and the area (A) covered by the oil was 1/2 acre = 2.0×10^7 cm^2. Let's assume that the oil molecules are tiny cubes that pack closely together and form a layer only one molecule thick. As shown in the accompanying figure, the volume of the oil equals the surface area of the layer times the length (l) of the side of one molecule: $V = A \times l$. Rearranging this equation to find the length then gives us an estimate of molecular size:

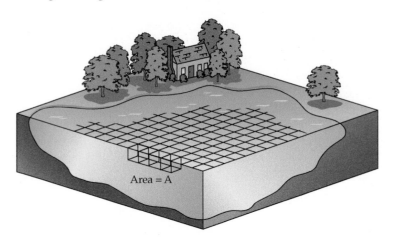

Area = A

2. The area of the oil layer is the area of the side of one molecule (l^2) times the number of molecules (N) of oil: $A = l^2 \times N$. Rearranging this equation gives the number of molecules:

$$N = \frac{A}{l^2} = \frac{2.0 \times 10^7 \text{ cm}^2}{(2.4 \times 10^{-7} \text{ cm})^2} = 3.5 \times 10^{20} \text{ molecules}$$

3. To calculate the number of moles, we first need to know the mass (m) of the oil. This could have been determined by weighing, but Franklin neglected to do so. Let's therefore estimate the mass by multiplying the volume (V) of the oil by the density (D) of a typical oil, 0.95 g/cm^3. [Since oil floats on water, the density of oil must be a bit less than the density of water (1.00 g/cm^3).]

$$m = V \times D = 4.9 \text{ cm}^3 \times 0.95 \frac{\text{g}}{\text{cm}^3} = 4.7 \text{ g}$$

4. We now have to make one final assumption about the molecular mass of the oil before completing the calculation. Assuming that a typical oil has molec. mass = 900 amu, then the mass of 1 mol of oil is 900 g. Dividing the mass of the oil by the mass of one mole gives the number of moles of oil:

$$\text{Moles of oil} = \frac{4.7 \text{ g}}{900 \text{ g/mol}} = 0.0052 \text{ mol}$$

5. Finally, the number of molecules per mole—Avogadro's number—can be obtained:

$$\text{Avogadro's number} = \frac{3.5 \times 10^{20} \text{ molecules}}{0.0052 \text{ mol}} = 6.7 \times 10^{22}$$

The calculation is not very accurate, but Franklin wasn't really intending for us to calculate Avogadro's number when he made a rough estimate of how much his oil spread out. Nevertheless, the result isn't too bad for such a simple experiment.

▶ **PROBLEM 3.28** What do you think are the main sources of error in calculating Avogadro's number by spreading oil on a pond?

▶ **PROBLEM 3.29** Recalculate Avogadro's number assuming that the oil molecules are shaped like tall rectangular boxes rather than cubes, with two edges of equal length and the third edge four times the length of the other two. Assume also that the molecules stand on end in the water.

SUMMARY

Because mass is neither created nor destroyed in chemical reactions, all chemical equations must be **balanced**—that is, the numbers and kinds of atoms on both sides of the reaction arrow must be the same. A balanced equation tells the number ratio of reactant and product **formula units** in a reaction.

Just as atomic mass is the mass of an atom, **molecular mass** is the mass of a molecule. The analogous term **formula mass** is used for ionic and other nonmolecular substances. Molecular mass is the sum of the atomic masses of all atoms in the molecule. One mole of a substance is the amount whose mass in grams is numerically equal to the substance's molecular or formula mass. Carrying out chemical calculations using mass–mole relationships is called **stoichiometry** and is done using molar masses as conversion factors.

The amount of product actually formed in a reaction—the reaction's **yield**—is often less than the amount theoretically possible. Dividing the actual amount by the theoretical amount and multiplying by 100% gives the reaction's **percent yield**. Often, reactions are carried out with an excess of one reactant beyond that called for by the balanced equation. In such cases, the extent to which the reaction takes place depends on the reactant present in limiting amount, the **limiting reactant**.

The concentration of a substance in solution is usually expressed as **molarity (M)**, defined as the number of moles of a substance (the **solute**) dissolved per liter of solution. A solution's molarity acts as a conversion factor between solution volume and number of moles of solute, making it possible to carry out stoichiometry calculations on solutions. Often, chemicals are stored as concentrated aqueous solutions that are diluted before use. When carrying out a dilution, only the volume is changed by adding solvent; the amount of solute is unchanged. A solution's exact concentration can often be determined by **titration**.

The chemical makeup of a substance is described by its **percent composition**—the percentage of the substance's mass due to each of its constituent elements. Elemental analysis is used to calculate a substance's **empirical formula**, which gives the smallest whole-number ratio of atoms of the elements in the compound. To determine the **molecular formula**, which may be a simple multiple of the empirical formula, it's also necessary to know the substance's molecular mass. Molecular masses are usually determined by mass spectrometry.

KEY WORDS

balanced equation 75	**formula unit** 75	**molecular mass** 79	**stoichiometry** 80
coefficient 75	**limiting reactant** 86	**percent composition** 94	**titration** 92
empirical formula 95	**molarity (M)** 88	**percent yield** 83	**yield** 83
formula mass 79	**molecular formula** 95	**solute** 88	

CONCEPTUAL PROBLEMS

Problems 3.1–3.29 appear within the chapter.

3.30 Box **(a)** represents 1.0 mL of a solution of particles at a given concentration. Which of the boxes **(b)–(d)** represents 1.0 mL of the solution that results after **(a)** has been diluted by doubling the volume of its solvent?

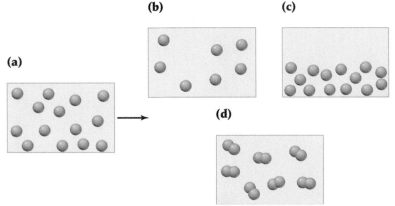

3.31 The reaction of A (red spheres) with B (blue spheres) is shown in the following diagram:

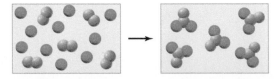

Which equation best describes the stoichiometry of the reaction?

(a) $A_2 + 2 B \longrightarrow A_2B_2$

(b) $10 A + 5 B_2 \longrightarrow 5 A_2B_2$

(c) $2 A + B_2 \longrightarrow A_2B_2$

(d) $5 A + 5 B_2 \longrightarrow 5 A_2B_2$

3.32 Cytosine, a constituent of deoxyribonucleic acid (DNA) can be represented by the following molecular model. If 0.001 mol of cytosine is submitted to combustion analysis, how many moles of CO_2 and how many moles of H_2O would be formed? (Gray = C, red = O, blue = N, ivory = H.)

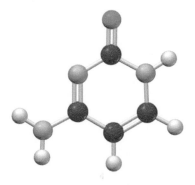

3.33 If blue spheres represent nitrogen atoms and red spheres represent oxygen atoms, which box represents reactants and which represents products for the reaction $2 NO(g) + O_2(g) \longrightarrow 2 NO_2(g)$?

(a)   **(b)**

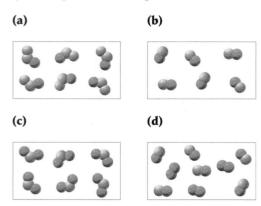

(c)   **(d)**

3.34 Fluoxetine, marketed as an antidepressant under the name *Prozac*, can be represented by the following ball-and-stick molecular model. Write the molecular formula for fluoxetine, and calculate its molecular mass (red = O, gray = C, blue = N, yellow-green = F, ivory = H).

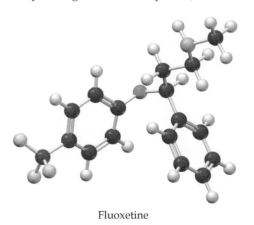

Fluoxetine

3.35 What is the percent composition of cysteine, one of the 20 amino acids commonly found in proteins? (Gray = C, red = O, blue = N, yellow = S, ivory = H.)

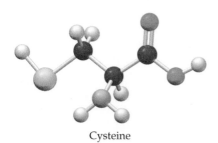

Cysteine

3.36 The following diagram represents the reaction of A_2 (red spheres) with B_2 (blue spheres):

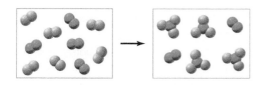

(a) Write a balanced equation for the reaction, and identify the limiting reactant.

(b) How many moles of product can be made from 1.0 mol of A_2 and 1.0 mol of B_2?

3.37 A hydrocarbon of unknown formula C_xH_y was submitted to combustion analysis with the following results. What is the empirical formula of the hydrocarbon?

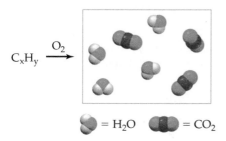

$C_xH_y \xrightarrow{O_2}$

 = H_2O = CO_2

SECTION PROBLEMS

Balancing Equations (Section 3.1)

3.38 Which of the following equations are balanced?

(a) The development reaction in silver-halide photography:

$$2 AgBr + 2 NaOH + C_6H_6O_2 \longrightarrow$$
$$2 Ag + H_2O + 2 NaBr + C_6H_4O_2$$

(b) The preparation of household bleach:

$$2 NaOH + Cl_2 \longrightarrow NaOCl + NaCl + H_2O$$

3.39 Which of the following equations are balanced? Balance any that need it.

(a) The thermite reaction, used in welding:

$$Al + Fe_2O_3 \longrightarrow Al_2O_3 + Fe$$

(b) The photosynthesis of glucose from CO_2:

$$6 CO_2 + 6 H_2O \longrightarrow C_6H_{12}O_6 + 6 O_2$$

(c) The separation of gold from its ore:

$$Au + 2 NaCN + O_2 + H_2O \longrightarrow$$
$$NaAu(CN)_2 + 3 NaOH$$

3.40 Balance the following equations:

(a) $Mg + HNO_3 \longrightarrow H_2 + Mg(NO_3)_2$

(b) $CaC_2 + H_2O \longrightarrow Ca(OH)_2 + C_2H_2$

(c) $S + O_2 \longrightarrow SO_3$

(d) $UO_2 + HF \longrightarrow UF_4 + H_2O$

3.41 Balance the following equations:

(a) The explosion of ammonium nitrate:

$$NH_4NO_3 \longrightarrow N_2 + O_2 + H_2O$$

(b) The spoilage of wine into vinegar:

$$C_2H_6O + O_2 \longrightarrow C_2H_4O_2 + H_2O$$

(c) The burning of rocket fuel:

$$C_2H_8N_2 + N_2O_4 \longrightarrow N_2 + CO_2 + H_2O$$

3.42 Balance the following equations:

(a) $SiCl_4 + H_2O \longrightarrow SiO_2 + HCl$

(b) $P_4O_{10} + H_2O \longrightarrow H_3PO_4$

(c) $CaCN_2 + H_2O \longrightarrow CaCO_3 + NH_3$

(d) $NO_2 + H_2O \longrightarrow HNO_3 + NO$

3.43 Balance the following equations:

(a) $VCl_3 + Na + CO \longrightarrow V(CO)_6 + NaCl$

(b) $RuI_3 + CO + Ag \longrightarrow Ru(CO)_5 + AgI$

(c) $CoS + CO + Cu \longrightarrow Co_2(CO)_8 + Cu_2S$

Molecular Masses and Stoichiometry (Section 3.3)

3.44 What are the molecular (formula) masses of the following substances?

(a) Hg_2Cl_2 (calomel, used at one time as a bowel purgative)

(b) $C_4H_8O_2$ (butyric acid, responsible for the odor of rancid butter)

(c) CF_2Cl_2 (a chlorofluorocarbon that destroys the stratospheric ozone layer)

3.45 What are the formulas of the following substances?

(a) $PCl_?$; Molec. mass = 137.3 amu

(b) Nicotine, $C_{10}H_{14}N_?$; Molec. mass = 162.2 amu

3.46 What are the molecular masses of the following pharmaceuticals?

(a) $C_{33}H_{35}FN_2O_5$ (atorvastatin, lowers blood cholesterol)

(b) $C_{22}H_{27}F_3O_4S$ (fluticasone, anti-inflammatory)

(c) $C_{16}H_{16}ClNO_2S$ (clopidogrel, inhibits blood clots)

3.47 What are the molecular masses of the following herbicides?

(a) $C_6H_6Cl_2O_3$ (2, 4-dichlorophenoxyacetic acid, effective on broadleaf plants)

(b) $C_{15}H_{22}ClNO_2$ (metolachlor, pre-emergent herbicide)

(c) $C_8H_6Cl_2O_3$ (dicamba, effective on broadleaf plants)

3.48 How many grams are in a mole of each of the following substances?

(a) Ti   (b) Br_2 (c) Hg   (d) H_2O

3.49 How many moles are in a gram of each of the following substances?

(a) Cr   (b) Cl_2 (c) Au   (d) NH_3

3.50 How many moles of ions are in 27.5 g of $MgCl_2$?

3.51 How many moles of anions are in 35.6 g of AlF_3?

3.52 What is the molecular mass of chloroform if 0.0275 mol weighs 3.28 g?

3.53 What is the molecular mass of cholesterol if 0.5731 mol weighs 221.6 g?

3.54 Iron(II) sulfate, $FeSO_4$, is prescribed for the treatment of anemia. How many moles of $FeSO_4$ are present in a standard 300 mg tablet? How many iron(II) ions?

3.55 The "lead" in lead pencils is actually almost pure carbon, and the mass of a period mark made by a lead pencil is about 0.0001 g. How many carbon atoms are in the period?

3.56 An average cup of coffee contains about 125 mg of caffeine, $C_8H_{10}N_4O_2$. How many moles of caffeine are in a cup? How many molecules of caffeine?

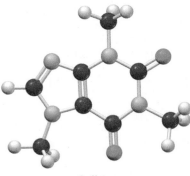

Caffeine

3.57 What is the mass in grams of each of the following samples?

(a) 0.0015 mol of sodium

(b) 0.0015 mol of lead

(c) 0.0015 mol of diazepam (Valium), $C_{16}H_{13}ClN_2O$

3.58 A sample that weighs 25.12 g contains 6.022×10^{23} particles. If 25.00% of the total number of particles are argon atoms and 75.00% are another element, what is the chemical identity of the other constituent?

3.59 A sample that weighs 107.75 g is a mixture of 30% helium atoms and 70% krypton atoms. How many particles are present in the sample?

3.60 Titanium metal is obtained from the mineral rutile, TiO_2. How many kilograms of rutile are needed to produce 100.0 kg of Ti?

3.61 Iron metal can be produced from the mineral hematite, Fe_2O_3, by reaction with carbon. How many kilograms of iron are present in 105 kg of hematite?

3.62 In the preparation of iron from hematite (Problem 3.61), Fe_2O_3 reacts with carbon:

$$Fe_2O_3 + C \longrightarrow Fe + CO_2 \qquad \text{Unbalanced}$$

(a) Balance the equation.

(b) How many moles of carbon are needed to react with 525 g of hematite?

(c) How many grams of carbon are needed to react with 525 g of hematite?

3.63 An alternative method for preparing pure iron from Fe_2O_3 (Problem 3.61) is by reaction with carbon monoxide:

$$Fe_2O_3 + CO \longrightarrow Fe + CO_2 \qquad \text{Unbalanced}$$

(a) Balance the equation.

(b) How many grams of CO are needed to react with 3.02 g of Fe_2O_3?

(c) How many grams of CO are needed to react with 1.68 mol of Fe_2O_3?

3.64 Magnesium metal burns in oxygen to form magnesium oxide, MgO.

(a) Write a balanced equation for the reaction.

(b) How many grams of oxygen are needed to react with 25.0 g of Mg? How many grams of MgO will result?

(c) How many grams of Mg are needed to react with 25.0 g of O_2? How many grams of MgO will result?

3.65 Ethylene gas, C_2H_4, reacts with water at high temperature to yield ethyl alcohol, C_2H_6O.

    (a) How many grams of ethylene are needed to react with 0.133 mol of H_2O? How many grams of ethyl alcohol will result?

    (b) How many grams of water are needed to react with 0.371 mol of ethylene? How many grams of ethyl alcohol will result?

3.66 Pure oxygen was first made by heating mercury(II) oxide:

$$HgO \xrightarrow{\text{Heat}} Hg + O_2 \quad \text{Unbalanced}$$

    (a) Balance the equation.

    (b) How many grams of mercury and how many grams of oxygen are formed from 45.5 g of HgO?

    (c) How many grams of HgO would you need to obtain 33.3 g of O_2?

3.67 Titanium dioxide (TiO_2), the substance used as the pigment in white paint, is prepared industrially by reaction of $TiCl_4$ with O_2 at high temperature.

$$TiCl_4 + O_2 \xrightarrow{\text{Heat}} TiO_2 + 2\,Cl_2$$

    How many kilograms of TiO_2 can be prepared from 5.60 kg of $TiCl_4$?

3.68 Silver metal reacts with chlorine (Cl_2) to yield silver chloride. If 2.00 g of Ag reacts with 0.657 g of Cl_2, what is the empirical formula of silver chloride?

3.69 Aluminum reacts with oxygen to yield aluminum oxide. If 5.0 g of Al reacts with 4.45 g of O_2, what is the empirical formula of aluminum oxide?

3.70 The industrial production of hydriodic acid takes place by treatment of iodine with hydrazine (N_2H_4):

$$2\,I_2 + N_2H_4 \longrightarrow 4\,HI + N_2$$

    (a) How many grams of I_2 are needed to react with 36.7 g of N_2H_4?

    (b) How many grams of HI are produced from the reaction of 115.7 g of N_2H_4 with excess iodine?

3.71 An alternative method for producing hydriodic acid (Problem 3.70) is the reaction of iodine with hydrogen sulfide:

$$H_2S + I_2 \longrightarrow 2\,HI + S$$

    (a) How many grams of I_2 are needed to react with 49.2 g of H_2S?

    (b) How many grams of HI are produced from the reaction of 95.4 g of H_2S with excess I_2?

Limiting Reactants and Reaction Yield (Sections 3.4 and 3.5)

3.72 Assume that you have 1.39 mol of H_2 and 3.44 mol of N_2. How many grams of ammonia (NH_3) can you make, and how many grams of which reactant will be left over?

$$3\,H_2 + N_2 \longrightarrow 2\,NH_3$$

3.73 Hydrogen and chlorine react to yield hydrogen chloride: $H_2 + Cl_2 \rightarrow 2\,HCl$. How many grams of HCl are formed from reaction of 3.56 g of H_2 with 8.94 g of Cl_2? Which reactant is limiting?

3.74 How many grams of the dry-cleaning solvent 1,2-dichloroethane (also called ethylene chloride), $C_2H_4Cl_2$, can be prepared by reaction of 15.4 g of ethylene, C_2H_4, with 3.74 g of Cl_2?

$$C_2H_4 + Cl_2 \longrightarrow C_2H_4Cl_2$$

1,2-Dichloroethane
(ethylene chloride)

3.75 How many grams of each product result from the following reactions, and how many grams of which reactant is left over?

    (a) $(1.3\text{ g NaCl}) + (3.5\text{ g AgNO}_3) \longrightarrow$
$$(x\text{ g AgCl}) + (y\text{ g NaNO}_3)$$

    (b) $(2.65\text{ g BaCl}_2) + (6.78\text{ g H}_2\text{SO}_4) \longrightarrow$
$$(x\text{ g BaSO}_4) + (y\text{ g HCl})$$

3.76 Nickel(II) sulfate, used for nickel plating, is prepared by treatment of nickel(II) carbonate with sulfuric acid:

$$NiCO_3 + H_2SO_4 \longrightarrow NiSO_4 + CO_2 + H_2O$$

    (a) How many grams of H_2SO_4 are needed to react with 14.5 g of $NiCO_3$?

    (b) How many grams of $NiSO_4$ are obtained if the yield is 78.9%?

3.77 Hydrazine, N_2H_4, once used as a rocket propellant, reacts with oxygen:

$$N_2H_4 + O_2 \longrightarrow N_2 + 2\,H_2O$$

    (a) How many grams of O_2 are needed to react with 50.0 g of N_2H_4?

    (b) How many grams of N_2 are obtained if the yield is 85.5%?

3.78 Limestone ($CaCO_3$) reacts with hydrochloric acid according to the equation $CaCO_3 + 2\,HCl \rightarrow CaCl_2 + H_2O + CO_2$. If 1.00 mol of CO_2 has a volume of 22.4 L under the reaction conditions, how many liters of gas can be formed by reaction of 2.35 g of $CaCO_3$ with 2.35 g of HCl? Which reactant is limiting?

3.79 Sodium azide (NaN_3) yields N_2 gas when heated to 300 °C, a reaction used in automobile air bags. If 1.00 mol of N_2 has a volume of 47.0 L under the reaction conditions, how many liters of gas can be formed by heating 38.5 g of NaN_3? The reaction is

$$2\,NaN_3 \longrightarrow 3\,N_2(g) + 2\,Na$$

3.80 Acetic acid (CH_3CO_2H) reacts with isopentyl alcohol ($C_5H_{12}O$) to yield isopentyl acetate ($C_7H_{14}O_2$), a fragrant substance with the odor of bananas. If the yield from the reaction of acetic acid with isopentyl alcohol is 45%, how many grams of isopentyl acetate are formed from 3.58 g of acetic acid and 4.75 g of isopentyl alcohol? The reaction is

$$CH_3CO_2H + C_5H_{12}O \longrightarrow C_7H_{14}O_2 + H_2O$$

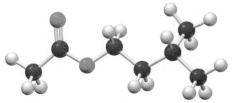

Isopentyl acetate

3.81 Cisplatin [Pt(NH$_3$)$_2$Cl$_2$], a compound used in cancer treatment, is prepared by reaction of ammonia with potassium tetrachloroplatinate:

$$K_2PtCl_4 + 2\,NH_3 \longrightarrow 2\,KCl + Pt(NH_3)_2Cl_2$$

How many grams of cisplatin are formed from 55.8 g of K$_2$PtCl$_4$ and 35.6 g of NH$_3$ if the reaction takes place in 95% yield based on the limiting reactant?

3.82 If 1.87 g of acetic acid reacts with 2.31 g of isopentyl alcohol to give 2.96 g of isopentyl acetate (Problem 3.80), what is the percent yield of the reaction?

3.83 If 3.42 g of K$_2$PtCl$_4$ and 1.61 g of NH$_3$ give 2.08 g of cisplatin (Problem 3.81), what is the percent yield of the reaction?

Molarity, Solution Stoichiometry, Dilution, and Titration (Sections 3.6–3.9)

3.84 How many moles of solute are present in each of the following solutions?
(a) 35.0 mL of 1.200 M HNO$_3$
(b) 175 mL of 0.67 M glucose (C$_6$H$_{12}$O$_6$)

3.85 How many grams of solute would you use to prepare each of the following solutions?
(a) 250.0 mL of 0.600 M ethyl alcohol (C$_2$H$_6$O)
(b) 167 mL of 0.200 M boric acid (H$_3$BO$_3$)

3.86 How many milliliters of a 0.45 M BaCl$_2$ solution contain 15.0 g of BaCl$_2$?

3.87 How many milliliters of a 0.350 M KOH solution contain 0.0171 mol of KOH?

3.88 The sterile saline solution used to rinse contact lenses can be made by dissolving 400 mg of NaCl in sterile water and diluting to 100 mL. What is the molarity of the solution?

3.89 The concentration of glucose (C$_6$H$_{12}$O$_6$) in normal blood is approximately 90 mg per 100 mL. What is the molarity of the glucose?

3.90 Copper reacts with dilute nitric acid according to the following equation:

$$3\,Cu(s) + 8\,HNO_3(aq) \longrightarrow$$
$$3\,Cu(NO_3)_2(aq) + 2\,NO(g) + 4\,H_2O(l)$$

If a copper penny weighing 3.045 g is dissolved in a small amount of nitric acid and the resultant solution is diluted to 50.0 mL with water, what is the molarity of the Cu(NO$_3$)$_2$?

3.91 Pennies minted after 1982 are mostly zinc (97.5%) with a copper cover. If a post-1982 penny is dissolved in a small amount of nitric acid, the copper coating reacts as in Problem 3.90 and the exposed zinc reacts according to the following equation:

$$Zn(s) + 2\,HNO_3(aq) \longrightarrow Zn(NO_3)_2(aq) + H_2(g)$$

For a penny that weighs 2.482 g, what is the molarity of the Zn(NO$_3$)$_2$ if the resultant solution is diluted to 250.0 mL with water?

3.92 A bottle of 12.0 M hydrochloric acid has only 35.7 mL left in it. What will the HCl concentration be if the solution is diluted to 250.0 mL?

3.93 What is the volume of the solution that would result by diluting 70.00 mL of 0.0913 M NaOH to a concentration of 0.0150 M?

3.94 A flask containing 450 mL of 0.500 M HBr was accidentally knocked to the floor. How many grams of K$_2$CO$_3$ would you need to put on the spill to neutralize the acid according to the following equation?

$$2\,HBr(aq) + K_2CO_3(aq) \longrightarrow 2\,KBr(aq) + CO_2(g) + H_2O(l)$$

3.95 The odor of skunks is caused by chemical compounds called *thiols*. These compounds, of which butanethiol (C$_4$H$_{10}$S) is a representative example, can be deodorized by reaction with household bleach (NaOCl) according to the following equation:

$$2\,C_4H_{10}S + NaOCl(aq) \longrightarrow C_8H_{18}S_2 + NaCl + H_2O(aq)$$

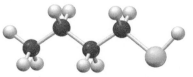

Butanethiol

How many grams of butanethiol can be deodorized by reaction with 5.00 mL of 0.0985 M NaOCl?

3.96 Potassium permanganate (KMnO$_4$) reacts with oxalic acid (H$_2$C$_2$O$_4$) in aqueous sulfuric acid according to the following equation:

$$2\,KMnO_4 + 5\,H_2C_2O_4 + 3\,H_2SO_4 \longrightarrow$$
$$2\,MnSO_4 + 10\,CO_2 + 8\,H_2O + K_2SO_4$$

How many milliliters of a 0.250 M KMnO$_4$ solution are needed to react completely with 3.225 g of oxalic acid?

3.97 Oxalic acid, H$_2$C$_2$O$_4$, is a toxic substance found in spinach leaves. What is the molarity of a solution made by dissolving 12.0 g of oxalic acid in enough water to give 400.0 mL of solution? How many milliliters of 0.100 M KOH would you need to titrate 25.0 mL of the oxalic acid solution according to the following equation?

$$H_2C_2O_4(aq) + 2\,KOH(aq) \longrightarrow K_2C_2O_4(aq) + 2\,H_2O(l)$$

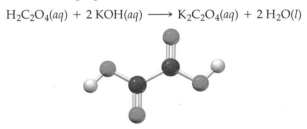

Oxalic acid

Formulas and Elemental Analysis (Sections 3.10 and 3.11)

3.98 Urea, a substance commonly used as a fertilizer, has the formula CH$_4$N$_2$O. What is its percent composition by mass?

Urea

3.99 Calculate the mass percent composition of each of the following substances:
(a) Malachite, a copper-containing mineral: Cu$_2$(OH)$_2$CO$_3$
(b) Acetaminophen, a headache remedy: C$_8$H$_9$NO$_2$
(c) Prussian blue, an ink pigment: Fe$_4$[Fe(CN)$_6$]$_3$

3.100 An unknown liquid is composed of 5.57% H, 28.01% Cl, and 66.42% C. The molecular mass found by mass spectrometry is 126.58 amu. What is the molecular formula of the compound?

3.101 An unknown liquid is composed of 34.31% C, 5.28% H, and 60.41% I. The molecular mass found by mass spectrometry is 210.06 amu. What is the molecular formula of the compound?

3.102 What is the empirical formula of stannous fluoride, the first fluoride compound added to toothpaste to protect teeth against decay? Its mass percent composition is 24.25% F, 75.75% Sn.

3.103 What are the empirical formulas of each of the following substances?

(a) Ibuprofen, a headache remedy: 75.69% C, 15.51% O, 8.80% H

(b) Magnetite, a naturally occurring magnetic mineral: 72.36% Fe, 27.64% O

(c) Zircon, a mineral from which cubic zirconia is made: 34.91% O, 15.32% Si, 49.77% Zr

3.104 Combustion analysis of 45.62 mg of toluene, a commonly used solvent, gives 35.67 mg of H_2O and 152.5 mg of CO_2. What is the empirical formula of toluene?

3.105 Coniine, a toxic substance isolated from poison hemlock, contains only carbon, hydrogen, and nitrogen. Combustion analysis of a 5.024 mg sample yields 13.90 mg of CO_2 and 6.048 mg of H_2O. What is the empirical formula of coniine?

3.106 Cytochrome c is an iron-containing enzyme found in the cells of all aerobic organisms. If cytochrome c is 0.43% Fe by mass, what is its minimum molecular mass?

3.107 Nitrogen fixation in the root nodules of peas and other leguminous plants is carried out by the molybdenum-containing enzyme *nitrogenase*. What is the molecular mass of nitrogenase if the enzyme contains two molybdenum atoms and is 0.0872% Mo by mass?

3.108 Disilane, Si_2H_x, is analyzed and found to contain 90.28% silicon by mass. What is the value of x?

3.109 A certain metal sulfide, MS_2, is used extensively as a high-temperature lubricant. If MS_2 is 40.06% sulfur by mass, what is the identity of the metal M?

3.110 The mass of an organic compound was found by mass spectrometry to be 70.042 11 amu. Is the sample C_5H_{10}, C_4H_6O, or $C_3H_6N_2$? Exact masses of elements are: 1.007 825 (^1H); 12.000 00 (^{12}C); 14.003 074 (^{14}N); 15.994 915 (^{16}O).

3.111 The mass of an organic compound was found by mass spectrometry to be 58.077 46 amu. Is the sample C_4H_{10}, C_3H_6O, or $C_2H_6N_2$? Exact masses of elements are: 1.007 825 (^1H); 12.000 00 (^{12}C); 14.003 074 (^{14}N); 15.994 915 (^{16}O).

3.112 Combustion analysis of a 31.472 mg sample of the widely used flame retardant Decabrom gave 1.444 mg of CO_2. Is the molecular formula of Decabrom $C_{12}Br_{10}$ or $C_{12}Br_{10}O$?

3.113 The stimulant amphetamine contains only carbon, hydrogen, and nitrogen. Combustion analysis of a 42.92 mg sample of amphetamine gives 37.187 mg of H_2O and 125.75 mg of CO_2. If the molar mass of amphetamine is less than 160 g/mol, what is its molecular formula?

Amphetamine

CHAPTER PROBLEMS

3.114 *Ringer's solution*, used in the treatment of burns and wounds, is prepared by dissolving 4.30 g of NaCl, 0.150 g of KCl, and 0.165 g of $CaCl_2$ in water and diluting to a volume of 500.0 mL. What is the molarity of each of the component ions in the solution?

3.115 Balance the following equations:

(a) $C_6H_5NO_2 + O_2 \longrightarrow CO_2 + H_2O + NO_2$

(b) $Au + H_2SeO_4 \longrightarrow Au_2(SeO_4)_3 + H_2SeO_3 + H_2O$

(c) $NH_4ClO_4 + Al \longrightarrow Al_2O_3 + N_2 + Cl_2 + H_2O$

3.116 The estimated concentration of gold in the oceans is 1.0×10^{-11} g/mL.

(a) Express the concentration in mol/L.

(b) Assuming that the volume of the oceans is 1.3×10^{21} L, estimate the amount of dissolved gold in grams in the oceans.

3.117 Silver sulfide, the tarnish on silverware, comes from reaction of silver metal with hydrogen sulfide (H_2S):

$$Ag + H_2S + O_2 \longrightarrow Ag_2S + H_2O \quad \text{Unbalanced}$$

(a) Balance the equation.

(b) If the reaction were used intentionally to prepare Ag_2S, how many grams would be formed from 496 g of Ag, 80.0 g of H_2S, and 40.0 g of O_2 if the reaction takes place in 95% yield based on the limiting reactant?

3.118 Give the percent composition of each of the following substances:

(a) Glucose, $C_6H_{12}O_6$

(b) Sulfuric acid, H_2SO_4

(c) Potassium permanganate, $KMnO_4$

(d) Saccharin, $C_7H_5NO_3S$

3.119 What are the empirical formulas of substances with the following mass percent compositions?

(a) Aspirin: 4.48% H, 60.00% C, 35.52% O

(b) Ilmenite (a titanium-containing ore): 31.63% O, 31.56% Ti, 36.81% Fe

(c) Sodium thiosulfate (photographic "fixer"): 30.36% O, 29.08% Na, 40.56% S

3.120 The reaction of tungsten hexachloride (WCl_6) with bismuth gives hexatungsten dodecachloride (W_6Cl_{12}).

$$WCl_6 + Bi \longrightarrow W_6Cl_{12} + BiCl_3 \quad \text{Unbalanced}$$

(a) Balance the equation.

(b) How many grams of bismuth react with 150.0 g of WCl_6?

(c) When 228 g of WCl_6 react with 175 g of Bi, how much W_6Cl_{12} is formed based on the limiting reactant?

3.121 Sodium borohydride, $NaBH_4$, a substance used in the synthesis of many pharmaceutical agents, can be prepared by reaction of NaH with B_2H_6 according to the equation $2 NaH + B_2H_6 \rightarrow 2 NaBH_4$.

(a) How many grams of $NaBH_4$ can be prepared by reaction between 8.55 g of NaH and 6.75 g of B_2H_6?

(b) Which reactant is limiting, and how many grams of the excess reactant will be left over?

3.122 Ferrocene, a substance proposed for use as a gasoline additive, has the percent composition 5.42% H, 64.56% C, and 30.02% Fe. What is the empirical formula of ferrocene?

3.123 The molar mass of HCl is 36.5 g/mol, and the average mass per HCl molecule is 36.5 amu. Use the fact that 1 amu = 1.6605×10^{-24} g to calculate Avogadro's number.

3.124 What is the molarity of each ion in a solution prepared by dissolving 0.550 g of Na_2SO_4, 1.188 g of Na_3PO_4, and 0.223 g of Li_2SO_4 in water and diluting to a volume of 100.00 mL?

3.125 Ethylene glycol, commonly used as automobile antifreeze, contains only carbon, hydrogen, and oxygen. Combustion analysis of a 23.46 mg sample yields 20.42 mg of H_2O and 33.27 mg of CO_2. What is the empirical formula of ethylene glycol? What is its molecular formula if it has a molecular mass of 62.0 amu?

3.126 The molecular mass of ethylene glycol (Problem 3.125) is 62.0689 amu when calculated using the atomic masses found in a standard periodic table, yet the molecular mass determined experimentally by high-resolution mass spectrometry is 62.0368 amu. Explain the discrepancy.

3.127 Balance the following equations:

(a) $CO(NH_2)_2(aq) + HOCl(aq) \longrightarrow$
$$NCl_3(aq) + CO_2(aq) + H_2O(l)$$

(b) $Ca_3(PO_4)_2(s) + SiO_2(s) + C(s) \longrightarrow$
$$P_4(g) + CaSiO_3(l) + CO(g)$$

3.128 Assume that gasoline has the formula C_8H_{18} and has a density of 0.703 g/mL. How many pounds of CO_2 are produced from the complete combustion of 1.00 gal of gasoline?

3.129 A sample of $CaCO_3$ with a mass of 6.35 g is placed in 500.0 mL of 0.31 M HCl, forming $CaCl_2$, H_2O, and CO_2. What mass in grams of CO_2 is produced?

3.130 Compound X contains only carbon, hydrogen, nitrogen, and chlorine. When 1.00 g of X is dissolved in water and allowed to react with excess silver nitrate, $AgNO_3$, all the chlorine in X reacts and 1.95 g of solid AgCl is formed. When 1.00 g of X undergoes complete combustion, 0.900 g of CO_2 and 0.735 g of H_2O are formed. What is the empirical formula of X?

3.131 A pulverized rock sample believed to be pure calcium carbonate, $CaCO_3$, is subjected to chemical analysis and found to contain 51.3% Ca, 7.7% C, and 41.0% O by mass. Why can't this rock sample be pure $CaCO_3$?

3.132 Salicylic acid, used in the manufacture of aspirin, contains only the elements C, H, and O and has only one acidic hydrogen that reacts with NaOH. When 1.00 g of salicylic acid undergoes complete combustion, 2.23 g CO_2 and 0.39 g H_2O are obtained. When 1.00 g of salicylic acid is titrated with 0.100 M NaOH, 72.4 mL of base is needed for complete reaction. What are the empirical and molecular formulas of salicylic acid?

3.133 Compound X contains only the elements C, H, O, and S. A 5.00 g sample undergoes complete combustion to give 4.83 g of CO_2, 1.48 g of H_2O, and a certain amount of SO_2 that is further oxidized to SO_3 and dissolved in water to form sulfuric acid, H_2SO_4. On titration of the H_2SO_4, 109.8 mL of 1.00 M NaOH is needed for complete reaction. (Both H atoms in sulfuric acid are acidic and react with NaOH.)

(a) What is the empirical formula of X?

(b) When 5.00 g of X is titrated with NaOH, it is found that X has two acidic hydrogens that react with NaOH and that 54.9 mL of 1.00 M NaOH is required to completely neutralize the sample. What is the molecular formula of X?

3.134 Assume that you have 1.00 g of a mixture of benzoic acid (molec. mass = 122 amu) and gallic acid (molec. mass = 170 amu), both of which contain one acidic hydrogen that reacts with NaOH. On titrating the mixture with 0.500 M NaOH, 14.7 mL of base is needed to completely react with both acids. What mass in grams of each acid is present in the original mixture?

3.135 A certain alcoholic beverage contains only ethanol (C_2H_6O) and water. When a sample of this beverage undergoes combustion, the ethanol burns but the water simply evaporates and is collected along with the water produced by combustion. The combustion reaction is

$$C_2H_6O(l) + 3 O_2(g) \longrightarrow 2 CO_2(g) + 3 H_2O(g)$$

When a 10.00 g sample of this beverage is burned, 11.27 g of water is collected. What is the mass in grams of ethanol, and what is the mass of water in the original sample?

3.136 A mixture of FeO and Fe_2O_3 with a mass of 10.0 g is converted to 7.43 g of pure Fe metal. What are the amounts in grams of FeO and Fe_2O_3 in the original sample?

3.137 A compound of formula XCl_3 reacts with aqueous $AgNO_3$ to yield solid AgCl according to the following equation:

$$XCl_3(aq) + 3 AgNO_3(aq) \longrightarrow X(NO_3)_3(aq) + 3 AgCl(s)$$

When a solution containing 0.634 g of XCl_3 was allowed to react with an excess of aqueous $AgNO_3$, 1.68 g of solid AgCl was formed. What is the identity of the atom X?

3.138 When eaten, dietary carbohydrates are digested to yield glucose ($C_6H_{12}O_6$), which is then metabolized to yield carbon dioxide and water:

$$C_6H_{12}O_6 + O_2 \longrightarrow CO_2 + H_2O \quad \text{Unbalanced}$$

Balance the equation, and calculate both the mass in grams and the volume in liters of the CO_2 produced from 66.3 g of glucose, assuming that 1 mol of CO_2 has a volume of 25.4 L at normal body temperature.

3.139 Other kinds of titrations are possible in addition to acid–base titrations. For example, the concentration of a solution of potassium permanganate, $KMnO_4$, can be determined by titration against a known amount of oxalic acid, $H_2C_2O_4$, according to the following equation:

$$5\,H_2C_2O_4(aq) + 2\,KMnO_4(aq) + 3\,H_2SO_4(aq) \longrightarrow$$
$$10\,CO_2(g) + 2\,MnSO_4(aq) + K_2SO_4(aq) + 8\,H_2O(l)$$

What is the concentration of a $KMnO_4$ solution if 22.35 mL reacts with 0.5170 g of oxalic acid?

3.140 A copper wire having a mass of 2.196 g was allowed to react with an excess of sulfur. The excess sulfur was then burned, yielding SO_2 gas. The mass of the copper sulfide produced was 2.748 g.

(a) What is the percent composition of copper sulfide?

(b) What is its empirical formula?

(c) Calculate the number of copper ions per cubic centimeter if the density of the copper sulfide is 5.6 g/cm^3.

3.141 Element X, a member of group 5A, forms two chlorides, XCl_3 and XCl_5. Reaction of an excess of Cl_2 with 8.729 g of XCl_3 yields 13.233 g of XCl_5. What is the atomic mass and the identity of the element X?

3.142 A mixture of XCl_3 and XCl_5 (see Problem 3.141) weighing 10.00 g contains 81.04% Cl by mass. How many grams of XCl_3 and how many grams of XCl_5 are present in the mixture?

3.143 A 1.268 g sample of a metal carbonate (MCO_3) was treated with 100.00 mL of 0.1083 M sulfuric acid (H_2SO_4), yielding CO_2 gas and an aqueous solution of the metal sulfate (MSO_4). The solution was boiled to remove all the dissolved CO_2 and was then titrated with 0.1241 M NaOH. A 71.02 mL volume of NaOH was required to neutralize the excess H_2SO_4.

(a) What is the identity of the metal M?

(b) How many liters of CO_2 gas were produced if the density of CO_2 is 1.799 g/L?

3.144 Ammonium nitrate, a potential ingredient of terrorist bombs, can be made nonexplosive by addition of diammonium hydrogen phosphate, $(NH_4)_2HPO_4$. Analysis of such a $NH_4NO_3-(NH_4)_2HPO_4$ mixture showed the mass percent of nitrogen to be 30.43%. What is the mass ratio of the two components in the mixture?

3.145 Window glass is typically made by mixing soda ash (Na_2CO_3), limestone ($CaCO_3$), and silica sand (SiO_2) and then heating to 1500 °C to drive off CO_2 from the Na_2CO_3 and $CaCO_3$. The resultant glass consists of about 12% Na_2O by mass, 13% CaO by mass, and 75% SiO_2 by mass. How much of each reactant would you start with to prepare 0.35 kg of glass?

3.146 An unidentified metal M reacts with an unidentified halogen X to form a compound MX_2. When heated, the compound decomposes by the reaction:

$$2\,MX_2(s) \longrightarrow 2\,MX(s) + X_2(g)$$

When 1.12 g of MX_2 is heated, 0.720 g of MX is obtained, along with 56.0 mL of X_2 gas. Under the conditions used, 1.00 mol of the gas has a volume of 22.41 L.

(a) What is the atomic mass and identity of the halogen X?

(b) What is the atomic mass and identity of the metal M?

3.147 A compound with the formula $XOCl_2$ reacts with water, yielding HCl and another acid H_2XO_3, which has two acidic hydrogens that react with NaOH. When 0.350 g of $XOCl_2$ was added to 50.0 mL of water and the resultant solution was titrated, 96.1 mL of 0.1225 M NaOH was required to react with all the acid.

(a) Write a balanced equation for the reaction of $XOCl_2$ with H_2O.

(b) What are the atomic mass and identity of element X?

3.148 Element M is prepared industrially by a two-step procedure according to the following (unbalanced) equations:

(1) $M_2O_3(s) + C(s) + Cl_2(g) \longrightarrow MCl_3(l) + CO(g)$

(2) $MCl_3(l) + H_2(g) \longrightarrow M(s) + HCl(g)$

Assume that 0.855 g of M_2O_3 is submitted to the reaction sequence. When the HCl produced in step (2) is dissolved in water and titrated with 0.511 M NaOH, 144.2 mL of the NaOH solution is required to neutralize the HCl.

(a) Balance both equations.

(b) What is the atomic mass of element M, and what is its identity?

(c) What mass of M in grams is produced in the reaction?

CHAPTER

4

Reactions in Aqueous Solution

The corrosion evident on this sunken boat occurs by a typical oxidation–reduction reaction of the kind discussed in this chapter.

CONTENTS

Ours is a world based on water. Approximately 71% of the Earth's surface is covered by water, and another 3% is covered by ice; 66% of the mass of an adult human body is water, and water is needed to sustain all living organisms. It's therefore not surprising that a large amount of important chemistry takes place in water—that is, in *aqueous solution*.

We saw in the previous chapter how chemical reactions are described and how specific mass relationships among reactant and product substances must be obeyed when reactions occur. In this chapter, we'll continue our study of chemical reactions by seeing how different reactions can be classified and by learning some of the general ways reactions take place.

4.1 SOME WAYS THAT CHEMICAL REACTIONS OCCUR

In beginning a study of chemical reactions in aqueous solution, it's useful to classify them into three general categories: *precipitation reactions, acid–base neutralization reactions*, and *oxidation–reduction reactions*. Let's look briefly at an example of each before studying them in more detail in subsequent sections.

▲ Reaction of aqueous $Pb(NO_3)_2$ with aqueous KI gives a yellow precipitate of PbI_2.

- **Precipitation reactions** are processes in which soluble ionic reactants yield an insoluble solid product that drops out of the solution, thereby removing some of the dissolved ions. Most precipitations take place when the anions and cations of two ionic compounds change partners. For example, an aqueous solution of lead(II) nitrate reacts with an aqueous solution of potassium iodide to yield an aqueous solution of potassium nitrate plus an insoluble yellow precipitate of lead iodide:

$$Pb(NO_3)_2(aq) + 2\,KI(aq) \longrightarrow 2\,KNO_3(aq) + PbI_2(s)$$

- **Acid–base neutralization reactions** are processes in which an acid reacts with a base to yield water plus an ionic compound called a *salt*. Acids, as we'll see shortly, are compounds that produce H^+ ions when dissolved in water, and bases are compounds that produce OH^- ions when dissolved in water. Thus, a neutralization reaction removes H^+ and OH^- ions from solution, just as a precipitation reaction removes metal and nonmetal ions. The reaction between hydrochloric acid and aqueous sodium hydroxide to yield water plus aqueous sodium chloride is a typical example:

$$HCl(aq) + NaOH(aq) \longrightarrow H_2O(l) + NaCl(aq)$$

- **Oxidation–reduction reactions**, or **redox reactions**, are processes in which one or more electrons are transferred between reaction partners (atoms, molecules, or ions). As a result of this electron transfer, the charges on atoms in the various reactants change. When metallic magnesium reacts with aqueous hydrochloric acid, for instance, a magnesium atom gives an electron to each of two H^+ ions, forming an Mg^{2+} ion and an H_2 molecule. The charge on the magnesium changes from 0 to +2, and the charge on each hydrogen changes from +1 to 0:

$$Mg(s) + 2\,HCl(aq) \longrightarrow MgCl_2(aq) + H_2(g)$$

▶ **PROBLEM 4.1**   Classify each of the following processes as a precipitation, acid–base neutralization, or redox reaction:

(a) $AgNO_3(aq) + KCl(aq) \longrightarrow AgCl(s) + KNO_3(aq)$

(b) $Cl_2(g) + 2\,NaBr(aq) \longrightarrow Br_2(aq) + 2\,NaCl(aq)$

(c) $Ca(OH)_2(aq) + 2\,HNO_3(aq) \longrightarrow 2\,H_2O(l) + Ca(NO_3)_2(aq)$

4.2 ELECTROLYTES IN AQUEOUS SOLUTION

We all know from experience that both sugar (sucrose) and table salt (NaCl) dissolve in water. The solutions that result, though, are quite different. When sucrose, a molecular substance, dissolves in water, the resulting solution contains neutral sucrose *molecules* surrounded by water. When NaCl, an ionic substance, dissolves in water, the solution contains separate Na^+ and Cl^- *ions* surrounded by water. Because of the presence of the charged ions, the NaCl solution conducts an electric current, but the sucrose solution does not.

$$C_{12}H_{22}O_{11}(s) \xrightarrow{H_2O} C_{12}H_{22}O_{11}(aq)$$
$$\text{Sucrose}$$

$$NaCl(s) \xrightarrow{H_2O} Na^+(aq) + Cl^-(aq)$$

The electrical conductivity of an aqueous NaCl solution is easy to demonstrate using a battery, a lightbulb, and several pieces of wire, connected as shown in **Figure 4.1**. When the wires are dipped into an aqueous NaCl solution, the positively charged Na^+ ions move through the solution toward the wire connected to the negatively charged terminal of the battery and the negatively charged Cl^- ions move toward the wire connected to the positively charged terminal of the battery. The resulting movement of electrical charges allows a current to flow, so the bulb lights. When the wires are dipped into an aqueous sucrose solution, however, there are no ions to carry the current, so the bulb remains dark.

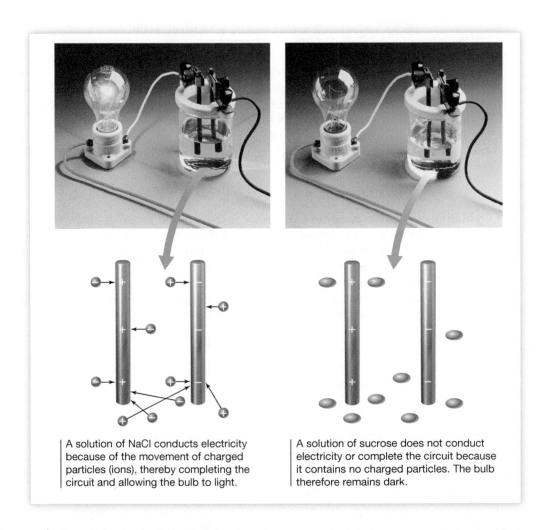

| A solution of NaCl conducts electricity because of the movement of charged particles (ions), thereby completing the circuit and allowing the bulb to light. | A solution of sucrose does not conduct electricity or complete the circuit because it contains no charged particles. The bulb therefore remains dark. |

Figure 4.1
Testing the conductivity of aqueous solutions.

Substances such as NaCl or KBr, which dissolve in water to produce conducting solutions of ions, are called **electrolytes**. Substances such as sucrose or ethyl alcohol, which do not produce ions in aqueous solution, are **nonelectrolytes**. Most electrolytes are ionic compounds, but some are molecular. Hydrogen chloride, for instance, is a gaseous molecular compound when pure but **dissociates**, or splits apart to give H^+ and Cl^- ions, when it dissolves in water.

$$HCl(g) \xrightarrow{\text{H}_2\text{O}} H^+(aq) + Cl^-(aq)$$

Compounds that dissociate to a large extent (70–100%) into ions when dissolved in water are said to be **strong electrolytes**, while compounds that dissociate to only a small extent are **weak electrolytes**. Potassium chloride and most other ionic compounds, for instance, are largely dissociated in dilute solution and are thus strong electrolytes. Acetic acid (CH_3CO_2H), by contrast, dissociates only to the extent of about 1.3% in a 0.10 M solution and is a weak electrolyte. As a result, a 0.10 M solution of acetic acid is only weakly conducting.

For 0.10 M solutions:

$$KCl(aq) \rightleftharpoons K^+(aq) + Cl^-(aq) \quad \text{—} \quad \text{Strong electrolyte}$$
(2%)   (98%)

$$CH_3CO_2H(aq) \rightleftharpoons H^+(aq) + CH_3CO_2^-(aq) \quad \text{—} \quad \text{Weak electrolyte}$$
(99%)   (1%)

Note that when we write a dissociation equation, we often use a forward-and-backward double arrow ($\rightleftharpoons$) to indicate that the reaction takes place in both directions. That is, dissociation is a dynamic process in which an *equilibrium* is established between the forward and reverse reactions. The balance between the two opposing reactions defines the exact concentrations of the various species in solution. We'll learn much more about chemical equilibria in Chapters 13 and 14.

A brief list of some common substances classified according to their electrolyte strength is given in Table 4.1. Note that pure water is a nonelectrolyte because it does not dissociate appreciably into H^+ and OH^- ions. We'll explore the dissociation of water in more detail in Section 14.4.

TABLE 4.1   Electrolyte Classification of Some Common Substances

Strong Electrolytes	Weak Electrolytes	Nonelectrolytes
HCl, HBr, HI	CH_3CO_2H	H_2O
$HClO_4$	HF	CH_3OH (methyl alcohol)
HNO_3	HCN	C_2H_5OH (ethyl alcohol)
H_2SO_4		$C_{12}H_{22}O_{11}$ (sucrose)
KBr		Most compounds of carbon
NaCl		(organic compounds)
NaOH, KOH		
Other soluble ionic compounds		

WORKED EXAMPLE 4.1

CALCULATING THE CONCENTRATION OF IONS IN A SOLUTION

What is the total molar concentration of ions in a 0.350 M solution of the strong electrolyte Na_2SO_4, assuming complete dissociation?

STRATEGY

First, we need to know how many ions are produced by dissociation of Na_2SO_4. Writing the equation for dissolving Na_2SO_4 in water shows that 3 mol of ions are formed: 2 mol of Na^+ and 1 mol of SO_4^{2-}.

$$Na_2SO_4(s) \xrightarrow{\text{H}_2\text{O}} 2\,Na^+(aq) + SO_4^{2-}(aq)$$

continued on next page

SOLUTION

Assuming complete dissociation, the total molar concentration of ions is three times the molarity of Na_2SO_4, or 1.05 M:

$$\frac{0.350 \text{ mol } Na_2SO_4}{1 \text{ L}} \times \frac{3 \text{ mol ions}}{1 \text{ mol } Na_2SO_4} = 1.05 \text{ M}$$

▶ **PROBLEM 4.2** What is the molar concentration of Br^- ions in a 0.225 M aqueous solution of $FeBr_3$, assuming complete dissociation?

CONCEPTUAL PROBLEM 4.3 Three different substances A_2X, A_2Y, and A_2Z are dissolved in water, with the following results. (Water molecules are omitted for clarity.) Which of the substances is the strongest electrolyte, and which is the weakest? Explain.

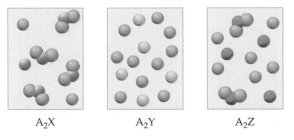

A_2X A_2Y A_2Z

4.3 AQUEOUS REACTIONS AND NET IONIC EQUATIONS

Remember...

The physical state of a substance in a chemical reaction is often indicated with a parenthetical **(s)** for solid, **(l)** for liquid, **(g)** for gas, and **(aq)** for aqueous solution. (Section 3.3)

The equations we've been writing up to this point have all been **molecular equations**. That is, all the substances involved in the reactions have been written using their complete formulas as if they were *molecules*. In Section 4.1, for instance, we wrote the precipitation reaction of lead(II) nitrate with potassium iodide to yield solid PbI_2 using only the parenthetical **(aq)** to indicate that the substances are dissolved in aqueous solution. Nowhere in the equation was it indicated that ions are involved.

A molecular equation

$$Pb(NO_3)_2(aq) + 2 \text{ KI}(aq) \longrightarrow 2 \text{ KNO}_3(aq) + PbI_2(s)$$

In fact, lead nitrate, potassium iodide, and potassium nitrate are strong electrolytes that dissolve in water to yield solutions of ions. Thus, it's more accurate to write the precipitation reaction as an **ionic equation**, in which all the ions are explicitly shown.

An ionic equation

$$Pb^{2+}(aq) + 2 \text{ NO}_3{}^-(aq) + 2 \text{ K}^+(aq) + 2 \text{ I}^-(aq) \longrightarrow 2 \text{ K}^+(aq) + 2 \text{ NO}_3{}^-(aq) + PbI_2(s)$$

A look at this ionic equation shows that the $NO_3{}^-$ and K^+ ions undergo no change during the reaction. Instead, they appear on both sides of the reaction arrow and act merely as **spectator ions**, whose only role is to balance the charge. The actual reaction, when stripped to its essentials, can be described more simply by writing a **net ionic equation**, in which only the ions undergoing change are shown—the Pb^{2+} and I^- ions in this instance. The spectator ions are not shown in a net ionic equation.

An ionic equation

$$Pb^{2+}(aq) + 2\,\cancel{NO_3{}^-}(aq) + 2\,\cancel{K^+}(aq) + 2 \text{ I}^-(aq) \longrightarrow 2\,\cancel{K^+}(aq) + 2\,\cancel{NO_3{}^-}(aq) + PbI_2(s)$$

A net ionic equation

$$Pb^{2+}(aq) + 2 \text{ I}^-(aq) \longrightarrow PbI_2(s)$$

Leaving the spectator ions out of a net ionic equation doesn't imply that their presence is irrelevant. If a reaction occurs by mixing a solution of Pb^{2+} ions with a solution of I^- ions, then those solutions must also contain additional ions to balance the charge in each. The Pb^{2+} solution must also contain an anion, and the I^- solution must also contain a cation. Leaving these other ions out of the net ionic equation only implies that their specific identity is not important. Any nonreactive spectator ions could fill the same role.

WORKED EXAMPLE 4.2

WRITING A NET IONIC EQUATION

Aqueous hydrochloric acid reacts with zinc metal to yield hydrogen gas and aqueous zinc chloride. Write a net ionic equation for the process.

$$2\,HCl(aq) + Zn(s) \longrightarrow H_2(g) + ZnCl_2(aq)$$

STRATEGY

First, write the ionic equation, listing all the species present in solution. Both HCl (a molecular compound; Table 4.1) and $ZnCl_2$ (an ionic compound) are strong electrolytes that exist as ions in solution. Then find the ions that are present on both sides of the reaction arrow—the spectator ions—and cancel them, leaving the net ionic equation.

SOLUTION

Ionic equation

$$2\,H^+(aq) + 2\,\cancel{Cl^-}(aq) + Zn(s) \longrightarrow H_2(g) + Zn^{2+}(aq) + 2\,\cancel{Cl^-}(aq)$$

Net ionic equation

$$2\,H^+(aq) + Zn(s) \longrightarrow H_2(g) + Zn^{2+}(aq)$$

▶ **PROBLEM 4.4** Write net ionic equations for the following reactions:

(a) $2\,AgNO_3(aq) + Na_2CrO_4(aq) \longrightarrow Ag_2CrO_4(s) + 2\,NaNO_3(aq)$

(b) $H_2SO_4(aq) + MgCO_3(s) \longrightarrow H_2O(l) + CO_2(g) + MgSO_4(aq)$

(c) $Hg(NO_3)_2(aq) + 2\,NH_4I(aq) \longrightarrow HgI_2(s) + 2\,NH_4NO_3(aq)$

▲ Zinc metal reacts with aqueous hydrochloric acid to give hydrogen gas and aqueous Zn^{2+} ions.

4.4 PRECIPITATION REACTIONS AND SOLUBILITY GUIDELINES

To predict whether a precipitation reaction will occur on mixing aqueous solutions of two substances, you must know the **solubility** of each potential product—how much of each compound will dissolve in a given amount of solvent at a given temperature. If a substance has a low solubility in water, it's likely to precipitate from an aqueous solution. If a substance has a high solubility in water, no precipitate will form.

Solubility is a complex matter, and it's not always possible to make correct predictions about a substance. In addition, solubilities depend on the concentrations of the reactant ions, and the very words *soluble* and *insoluble* are imprecise. Using a concentration of 0.01 M as the lower limit a substance can have to be considered soluble, a compound is probably soluble if it meets either (or both) of the following criteria:

1. **A compound is probably soluble if it contains one of the following cations:**
   - Li^+, Na^+, K^+, Rb^+, Cs^+ (group 1A cations)
   - NH_4^+ (ammonium ion)

   That is, essentially all ionic compounds containing an alkali metal or ammonium cation are soluble in water and will not precipitate, regardless of the anions present.

2. **A compound is probably soluble if it contains one of the following anions:**
   - Cl^-, Br^-, I^- (halide)
     except: Ag^+, Hg_2^{2+}, and Pb^{2+} halides
   - NO_3^- (nitrate), ClO_4^- (perchlorate), $CH_3CO_2^-$ (acetate), and SO_4^{2-} (sulfate)
     except: Sr^{2+}, Ba^{2+}, Hg_2^{2+}, and Pb^{2+} sulfates

   That is, most ionic compounds containing a halide, nitrate, perchlorate, acetate, or sulfate anion are soluble in water and will not precipitate regardless of the cations present. The exceptions that *will* precipitate are silver (I), mercury(I), and Pb(II) halides, and strontium, barium, mercury(I), and lead(II) sulfates.

Looked at from the other side, a compound that does *not* contain one of the cations or anions listed above is probably *not* soluble. Thus, carbonates (CO_3^{2-}), sulfides (S^{2-}). phosphates (PO_4^{3-}), and hydroxides (OH^-) are generally not soluble unless they contain an alkali metal or ammonium cation. The main exceptions are the sulfides and hydroxides of Ca^{2+}, Sr^{2+}, Ba^{2+}. These guidelines are summarized in Table 4.2.

TABLE 4.2   Solubility Guidelines for Ionic Compounds in Water

Soluble Compounds	Common Exceptions
Li^+, Na^+, K^+, Rb^+, Cs^+ (group 1A cations)	None
NH_4^+ (ammonium ion)	None
Cl^-, Br^-, I^- (halide)	Halides of Ag^+, Hg_2^{2+}, Pb^{2+}
NO_3^- (nitrate)	None
ClO_4^- (perchlorate)	None
$CH_3CO_2^-$ (acetate)	None
SO_4^{2-} (sulfate)	Sulfates of Sr^{2+}, Ba^{2+}, Hg_2^{2+}, Pb^{2+}
Insoluble Compounds	**Common Exceptions**
CO_3^{2-} (carbonate)	Carbonates of group 1A cations, NH_4^+
S^{2-} (sulfide)	Sulfides of group 1A cations, NH_4^+, Ca^{2+}, Sr^{2+}, and Ba^{2+}
PO_4^{3-} (phosphate)	Phosphates of group 1A cations, NH_4^+
OH^- (hydroxide)	Hydroxides of group 1A cations, NH_4^+, Ca^{2+}, Sr^{2+}, and Ba^{2+}

You might notice that most of the ions that impart solubility to compounds are singly charged—either singly positive (Li^+, Na^+, K^+, Rb^+, Cs^+, NH_4^+) or singly negative (Cl^-, Br^-, I^-, NO_3^-, ClO_4^-, $CH_3CO_2^-$). Very few doubly charged ions or triply charged ions form soluble compounds. This solubility behavior arises because of the relatively strong ionic bonds in compounds containing ions with multiple charges. The greater the strength of the ionic bonds holding ions together in a crystal, the more difficult it is to break those bonds apart during the solution process. We'll return to this topic in Section 6.8.

The solubility guidelines not only let us predict whether a precipitate will form when solutions of two ionic compounds are mixed but also let us prepare a specific compound by purposefully carrying out a precipitation. If, for example, you wanted to prepare a sample of solid silver carbonate, Ag_2CO_3, you could mix a solution of $AgNO_3$ with a solution of Na_2CO_3. Both starting compounds are soluble in water, as is $NaNO_3$. Silver carbonate is the only insoluble combination of ions and will therefore precipitate from solution.

▲ Reaction of aqueous $AgNO_3$ with aqueous Na_2CO_3 gives a white precipitate of Ag_2CO_3.

$$2\,AgNO_3(aq) + Na_2CO_3(aq) \longrightarrow Ag_2CO_3(s) + 2\,NaNO_3(aq)$$

WORKED EXAMPLE 4.3

PREDICTING THE PRODUCT OF A PRECIPITATION REACTION

Will a precipitation reaction occur when aqueous solutions of $CdCl_2$ and $(NH_4)_2S$ are mixed? If so, write the net ionic equation.

STRATEGY

Write the possible reaction, identify the two potential products, and predict the solubility of each. In the present instance, $CdCl_2$ and $(NH_4)_2S$ might give CdS and NH_4Cl:

$$??\quad CdCl_2(aq) + (NH_4)_2S(aq) \longrightarrow CdS + 2\,NH_4Cl\quad ??$$

SOLUTION

Of the two possible products, the solubility guidelines predict that CdS, a sulfide, is insoluble and that NH_4Cl, an ammonium compound and a halide, is soluble. Thus, a precipitation reaction will likely occur:

$$Cd^{2+}(aq) + S^{2-}(aq) \longrightarrow CdS(s)$$

WORKED EXAMPLE 4.4

USING A PRECIPITATION REACTION TO PREPARE A SUBSTANCE

How might you use a precipitation reaction to prepare a sample of $CuCO_3$? Write the net ionic equation.

STRATEGY

To prepare a precipitate of $CuCO_3$, a soluble Cu^{2+} compound must react with a soluble CO_3^{2-} compound.

SOLUTION

A look at the solubility guidelines suggests that a soluble copper compound, such as $Cu(NO_3)_2$, and a soluble carbonate, such as Na_2CO_3, might work. (There are many other possibilities.)

$$Cu(NO_3)_2(aq) + Na_2CO_3(aq) \longrightarrow 2\,NaNO_3(aq) + CuCO_3(s)$$
$$Cu^{2+}(aq) + CO_3^{2-}(aq) \longrightarrow CuCO_3(s)$$

WORKED CONCEPTUAL EXAMPLE 4.5

IDENTIFYING PRECIPITATION REACTIONS

When aqueous solutions of two ionic compounds are mixed, the following results are obtained. (Only the anion of the first compound, represented by blue spheres, and the cation of the second compound, represented by red spheres, are shown.) Which cations and anions, chosen from the following lists, are compatible with the observed results?

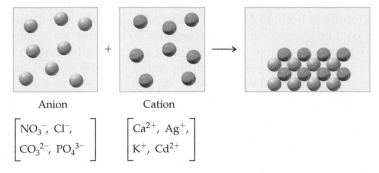

Anion

$$\begin{bmatrix} NO_3^-, Cl^-, \\ CO_3^{2-}, PO_4^{3-} \end{bmatrix}$$

Cation

$$\begin{bmatrix} Ca^{2+}, Ag^+, \\ K^+, Cd^{2+} \end{bmatrix}$$

STRATEGY

The process represented in the drawing is a precipitation reaction because ions in solution drop to the bottom of the container in an ordered arrangement. Counting the spheres shows that the cation and anion react in equal numbers (8 of each), so they must have the same number of charges—either both singly charged or both doubly charged. (There is no triply charged cation in the list.) Look at all the possible combinations, and decide which would precipitate.

SOLUTION

> Possible combinations of singly charged ions: $AgNO_3$, KNO_3, $AgCl$, KCl
> Possible combinations of doubly charged ions: $CaCO_3$, $CdCO_3$

Of the possible combinations, $AgCl$, $CaCO_3$, and $CdCO_3$ are insoluble, so the anion might be Cl^- or CO_3^{2-} and the cation might be Ag^+, Ca^{2+}, or Cd^{2+}.

▶ **PROBLEM 4.5** Predict whether each of the following compounds is likely to be soluble in water:

(a) $CdCO_3$ (b) MgO (c) Na_2S
(d) $PbSO_4$ (e) $(NH_4)_3PO_4$ (f) $HgCl_2$

▶ **PROBLEM 4.6** Predict whether a precipitation reaction will occur in each of the following situations. Write a net ionic equation for each reaction that occurs.

(a) $NiCl_2(aq) + (NH_4)_2S(aq) \longrightarrow$? (b) $Na_2CrO_4(aq) + Pb(NO_3)_2(aq) \longrightarrow$?
(c) $AgClO_4(aq) + CaBr_2(aq) \longrightarrow$? (d) $ZnCl_2(aq) + K_2CO_3(aq) \longrightarrow$?

▶ **PROBLEM 4.7**   How might you use a precipitation reaction to prepare a sample of $Ca_3(PO_4)_2$? Write the net ionic equation.

CONCEPTUAL PROBLEM 4.8   An aqueous solution containing an anion, represented by blue spheres, is added to another solution containing a cation, represented by red spheres, and the following result is obtained. Which cations and anions, chosen from the following lists, are compatible with the observed results?

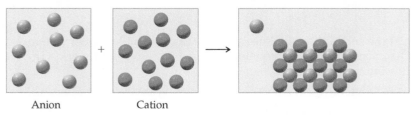

Anion   Cation

Anions: S^{2-}, PO_4^{3-}, SO_4^{2-}, ClO_4^-

Cations: Mg^{2+}, Fe^{3+}, NH_4^+, Zn^{2+}

4.5   ACIDS, BASES, AND NEUTRALIZATION REACTIONS

We've mentioned acids and bases briefly on several previous occasions, but now let's look more carefully at both. In 1777, the French chemist Antoine Lavoisier proposed that all acids contain a common element: oxygen. In fact, the word *oxygen* is derived from a Greek phrase meaning "acid former." Lavoisier's idea had to be modified, however, when the English chemist Sir Humphrey Davy (1778–1829) showed in 1810 that muriatic acid (now called hydrochloric acid) contains only hydrogen and chlorine but no oxygen. Davy's studies thus suggested that the common element in acids is *hydrogen*, not oxygen.

The relationship between acidic behavior and the presence of hydrogen in a compound was clarified in 1887 by the Swedish chemist Svante Arrhenius (1859–1927). Arrhenius proposed that an **acid** is a substance that dissociates in water to give hydrogen ions (H^+) and a **base** is a substance that dissociates in water to give hydroxide ions (OH^-):

An acid $HA(aq) \longrightarrow H^+(aq) + A^-(aq)$

A base $MOH(aq) \longrightarrow M^+(aq) + OH^-(aq)$

In these equations, HA is a general formula for an acid—for example, HCl or HNO_3—and MOH is a general formula for a metal hydroxide—for example, NaOH or KOH.

Although convenient to use in equations, the symbol $H^+(aq)$ does not really represent the structure of the ion present in aqueous solution. As a bare hydrogen nucleus (a proton) with no electron nearby, H^+ is much too reactive to exist by itself. Rather, the H^+ bonds to the oxygen atom of a water molecule, giving the more stable **hydronium ion, H_3O^+**. We'll sometimes write $H^+(aq)$ for convenience, particularly when balancing equations, but will more often write $H_3O^+(aq)$ to represent an aqueous acid solution. Hydrogen chloride, for instance, gives $Cl^-(aq)$ and $H_3O^+(aq)$ when it dissolves in water.

HCl H_2O H_3O^+ Cl^-

Different acids dissociate to different extents in aqueous solution. Acids that dissociate to a large extent are strong electrolytes and **strong acids**, whereas acids that dissociate to only a small extent are weak electrolytes and **weak acids**. We've already seen in Table 4.1, for instance, that HCl, HClO$_4$, HNO$_3$, and H$_2$SO$_4$ are strong electrolytes and therefore strong acids, while CH$_3$CO$_2$H and HF are weak electrolytes and therefore weak acids. You might note that acetic acid actually contains four hydrogens, but only the one bonded to the oxygen atom dissociates.

Acetic Acid

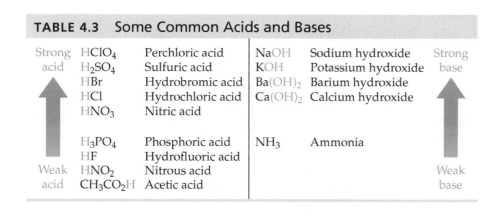

Different acids can have different numbers of acidic hydrogens and yield different numbers of H$_3$O$^+$ ions in solution. Hydrochloric acid (HCl) is said to be a **monoprotic acid** because it provides only one H$^+$ ion, but sulfuric acid (H$_2$SO$_4$) is a **diprotic acid** because it can provide two H$^+$ ions. Phosphoric acid (H$_3$PO$_4$) is a **triprotic acid** and can provide three H$^+$ ions. With sulfuric acid, the first dissociation of an H$^+$ is complete—all H$_2$SO$_4$ molecules lose one H$^+$—but the second dissociation is incomplete, as indicated by the double arrow in the following equation:

Sulfuric acid:
$$H_2SO_4(aq) + H_2O(l) \longrightarrow HSO_4^-(aq) + H_3O^+(aq)$$
$$HSO_4^-(aq) + H_2O(l) \rightleftharpoons SO_4^{2-}(aq) + H_3O^+(aq)$$

With phosphoric acid, none of the three dissociations is complete:

Phosphoric acid:
$$H_3PO_4(aq) + H_2O(l) \rightleftharpoons H_2PO_4^-(aq) + H_3O^+(aq)$$
$$H_2PO_4^-(aq) + H_2O(l) \rightleftharpoons HPO_4^{2-}(aq) + H_3O^+(aq)$$
$$HPO_4^{2-}(aq) + H_2O(l) \rightleftharpoons PO_4^{3-}(aq) + H_3O^+(aq)$$

Bases, like acids, can also be either strong or weak, depending on the extent to which they dissociate and produce OH$^-$ ions in aqueous solution. Most metal hydroxides, such as NaOH and Ba(OH)$_2$, are strong electrolytes and **strong bases**, but ammonia (NH$_3$) is a weak electrolyte and a **weak base**. Ammonia is weakly basic, not because it contains OH$^-$ ions in its formula, but because it reacts to a small extent with water to yield NH$_4^+$ and OH$^-$ ions. In fact, aqueous solutions of ammonia are often called *ammonium hydroxide*, although this is really a misnomer because the concentrations of NH$_4^+$ and OH$^-$ ions are low.

$$NH_3(g) + H_2O(l) \rightleftharpoons NH_4^+(aq) + OH^-(aq)$$

As with the dissociation of acetic acid, discussed in Section 4.2, the reaction of ammonia with water takes place only to a small extent (about 1%). Most of the ammonia remains unreacted, and we therefore write the reaction with a double arrow to show that a dynamic equilibrium exists between the forward and reverse reactions.

Table 4.3 summarizes the names, formulas, and classification of some common acids and bases.

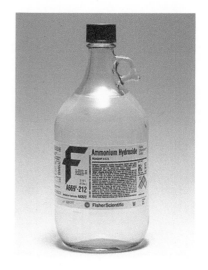

▲ Shouldn't this bottle be labeled "Aqueous Ammonia" rather than "Ammonium Hydroxide"?

TABLE 4.3 Some Common Acids and Bases

Strong acid	HClO$_4$	Perchloric acid	NaOH	Sodium hydroxide	Strong base
	H$_2$SO$_4$	Sulfuric acid	KOH	Potassium hydroxide	
	HBr	Hydrobromic acid	Ba(OH)$_2$	Barium hydroxide	
	HCl	Hydrochloric acid	Ca(OH)$_2$	Calcium hydroxide	
	HNO$_3$	Nitric acid			
	H$_3$PO$_4$	Phosphoric acid	NH$_3$	Ammonia	
	HF	Hydrofluoric acid			
Weak acid	HNO$_2$	Nitrous acid			Weak base
	CH$_3$CO$_2$H	Acetic acid			

Naming Acids

Most acids are **oxoacids**, meaning that they contain oxygen in addition to hydrogen and another element. When dissolved in water, an oxoacid yields one or more H^+ ions and an oxoanion like those we saw in Section 2.12 (Table 2.4).

TABLE 4.4   Common Oxoacids and Their Anions

Oxoacid		Oxoanion	
HNO_2	Nitrous acid	NO_2^-	Nitrite ion
HNO_3	Nitric acid	NO_3^-	Nitrate ion
H_3PO_4	Phosphoric acid	PO_4^{3-}	Phosphate ion
H_2SO_3	Sulfurous acid	SO_3^{2-}	Sulfite ion
H_2SO_4	Sulfuric acid	SO_4^{2-}	Sulfate ion
HClO	Hypochlorous acid	ClO^-	Hypochlorite ion
$HClO_2$	Chlorous acid	ClO_2^-	Chlorite ion
$HClO_3$	Chloric acid	ClO_3^-	Chlorate ion
$HClO_4$	Perchloric acid	ClO_4^-	Perchlorate ion

The names of oxoacids are related to the names of the corresponding oxoanions, with the -*ite* or -*ate* ending of the anion name replaced by -*ous acid* or -*ic acid*, respectively. In other words, the acid with fewer oxygens has an -*ous* ending, and the acid with more oxygens has an -*ic* ending. The compound HNO_2, for example, is called *nitrous acid* because it has fewer oxygens and yields the nit*rite* ion (NO_2^-) when dissolved in water, while HNO_3 is called *nitric acid* because it has more oxygens and yields the nit*rate* ion (NO_3^-) when dissolved in water.

Nit*rous* acid gives nit*rite* ion

$$HNO_2(aq) + H_2O(l) \rightleftharpoons H_3O^+(aq) + NO_2^-(aq)$$

Nit*ric* acid gives nit*rate* ion

$$HNO_3(aq) + H_2O(l) \longrightarrow H_3O^+(aq) + NO_3^-(aq)$$

In a similar way, hypochlor*ous* acid yields the hypochlor*ite* ion, chlor*ous* acid yields the chlor*ite* ion, chlor*ic* acid yields the chlor*ate* ion, and perchlor*ic* acid yields the perchlor*ate* ion (Table 4.4).

In addition to the oxoacids, there are a small number of other common acids, such as HCl, that do not contain oxygen. For such compounds, the prefix *hydro-* and the suffix -*ic acid* are used for the aqueous solution.

Hydrogen chloride gives *hydrochloric acid*

$$HCl(g) + H_2O(l) \xrightarrow{\text{Dissolve in water}} H_3O^+(aq) + Cl^-(aq)$$

Hydrogen cyanide gives *hydrocyanic acid*

$$HCN(g) + H_2O(l) \xrightleftharpoons{\text{Dissolve in water}} H_3O^+(aq) + CN^-(aq)$$

WORKED EXAMPLE 4.6

NAMING ACIDS

Name the following acids:

(a) HBrO(*aq*)   **(b)** H_2S(*aq*)

STRATEGY

To name an acid, look at the formula and decide whether the compound is an oxoacid. If so, the name must reflect the number of oxygen atoms, according to Table 4.4. If the compound is not an oxoacid, it is named using the prefix *hydro-* and the suffix -*ic acid*.

SOLUTION

(a) This compound is an oxoacid that yields hypobromite ion (BrO^-) when dissolved in water. Its name is hypobromous acid.

(b) This compound is not an oxoacid but yields sulfide ion when dissolved in water. As a pure gas, H_2S is named hydrogen sulfide. In water solution, it is called hydrosulfuric acid.

▶ **PROBLEM 4.9** Name the following acids:

(a) HIO_4 (b) $HBrO_2$ (c) H_2CrO_4

▶ **PROBLEM 4.10** Give likely chemical formulas corresponding to the following names:

(a) Phosphorous acid   (b) Hydroselenic acid

Neutralization Reactions

When an acid and a base are mixed in the right stoichiometric proportion, both acidic and basic properties disappear because of a neutralization reaction that produces water and an ionic **salt**. The anion of the salt (A^-) comes from the acid, and the cation of the salt (M^+) comes from the base:

A neutralization reaction

$$\underset{\text{Acid}}{HA(aq)} + \underset{\text{Base}}{MOH(aq)} \longrightarrow \underset{\text{Water}}{H_2O(l)} + \underset{\text{A salt}}{MA(aq)}$$

Because salts are generally strong electrolytes in aqueous solution, we can write the neutralization reaction of a strong acid with a strong base as an ionic equation:

$$H^+(aq) + A^-(aq) + M^+(aq) + OH^-(aq) \longrightarrow H_2O(l) + M^+(aq) + A^-(aq)$$

Canceling the ions that appear on both sides of the ionic equation gives the net ionic equation, which describes the reaction of any strong acid with any strong base in water:

$$H^+(aq) + \cancel{A^-(aq)} + \cancel{M^+(aq)} + OH^-(aq) \longrightarrow H_2O(l) + \cancel{M^+(aq)} + \cancel{A^-(aq)}$$
$$H^+(aq) + OH^-(aq) \longrightarrow H_2O(l)$$
$$\text{or} \quad H_3O^+(aq) + OH^-(aq) \longrightarrow 2\,H_2O(l)$$

For the reaction of a weak acid with a strong base, a similar neutralization occurs, but we must write the molecular formula of the acid rather than simply $H^+(aq)$, because the dissociation of the acid in water is incomplete. Instead, the acid exists primarily as the neutral molecule. In the reaction of the weak acid HF with the strong base KOH, for example, we write the net ionic equation as

$$HF(aq) + OH^-(aq) \longrightarrow H_2O(l) + F^-(aq)$$

WORKED EXAMPLE 4.7

WRITING IONIC AND NET IONIC EQUATIONS FOR AN ACID–BASE REACTION

Write both an ionic equation and a net ionic equation for the neutralization reaction of aqueous HBr and aqueous $Ba(OH)_2$.

STRATEGY

Hydrogen bromide is a strong acid whose aqueous solution contains H^+ ions and Br^- ions. Barium hydroxide is a strong base whose aqueous solution contains Ba^{2+} and OH^- ions. Thus, we have a mixture of four different ions on the reactant side. Write the neutralization reaction as an ionic equation, and then cancel spectator ions to give the net ionic equation.

SOLUTION

Ionic equation

$$2\,H^+(aq) + 2\,Br^-(aq) + Ba^{2+}(aq) + 2\,OH^-(aq) \longrightarrow 2\,H_2O(l) + 2\,Br^-(aq) + Ba^{2+}(aq)$$

Net ionic equation

$$2\,H^+(aq) + 2\,OH^-(aq) \longrightarrow 2\,H_2O(l)$$
$$\text{or} \qquad H^+(aq) + OH^-(aq) \longrightarrow H_2O(l)$$

The reaction of HBr with $Ba(OH)_2$ involves the combination of a proton (H^+) from the acid with OH^- from the base to yield water and an aqueous salt ($BaBr_2$).

▶ **PROBLEM 4.11** Write a balanced ionic equation and net ionic equation for each of the following acid–base reactions:

(a) $2\,CsOH(aq) + H_2SO_4(aq) \longrightarrow$ **(b)** $Ca(OH)_2(aq) + 2\,CH_3CO_2H(aq) \longrightarrow$

CONCEPTUAL PROBLEM 4.12 The following pictures represent aqueous solutions of three acids HA (A = X, Y, or Z), with water molecules omitted for clarity. Which of the three is the strongest acid, and which is the weakest?

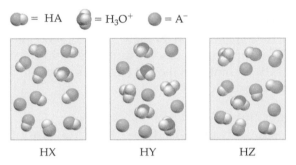

● = HA ● = H_3O^+ ● = A^-

HX HY HZ

4.6 OXIDATION–REDUCTION (REDOX) REACTIONS

Purple aqueous permanganate ion, MnO_4^-, reacts with aqueous Fe^{2+} ion to yield Fe^{3+} and pale pink Mn^{2+}. Magnesium metal burns in air with an intense white light to form solid magnesium oxide. Red phosphorus reacts with liquid bromine to form liquid phosphorus tribromide. Although these and many thousands of other reactions appear unrelated, and many don't even take place in aqueous solution, all are *oxidation–reduction (redox)* reactions.

$$MnO_4^-(aq) + 5\,Fe^{2+}(aq) + 8\,H^+(aq) \longrightarrow Mn^{2+}(aq) + 5\,Fe^{3+}(aq) + 4\,H_2O(l)$$

$$2\,Mg(s) + O_2(g) \longrightarrow 2\,MgO(s)$$

$$2\,P(s) + 3\,Br_2(l) \longrightarrow 2\,PBr_3(l)$$

▲ Aqueous potassium permanganate, deep purple in color, is frequently used as an *oxidizing agent*, as described in the text.

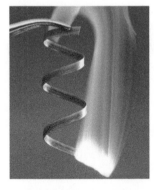

▲ Magnesium metal burns in air to give MgO.

▲ Elemental phosphorus reacts spectacularly with bromine to give PBr_3.

Historically, the word *oxidation* referred to the combination of an element with oxygen to yield an oxide, and the word *reduction* referred to the removal of oxygen from an oxide to yield the element. Such oxidation–reduction processes have been crucial to the development of human civilization and still have enormous commercial value. The oxidation (rusting) of iron metal by reaction with moist air has been known for millennia and is still a serious problem that causes enormous structural damage to buildings, boats, and bridges. The reduction of iron ore (Fe_2O_3) with charcoal (C) to make iron metal has been carried out since prehistoric times and is still used today in the initial stages of steelmaking.

$$4\,Fe(s) + 3\,O_2(g) \longrightarrow 2\,Fe_2O_3(s)$$ Rusting of iron: an **oxidation** of Fe

$$2\,Fe_2O_3(s) + 3\,C(s) \longrightarrow 4\,Fe(s) + 3\,CO_2(g)$$ Manufacture of iron: a **reduction** of Fe_2O_3

Today, the words oxidation and reduction have taken on a much broader meaning. An **oxidation** is now defined as the loss of one or more electrons by a substance, whether element, compound, or ion, and a **reduction** is the gain of one or more electrons by a substance. Thus, an **oxidation–reduction**, or **redox**, **reaction** is any process in which electrons are transferred from one substance to another.

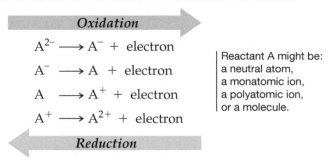

Oxidation

$$A^{2-} \longrightarrow A^- + \text{electron}$$
$$A^- \longrightarrow A + \text{electron}$$
$$A \longrightarrow A^+ + \text{electron}$$
$$A^+ \longrightarrow A^{2+} + \text{electron}$$

Reduction

Reactant A might be: a neutral atom, a monatomic ion, a polyatomic ion, or a molecule.

How can you tell when a redox reaction takes place? The answer is that we can assign to each atom in a compound a value called an **oxidation number** (or *oxidation state*), which indicates whether the atom is neutral, electron-rich, or electron-poor. By comparing the oxidation number of an atom before and after reaction, we can tell whether the atom has gained or lost electrons. Note that oxidation numbers don't necessarily imply ionic charges; they are just a convenient device to help keep track of electrons during redox reactions.

The rules for assigning oxidation numbers are as follows:

1. **An atom in its elemental state has an oxidation number of 0.** For example:

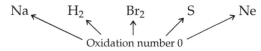

$$\text{Na} \qquad \text{H}_2 \qquad \text{Br}_2 \qquad \text{S} \qquad \text{Ne}$$

Oxidation number 0

2. **An atom in a monatomic ion has an oxidation number identical to its charge.** Review Section 2.12 to see the charges on some common ions. For example:

$$\text{Na}^+ \qquad \text{Ca}^{2+} \qquad \text{Al}^{3+} \qquad \text{Cl}^- \qquad \text{O}^{2-}$$
$$\;\;\;+1 \qquad\;\; +2 \qquad\;\;\; +3 \qquad\;\;\; -1 \qquad\;\;\; -2$$

3. **An atom in a polyatomic ion or in a molecular compound usually has the same oxidation number it would have if it were a monatomic ion.** In the hydroxide ion (OH^-), for instance, the hydrogen atom has an oxidation number of +1, as if it were H^+, and the oxygen atom has an oxidation number of −2, as if it were a monatomic O^{2-} ion.

$$\text{H}-\text{O}-\text{H} \qquad\quad [\text{O}-\text{H}]^- \qquad\quad \begin{array}{c} \text{H} \leftarrow {\scriptstyle +1} \\ | \\ \text{H}-\text{N}-\text{H} \end{array}$$
$$\;\;+1 \;\;\; -2 \;\;\; +1 \qquad\quad -2 \;\;\;\; +1 \qquad\quad +1 \;\;\; -3 \;\;\; +1$$

In general, the farther left an element is in the periodic table, the more probable that it will be "cationlike." Metals, therefore, usually have positive oxidation numbers. The farther right an element is in the periodic table, the more probable that it will be "anionlike." Nonmetals, such as O, N, and the halogens, usually have negative oxidation numbers. We'll see the reasons for these trends in Sections 6.3–6.5.

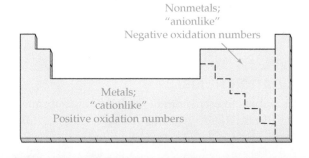

Nonmetals; "anionlike" Negative oxidation numbers

Metals; "cationlike" Positive oxidation numbers

(a) **Hydrogen can be either +1 or −1.** When bonded to a metal, such as Na or Ca, hydrogen has an oxidation number of −1. When bonded to a nonmetal, such as C, N, O, or Cl, hydrogen has an oxidation number of +1.

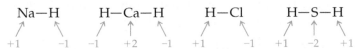

$$\underset{+1}{Na}-\underset{-1}{H} \qquad \underset{-1}{H}-\underset{+2}{Ca}-\underset{-1}{H} \qquad \underset{+1}{H}-\underset{-1}{Cl} \qquad \underset{+1}{H}-\underset{-2}{S}-\underset{+1}{H}$$

(b) **Oxygen usually has an oxidation number of −2.** The major exception is in compounds called *peroxides*, which contain either the O_2^{2-} ion or an O—O covalent bond in a molecule. Both oxygen atoms in a peroxide have an oxidation number of −1.

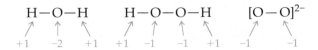

$$\underset{+1}{H}-\underset{-2}{O}-\underset{+1}{H} \qquad \underset{+1}{H}-\underset{-1}{O}-\underset{-1}{O}-\underset{+1}{H} \qquad [\underset{-1}{O}-\underset{-1}{O}]^{2-}$$

(c) **Halogens usually have an oxidation number of −1.** The major exception is in compounds of chlorine, bromine, or iodine in which the halogen atom is bonded to oxygen. In such cases, the oxygen has an oxidation number of −2, and the halogen has a positive oxidation number. In Cl_2O, for instance, the O atom has an oxidation number of −2 and each Cl atom has an oxidation number of +1.

$$\underset{+1}{Cl}-\underset{-2}{O}-\underset{+1}{Cl} \qquad \underset{+1}{H}-\underset{-2}{O}-\underset{+1}{Br}$$

4. **The sum of the oxidation numbers is 0 for a neutral compound and is equal to the net charge for a polyatomic ion.** This rule is particularly useful for finding the oxidation number of an atom in difficult cases. The general idea is to assign oxidation numbers to the "easy" atoms first and then find the oxidation number of the "difficult" atom by subtraction. For example, suppose we need to know the oxidation number of the sulfur atom in sulfuric acid (H_2SO_4). Since each H atom is +1 and each O atom is −2, the S atom must have an oxidation number of +6 for the compound to have no net charge:

$$\underset{+1}{H_2}\underset{?}{S}\underset{-2}{O_4} \qquad 2(+1) + (?) + 4(-2) = 0 \text{ net charge}$$
$$? = 0 - 2(+1) - 4(-2) = +6$$

To find the oxidation number of the chlorine atom in the perchlorate anion (ClO_4^-), we know that each oxygen is −2, so the Cl atom must have an oxidation number of +7 for there to be a net charge of −1 on the ion:

$$\underset{?}{Cl}\underset{-2}{O_4^-} \qquad ? + 4(-2) = -1 \text{ net charge}$$
$$? = -1 - 4(-2) = +7$$

To find the oxidation number of the nitrogen atom in the ammonium cation (NH_4^+), we know that each H atom is +1, so the N atom must have an oxidation number of −3 for the ion to have a net charge of +1:

$$\underset{?}{N}\underset{+1}{H_4^+} \qquad ? + 4(+1) = +1 \text{ net charge}$$
$$? = +1 - 4(+1) = -3$$

WORKED EXAMPLE 4.8

ASSIGNING OXIDATION NUMBERS

Assign oxidation numbers to each atom in the following substances:

(a) CdS   (b) AlH_3 (c) $S_2O_3^{2-}$ (d) $Na_2Cr_2O_7$

STRATEGY

(a) The sulfur atom in S^{2-} has an oxidation number of -2, so Cd must be $+2$.
(b) H bonded to a metal has the oxidation number -1, so Al must be $+3$.
(c) O usually has the oxidation number -2, so S must be $+2$ for the anion to have a net charge of -2: for $(2\,S^{+2})\,(3\,O^{-2})$, $2(+2) + 3(-2) = -2$ net charge.
(d) Na is always $+1$, and oxygen is -2, so Cr must be $+6$ for the compound to be neutral: for $(2\,Na^{+})\,(2\,Cr^{+6})\,(7\,O^{-2})$, $2(+1) + 2(+6) + 7(-2) = 0$ net charge.

SOLUTION

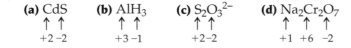

(a) CdS
  ↑ ↑
  +2 −2

(b) AlH_3
  ↑ ↑
  +3 −1

(c) $S_2O_3{}^{2-}$
  ↑ ↑
  +2 −2

(d) $Na_2Cr_2O_7$
  ↑ ↑ ↑
  +1 +6 −2

▶ **PROBLEM 4.13** Assign an oxidation number to each atom in the following compounds:
(a) $SnCl_4$
(b) CrO_3
(c) $VOCl_3$
(d) V_2O_3
(e) HNO_3
(f) $FeSO_4$

4.7 IDENTIFYING REDOX REACTIONS

Once oxidation numbers are assigned, it's clear why all the reactions mentioned in the previous section are redox processes. Take the rusting of iron, for example. Two of the reactants, Fe and O_2, are elements, and both therefore have an oxidation number of 0. In the product, however, the oxygen atoms have an oxidation number of -2 and the iron atoms have an oxidation number of $+3$. Thus, Fe has undergone a change from 0 to $+3$ (a loss of electrons, or oxidation), and O has undergone a change from 0 to -2 (a gain of electrons, or reduction). Note that the total number of electrons given up by the atoms being oxidized (4 Fe $\times$ 3 electrons/Fe = 12 electrons) is the same as the number gained by the atoms being reduced (6 O $\times$ 2 electrons/O = 12 electrons).

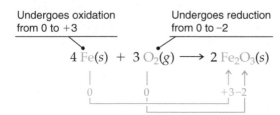

Undergoes oxidation
from 0 to +3

Undergoes reduction
from 0 to −2

$$4\,Fe(s) + 3\,O_2(g) \longrightarrow 2\,Fe_2O_3(s)$$

0   0   +3 −2

A similar analysis can be carried out for the production of iron metal from its ore. The iron atom is reduced because it goes from an oxidation number of $+3$ in the reactant (Fe_2O_3) to 0 in the product (Fe). At the same time, the carbon atom is oxidized because it goes from an oxidation number of 0 in the reactant (C) to $+4$ in the product (CO_2).

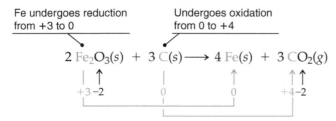

Fe undergoes reduction
from +3 to 0

Undergoes oxidation
from 0 to +4

$$2\,Fe_2O_3(s) + 3\,C(s) \longrightarrow 4\,Fe(s) + 3\,CO_2(g)$$

+3 −2   0   0   +4 −2

The oxygen atoms undergo no change because they have an oxidation number of -2 in both reactant and product. The total number of electrons given up by the atoms being oxidized (3 C $\times$ 4 electrons/C = 12 electrons) is the same as the number gained by the atoms being reduced (4 Fe $\times$ 3 electrons/Fe = 12 electrons).

As these examples show, oxidations and reductions always occur together. Whenever one atom loses one or more electrons, another atom must gain those

▲ The iron used in this prehistoric dagger handle was made by the reduction of iron ore with charcoal.

electrons. The substance that *causes* a reduction by giving up electrons—the iron atom in the reaction of Fe with O_2 and the carbon atom in the reaction of C with Fe_2O_3—is called a **reducing agent**. The substance that causes an oxidation by accepting electrons—the oxygen atom in the reaction of Fe with O_2 and the iron atom in the reaction of C with Fe_2O_3—is called an **oxidizing agent**. The reducing agent is itself oxidized when it gives up electrons, and the oxidizing agent is itself reduced when it accepts electrons.

Reducing agent:
- Causes reduction
- Loses one or more electrons
- Undergoes oxidation
- Oxidation number of atom increases

Oxidizing agent:
- Causes oxidation
- Gains one or more electrons
- Undergoes reduction
- Oxidation number of atom decreases

We'll see in later chapters that redox reactions are common for almost every element in the periodic table except for the noble gas elements of group 8A. In general, metals give up electrons and act as reducing agents, while reactive nonmetals such as O_2 and the halogens accept electrons and act as oxidizing agents.

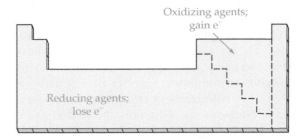

Different metals can give up different numbers of electrons in redox reactions. Lithium, sodium, and the other group 1A elements give up only one electron and become monopositive ions with oxidation numbers of +1. Beryllium, magnesium, and the other group 2A elements, however, typically give up two electrons and become dipositive ions. The transition metals in the middle of the periodic table can give up a variable number of electrons to yield more than one kind of ion depending on the exact reaction. Titanium, for example, can react with chlorine to yield either $TiCl_3$ or $TiCl_4$. Because a chloride ion has a -1 oxidation number, the titanium atom in $TiCl_3$ must have a +3 oxidation number and the titanium atom in $TiCl_4$ must be +4.

WORKED EXAMPLE 4.9

IDENTIFYING OXIDIZING AND REDUCING AGENTS

Assign oxidation numbers to all atoms, tell in each case which substance is undergoing oxidation and which reduction, and identify the oxidizing and reducing agents.

(a) $Ca(s) + 2 H^+(aq) \longrightarrow Ca^{2+}(aq) + H_2(g)$

(b) $2 Fe^{2+}(aq) + Cl_2(aq) \longrightarrow 2 Fe^{3+}(aq) + 2 Cl^-(aq)$

STRATEGY AND SOLUTION

(a) The elements Ca and H_2 have oxidation numbers of 0; Ca^{2+} is +2 and H^+ is +1:

$$\underset{0}{Ca(s)} + \underset{+1}{2 H^+(aq)} \longrightarrow \underset{+2}{Ca^{2+}(aq)} + \underset{0}{H_2(g)}$$

Ca is oxidized because its oxidation number increases from 0 to +2, and H^+ is reduced because its oxidation number decreases from +1 to 0. The reducing agent is the substance that gives away electrons, thereby going to a higher oxidation number, and the oxidizing agent is the substance that accepts electrons, thereby going to a lower oxidation number. In the present case, calcium is the reducing agent and H^+ is the oxidizing agent.

(b) Atoms of the neutral element Cl_2 have an oxidation number of 0; the monatomic ions have oxidation numbers equal to their charge:

$$2\ Fe^{2+}(aq)\ +\ Cl_2(aq) \longrightarrow 2\ Fe^{3+}(aq)\ +\ 2\ Cl^-(aq)$$
$$\quad\uparrow \qquad\qquad \uparrow \qquad\qquad \uparrow \qquad\qquad \uparrow$$
$$\quad +2 \qquad\qquad 0 \qquad\qquad +3 \qquad\qquad -1$$

Fe^{2+} is oxidized because its oxidation number increases from +2 to +3, and Cl_2 is reduced because its oxidation number decreases from 0 to −1. Fe^{2+} is the reducing agent, and Cl_2 is the oxidizing agent.

▶ **PROBLEM 4.14**   Aqueous copper(II) ion reacts with aqueous iodide ion to yield solid copper(I) iodide and aqueous iodine. Write the balanced net ionic equation, assign oxidation numbers to all species present, and identify the oxidizing and reducing agents.

▶ **PROBLEM 4.15**   In each of the following reactions, tell which substance is undergoing an oxidation and which a reduction, and identify the oxidizing and reducing agents.

(a) $SnO_2(s) + 2\,C(s) \longrightarrow Sn(s) + 2\,CO(g)$

(b) $Sn^{2+}(aq) + 2\,Fe^{3+}(aq) \longrightarrow Sn^{4+}(aq) + 2\,Fe^{2+}(aq)$

(c) $4\,NH_3(g) + 5\,O_2(g) \longrightarrow 4\,NO(g) + 6\,H_2O(l)$

4.8   THE ACTIVITY SERIES OF THE ELEMENTS

The reaction of an aqueous cation, usually a metal ion, with a free element to give a different cation and a different element is among the simplest of all redox processes. Aqueous copper(II) ion reacts with iron metal, for example, to give iron(II) ion and copper metal **(Figure 4.2)**:

$$Fe(s) + Cu^{2+}(aq) \longrightarrow Fe^{2+}(aq) + Cu(s)$$

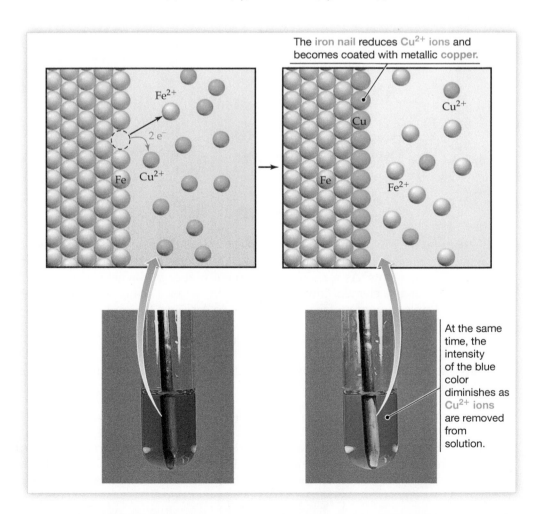

Figure 4.2
The redox reaction of iron with aqueous copper(II) ion.

Similarly, aqueous acid reacts with magnesium metal to yield magnesium ion and hydrogen gas:

$$Mg(s) + 2\,H^+(aq) \longrightarrow Mg^{2+}(aq) + H_2(g)$$

Whether a reaction occurs between a given ion and a given element depends on the relative ease with which the various substances gain or lose electrons—that is, on how easily each substance is reduced or oxidized. By noting the results from a succession of different reactions, it's possible to construct an **activity series**, which ranks the elements in order of their reducing ability in aqueous solution (Table 4.5).

TABLE 4.5   A Partial Activity Series of the Elements

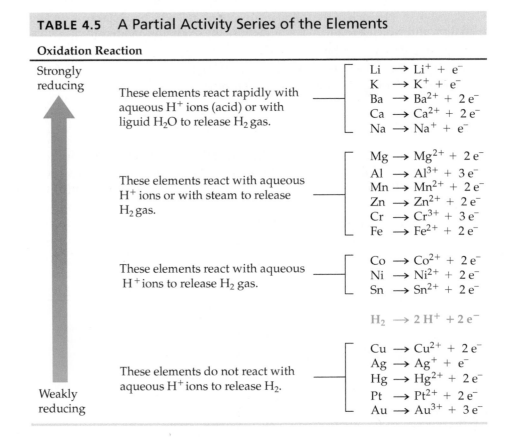

Elements at the top of Table 4.5 give up electrons readily and are stronger reducing agents, whereas elements at the bottom give up electrons less readily and are weaker reducing agents. As a result, any element higher in the activity series will reduce the ion of any element lower in the activity series. Because copper is above silver, for example, copper metal gives electrons to Ag^+ ions (Figure 4.3).

$$Cu(s) + 2\,Ag^+(aq) \longrightarrow Cu^{2+}(aq) + 2\,Ag(s)$$

Conversely, because gold is below silver in the activity series, gold metal does not give electrons to Ag^+ ions.

$$Au(s) + 3\,Ag^+(aq) \longrightarrow\!\!\!\!/ \;\; Au^{3+}(aq) + 3\,Ag(s) \quad \textit{Does not occur}$$

The position of hydrogen in the activity series is particularly important because it indicates which metals react with aqueous acid (H^+) to release H_2 gas. The metals at the top of the series—the alkali metals of group 1A and alkaline earth metals of

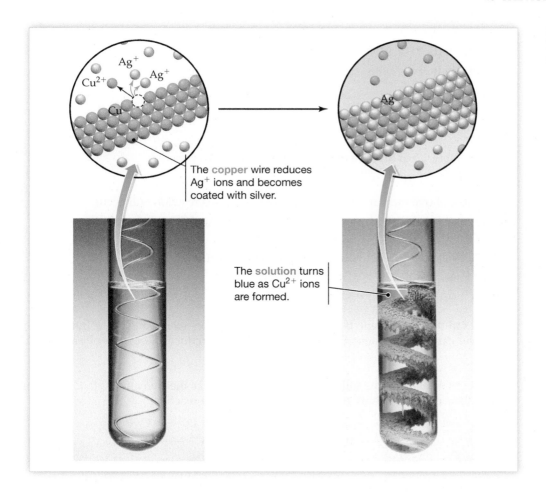

Figure 4.3
The redox reaction of copper with aqueous Ag$^+$ ion.

The **copper** wire reduces Ag$^+$ ions and becomes coated with silver.

The **solution** turns blue as Cu^{2+} ions are formed.

group 2A—are such powerful reducing agents that they react even with pure water, in which the concentration of H$^+$ is very low:

Oxidized   Reduced   Unchanged

$$2\,\text{Na}(s) \;+\; 2\,\text{H}_2\text{O}(l) \longrightarrow 2\,\text{Na}^+(aq) \;+\; 2\,\text{OH}^-(aq) \;+\; \text{H}_2(g)$$

| 0 | +1 −2 | +1 | −2 +1 | 0 |

In contrast, the metals in the middle of the series react with aqueous acid but not with water, and the metals at the bottom of the series react with neither aqueous acid nor water:

$$\text{Fe}(s) + 2\,\text{H}^+(aq) \longrightarrow \text{Fe}^{2+}(aq) + \text{H}_2(g)$$

$$\text{Ag}(s) + \text{H}^+(aq) \longrightarrow \text{No reaction}$$

Notice that the most easily oxidized metals—those at the top of the activity series—are on the left of the periodic table, whereas the least easily oxidized metals—those at the bottom of the activity series—are in the transition metal groups closer to the right side of the table. We'll see the reasons for this behavior in Chapter 6.

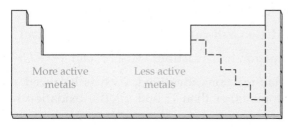

More active metals   Less active metals

WORKED EXAMPLE 4.10

PREDICTING THE PRODUCTS OF REDOX REACTIONS

Predict whether the following redox reactions will occur:

(a) $Hg^{2+}(aq) + Zn(s) \longrightarrow Hg(l) + Zn^{2+}(aq)$

(b) $2 H^+(aq) + Cu(s) \longrightarrow H_2(g) + Cu^{2+}(aq)$

STRATEGY

Look at Table 4.5 to find the relative reactivities of the elements.

SOLUTION

(a) Zinc is above mercury in the activity series, so this reaction will occur.

(b) Copper is below hydrogen in the activity series, so this reaction will not occur.

▶ **PROBLEM 4.16**   Predict whether the following reactions will occur:

(a) $2 H^+(aq) + Pt(s) \longrightarrow H_2(g) + Pt^{2+}(aq)$

(b) $Ca^{2+}(aq) + Mg(s) \longrightarrow Ca(s) + Mg^{2+}(aq)$

▶ **PROBLEM 4.17**   Element B will reduce the cation of element A (A^+) but will not reduce the cation of element C (C^+). Will element C reduce the cation of element A? Explain.

▶ **PROBLEM 4.18**   Use the following reactions to arrange the elements A, B, C, and D in order of their redox reactivity from most reactive to least reactive.

$$A + D^+ \longrightarrow A^+ + D \qquad\qquad C^+ + D \longrightarrow C + D^+$$
$$B^+ + D \longrightarrow B + D^+ \qquad\qquad B + C^+ \longrightarrow B^+ + C$$

4.9   BALANCING REDOX REACTIONS: THE HALF-REACTION METHOD

Simple redox reactions can often be balanced by the trial-and-error method described in Section 3.1, but many reactions are so complex that a more systematic approach is needed. A number of different methods are available, but we'll look only at the **half-reaction method**, which focuses on the transfer of electrons, a subject of particular interest when discussing batteries and other aspects of electrochemistry (Chapter 17).

The key to the half-reaction method is to realize that a redox reaction can be broken into two parts, or **half-reactions**. One half-reaction describes the oxidation part of the process, and the other describes the reduction part. Each half is balanced separately, and the two halves are then added to obtain the final equation. As an example, let's look at the reaction of aqueous potassium dichromate ($K_2Cr_2O_7$) with aqueous NaCl. The reaction occurs in acidic solution according to the unbalanced net ionic equation

$$Cr_2O_7{}^{2-}(aq) + Cl^-(aq) \longrightarrow Cr^{3+}(aq) + Cl_2(aq) \quad \text{Unbalanced}$$

The first step is to decide which atoms have been oxidized and which have been reduced. In the present case, the chloride ion is oxidized from −1 to 0, and the chromium atom is reduced from +6 to +3. Thus, we can write two unbalanced half-reactions that show the separate parts:

Oxidation half-reaction: $Cl^-(aq) \longrightarrow Cl_2(aq)$

Reduction half-reaction: $Cr_2O_7{}^{2-}(aq) \longrightarrow Cr^{3+}(aq)$

With the two half-reactions identified, each is balanced separately. Begin by balancing for all atoms other than H and O. The oxidation half-reaction needs a

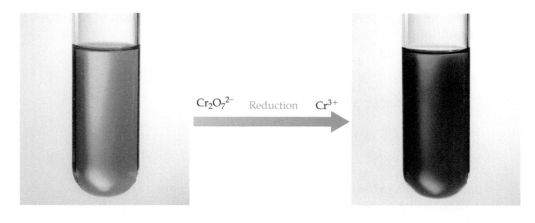

◀ The orange dichromate ion is reduced by addition of Cl⁻ to give the green Cr^{3+} ion.

coefficient of 2 before the Cl⁻, and the reduction half-reaction needs a coefficient of 2 before the Cr^{3+}.

Oxidation $\quad$ 2 Cl⁻(aq) $\longrightarrow$ Cl₂(aq)

Add this coefficient to balance for Cl.

Reduction $\quad$ $Cr_2O_7^{2-}$(aq) $\longrightarrow$ 2 Cr^{3+}(aq)

Add this coefficient to balance for Cr.

Next, balance both half-reactions for oxygen by adding H_2O to the side with less O, and then balance for hydrogen by adding H^+ to the side with less H. The oxidation half-reaction has no O or H, but the reduction half-reaction needs 7 H_2O on the product side to balance for O, and then 14 H^+ on the reactant side to balance for H:

Oxidation $\quad$ 2 Cl⁻(aq) $\longrightarrow$ Cl₂(aq)

Then, add 14 H^+ to balance for H.

First, add 7 H_2O to balance for O.

Reduction $\quad$ $Cr_2O_7^{2-}$(aq) + 14 H^+(aq) $\longrightarrow$ 2 Cr^{3+}(aq) + 7 H_2O(l)

Now, balance both half-reactions for charge by adding electrons (e⁻) to the side with the greater positive charge. The oxidation half-reaction has 2 minus charges on the reactant side (2 Cl⁻) and must therefore have 2 e⁻ added to the product side. The reduction half-reaction has a net of 12 positive charges on the reactant side and 6 positive charges on the product side and so must have 6 e⁻ added to the reactant side:

Add these electrons to balance for charge.

Oxidation $\quad$ 2 Cl⁻(aq) $\longrightarrow$ Cl₂(aq) + 2 e⁻

Add these electrons to balance for charge.

Reduction $\quad$ $Cr_2O_7^{2-}$(aq) + 14 H^+(aq) + 6 e⁻ $\longrightarrow$ 2 Cr^{3+}(aq) + 7 H_2O(l)

With both half-reactions now balanced, we need to multiply the equations by suitable coefficients so that the number of electrons is the same in both. That is, the number of electrons released in the oxidation half-reaction must be the same as the number consumed in the reduction half-reaction. Because the reduction half-reaction has 6 e⁻ but the oxidation half-reaction has only 2 e⁻, the oxidation half-reaction must be multiplied by 3:

Multiply by this coefficient to equalize the numbers of electrons in the two half-reactions.

Oxidation $3 \times [2\,Cl^-(aq) \longrightarrow Cl_2(aq) + 2\,e^-]$

or $6\,Cl^-(aq) \longrightarrow 3\,Cl_2(aq) + 6\,e^-$

Reduction $Cr_2O_7^{2-}(aq) + 14\,H^+(aq) + 6\,e^- \longrightarrow 2\,Cr^{3+}(aq) + 7\,H_2O(l)$

Adding the two half-reactions together and canceling the species that occur on both sides (only the electrons in this example) then gives the final balanced equation. Check the answer to make sure it is balanced both for atoms and for charge.

$$6\,Cl^-(aq) \longrightarrow 3\,Cl_2(aq) + \cancel{6\,e^-}$$

$$\underline{Cr_2O_7^{2-}(aq) + 14\,H^+(aq) + \cancel{6\,e^-} \longrightarrow 2\,Cr^{3+}(aq) + 7\,H_2O(l)}$$

$$Cr_2O_7^{2-}(aq) + 14\,H^+(aq) + 6\,Cl^-(aq) \longrightarrow 3\,Cl_2(aq) + 2\,Cr^{3+}(aq) + 7\,H_2O(l)$$

Charge: $(-2) + (+14) + (6 \times -1) = +6$ Charge: $(2 \times +3) = +6$

To summarize, balancing a redox reaction in acidic solution by the half-reaction method is a six-step process, followed by a check of the answer (**Figure 4.4.**)

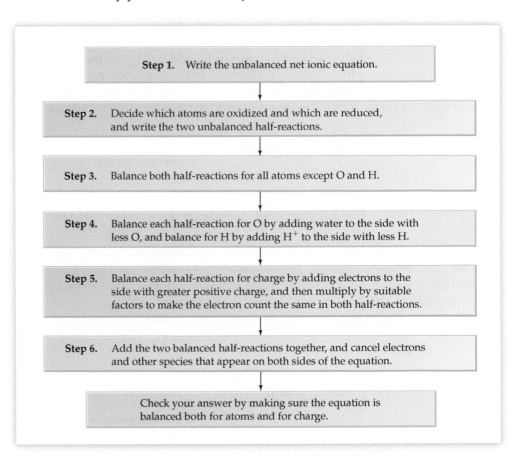

Step 1.   Write the unbalanced net ionic equation.

Step 2.   Decide which atoms are oxidized and which are reduced, and write the two unbalanced half-reactions.

Step 3.   Balance both half-reactions for all atoms except O and H.

Step 4.   Balance each half-reaction for O by adding water to the side with less O, and balance for H by adding H⁺ to the side with less H.

Step 5.   Balance each half-reaction for charge by adding electrons to the side with greater positive charge, and then multiply by suitable factors to make the electron count the same in both half-reactions.

Step 6.   Add the two balanced half-reactions together, and cancel electrons and other species that appear on both sides of the equation.

Check your answer by making sure the equation is balanced both for atoms and for charge.

Figure 4.4
Using the half-reaction method to balance redox equations for reactions in acidic solution.

Worked Example 4.12 shows how to use the method for balancing an equation for a reaction that takes place in basic solution. The procedure is the same as that used for balancing a reaction in acidic solution, but OH⁻ ions are added as a final step to neutralize any H⁺ ions that appear in the equation. This simply reflects the fact that basic solutions contain negligibly small amounts of H⁺ but relatively large amounts of OH⁻.

WORKED EXAMPLE 4.11

WRITING HALF-REACTIONS

Write unbalanced half-reactions for the following net ionic equations:

(a) $Mn^{2+}(aq) + ClO_3^-(aq) \longrightarrow MnO_2(s) + ClO_2(aq)$

(b) $Cr_2O_7^{2-}(aq) + Fe^{2+}(aq) \longrightarrow Cr^{3+}(aq) + Fe^{3+}(aq)$

STRATEGY

Look at each equation to see which atoms are being oxidized (increasing in oxidation number) and which are being reduced (decreasing in oxidation number).

SOLUTION

(a) Oxidation: $Mn^{2+}(aq) \longrightarrow MnO_2(s)$ Mn goes from +2 to +4

    Reduction: $ClO_3^-(aq) \longrightarrow ClO_2(aq)$ Cl goes from +5 to +4

(b) Oxidation: $Fe^{2+}(aq) \longrightarrow Fe^{3+}(aq)$ Fe goes from +2 to +3

    Reduction: $Cr_2O_7^{2-}(aq) \longrightarrow Cr^{3+}(aq)$ Cr goes from +6 to +3

WORKED EXAMPLE 4.12

BALANCING AN EQUATION FOR A REACTION IN BASE

Aqueous sodium hypochlorite (NaOCl; household bleach) is a strong oxidizing agent that reacts with chromite ion [$Cr(OH)_4^-$] in basic solution to yield chromate ion (CrO_4^{2-}) and chloride ion. The net ionic equation is

$$ClO^-(aq) + Cr(OH)_4^-(aq) \longrightarrow CrO_4^{2-}(aq) + Cl^-(aq) \qquad \text{Unbalanced}$$

Balance the equation using the half-reaction method.

STRATEGY

Follow the steps outlined in Figure 4.4.

SOLUTION

Steps 1 and 2. The unbalanced net ionic equation shows that chromium is oxidized (from +3 to +6) and chlorine is reduced (from +1 to −1). Thus, we can write the following half-reactions:

    Oxidation half-reaction: $Cr(OH)_4^-(aq) \longrightarrow CrO_4^{2-}(aq)$

    Reduction half-reaction: $ClO^-(aq) \longrightarrow Cl^-(aq)$

Step 3. The half-reactions are already balanced for atoms other than O and H.

Step 4. Balance both half-reactions for O by adding H_2O to the sides with less O, and then balance both for H by adding H^+ to the sides with less H:

    Oxidation: $Cr(OH)_4^-(aq) \longrightarrow CrO_4^{2-}(aq) + 4\,H^+(aq)$

    Reduction: $ClO^-(aq) + 2\,H^+(aq) \longrightarrow Cl^-(aq) + H_2O(l)$

Step 5. Balance both half-reactions for charge by adding electrons to the sides with the greater positive charge:

    Oxidation: $Cr(OH)_4^-(aq) \longrightarrow CrO_4^{2-}(aq) + 4\,H^+(aq) + 3\,e^-$

    Reduction: $ClO^-(aq) + 2\,H^+(aq) + 2\,e^- \longrightarrow Cl^-(aq) + H_2O(l)$

Next, multiply the half-reactions by factors that make the electron count in each the same. The oxidation half-reaction must be multiplied by 2, and the reduction half-reaction must be multiplied by 3 to give 6 e^- in both:

    Oxidation: $2 \times [Cr(OH)_4^-(aq) \longrightarrow CrO_4^{2-}(aq) + 4\,H^+(aq) + 3\,e^-]$

        or $2\,Cr(OH)_4^-(aq) \longrightarrow 2\,CrO_4^{2-}(aq) + 8\,H^+(aq) + 6\,e^-$

    Reduction: $3 \times [ClO^-(aq) + 2\,H^+(aq) + 2\,e^- \longrightarrow Cl^-(aq) + H_2O(l)]$

        or $3\,ClO^-(aq) + 6\,H^+(aq) + 6\,e^- \longrightarrow 3\,Cl^-(aq) + 3\,H_2O(l)$

continued on next page

Step 6. Add the balanced half-reactions:

$$2\,Cr(OH)_4{}^-(aq) \longrightarrow 2\,CrO_4{}^{2-}(aq) + 8\,H^+(aq) + 6\,e^-$$

$$3\,ClO^-(aq) + 6\,H^+(aq) + 6\,e^- \longrightarrow 3\,Cl^-(aq) + 3\,H_2O(l)$$

$$2\,Cr(OH)_4{}^-(aq) + 3\,ClO^-(aq) + 6\,H^+(aq) + 6\,e^- \longrightarrow$$
$$2\,CrO_4{}^{2-}(aq) + 3\,Cl^-(aq) + 3\,H_2O(l) + 8\,H^+(aq) + 6\,e^-$$

Now, cancel the species that appear on both sides of the equation:

$$2\,Cr(OH)_4{}^-(aq) + 3\,C1O^-(aq) \longrightarrow 2\,CrO_4{}^{2-}(aq) + 3\,C1^-(aq) + 3\,H_2O(l) + 2\,H^+(aq)$$

Finally, since we know that the reaction takes place in basic solution, we must add $2\,OH^-$ ions to both sides of the equation to neutralize the $2\,H^+$ ions on the right, giving 2 additional H_2O. The final net ionic equation, balanced for both atoms and charge, is

$$2\,Cr(OH)_4{}^-(aq) + 3\,ClO^-(aq) + 2\,OH^-(aq) \longrightarrow 2\,CrO_4{}^{2-}(aq) + 3\,Cl^-(aq) + 5\,H_2O(l)$$

Charge: $(2 \times -1) + (3 \times -1) + (2 \times -1) = -7$ Charge: $(2 \times -2) + (3 \times -1) = -7$

▶ **PROBLEM 4.19**   Write unbalanced half-reactions for the following net ionic equations:

(a) $MnO_4{}^-(aq) + IO_3{}^-(aq) \longrightarrow MnO_2(s) + IO_4{}^-(aq)$

(b) $NO_3{}^-(aq) + SO_2(aq) \longrightarrow SO_4{}^{2-}(aq) + NO_2(g)$

▶ **PROBLEM 4.20**   Balance the following net ionic equation by the half-reaction method. The reaction takes place in acidic solution.

$$NO_3{}^-(aq) + Cu(s) \longrightarrow NO(g) + Cu^{2+}(aq) \quad \text{Unbalanced}$$

▶ **PROBLEM 4.21**   Balance the following equation by the half-reaction method. The reaction takes place in basic solution.

$$Fe(OH)_2(s) + O_2(g) \longrightarrow Fe(OH)_3(s) \quad \text{Unbalanced}$$

4.10 REDOX STOICHIOMETRY

Remember...

The reaction used for a **titration** must go to completion and have a yield of 100%. (Section 3.9)

We saw in Section 3.9 that the concentration of an acid or base solution can be determined by **titration**. A measured volume of the acid or base solution of unknown concentration is placed in a flask, and a base or acid solution of known concentration is slowly added from a buret. By measuring the volume of the added solution necessary for a complete reaction, as signaled by the color change of an indicator, the unknown concentration can be calculated.

A similar procedure can be carried out to determine the concentration of many oxidizing or reducing agents using a *redox titration*. All that's necessary is that the substance whose concentration you want to determine undergo an oxidation or reduction reaction in 100% yield and that there be some means, such as a color change, to indicate when the reaction is complete. The color change might be due to one of the substances undergoing reaction or to some added indicator.

Let's imagine that we have a potassium permanganate solution whose concentration we want to find. Aqueous $KMnO_4$ reacts with oxalic acid, $H_2C_2O_4$, in acidic solution according to the net ionic equation

$$5\,H_2C_2O_4(aq) + 2\,MnO_4{}^-(aq) + 6\,H^+(aq) \longrightarrow 10\,CO_2(g) + 2\,Mn^{2+}(aq) + 8\,H_2O(l)$$

The reaction takes place in 100% yield and is accompanied by a sharp color change when the intense purple color of the $MnO_4{}^-$ ion disappears.

The strategy used is outlined in **Figure 4.5**. As with acid–base titrations, the general idea is to measure a known amount of one substance—in this case, $H_2C_2O_4$—and use mole ratios from the balanced equation to find the number of moles of the second substance—in this case, $KMnO_4$—necessary for complete reaction. With the molar

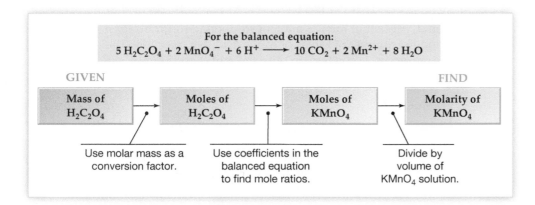

For the balanced equation:
$$5 H_2C_2O_4 + 2 MnO_4^- + 6 H^+ \longrightarrow 10 CO_2 + 2 Mn^{2+} + 8 H_2O$$

GIVEN   FIND

| Mass of $H_2C_2O_4$ | → | Moles of $H_2C_2O_4$ | → | Moles of $KMnO_4$ | → | Molarity of $KMnO_4$ |

Use molar mass as a conversion factor.

Use coefficients in the balanced equation to find mole ratios.

Divide by volume of $KMnO_4$ solution.

Figure 4.5
A summary of calculations for determining the concentration of a $KMnO_4$ solution by redox titration of $H_2C_2O_4$.

amount of $KMnO_4$ thus known, titration gives the volume of solution containing that amount. Dividing the number of moles by the volume gives the concentration.

As an example of how the procedure works, let's carefully weigh some amount of $H_2C_2O_4$—say, 0.2585 g—and dissolve it in approximately 100 mL of 0.5 M H_2SO_4. The exact volume isn't important because we're concerned only with the amount of dissolved $H_2C_2O_4$, not with its concentration. Next, we place an aqueous $KMnO_4$ solution of unknown concentration in a buret and slowly add it to the $H_2C_2O_4$ solution. The purple color of MnO_4^- initially disappears as reaction occurs, but we continue the addition until a faint color persists, indicating that all the $H_2C_2O_4$ has reacted and that MnO_4^- ion is no longer being reduced. At this equivalence point, or *end point*, of the titration, we might find that 22.35 mL of the $KMnO_4$ solution has been added (Figure 4.6).

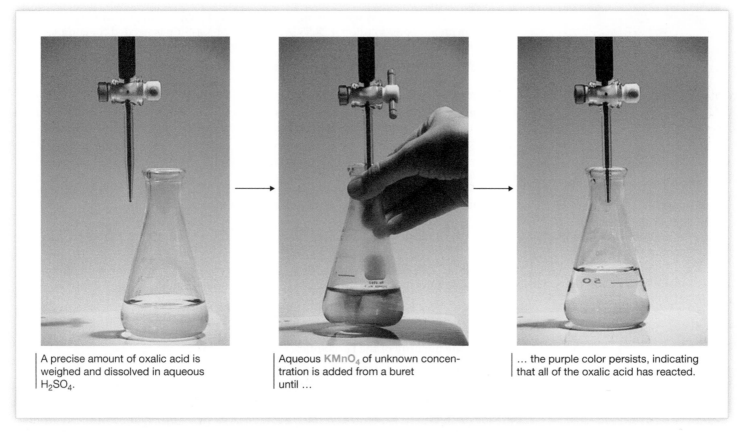

A precise amount of oxalic acid is weighed and dissolved in aqueous H_2SO_4.

Aqueous $KMnO_4$ of unknown concentration is added from a buret until …

… the purple color persists, indicating that all of the oxalic acid has reacted.

Figure 4.6
The redox titration of oxalic acid, $H_2C_2O_4$, with $KMnO_4$.

To calculate the molarity of the $KMnO_4$ solution, we need to find the number of moles of $KMnO_4$ present in the 22.35 mL of solution used for titration. We do this by first calculating the number of moles of oxalic acid that react with the permanganate ion, using a gram-to-mole conversion with the molar mass of $H_2C_2O_4$ as the conversion factor:

$$\text{Moles of } H_2C_2O_4 = 0.2585 \text{ g } H_2C_2O_4 \times \frac{1 \text{ mol } H_2C_2O_4}{90.04 \text{ g } H_2C_2O_4}$$

$$= 2.871 \times 10^{-3} \text{ mol } H_2C_2O_4$$

According to the balanced equation, 5 mol of oxalic acid react with 2 mol of permanganate ion. Thus, we can calculate the number of moles of $KMnO_4$ that react with 2.871×10^{-3} mol of $H_2C_2O_4$:

$$\text{Moles of } KMnO_4 = 2.871 \times 10^{-3} \text{ mol } H_2C_2O_4 \times \frac{2 \text{ mol } KMnO_4}{5 \text{ mol } H_2C_2O_4}$$

$$= 1.148 \times 10^{-3} \text{ mol } KMnO_4$$

Knowing both the number of moles of $KMnO_4$ that react (1.148×10^{-3} mol) and the volume of the $KMnO_4$ solution (22.35 mL), we can calculate the molarity:

$$\text{Molarity} = \frac{1.148 \times 10^{-3} \text{ mol } KMnO_4}{22.35 \text{ mL}} \times \frac{1000 \text{ mL}}{1 \text{ L}} = 0.051\ 36 \text{ M}$$

The molarity of the $KMnO_4$ solution is 0.051 36 M.

WORKED EXAMPLE 4.13

USING A REDOX REACTION TO DETERMINE A SOLUTION'S CONCENTRATION

The concentration of an aqueous I_3^- solution can be determined by titration with aqueous sodium thiosulfate, $Na_2S_2O_3$, in the presence of a starch indicator, which turns from deep blue to colorless when all the I_3^- has reacted. What is the molar concentration of I_3^- in an aqueous solution if 24.55 mL of 0.102 M $Na_2S_2O_3$ is needed for complete reaction with 10.00 mL of the I_3^- solution? The net ionic equation is

$$2\,S_2O_3^{2-}(aq) + I_3^-(aq) \longrightarrow S_4O_6^{2-}(aq) + 3\,I^-(aq)$$

STRATEGY AND SOLUTION

The procedure is similar to that outlined in Figure 4.5. We first need to find the number of moles of thiosulfate ion used for the titration:

$$24.55 \text{ mL} \times \frac{1 \text{ L}}{1000 \text{ mL}} \times \frac{0.102 \text{ mol } S_2O_3^{2-}}{1 \text{ L}} = 2.50 \times 10^{-3} \text{ mol } S_2O_3^{2-}$$

According to the balanced equation, 2 mol of $S_2O_3^{2-}$ ion react with 1 mol of I_3^- ion. Thus, we can find the number of moles of I_3^- ion:

$$2.50 \times 10^{-3} \text{ mol } S_2O_3^{2-} \times \frac{1 \text{ mol } I_3^-}{2 \text{ mol } S_2O_3^{2-}} = 1.25 \times 10^{-3} \text{ mol } I_3^-$$

Knowing both the number of moles of I_3^- (1.25×10^{-3} mol) and the volume of the I_3^- solution (10.00 mL) then lets us calculate molarity:

$$\frac{1.25 \times 10^{-3} \text{ mol } I_3^-}{10.00 \text{ mL}} \times \frac{10^3 \text{ mL}}{1 \text{ L}} = 0.125 \text{ M}$$

The molarity of the I_3^- solution is 0.125 M.

BALLPARK CHECK

According to the balanced equation, the amount of $S_2O_3^{2-}$ needed for the reaction (2 mol) is twice the amount of I_3^- (1 mol). The titration results indicate that the volume of the $S_2O_3^{2-}$ solution (24.55 mL) is a little over twice the volume of the I_3^- solution (10.00 mL). Thus, the concentrations of the two solutions must be about the same—approximately 0.1 M.

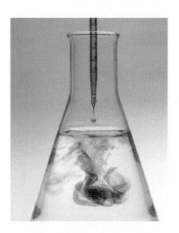

▲ The reddish I_3^- solution turns a deep blue color when it is added to a solution containing a small amount of starch.

INQUIRY HOW CAN CHEMISTRY BE GREEN?

Chemistry has made our lives longer, safer, and far more comfortable than they would otherwise be. The medicines, fertilizers, insecticides, adhesives, textiles, dyes, building materials, and polymers that we take for granted are all products of the chemical industry. But these benefits have not come without a price. Many chemical processes produce hazardous wastes that must be dealt with—reaction solvents and byproducts that might evaporate into the air or leach into groundwater if not disposed of properly.

It's unlikely that all chemical processes will ever be completely benign, but awareness of the environmental problems caused by chemistry has grown dramatically in recent years, giving rise to a movement called *green chemistry*. Green chemistry is the design and implementation of chemical processes that reduce waste and minimize or eliminate the generation of hazardous substances. Twelve principles form the foundation of green chemistry:

▲ Green chemistry can help prevent this kind of problem in the future.

Prevent waste—Waste should be prevented rather than cleaned up after it has been created.

Maximize atom economy—Processes should maximize the incorporation of all reactant atoms into the final product to minimize leftover waste.

Use less-hazardous processes—Methods of chemical synthesis should use non-toxic reactants and generate nontoxic wastes.

Design safer chemicals—Chemical products should be designed from the beginning to have minimal toxicity.

Use safer solvents—Solvents and other auxiliary substances used in reactions should be safe and used sparingly.

Design for energy efficiency—Energy usage in chemical processes should be minimized, with reactions carried out at room temperature if possible.

Use renewable feedstocks—Raw materials should come from renewable sources when feasible.

Minimize derivatives—Syntheses should be designed with minimal use of protecting groups to avoid extra steps and reduce waste.

Use catalysis—Reactions should be catalytic rather than stoichiometric.

Design for degradation—Products should be designed to be biodegradable at the end of their useful lifetimes.

Monitor pollution in real time—Processes should be monitored in real time for the formation of hazardous substances.

Prevent accidents—Chemical substances and processes should minimize the potential for fires, explosions, or other accidents.

The 12 principles of green chemistry won't all be met in most applications, but they provide goals to aim for and they can make chemists think more carefully about the environmental implications of their work. Among the successes already recorded is a new process for converting glycerin, a by-product of producing biodiesel fuel from vegetable oil, into propylene glycol, which is used in automobile antifreeze. The process occurs in a single step and gives only water as the by-product.

$$\text{Glycerin} \xrightarrow[\substack{\text{Copper} \\ \text{chromite} \\ \text{catalyst}}]{H_2} \text{Propylene glycol} + H_2O$$

▶ **PROBLEM 4.24** Many dozens of different solvents are used in various chemical processes. If you were designing a green process that required a solvent, what properties would you look for, and what solvent might you choose?

SUMMARY

Many reactions, particularly those that involve ionic compounds, take place in aqueous solution. Substances whose aqueous solutions contain ions conduct electricity and are called **electrolytes**. Ionic compounds, such as NaCl, and molecular compounds that **dissociate** substantially into ions when dissolved in water are **strong electrolytes**. Substances that dissociate to only a small extent are **weak electrolytes**, and substances that do not produce ions in aqueous solution are **nonelectrolytes**.

Acids are compounds that dissociate in aqueous solutions to yield an anion and a **hydronium ion, H_3O^+**. Acids that dissociate to a large extent are **strong acids**; acids that dissociate to a small extent are **weak acids**. Similarly, **bases** are compounds that dissociate in aqueous solution to yield a cation and hydroxide ion, OH^-.

There are three important classes of aqueous reactions. **Precipitation reactions** occur when solutions of two ionic substances are mixed and a precipitate falls from solution. To predict whether a precipitate will form, you must know the **solubility** of each potential product. **Acid–base neutralization reactions** occur when an acid is mixed with a base, yielding water and an ionic **salt**. The neutralization of a strong acid with a strong base can be written as a **net ionic equation**, in which nonparticipating, **spectator ions** are not specified:

$$H^+(aq) + OH^-(aq) \longrightarrow H_2O(l)$$

Oxidation–reduction reactions, or **redox reactions**, are processes in which one or more electrons are transferred between reaction partners. An **oxidation** is the loss of one or more electrons; a **reduction** is the gain of one or more electrons. Redox reactions can be identified by assigning to each atom in a substance an **oxidation number**, which provides a measure of whether the atom is neutral, electron rich, or electron poor. Comparing the oxidation numbers of an atom before and after reaction shows whether the atom has gained or lost electrons.

Oxidations and reductions must occur together. Whenever one substance loses one or more electrons (is oxidized), another substance gains the electrons (is reduced). The substance that causes a reduction by giving up electrons is called a **reducing agent**. The substance that causes an oxidation by accepting electrons is called an **oxidizing agent**. The reducing agent is itself oxidized when it gives up electrons, and the oxidizing agent is itself reduced when it accepts electrons.

Among the simplest of redox processes is the reaction of an aqueous cation, usually a metal ion, with a free element to give a different ion and a different element. Noting the results from a succession of different reactions makes it possible to organize an **activity series**, which ranks the elements in order of their reducing ability in aqueous solution.

Redox reactions can be balanced using the **half-reaction method**, which divides a reaction into oxidation and reduction parts and focuses on equalizing the transfer of electrons between the parts. The concentration of an oxidizing agent or a reducing agent in solution can be determined by a redox titration.

KEY WORDS

CONCEPTUAL PROBLEMS

Problems 4.1–4.24 appear within the chapter.

4.25 Assume that an aqueous solution of a cation, represented as a red sphere, is allowed to mix with a solution of an anion, represented as a yellow sphere. Three possible outcomes are represented by boxes (1)–(3):

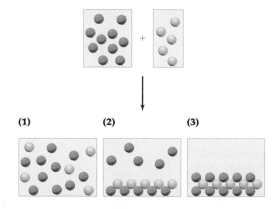

Which outcome corresponds to each of the following reactions?

(a) $2\,Na^+(aq) + CO_3^{2-}(aq) \longrightarrow$

(b) $Ba^{2+}(aq) + CrO_4^{2-}(aq) \longrightarrow$

(c) $2\,Ag^+(aq) + SO_3^{2-}(aq) \longrightarrow$

4.26 Assume that an aqueous solution of a cation, represented as a blue sphere, is allowed to mix with a solution of an anion, represented as a red sphere, and that the following result is obtained:

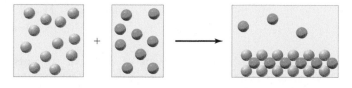

Which combinations of cation and anion, chosen from the following lists, are compatible with the observed results? Explain.

Cations: Na^+, Ca^{2+}, Ag^+, Ni^{2+}

Anions: Cl^-, CO_3^{2-}, CrO_4^{2-}, NO_3^-

4.27 Assume that an aqueous solution of OH^-, represented as a blue sphere, is allowed to mix with a solution of an acid H_nA, represented as a red sphere. Three possible outcomes are depicted by boxes (1)–(3), where the green spheres represent A^{n-}, the anion of the acid:

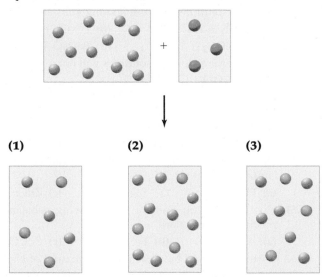

Which outcome corresponds to each of the following reactions?

(a) $HF + OH^- \longrightarrow H_2O + F^-$

(b) $H_2SO_3 + 2\,OH^- \longrightarrow 2\,H_2O + SO_3^{2-}$

(c) $H_3PO_4 + 3\,OH^- \longrightarrow 3\,H_2O + PO_4^{3-}$

4.28 The concentration of an aqueous solution of NaOCl (sodium hypochlorite; the active ingredient in household bleach) can be determined by a redox titration with iodide ion in acidic solution:

$OCl^-(aq) + 2\,I^-(aq) + 2\,H^+(aq) \longrightarrow$
$$Cl^-(aq) + I_2(aq) + H_2O(l)$$

Assume that the blue spheres in the buret represent I^- ions, the red spheres in the flask represent OCl^- ions, the concentration of the I^- ions in the buret is 0.120 M, and the volumes in the buret and the flask are identical. What is the concentration of NaOCl in the flask? What percentage of the I^- solution in the buret must be added to the flask to react with all the OCl^- ions?

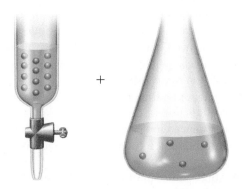

4.29 Assume that the electrical conductivity of a solution depends on the total concentration of dissolved ions and that you measure the conductivity of three different solutions while carrying out titration procedures:

(a) Begin with 1.00 L of 0.100 M KCl, and titrate by adding 0.100 M AgNO₃.

(b) Begin with 1.00 L of 0.100 M HF, and titrate by adding 0.100 M KOH.

(c) Begin with 1.00 L of 0.100 M BaCl₂, and titrate by adding 0.100 M Na₂SO₄.

Which of the following graphs corresponds to which titration?

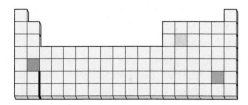

4.30 Based on the positions in the periodic table, which of the following reactions would you expect to occur?

(a) $Red^+ + Green \longrightarrow Red + Green^+$

(b) $Blue + Green^+ \longrightarrow Blue^+ + Green$

(c) $Red + Blue^+ \longrightarrow Red^+ + Blue$

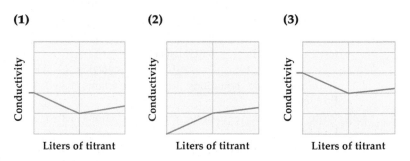

4.31 The following two redox reactions occur between aqueous cations and solid metals. Will a solution of green cations react with solid blue metal? Explain.

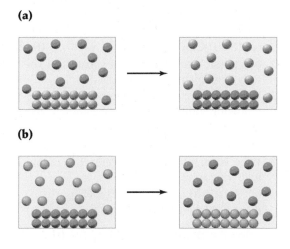

SECTION PROBLEMS

Aqueous Reactions, Net Ionic Equations, and Electrolytes (Sections 4.2 and 4.3)

4.32 Classify each of the following reactions as a precipitation, acid–base neutralization, or oxidation–reduction:

(a) $Hg(NO_3)_2(aq) + 2\,NaI(aq) \longrightarrow 2\,NaNO_3(aq) + HgI_2(s)$

(b) $2\,HgO(s) \xrightarrow{\text{heat}} 2\,Hg(l) + O_2(g)$

(c) $H_3PO_4(aq) + 3\,KOH(aq) \longrightarrow K_3PO_4(aq) + 3\,H_2O(l)$

4.33 Classify each of the following reactions as a precipitation, acid–base neutralization, or oxidation–reduction:

(a) $S_8(s) + 8\,O_2(g) \longrightarrow 8\,SO_2(g)$

(b) $NiCl_2(aq) + Na_2S(aq) \longrightarrow NiS(s) + 2\,NaCl(aq)$

(c) $2\,CH_3CO_2H(aq) + Ba(OH)_2(aq) \longrightarrow$
$\qquad\qquad (CH_3CO_2)_2Ba(aq) + 2\,H_2O(l)$

4.34 Write net ionic equations for the reactions listed in Problem 4.32.

4.35 Write net ionic equations for the reactions listed in Problem 4.33.

4.36 The following aqueous solutions were tested with a light-bulb conductivity apparatus, as shown in Figure 4.1. What result—dark, dim, or bright—do you expect from each?

(a) 0.10 M potassium chloride   (b) 0.10 M methanol

(c) 0.10 M acetic acid

4.37 The following aqueous solutions were tested with a light-bulb conductivity apparatus, as shown in Figure 4.1. What result—dark, dim, or bright—do you expect from each?

(a) 0.10 M hydrofluoric acid

(b) 0.10 M sodium chloride

(c) 0.10 M glucose ($C_6H_{12}O_6$)

4.38 Individual solutions of $Ba(OH)_2$ and H_2SO_4 both conduct electricity, but the conductivity disappears when equal molar amounts of the solutions are mixed. Explain.

4.39 A solution of HCl in water conducts electricity, but a solution of HCl in chloroform, $CHCl_3$, does not. What does this observation tell you about how HCl exists in water and how it exists in chloroform?

4.40 Classify each of the following substances as either a strong electrolyte, weak electrolyte, or nonelectrolyte:

(a) HBr   (b) HF   (c) $NaClO_4$

(d) $(NH_4)_2CO_3$ (e) NH_3 (f) Ethyl alcohol

4.41 Is it possible for a molecular substance to be a strong electrolyte? Explain.

4.42 What is the total molar concentration of ions in each of the following solutions, assuming complete dissociation?

(a) A 0.750 M solution of K_2CO_3

(b) A 0.355 M solution of $AlCl_3$

4.43 What is the total molar concentration of ions in each of the following solutions?

(a) A 1.250 M solution of CH_3OH

(b) A 0.225 M solution of $HClO_4$

Precipitation Reactions and Solubility Guidelines (Section 4.4)

4.44 Which of the following substances are likely to be soluble in water?

(a) Ag_2O (b) $Ba(NO_3)_2$ (c) $SnCO_3$ (d) Fe_2O_3

4.45 Which of the following substances are likely to be soluble in water?

(a) ZnS   (b) $Au_2(CO_3)_3$ (c) $PbCl_2$ (d) MnO_2

4.46 Predict whether a precipitation reaction will occur when aqueous solutions of the following substances are mixed:

(a) $NaOH + HClO_4$ (b) $FeCl_2 + KOH$

(c) $(NH_4)_2SO_4 + NiCl_2$ (d) $CH_3CO_2Na + HCl$

4.47 Predict whether a precipitation reaction will occur when aqueous solutions of the following substances are mixed:

(a) $MnCl_2 + Na_2S$ (b) $HNO_3 + CuSO_4$

(c) $Hg(NO_3)_2 + Na_3PO_4$ (d) $Ba(NO_3)_2 + KOH$

4.48 Which of the following solutions will not form a precipitate when added to 0.10 M $BaCl_2$?

(a) 0.10 M $LiNO_3$ (b) 0.10 M K_2SO_4 (c) 0.10 M $AgNO_3$

4.49 Which of the following solutions will not form a precipitate when added to 0.10 M NaOH?

(a) 0.10 M $MgBr_2$ (b) 0.10 M NH_4Br (c) 0.10 M $FeCl_2$

4.50 How would you prepare the following substances by a precipitation reaction?

(a) $PbSO_4$ (b) $Mg_3(PO_4)_2$ (c) $ZnCrO_4$

4.51 How would you prepare the following substances by a precipitation reaction?

(a) $Al(OH)_3$ (b) FeS   (c) $CoCO_3$

4.52 Assume that you have an aqueous mixture of $NaNO_3$ and $AgNO_3$. How could you use a precipitation reaction to separate the two metal ions?

4.53 Assume that you have an aqueous mixture of $BaCl_2$ and $CuCl_2$. How could you use a precipitation reaction to separate the two metal ions?

4.54 Assume that you have an aqueous solution of an unknown salt. Treatment of the solution with dilute NaOH, Na_2SO_4, and KCl produces no precipitate. Which of the following cations might the solution contain?

(a) Ag^+ (b) Cs^+ (c) Ba^{2+} (d) NH_4^+

4.55 Assume that you have an aqueous solution of an unknown salt. Treatment of the solution with dilute $BaCl_2$, $AgNO_3$, and $Cu(NO_3)_2$ produces no precipitate. Which of the following anions might the solution contain?

(a) Cl^- (b) NO_3^- (c) OH^- (d) SO_4^{2-}

Acids, Bases, and Neutralization Reactions (Section 4.5)

4.56 Assume that you are given a solution of an unknown acid or base. How can you tell whether the unknown substance is acidic or basic?

4.57 Why do we use a double arrow ($\rightleftharpoons$) to show the dissociation of a weak acid or weak base in aqueous solution?

4.58 Write balanced ionic equations for the following reactions:

(a) Aqueous perchloric acid is neutralized by aqueous calcium hydroxide.

(b) Aqueous sodium hydroxide is neutralized by aqueous acetic acid.

4.59 Write balanced ionic equations for the following reactions:

(a) Aqueous hydrobromic acid is neutralized by aqueous calcium hydroxide.

(b) Aqueous barium hydroxide is neutralized by aqueous nitric acid.

4.60 Write balanced net ionic equations for the following reactions:

(a) $LiOH(aq) + HI(aq) \longrightarrow$?

(b) $HBr(aq) + Ca(OH)_2(aq) \longrightarrow$?

4.61 Write balanced net ionic equations for the following reactions. Note that $HClO_3$ is a strong acid.

(a) $Fe(OH)_3(s) + H_2SO_4(aq) \longrightarrow$?

(b) $HClO_3(aq) + NaOH(aq) \longrightarrow$?

4.62 If the following solutions are mixed, is the resulting solution acidic, basic, or neutral?

(a) 50.0 mL of 0.100 M HBr and 30.0 mL of 0.200 M KOH

(b) 100.0 mL of 0.0750 M HCl and 75.0 mL of 0.100 M $Ba(OH)_2$

4.63 If the following solutions are mixed, is the resulting solution acidic, basic, or neutral?

(a) 65.0 mL of 0.0500 M $HClO_4$ and 40.0 mL of 0.0750 M NaOH

(b) 125.0 mL of 0.100 M HNO_3 and 90.0 mL of 0.0750 M $Ca(OH)_2$

4.64 How many milliliters of 1.00 M KOH must be added to neutralize the following solutions?

(a) a mixture of 0.240 M LiOH (25.0 mL) and 0.200 M HBr (75.0 mL)

(b) a mixture of 0.300 M HCl (45.0 mL) and 0.250 M NaOH (10.0 mL)

4.65 How many milliliters of 2.00 M HCl must be added to neutralize the following solutions?

(a) a mixture of 0.160 M HNO_3 (100.0 mL) and 0.100 M KOH (400.0 mL)

(b) a mixture of 0.120 M NaOH (350.0 mL) and 0.190 M HBr (150.0 mL)

Redox Reactions and Oxidation Numbers (Sections 4.6–4.8)

4.66 Where in the periodic table are the best reducing agents found? The best oxidizing agents?

4.67 Where in the periodic table are the most easily reduced elements found? The most easily oxidized?

4.68 In each of the following instances, tell whether the substance gains electrons or loses electrons in a redox reaction:

(a) An oxidizing agent

(b) A reducing agent

(c) A substance undergoing oxidation

(d) A substance undergoing reduction

4.69 Tell for each of the following substances whether the oxidation number increases or decreases in a redox reaction:

(a) An oxidizing agent

(b) A reducing agent

(c) A substance undergoing oxidation

(d) A substance undergoing reduction

4.70 Assign oxidation numbers to each element in the following compounds:

(a) NO_2 (b) SO_3 (c) $COCl_2$

(d) CH_2Cl_2 (e) $KClO_3$ (f) HNO_3

4.71 Assign oxidation numbers to each element in the following compounds:

(a) $VOCl_3$ (b) $CuSO_4$ (c) CH_2O

(d) Mn_2O_7 (e) OsO_4 (f) H_2PtCl_6

4.72 Assign oxidation numbers to each element in the following ions:

(a) ClO_3^- (b) SO_3^{2-} (c) $C_2O_4^{2-}$

(d) NO_2^- (e) BrO^- (f) AsO_4^{3-}

4.73 Assign oxidation numbers to each element in the following ions:

(a) $Cr(OH)_4^-$ (b) $S_2O_3^{2-}$ (c) NO_3^-

(d) MnO_4^{2-} (e) HPO_4^{2-} (f) $V_2O_7^{4-}$

4.74 Which element is oxidized and which is reduced in each of the following reactions?

(a) $Ca(s) + Sn^{2+}(aq) \longrightarrow Ca^{2+}(aq) + Sn(s)$

(b) $ICl(s) + H_2O(l) \longrightarrow HCl(aq) + HOI(aq)$

4.75 Which element is oxidized and which is reduced in each of the following reactions?

(a) $Si(s) + 2\,Cl_2(g) \longrightarrow SiCl_4(l)$

(b) $Cl_2(g) + 2\,NaBr(aq) \longrightarrow Br_2(aq) + 2\,NaCl(aq)$

4.76 Use the activity series of metals (Table 4.5; page 130) to predict the outcome of each of the following reactions. If no reaction occurs, write N.R.

(a) $Na^+(aq) + Zn(s) \longrightarrow$?   (b) $HCl(aq) + Pt(s) \longrightarrow$?

(c) $Ag^+(aq) + Au(s) \longrightarrow$?   (d) $Au^{3+}(aq) + Ag(s) \longrightarrow$?

4.77 Neither strontium (Sr) nor antimony (Sb) is shown in the activity series of Table 4.5. Based on their positions in the periodic table, which would you expect to be the better reducing agent? Will the following reaction occur? Explain.

$$2\,Sb^{3+}(aq) + 3\,Sr(s) \longrightarrow 2\,Sb(s) + 3\,Sr^{2+}(aq)$$

4.78 (a) Use the following reactions to arrange the elements A, B, C, and D in order of their decreasing ability as reducing agents:

$A + B^+ \longrightarrow A^+ + B$ $C^+ + D \longrightarrow$ no reaction

$B + D^+ \longrightarrow B^+ + D$ $B + C^+ \longrightarrow B^+ + C$

(b) Which of the following reactions would you expect to occur according to the activity series you established in part (a)?

(1) $A^+ + C \longrightarrow A + C^+$ (2) $A^+ + D \longrightarrow A + D^+$

4.79 (a) Use the following reactions to arrange the elements A, B, C, and D in order of their decreasing ability as reducing agents:

$2\,A + B^{2+} \longrightarrow 2\,A^+ + B$ $B + D^{2+} \longrightarrow B^{2+} + D$

$A^+ + C \longrightarrow$ no reaction $2\,C + B^{2+} \longrightarrow 2\,C^+ + B$

(b) Which of the following reactions would you expect to occur according to the activity series you established in part (a)?

(1) $2\,A^+ + D \longrightarrow 2\,A + D^{2+}$

(2) $D^{2+} + 2\,C \longrightarrow D + 2\,C^+$

Balancing Redox Reactions (Section 4.9)

4.80 Classify each of the following unbalanced half-reactions as either an oxidation or a reduction:

(a) $NO_3^-(aq) \longrightarrow NO(g)$ (b) $Zn(s) \longrightarrow Zn^{2+}(aq)$

(c) $Ti^{3+}(aq) \longrightarrow TiO_2(s)$ (d) $Sn^{4+}(aq) \longrightarrow Sn^{2+}(aq)$

4.81 Classify each of the following unbalanced half-reactions as either an oxidation or a reduction:

(a) $O_2(g) \longrightarrow OH^-(aq)$ (b) $H_2O_2(aq) \longrightarrow O_2(g)$

(c) $MnO_4^-(aq) \longrightarrow MnO_4^{2-}(aq)$

(d) $CH_3OH(aq) \longrightarrow CH_2O(aq)$

4.82 Balance the half-reactions in Problem 4.80, assuming that they occur in acidic solution.

4.83 Balance the half-reactions in Problem 4.81, assuming that they occur in basic solution.

4.84 Write unbalanced oxidation and reduction half-reactions for the following processes:

(a) $Te(s) + NO_3^-(aq) \longrightarrow TeO_2(s) + NO(g)$

(b) $H_2O_2(aq) + Fe^{2+}(aq) \longrightarrow Fe^{3+}(aq) + H_2O(l)$

4.85 Write unbalanced oxidation and reduction half-reactions for the following processes:

(a) $Mn(s) + NO_3^-(aq) \longrightarrow Mn^{2+}(aq) + NO_2(g)$

(b) $Mn^{3+}(aq) \longrightarrow MnO_2(s) + Mn^{2+}(aq)$

4.86 Balance the following half-reactions:

(a) (acidic) $Cr_2O_7^{2-}(aq) \longrightarrow Cr^{3+}(aq)$

(b) (basic) $CrO_4^{2-}(aq) \longrightarrow Cr(OH)_4^-(aq)$

(c) (basic) $Bi^{3+}(aq) \longrightarrow BiO_3^-(aq)$

(d) (basic) $ClO^-(aq) \longrightarrow Cl^-(aq)$

4.87 Balance the following half-reactions:

(a) (acidic) $VO^{2+}(aq) \longrightarrow V^{3+}(aq)$

(b) (basic) $Ni(OH)_2(s) \longrightarrow Ni_2O_3(s)$

(c) (acidic) $NO_3^-(aq) \longrightarrow NO_2(aq)$

(d) (basic) $Br_2(aq) \longrightarrow BrO_3^-(aq)$

4.88 Write balanced net ionic equations for the following reactions in basic solution:

(a) $MnO_4^-(aq) + IO_3^-(aq) \longrightarrow MnO_2(s) + IO_4^-(aq)$

(b) $Cu(OH)_2(s) + N_2H_4(aq) \longrightarrow Cu(s) + N_2(g)$

(c) $Fe(OH)_2(s) + CrO_4^{2-}(aq) \longrightarrow$
$\qquad\qquad\qquad Fe(OH)_3(s) + Cr(OH)_4^-(aq)$

(d) $H_2O_2(aq) + ClO_4^-(aq) \longrightarrow ClO_2^-(aq) + O_2(g)$

4.89 Write balanced net ionic equations for the following reactions in basic solution:

(a) $S_2O_3^{2-}(aq) + I_2(aq) \longrightarrow S_4O_6^{2-}(aq) + I^-(aq)$

(b) $Mn^{2+}(aq) + H_2O_2(aq) \longrightarrow MnO_2(s) + H_2O(l)$

(c) $Zn(s) + NO_3^-(aq) \longrightarrow NH_3(aq) + Zn(OH)_4^{2-}(aq)$

(d) $Bi(OH)_3(s) + Sn(OH)_3^-(aq) \longrightarrow Bi(s) + Sn(OH)_6^{2-}(aq)$

4.90 Write balanced net ionic equations for the following reactions in acidic solution:

(a) $Zn(s) + VO^{2+}(aq) \longrightarrow Zn^{2+}(aq) + V^{3+}(aq)$

(b) $Ag(s) + NO_3^-(aq) \longrightarrow Ag^+(aq) + NO_2(g)$

(c) $Mg(s) + VO_4^{3-}(aq) \longrightarrow Mg^{2+}(aq) + V^{2+}(aq)$

(d) $I^-(aq) + IO_3^-(aq) \longrightarrow I_3^-(aq)$

4.91 Write balanced net ionic equations for the following reactions in acidic solution:

(a) $MnO_4^-(aq) + C_2H_5OH(aq) \longrightarrow$
$\qquad\qquad\qquad Mn^{2+}(aq) + CH_3CO_2H(aq)$

(b) $H_2O_2(aq) + Cr_2O_7^{2-}(aq) \longrightarrow O_2(g) + Cr^{3+}(aq)$

(c) $Sn^{2+}(aq) + IO_4^-(aq) \longrightarrow Sn^{4+}(aq) + I^-(aq)$

(d) $PbO_2(s) + Cl^-(aq) \longrightarrow PbCl_2(s) + O_2(g)$

Redox Titrations (Section 4.10)

4.92 Iodine, I_2, reacts with aqueous thiosulfate ion in neutral solution according to the balanced equation

$$I_2(aq) + 2 S_2O_3^{2-}(aq) \longrightarrow S_4O_6^{2-}(aq) + 2 I^-(aq)$$

How many grams of I_2 are present in a solution if 35.20 mL of 0.150 M $Na_2S_2O_3$ solution is needed to titrate the I_2 solution?

4.93 How many milliliters of 0.250 M $Na_2S_2O_3$ solution is needed for complete reaction with 2.486 g of I_2 according to the equation in Problem 4.92?

4.94 Dichromate ion, $Cr_2O_7^{2-}$, reacts with aqueous iron(II) ion in acidic solution according to the balanced equation

$$Cr_2O_7^{2-}(aq) + 6 Fe^{2+}(aq) + 14 H^+(aq) \longrightarrow$$
$$2 Cr^{3+}(aq) + 6 Fe^{3+}(aq) + 7 H_2O(l)$$

What is the concentration of Fe^{2+} if 46.99 mL of 0.2004 M $K_2Cr_2O_7$ is needed to titrate 50.00 mL of the Fe^{2+} solution?

4.95 A volume of 18.72 mL of 0.1500 M $K_2Cr_2O_7$ solution was required to titrate a sample of $FeSO_4$ according to the equation in Problem 4.94. What is the mass of the sample?

4.96 What is the molar concentration of As(III) in a solution if 22.35 mL of 0.100 M $KBrO_3$ is needed for complete reaction with 50.00 mL of the As(III) solution? The balanced equation is:

$$3 H_3AsO_3(aq) + BrO_3^-(aq) \longrightarrow Br^-(aq) + 3 H_3AsO_4(aq)$$

4.97 Standardized solutions of $KBrO_3$ are frequently used in redox titrations. The necessary solution can be made by dissolving $KBrO_3$ in water and then titrating it with an As(III) solution. What is the molar concentration of a $KBrO_3$ solution if 28.55 mL of the solution is needed to titrate 1.550 g of As_2O_3? See Problem 4.96 for the balanced equation. (As_2O_3 dissolves in aqueous acid solution to yield H_3AsO_3: $As_2O_3 + 3 H_2O \longrightarrow 2 H_3AsO_3$.)

4.98 The metal content of iron in ores can be determined by a redox procedure in which the sample is first oxidized with Br_2 to convert all the iron to Fe^{3+} and then titrated with Sn^{2+} to reduce the Fe^{3+} to Fe^{2+}. The balanced equation is:

$$2 Fe^{3+}(aq) + Sn^{2+}(aq) \longrightarrow 2 Fe^{2+}(aq) + Sn^{4+}(aq)$$

What is the mass percent Fe in a 0.1875 g sample of ore if 13.28 mL of a 0.1015 M Sn^{2+} solution is needed to titrate the Fe^{3+}?

4.99 The concentration of the Sn^{2+} solution used in Problem 4.98 can be found by letting it react with a known amount of Fe^{3+}. What is the molar concentration of an Sn^{2+} solution if 23.84 mL is required for complete reaction with 1.4855 g of Fe_2O_3?

4.100 Alcohol levels in blood can be determined by a redox reaction with potassium dichromate according to the balanced equation

$$C_2H_5OH(aq) + 2 Cr_2O_7^{2-}(aq) + 16 H^+(aq) \longrightarrow$$
$$2 CO_2(g) + 4 Cr^{3+}(aq) + 11 H_2O(l)$$

What is the blood alcohol level in mass percent if 8.76 mL of 0.049 88 M $K_2Cr_2O_7$ is required for complete reaction with a 10.002 g sample of blood?

4.101 Calcium levels in blood can be determined by adding oxalate ion to precipitate calcium oxalate, CaC_2O_4, followed by dissolving the precipitate in aqueous acid and titrating the resulting oxalic acid ($H_2C_2O_4$) with $KMnO_4$:

$$5 H_2C_2O_4(aq) + 2 MnO_4^-(aq) + 6 H^+(aq) \longrightarrow$$
$$10 CO_2(g) + 2 Mn^{2+}(aq) + 8 H_2O(l)$$

How many milligrams of Ca^{2+} are present in 10.0 mL of blood if 21.08 mL of 0.000 988 M $KMnO_4$ solution is needed for the titration?

CHAPTER PROBLEMS

4.102 Balance the equations for the following reactions in basic solution:

(a) $[Fe(CN)_6]^{3-}(aq) + N_2H_4(aq) \longrightarrow [Fe(CN)_6]^{4-}(aq) + N_2(g)$

(b) $SeO_3^{2-}(aq) + Cl_2(g) \longrightarrow SeO_4^{2-}(aq) + Cl^-(aq)$

(c) $Co^{2+}(aq) + HO_2^-(aq) \longrightarrow Co(OH)_3(s)$

4.103 An alternative procedure to that given in Problem 4.98 for determining the amount of iron in a sample is to convert the iron to Fe^{2+} and then titrate it with a solution of $Ce(NH_4)_2(NO_3)_6$:

$$Fe^{2+}(aq) + Ce^{4+}(aq) \longrightarrow Fe^{3+}(aq) + Ce^{3+}(aq)$$

What is the mass percent of iron in a sample if 1.2284 g of the sample requires 57.91 mL of 0.1018 M $Ce(NH_4)_2(NO_3)_6$ for complete reaction?

4.104 Assign oxidation numbers to each atom in the following substances:

(a) Ethane, C_2H_6, a constituent of natural gas

(b) Borax, $Na_2B_4O_7$, a mineral used in laundry detergents

(c) $Mg_2Si_2O_6$, a silicate mineral

4.105 Balance the equations for the following reactions in acidic solution:

(a) $PbO_2(s) + Mn^{2+}(aq) \longrightarrow Pb^{2+}(aq) + MnO_4^-(aq)$

(b) $As_2O_3(s) + NO_3^-(aq) \longrightarrow H_3AsO_4(aq) + HNO_2(aq)$

(c) $Br_2(aq) + SO_2(g) \longrightarrow Br^-(aq) + HSO_4^-(aq)$

(d) $NO_2^-(aq) + I^-(aq) \longrightarrow I_2(s) + NO(g)$

4.106 (a) Use the following reactions to arrange the elements A, B, C, and D in order of their decreasing ability as reducing agents:

$C + B^+ \longrightarrow C^+ + B \qquad A^+ + D \longrightarrow$ No reaction

$C^+ + A \longrightarrow$ No reaction $\qquad D + B^+ \longrightarrow D^+ + B$

(b) Which of the following reactions would you expect to occur according to the activity series you established in part (a)?

(1) $A^+ + C \longrightarrow A + C^+$

(2) $A^+ + B \longrightarrow A + B^+$

4.107 Some metals occur naturally in their elemental state while others occur as compounds in ores. Gold, for instance, is found as the free metal; mercury is obtained by heating mercury(II) sulfide ore in oxygen; and zinc is obtained by heating zinc(II) oxide ore with coke (carbon). Judging from their positions in the activity series, which of the metals silver, platinum, and chromium would probably be obtained by

(a) finding it in its elemental state

(b) heating its sulfide with oxygen

(c) heating its oxide with coke

4.108 A sample weighing 14.98 g and containing a small amount of copper was treated to give a solution containing aqueous Cu^{2+} ions. Sodium iodide was then added to yield solid copper(I) iodide plus I_3^- ion, and the I_3^- was titrated with thiosulfate, $S_2O_3^{2-}$. The titration required 10.49 mL of 0.100 M $Na_2S_2O_3$ for complete reaction. What is the mass percent copper in the sample? The balanced equations are

$$2\, Cu^{2+}(aq) + 5\, I^-(aq) \longrightarrow 2\, CuI(s) + I_3^-(aq)$$

$$I_3^-(aq) + 2\, S_2O_3^{2-}(aq) \longrightarrow 3\, I^-(aq) + S_4O_6^{2-}(aq)$$

4.109 The solubility of an ionic compound can be described quantitatively by a value called the *solubility product constant*, K_{sp}. For the general process $A_aB_b \rightleftharpoons a\, A^{n+} + b\, B^{m-}$, $K_{sp} = [A^{n+}]^a\, [B^{m-}]^b$. The brackets refer to concentrations in moles per liter.

(a) Write the expression for the solubility product constant of Ag_2CrO_4.

(b) If $K_{sp} = 1.1 \times 10^{-12}$ for Ag_2CrO_4, what are the molar concentrations of Ag^+ and CrO_4^{2-} in a saturated solution?

4.110 Write the expression for the solubility product constant of MgF_2 (see Problem 4.109). If $[Mg^{2+}] = 2.6 \times 10^{-4}$ mol/L in a saturated solution, what is the value of K_{sp}?

4.111 Succinic acid, an intermediate in the metabolism of food molecules, has molecular mass = 118.1 amu. When 1.926 g of succinic acid was dissolved in water and titrated, 65.20 mL of 0.5000 M NaOH solution was required to neutralize the acid. How many acidic hydrogens are there in a molecule of succinic acid?

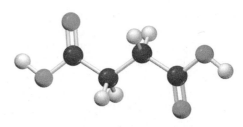

Succinic acid

4.112 How could you use a precipitation reaction to separate each of the following pairs of cations? Write the formula for each reactant you would add, and write a balanced net ionic equation for each reaction.

(a) K^+ and Hg_2^{2+} (b) Pb^{2+} and Ni^{2+}

(c) Ca^{2+} and NH_4^+ (d) Fe^{2+} and Ba^{2+}

4.113 How could you use a precipitation reaction to separate each of the following pairs of anions? Write the formula for each reactant you would add, and write a balanced net ionic equation for each reaction.

(a) Cl^- and NO_3^- (b) S^{2-} and SO_4^{2-}

(c) SO_4^{2-} and CO_3^{2-} (d) OH^- and ClO_4^-

4.114 Write a balanced net ionic equation for each of the following reactions:

(a) $Mn(OH)_2(s) + H_2O_2(aq) \xrightarrow{Base} Mn(OH)_3(s)$

(b) $MnO_4^{2-}(aq) \xrightarrow{Acid} MnO_2(s) + MnO_4^-(aq)$

(c) $IO_3^-(aq) + I^-(aq) \xrightarrow{Acid} I_3^-(aq)$

(d) $P(s) + PO_4^{3-}(aq) \xrightarrow{Base} HPO_3^{2-}(aq)$

4.115 A 100.0 mL solution containing aqueous HCl and HBr was titrated with 0.1235 M NaOH. The volume of base required to neutralize the acid was 47.14 mL. Aqueous $AgNO_3$ was then added to precipitate the Cl^- and Br^- ions as AgCl and AgBr. The mass of the silver halides obtained was 0.9974 g. What are the molarities of the HCl and HBr in the original solution?

4.116 Write balanced net ionic equations for the following reactions in acidic solution:

(a) $S_4O_6^{2-}(aq) + Al(s) \longrightarrow H_2S(aq) + Al^{3+}(aq)$

(b) $S_2O_3^{2-}(aq) + Cr_2O_7^{2-}(aq) \longrightarrow S_4O_6^{2-}(aq) + Cr^{3+}(aq)$

(c) $ClO_3^{-}(aq) + As_2S_3(s) \longrightarrow$
$$Cl^{-}(aq) + H_2AsO_4^{-}(aq) + HSO_4^{-}(aq)$$

(d) $IO_3^{-}(aq) + Re(s) \longrightarrow ReO_4^{-}(aq) + I^{-}(aq)$

(e) $HSO_4^{-}(aq) + As_4(s) + Pb_3O_4(s) \longrightarrow$
$$PbSO_4(s) + H_2AsO_4^{-}(aq)$$

(f) $HNO_2(aq) \longrightarrow NO_3^{-}(aq) + NO(g)$

4.117 Write balanced net ionic equations for the following reactions in basic solution:

(a) $C_4H_4O_6^{2-}(aq) + ClO_3^{-}(aq) \longrightarrow CO_3^{2-}(aq) + Cl^{-}(aq)$

(b) $Al(s) + BiONO_3(s) \longrightarrow$
$$Bi(s) + NH_3(aq) + Al(OH)_4^{-}(aq)$$

(c) $H_2O_2(aq) + Cl_2O_7(aq) \longrightarrow ClO_2^{-}(aq) + O_2(g)$

(d) $Tl_2O_3(s) + NH_2OH(aq) \longrightarrow TlOH(s) + N_2(g)$

(e) $Cu(NH_3)_4^{2+}(aq) + S_2O_4^{2-}(aq) \longrightarrow$
$$SO_3^{2-}(aq) + Cu(s) + NH_3(aq)$$

(f) $Mn(OH)_2(s) + MnO_4^{-}(aq) \longrightarrow MnO_2(s)$

4.118 A mixture of CuO and Cu_2O with a mass of 10.50 g is reduced to give 8.66 g of pure Cu metal. What are the amounts in grams of CuO and Cu_2O in the original mixture?

4.119 When 75.0 mL of a 0.100 M lead(II) nitrate solution is mixed with 100.0 mL of a 0.190 M potassium iodide solution, a yellow-orange precipitate of lead(II) iodide is formed.

(a) What mass in grams of lead(II) iodide is formed, assuming the reaction goes to completion?

(b) What is the molarity of each of the ions Pb^{2+}, K^+, NO_3^-, and I^- in the resulting solution?

4.120 A sample of metal (M) reacted with both steam and aqueous HCl to release H_2, but did not react with water at room temperature. When 1.000 g of the metal was burned in oxygen, it formed 1.890 g of a metal oxide, M_2O_3. What is the identity of the metal?

4.121 An unknown metal (M) was found not to react with either water or steam, but its reactivity with aqueous acid was not investigated. When a 1.000 g sample of the metal was burned in oxygen and the resulting metal oxide converted to a metal sulfide, 1.504 g of sulfide was obtained. What is the identity of the metal?

4.122 Hydrogen peroxide can be either an oxidizing or reducing agent depending on the circumstances. Write balanced net ionic equations for each of the following reactions, and determine in each case whether hydrogen peroxide is oxidized (acts as a reducing agent) or reduced (acts as an oxidizing agent).

(a) $HCl(aq) + H_2O_2(aq) \longrightarrow Cl_2(aq) + H_2O(l)$

(b) (acidic) $MnO_4^{-}(aq) + H_2O_2(aq) \longrightarrow Mn^{2+}(aq) + O_2(g)$

(c) $H_2O_2(aq) + Cl_2(aq) \longrightarrow HCl(aq) + O_2(g)$

4.123 A mixture of acetic acid (CH_3CO_2H; monoprotic) and oxalic acid ($H_2C_2O_4$; diprotic) requires 27.15 mL of 0.100 M NaOH to neutralize it. When an identical amount of the mixture is titrated, 15.05 mL of 0.0247 M $KMnO_4$ is needed for complete reaction. What is the mass percent of each acid in the mixture? (Acetic acid does not react with MnO_4^-. The equation for the reaction of oxalic acid with MnO_4^- was given in Problem 4.101.)

4.124 Iron content in ores can be determined by a redox procedure in which the sample is first reduced with Sn^{2+}, as in Problem 4.98, and then titrated with $KMnO_4$ to oxidize the Fe^{2+} to Fe^{3+}. The balanced equation is

$$MnO_4^{-}(aq) + 5\,Fe^{2+}(aq) + 8\,H^+(aq) \longrightarrow$$
$$Mn^{2+}(aq) + 5\,Fe^{3+}(aq) + 4\,H_2O(l)$$

What is the mass percent Fe in a 2.368 g sample if 48.39 mL of a 0.1116 M $KMnO_4$ solution is needed to titrate the Fe^{3+}?

4.125 A mixture of $FeCl_2$ and NaCl is dissolved in water, and addition of aqueous silver nitrate then yields 7.0149 g of a precipitate. When an identical amount of the mixture is titrated with MnO_4^-, 14.28 mL of 0.198 M $KMnO_4$ is needed for complete reaction. What are the mass percents of the two compounds in the mixture? Na^+ and Cl^- do not react with MnO_4^-. The equation for the reaction of Fe^{2+} with MnO_4^- was given in Problem 4.124.

MULTICONCEPT PROBLEMS

4.126 Assume that you dissolve 10.0 g of a mixture of NaOH and $Ba(OH)_2$ in 250.0 mL of water and titrate with 1.50 M hydrochloric acid. The titration is complete after 108.9 mL of the acid has been added. What is the mass in grams of each substance in the mixture?

4.127 The following three solutions are mixed: 100.0 mL of 0.100 M Na_2SO_4, 50.0 mL of 0.300 M $ZnCl_2$, and 100.0 mL of 0.200 M $Ba(CN)_2$.

(a) What ionic compounds will precipitate out of solution?

(b) What is the molarity of each ion remaining in the solution assuming complete precipitation of all insoluble compounds?

4.128 A 250.0 g sample of a white solid is known to be a mixture of KNO_3, $BaCl_2$, and NaCl. When 100.0 g of this mixture is dissolved in water and allowed to react with excess H_2SO_4, 67.3 g of a white precipitate is collected. When the remain-

ing 150.0 g of the mixture is dissolved in water and allowed to react with excess $AgNO_3$, 197.6 g of a second precipitate is collected.

(a) What are the formulas of the two precipitates?

(b) What is the mass of each substance in the original 250 g mixture?

4.129 Four solutions are prepared and mixed in the following order:

(1) Start with 100.0 mL of 0.100 M $BaCl_2$

(2) Add 50.0 mL of 0.100 M $AgNO_3$

(3) Add 50.0 mL of 0.100 M H_2SO_4

(4) Add 250.0 mL of 0.100 M NH_3

Write an equation for any reaction that occurs after each step, and calculate the concentrations of Ba^{2+}, Cl^-, NO_3^-, NH_3, and NH_4^+ in the final solution, assuming that all reactions go to completion.

4.130 To 100.0 mL of a solution that contains 0.120 M $Cr(NO_3)_2$ and 0.500 M HNO_3 is added 20.0 mL of 0.250 M $K_2Cr_2O_7$. The dichromate and chromium(II) ions react to give chromium(III) ions.

(a) Write a balanced net ionic equation for the reaction.

(b) Calculate the concentrations of all ions in the solution after reaction. Check your concentrations to make sure that the solution is electrically neutral.

4.131 Sodium nitrite, $NaNO_2$, is frequently added to processed meats as a preservative. The amount of nitrite ion in a sample can be determined by acidifying to form nitrous acid (HNO_2), letting the nitrous acid react with an excess of iodide ion, and then titrating the I_3^- ion that results with thiosulfate solution in the presence of a starch indicator. The unbalanced equations are

(1) $HNO_2 + I^- \longrightarrow NO + I_3^-$ (in acidic solution)

(2) $I_3^- + S_2O_3^{2-} \longrightarrow I^- + S_4O_6^{2-}$

(a) Balance the two redox equations.

(b) When a nitrite-containing sample with a mass of 2.935 g was analyzed, 18.77 mL of 0.1500 M $Na_2S_2O_3$ solution was needed for the reaction. What is the mass percent of NO_2^- ion in the sample?

4.132 Brass is an approximately 4:1 alloy of copper and zinc, along with small amounts of tin, lead, and iron. The mass percents of copper and zinc can be determined by a procedure that begins with dissolving the brass in hot nitric acid. The resulting solution of Cu^{2+} and Zn^{2+} ions is then treated with aqueous ammonia to lower its acidity, followed by addition of sodium thiocyanate (NaSCN) and sulfurous acid (H_2SO_3) to precipitate copper(I) thiocyanate (CuSCN). The solid CuSCN is collected, dissolved in aqueous acid, and treated with potassium iodate (KIO_3) to give iodine, which is then titrated with aqueous sodium thiosulfate ($Na_2S_2O_3$). The filtrate remaining after CuSCN has been removed is neutralized by addition of aqueous ammonia, and a solution of diammonium hydrogen phosphate $[(NH_4)_2HPO_4]$ is added to yield a precipitate of zinc ammonium phosphate ($ZnNH_4PO_4$). Heating the precipitate to 900 °C converts it to zinc pyrophosphate ($Zn_2P_2O_7$), which is weighed. The equations are

(1) $Cu(s) + NO_3^-(aq) \longrightarrow Cu^{2+}(aq) + NO(g)$ (in acid)

(2) $Cu^{2+}(aq) + SCN^-(aq) + HSO_3^-(aq) \longrightarrow$ $CuSCN(s) + HSO_4^-(aq)$ (in acid)

(3) $Cu^+(aq) + IO_3^-(aq) \longrightarrow Cu^{2+}(aq) + I_2(aq)$ (in acid)

(4) $I_2(aq) + S_2O_3^{2-}(aq) \longrightarrow I^-(aq) + S_4O_6^{2-}(aq)$ (in acid)

(5) $ZnNH_4PO_4(s) \longrightarrow Zn_2P_2O_7(s) + H_2O(g) + NH_3(g)$

(a) Balance all equations.

(b) When a brass sample with a mass of 0.544 g was subjected to the preceding analysis, 10.82 mL of 0.1220 M sodium thiosulfate was required for the reaction with iodine. What is the mass percent copper in the brass?

(c) The brass sample in part (b) yielded 0.246 g of $Zn_2P_2O_7$. What is the mass percent zinc in the brass?

4.133 A certain metal sulfide, MS_n (where n is a small integer), is widely used as a high-temperature lubricant. The substance is prepared by reaction of the metal pentachloride (MCl_5) with sodium sulfide (Na_2S). Heating the metal sulfide to 700 °C in air gives the metal trioxide (MO_3) and sulfur dioxide (SO_2), which reacts with Fe^{3+} ion under aqueous acidic conditions to give sulfate ion (SO_4^{2-}). Addition of aqueous $BaCl_2$ then forms a precipitate of $BaSO_4$. The unbalanced equations are:

(1) $MCl_5(s) + Na_2S(s) \longrightarrow MS_n(s) + S(l) + NaCl(s)$

(2) $MS_n(s) + O_2(g) \longrightarrow MO_3(s) + SO_2(g)$

(3) $SO_2(g) + Fe^{3+}(aq) \longrightarrow Fe^{2+}(aq) + SO_4^{2-}(aq)$ (in acid)

(4) $SO_4^{2-}(aq) + Ba^{2+}(aq) \longrightarrow BaSO_4(s)$

Assume that you begin with 4.61 g of MCl_5 and that reaction (1) proceeds in 91.3% yield. After oxidation of the MS_n product, oxidation of SO_2, and precipitation of sulfate ion, 7.19 g of $BaSO_4(s)$ is obtained.

(a) How many moles of sulfur are present in the MS_n sample?

(b) Assuming several possible values for n ($n = 1, 2, 3$ . . .), what is the atomic mass of M in each case?

(c) What is the likely identity of the metal M, and what is the formula of the metal sulfide MS_n?

(d) Balance all equations.

4.134 On heating a 0.200 g sample of a certain semimetal in air, the corresponding oxide M_2O_3 was obtained. When the oxide was dissolved in aqueous acid and titrated with $KMnO_4$, 10.7 mL of 0.100 M MnO_4^- was required for complete reaction. The unbalanced equation is

$H_3MO_3(aq) + MnO_4^-(aq) \longrightarrow$
$$H_3MO_4(aq) + Mn^{2+} \quad \text{(in acid)}$$

(a) Balance the equation.

(b) How many moles of oxide were formed, and how many moles of semimetal were in the initial 0.200 g sample?

(c) What is the identity of the semimetal M?

CHAPTER 5

Periodicity and the Electronic Structure of Atoms

Periodicity, the presence of repeating patterns, is common throughout nature, as seen here in these basalt columns at the biosphere reserve, Gangolfsberg, Bavaria.

CONTENTS

The periodic table, introduced in Section 1.3, is the most important organizing principle in chemistry. If you know the properties of any one element in a group, or column, of the periodic table, you can make a good guess at the properties of every other element in the same group and even of the elements in neighboring groups. Although the periodic table was originally constructed from empirical observations, its scientific underpinnings have long been established and are well understood.

To see why it's called the *periodic* table, look at the graph of atomic radius versus atomic number in Figure 5.1, which shows a periodic rise-and-fall pattern. Beginning on the left with atomic number 1 (hydrogen), the size of the atoms increases to a maximum at atomic number 3 (lithium), then decreases to a minimum, then increases again to a maximum at atomic number 11 (sodium), then decreases, and so on. It turns out that all the maxima occur for atoms of group 1A elements—Li, Na, K, Rb, Cs, and Fr—and that the minima occur for atoms of the group 7A elements—F, Cl, Br, and I.

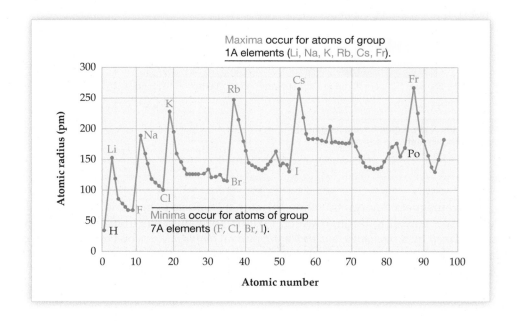

Figure 5.1

A graph of atomic radius in picometers (pm) versus atomic number. A clear rise-and-fall pattern of periodicity is evident. (Accurate data are not available for the group 8A elements.)

There's nothing unique about the periodicity of atomic radii shown in Figure 5.1. Any of several dozen other physical or chemical properties could be plotted in a similar way with similar results. We'll look at several examples of such periodicity in this chapter and the next.

5.1 LIGHT AND THE ELECTROMAGNETIC SPECTRUM

What fundamental property of atoms is responsible for the periodic variations we observe in atomic radii and in so many other characteristics of the elements? This question occupied the thoughts of chemists for more than 50 years after Mendeleev, and it was not until well into the 1920s that the answer was established. To understand how the answer slowly emerged, it's necessary to look first at the nature of visible light and other forms of radiant energy. Historically, studies of the interaction of radiant energy with matter have provided immense insight into atomic structure.

Although they appear quite different to our senses, visible light, infrared radiation, microwaves, radio waves, X rays, and other forms of radiant energy are all different kinds of **electromagnetic energy**. Collectively, they make up the **electromagnetic spectrum**, shown in Figure 5.2.

Figure 5.2
Figure 5.2
The electromagnetic spectrum. The spectrum consists of a continuous range of wavelengths and frequencies, from radio waves at the low-frequency end to gamma rays at the high-frequency end.

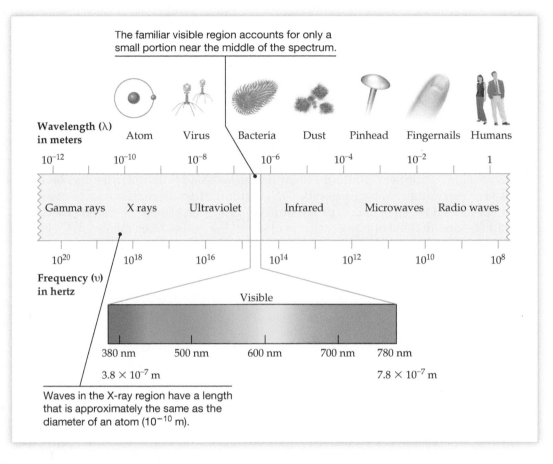

The familiar visible region accounts for only a small portion near the middle of the spectrum.

Wavelength (λ) in meters

| Atom | Virus | Bacteria | Dust | Pinhead | Fingernails | Humans |

10^{-12} 10^{-10} 10^{-8} 10^{-6} 10^{-4} 10^{-2} 1

| Gamma rays | X rays | Ultraviolet | Infrared | Microwaves | Radio waves |

10^{20} 10^{18} 10^{16} 10^{14} 10^{12} 10^{10} 10^{8}

Frequency (υ) in hertz

Visible

380 nm   500 nm   600 nm   700 nm   780 nm

3.8×10^{-7} m 7.8×10^{-7} m

Waves in the X-ray region have a length that is approximately the same as the diameter of an atom (10^{-10} m).

Electromagnetic energy traveling through a vacuum behaves in some ways like ocean waves traveling through water. Like ocean waves, electromagnetic energy is characterized by a *frequency*, a *wavelength*, and an *amplitude*. If you could stand in one place and look at a sideways, cutaway view of an ocean wave moving through the water, you would see a regular rise-and-fall pattern like that in **Figure 5.3**.

▲ Ocean waves, like electromagnetic waves, are characterized by a wavelength, a frequency, and an amplitude.

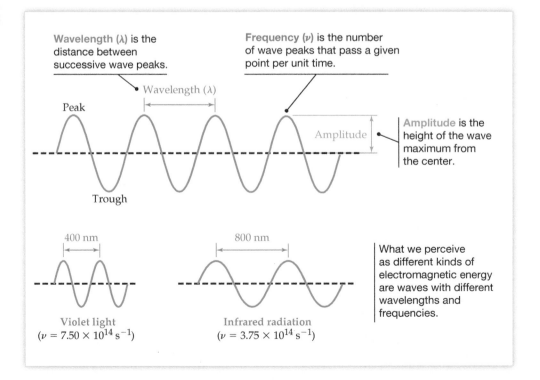

Wavelength (λ) is the distance between successive wave peaks.

Frequency (ν) is the number of wave peaks that pass a given point per unit time.

Wavelength (λ)

Peak

Amplitude

Amplitude is the height of the wave maximum from the center.

Trough

400 nm   800 nm

What we perceive as different kinds of electromagnetic energy are waves with different wavelengths and frequencies.

Violet light
($\nu = 7.50 \times 10^{14}$ s^{-1})

Infrared radiation
($\nu = 3.75 \times 10^{14}$ s^{-1})

Figure 5.3
The nature of electromagnetic waves. The waves are characterized by a wavelength, a frequency, and an amplitude.

The **frequency** (ν, Greek nu) of a wave is simply the number of wave peaks that pass by a given point per unit time, usually expressed in units of reciprocal seconds, or **hertz** (**Hz**; 1 Hz $= 1$ s^{-1}). The **wavelength** (λ, Greek lambda) of the wave is the distance from one wave peak to the next, and the **amplitude** of the wave is the height of the wave, measured from the center line between peak and trough. Physically, what we perceive as the intensity of electromagnetic energy is proportional to the square of the wave amplitude. A feeble beam and a blinding glare of light may have the same wavelength and frequency, but they differ greatly in amplitude.

Multiplying the wavelength of a wave in meters (m) by its frequency in reciprocal seconds (s^{-1}) gives the speed of the wave in meters per second (m/s). The rate of travel of all electromagnetic energy in a vacuum is a constant value, commonly called the speed of light and abbreviated c. Its numerical value is defined as exactly $2.997\ 924\ 58 \times 10^8$ m/s, usually rounded off to 3.00×10^8 m/s:

$$\text{Wavelength} \times \text{Frequency} = \text{Speed}$$

$$\lambda \text{ (m)} \times \nu \text{ (s}^{-1}) = c \text{ (m/s)}$$

which can be rewritten as:

$$\lambda = \frac{c}{\nu} \quad \text{or} \quad \nu = \frac{c}{\lambda}$$

This equation says that frequency and wavelength are inversely related: Electromagnetic energy with a longer wavelength has a lower frequency, and energy with a shorter wavelength has a higher frequency.

WORKED EXAMPLE 5.1

CALCULATING A FREQUENCY FROM A WAVELENGTH

The light blue glow given off by mercury streetlamps has a wavelength of 436 nm. What is its frequency in hertz?

STRATEGY

We are given a wavelength and need to find the corresponding frequency. Wavelength and frequency are inversely related by the equation $\lambda\nu = c$, which can be solved for ν. Don't forget to convert from nanometers to meters.

SOLUTION

$$\nu = \frac{c}{\lambda} = \frac{\left(3.00 \times 10^8 \, \frac{m}{s}\right)}{(436 \text{ nm})\left(\frac{1 \text{ m}}{10^9 \text{ nm}}\right)}$$

$$= 6.88 \times 10^{14} \text{ s}^{-1} = 6.88 \times 10^{14} \text{ Hz}$$

The frequency of the light is 6.88×10^{14} s^{-1}, or 6.88×10^{14} Hz.

▲ Does the blue glow from this mercury lamp correspond to a longer or shorter wavelength than the yellow glow from a sodium lamp?

▶ **PROBLEM 5.1** What is the frequency of a gamma ray with $\lambda = 3.56 \times 10^{-11}$ m? Of a radar wave with $\lambda = 10.3$ cm?

▶ **PROBLEM 5.2** What is the wavelength in meters of an FM radio wave with frequency $\nu = 102.5$ MHz? Of a medical X ray with $\nu = 9.55 \times 10^{17}$ Hz?

CONCEPTUAL PROBLEM 5.3 Two electromagnetic waves are represented to the right.

(a) Which wave has the higher frequency?

(b) Which wave represents a more intense beam of light?

(c) Which wave represents blue light, and which represents red light?

(a)

(b)

5.2 ELECTROMAGNETIC ENERGY AND ATOMIC LINE SPECTRA

The light that we see from the sun or from a typical lightbulb is "white" light, meaning that it consists of an essentially continuous distribution of wavelengths spanning the entire visible region of the electromagnetic spectrum. When a narrow beam of white light is passed through a glass prism, the different wavelengths travel through the glass at different rates. As a result, the white light is separated into its component colors, ranging from red at the long-wavelength end of the spectrum (780 nm) to violet at the short-wavelength end (380 nm) (Figure 5.4a). This separation into colors also occurs when light travels through water droplets in the air, forming a rainbow, or through oriented ice crystals in clouds, causing a *parhelion*, or sundog (Figure 5.4b).

(a)   **(b)**

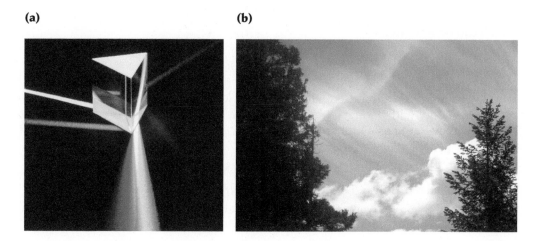

Figure 5.4
Separation of white light into its constituent colors. **(a)** When a narrow beam of ordinary white light is passed through a glass prism, different wavelengths travel through the glass at different rates and appear as different colors. A similar effect occurs when light passes through water droplets in the air, forming a rainbow, or **(b)** through ice crystals in clouds, causing an unusual weather phenomenon called a parhelion, or sundog.

▲ Excited hydrogen atoms give off a red light, and excited neon atoms emit orange light.

What do visible light and other kinds of electromagnetic energy have to do with atomic structure? It turns out that atoms give off light when heated or otherwise energetically excited, thereby providing a clue to their atomic makeup. Unlike the white light from the sun, though, the light given off by an energetically excited atom is not a continuous distribution of wavelengths. When passed first through a narrow slit and then through a prism, the light emitted by an excited atom is found to consist of only a few wavelengths rather than a full rainbow of colors, giving a series of discrete lines on an otherwise dark background—a so-called **line spectrum** that is unique for each element. Excited sodium atoms, produced by heating NaCl or some other sodium salt in the flame of a Bunsen burner, give off yellow light; hydrogen atoms give off a red light made of several different colors (Figure 5.5); and so on. In fact, the brilliant colors of fireworks are produced by mixtures of metal atoms that have been heated by explosive powder.

Soon after the discovery that energetic atoms emit light of specific wavelengths, chemists began cataloging the line spectra of various elements. They rapidly found that each element has its own unique spectral "signature, " and they began using the results to identify the elements present in minerals and other substances. Not until the work of the Swiss schoolteacher Johann Balmer in 1885, though, was a pattern discovered in atomic line spectra. It was known at the time that hydrogen produced a spectrum with four lines, as shown in Figure 5.5. The wavelengths of the four lines are 656.3 nm (red), 486.1 nm (blue-green), 434.0 nm (blue), and 410.1 nm (indigo).

Thinking about the hydrogen spectrum and trying by trial-and-error to organize the data in various ways, Balmer discovered that the wavelengths of the four lines in

Figure 5.5
Atomic line spectra.

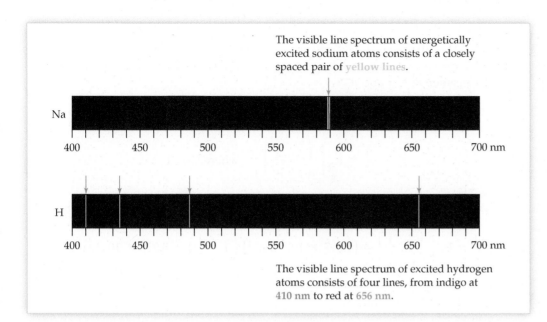

The visible line spectrum of energetically excited sodium atoms consists of a closely spaced pair of yellow lines.

The visible line spectrum of excited hydrogen atoms consists of four lines, from indigo at 410 nm to red at 656 nm.

the hydrogen spectrum can be expressed by the equation

$$\frac{1}{\lambda} = R_\infty\left[\frac{1}{2^2} - \frac{1}{n^2}\right] \qquad \text{or} \qquad \nu = R_\infty \cdot c\left[\frac{1}{2^2} - \frac{1}{n^2}\right]$$

where R_∞ is a constant (now called the *Rydberg constant*) equal to $1.097 \times 10^{-2}\,\text{nm}^{-1}$ and n is an integer greater than 2. The red spectral line at 656.3 nm, for example, results from Balmer's equation when $n = 3$:

$$\frac{1}{\lambda} = [1.097 \times 10^{-2}\,\text{nm}^{-1}]\left[\frac{1}{2^2} - \frac{1}{3^2}\right] = 1.524 \times 10^{-3}\,\text{nm}^{-1}$$

$$\lambda = \frac{1}{1.524 \times 10^{-3}\,\text{nm}^{-1}} = 656.3\,\text{nm}$$

Similarly, a value of $n = 4$ gives the blue-green line at 486.1 nm, a value of $n = 5$ gives the blue line at 434.0 nm, and so on. Solve Balmer's equation yourself to make sure.

Subsequent to the discovery of the Balmer series of lines in the visible region of the electromagnetic spectrum, it was found that many other spectral lines are also present in nonvisible regions of the spectrum. Hydrogen, for instance, shows a series of spectral lines in the ultraviolet region and several other series in the infrared region.

By adapting Balmer's equation, the Swedish physicist Johannes Rydberg was able to show that every line in the entire spectrum of hydrogen can be fit by a generalized **Balmer–Rydberg equation**:

Balmer–Rydberg equation $\quad \dfrac{1}{\lambda} = R_\infty\left[\dfrac{1}{m^2} - \dfrac{1}{n^2}\right] \qquad \text{or} \qquad \nu = R_\infty \cdot c\left[\dfrac{1}{m^2} - \dfrac{1}{n^2}\right]$

where m and n represent integers with $n > m$. If $m = 1$, then the ultraviolet series of lines results. If $m = 2$, then Balmer's series of visible lines results. If $m = 3$, an infrared series is described, and so forth for still larger values of m. Some of these other spectral lines are calculated in Worked Example 5.2.

We'll look further at the Balmer–Rydberg equation and ultimately see what the integers m and n represent in Section 5.8.

WORKED EXAMPLE 5.2

USING THE BALMER–RYDBERG EQUATION

What are the two longest-wavelength lines in nanometers in the series of the hydrogen spectrum when $m = 1$ and $n > 1$?

STRATEGY

The wavelength λ is greatest when n is smallest; that is, when $n = 2$ and $n = 3$.

$$\frac{1}{\lambda} = R_\infty \left[\frac{1}{m^2} - \frac{1}{n^2} \right] \quad \text{where } m = 1$$

SOLUTION

Solving the equation first for $n = 2$ gives

$$\frac{1}{\lambda} = R_\infty \left[\frac{1}{1^2} - \frac{1}{2^2} \right] = \left(1.097 \times 10^{-2}\,\text{nm}^{-1} \right) \left(1 - \frac{1}{4} \right) = 8.228 \times 10^{-3}\,\text{nm}^{-1}$$

or $\quad \lambda = \dfrac{1}{8.228 \times 10^{-3}\,\text{nm}^{-1}} = 121.5\,\text{nm}$

Solving the equation next for $n = 3$ gives

$$\frac{1}{\lambda} = R_\infty \left[\frac{1}{1^2} - \frac{1}{3^2} \right] = \left(1.097 \times 10^{-2}\,\text{nm}^{-1} \right) \left(1 - \frac{1}{9} \right) = 9.751 \times 10^{-3}\,\text{nm}^{-1}$$

$$\lambda = \frac{1}{9.751 \times 10^{-3}\,\text{nm}^{-1}} = 102.6\,\text{nm}$$

The two longest-wavelength lines are at 121.5 nm and 102.6 nm.

WORKED EXAMPLE 5.3

USING THE BALMER–RYDBERG EQUATION

What is the shortest-wavelength line in nanometers in the series of the hydrogen spectrum when $m = 1$ and $n > 1$?

STRATEGY

The shortest-wavelength line occurs when n is infinitely large so that $1/n^2$ is zero. That is, if $n = \infty$, then $1/n^2 = 0$.

SOLUTION

$$\frac{1}{\lambda} = R_\infty \left[\frac{1}{1^2} - \frac{1}{\infty^2} \right] = \left(1.097 \times 10^{-2}\,\text{nm}^{-1} \right)(1 - 0) = 1.097 \times 10^{-2}\,\text{nm}^{-1}$$

or $\quad \lambda = \dfrac{1}{1.097 \times 10^{-2}\,\text{nm}^{-1}} = 91.16\,\text{nm}$

The shortest-wavelength line is at 91.16 nm.

▶ PROBLEM 5.4 The Balmer equation can be extended beyond the visible portion of the electromagnetic spectrum to include lines in the ultraviolet. What is the wavelength in nanometers of ultraviolet light in the Balmer series corresponding to a value of $n = 7$?

▶ PROBLEM 5.5 What is the longest-wavelength line in nanometers in the infrared series for hydrogen where $m = 3$?

▶ PROBLEM 5.6 What is the shortest-wavelength line in nanometers in the infrared series for hydrogen where $m = 3$?

5.3 PARTICLELIKE PROPERTIES OF ELECTROMAGNETIC ENERGY

The existence of atomic line spectra and the fit of the visible hydrogen spectrum to the Balmer–Rydberg equation imply the existence of a general underlying principle about atomic structure, but it was years before that principle was found.

One important step toward developing a model of atomic structure came in 1905, when Albert Einstein (1879–1955) proposed an explanation of the *photoelectric effect*. Scientists had known since the late 1800s that irradiating a clean metal surface with light causes electrons to be ejected from the metal. Furthermore, the frequency of the light used for the irradiation must be above some threshold value, which is different for every metal. Blue light ($\nu \approx 6.5 \times 10^{14}$ Hz) causes metallic sodium to emit electrons, for example, but red light ($\nu \approx 4.5 \times 10^{14}$ Hz) has no effect on sodium.

Einstein explained the photoelectric effect by assuming that a beam of light behaves as if it were a stream of small particles, called **photons**, whose energy (E) is related to their frequency, ν, (or wavelength, λ) by the equation, $E = h\nu = hc/\lambda$. The proportionality constant h represents a fundamental physical constant that we now call Planck's constant and that has the value $h = 6.626 \times 10^{-34}$ J·s. For example, one photon of red light with a frequency $\nu = 4.62 \times 10^{14}\,\text{s}^{-1}$ (wavelength $\lambda = 649$ nm) has an energy of 3.06×10^{-19} J. [Recall from Section 1.11 that the SI unit for energy is the *joule* (J), where $1\,\text{J} = 1\,(\text{kg} \cdot \text{m}^2)/\text{s}^2$.]

$$E = h\nu = (6.626 \times 10^{-34}\,\text{J} \cdot \text{s})\,(4.62 \times 10^{14}\,\text{s}^{-1}) = 3.06 \times 10^{-19}\,\text{J}$$

You might also recall from Section 2.6 that 1 *mole* (mol) of anything is the amount that contains Avogadro's number (6.022×10^{23}) of entities. Thus, it's often convenient to express electromagnetic energy on a per-mole basis rather than a per-photon basis. Multiplying the per-photon energy of 3.06×10^{-19} J by Avogadro's number gives an energy of 184 kJ/mol.

$$\left(3.06 \times 10^{-19}\,\frac{\text{J}}{\text{photon}}\right)\left(6.022 \times 10^{23}\,\frac{\text{photon}}{\text{mol}}\right) = 1.84 \times 10^5\,\frac{\text{J}}{\text{mol}}$$

$$\left(1.84 \times 10^5\,\frac{\text{J}}{\text{mol}}\right)\left(\frac{1\,\text{kJ}}{1000\,\text{J}}\right) = 184\,\text{kJ/mol}$$

Higher frequencies and shorter wavelengths correspond to higher energy radiation, while lower frequencies and longer wavelengths correspond to lower energy. Blue light ($\lambda \approx 450$ nm), for instance, has a shorter wavelength and is more energetic than red light ($\lambda \approx 650$ nm). Similarly, an X ray ($\lambda \approx 1$ nm) has a shorter wavelength and is more energetic than an FM radio wave ($\lambda \approx 10^{10}$ nm, or 10 m).

If the frequency (or energy) of the photon striking a metal is below a minimum value, no electron is ejected. Above the threshold level, however, sufficient energy is transferred from the photon to an electron to overcome the attractive forces holding the electron to the metal (Figure 5.6).

Note again that the energy of an individual photon depends only on its frequency (or wavelength), not on the intensity of the light beam. The intensity of a light beam is a measure of the *number* of photons in the beam, whereas frequency is a measure of the *energies* of those photons. A low-intensity beam of high-energy photons might easily knock a few electrons loose from a metal, but a high-intensity beam of low-energy photons might not be able to knock loose a single electron.

As a rough analogy, think of throwing balls of different masses at a glass window. A thousand Ping-Pong balls (lower energy) would only bounce off the window, but a single baseball (higher energy) would break the glass. In the same way, low-energy photons bounce off the metal surface, but a single photon at or above a certain threshold energy can "break" the metal and dislodge an electron.

▲ A glass window can be broken by a single baseball, but a thousand Ping-Pong balls would only bounce off.

Figure 5.6
The photoelectric effect.

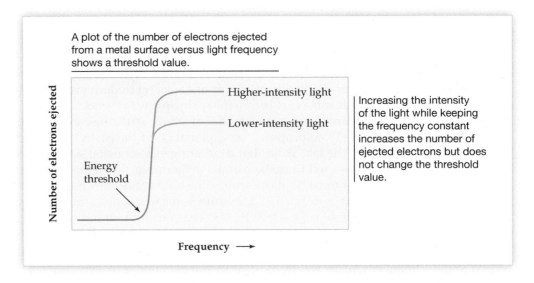

A plot of the number of electrons ejected from a metal surface versus light frequency shows a threshold value.

Higher-intensity light

Lower-intensity light

Energy threshold

Number of electrons ejected

Frequency →

Increasing the intensity of the light while keeping the frequency constant increases the number of ejected electrons but does not change the threshold value.

The main conclusion from Einstein's work was that the behavior of light and other forms of electromagnetic energy is more complex than had been formerly believed. In addition to behaving as waves, light energy can also behave as small particles. The idea might seem strange at first but becomes less so if you think of light as analogous to matter. Both are said to be *quantized*, meaning that both matter and electromagnetic energy occur only in discrete amounts. Just as there can be either 1 or 2 hydrogen atoms but not 1.5 or 1.8, there can be 1 or 2 photons of light but not 1.5 or 1.8. The amount, or **quantum**, of energy corresponding to one photon of light is almost inconceivably small, just as the amount of matter in one atom is inconceivably small, but the idea is the same.

An analogy of quantization from daily life is that of stairs versus a ramp. A ramp changes height continuously, but stairs change height only in discrete amounts and are thus quantized.

Understanding of the particlelike nature of electromagnetic energy explains in part the puzzle of atomic line spectra. Energetically excited atoms are unable to emit light of continuously varying wavelengths and therefore don't give a continuous spectrum. Instead, the atoms are constrained to emit quanta of only a few specific energies, and they therefore give a line spectrum.

Based on this insight, the Danish physicist Niels Bohr (1885–1962) proposed in 1914 a model of the hydrogen atom as a nucleus with an electron circling around it, much as a planet orbits the sun. According to Bohr, the energy levels of the orbits are quantized so that only certain specific orbits corresponding to certain specific energies for the electron are available. The observed spectral emission lines result when an electron falls from a higher-energy outer orbit to a lower-energy inner orbit, emitting a quantum of energy corresponding to the energy difference between the two allowed orbits (Figure 5.7).

▲ A ramp changes height continuously, but stairs are quantized, changing height only in discrete amounts. In the same way, electromagnetic energy is not continuous but is emitted only in discrete amounts.

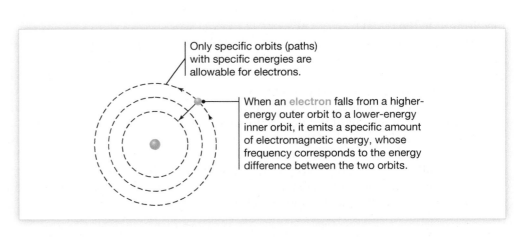

Only specific orbits (paths) with specific energies are allowable for electrons.

When an electron falls from a higher-energy outer orbit to a lower-energy inner orbit, it emits a specific amount of electromagnetic energy, whose frequency corresponds to the energy difference between the two orbits.

Figure 5.7
The Bohr model of the hydrogen atom.
In this model, an electron travels in a circular orbit around the nucleus.

WORKED EXAMPLE 5.4

CALCULATING THE ENERGY OF A PHOTON FROM ITS FREQUENCY

What is the energy in kilojoules per mole of radar waves with $\nu = 3.35 \times 10^8$ Hz?

STRATEGY

The energy of a photon with frequency ν can be calculated with the equation $E = h\nu$. To find the energy per mole of photons, the energy of one photon must be multiplied by Avogadro's number (Section 2.6).

SOLUTION

$$E = h\nu = (6.626 \times 10^{-34}\,\text{J} \cdot \text{s})(3.35 \times 10^8\,\text{s}^{-1}) \quad = 2.22 \times 10^{-25}\,\text{J}$$

$$\left(2.22 \times 10^{-25}\,\frac{\text{J}}{\text{photon}} \right)\left(6.022 \times 10^{23}\,\frac{\text{photon}}{\text{mol}} \right) = 0.134\,\text{J/mol}$$

$$= 1.34 \times 10^{-4}\,\text{kJ/mol}$$

▶ **PROBLEM 5.7**   What is the energy in kilojoules per mole of photons corresponding to the shortest-wavelength line in the series of the hydrogen spectrum when $m = 1$ and $n > 1$? (Worked Example 5.3)?

▶ **PROBLEM 5.8**   The biological effects of a given dose of electromagnetic energy generally become more serious as the energy of the radiation increases: Infrared radiation has a pleasant warming effect; ultraviolet radiation causes tanning and burning; and X rays can cause considerable tissue damage. What energies in kilojoules per mole are associated with the following wavelengths: infrared radiation with $\lambda = 1.55 \times 10^{-6}$ m, ultraviolet light with $\lambda = 250$ nm, and X rays with $\lambda = 5.49$ nm?

5.4 WAVELIKE PROPERTIES OF MATTER

The analogy between matter and radiant energy developed in the early 1900s was further extended in 1924 by the French physicist Louis de Broglie (1892–1987). de Broglie suggested that, if *light* can behave in some respects like *matter*, then perhaps *matter* can behave in some respects like *light*. That is, perhaps matter is wavelike as well as particlelike.

In developing his theory about the wavelike behavior of matter, de Broglie focused on the inverse relationship between energy and wavelength for photons:

$$\text{Since} \quad E = \frac{hc}{\lambda} \quad \text{then} \quad \lambda = \frac{hc}{E}$$

Using the famous equation $E = mc^2$ proposed in 1905 by Einstein as part of his special theory of relativity, and substituting for E, then gives

$$\lambda = \frac{hc}{E} = \frac{hc}{mc^2} = \frac{h}{mc}$$

de Broglie suggested that a similar equation might be applied to moving particles like electrons by replacing the speed of light, c, by the speed of the particle, v. The resultant **de Broglie equation** thus allows calculation of a "wavelength" of an electron or of any other particle or object of mass m moving at velocity v:

◀▦▶ **de Broglie equation** $\lambda = \dfrac{h}{mv}$

To see how the de Broglie equation can be used, look at the electron in a hydrogen atom. The mass of an electron is 9.11×10^{-31} kg, and the velocity v of an electron in a hydrogen atom is 2.2×10^6 m/s (about 1% of the speed of light). Thus, the de Broglie wavelength of an electron in a hydrogen atom is 3.3×10^{-10} m, or 330 pm. Note that

Planck's constant, which is usually expressed in units of joule seconds (J·s), is expressed for the present purposes in units of $(kg \cdot m^2)/s$ [1 J = 1 $(kg \cdot m^2)/s^2$].

$$\lambda = \frac{h}{mv} = \frac{6.626 \times 10^{-34} \frac{kg \cdot m^2}{s}}{(9.11 \times 10^{-31} \, kg)\left(2.2 \times 10^6 \, \frac{m}{s}\right)} = 3.3 \times 10^{-10} \, m$$

What does it mean to say that light and matter act both as waves and as particles? The answer is "not much," at least not on the everyday human scale, because dual wave/particle description of light and matter is really just a mathematical *model*. Since we can't see atoms and observe their behavior directly, the best we can do is to construct a set of mathematical equations that correctly account for atomic properties and behavior.

The problem in trying to understand the dual wave/particle description of light and matter is that our common sense isn't up to the task. Our intuition has been developed from personal experiences, using our eyes and other senses to tell us how light and matter are "supposed" to behave. We have no personal experience on the atomic scale, though, and thus have no common-sense way of dealing with the behavior of light and matter at that level. On the atomic scale, where distances and masses are so tiny, light and matter behave in a manner different from what we're used to.

▶ **PROBLEM 5.9** What is the de Broglie wavelength in meters of a small car with a mass of 1150 kg traveling at a velocity of 55.0 mi/h (24.6 m/s)? Is this wavelength longer or shorter than the diameter of an atom (approximately 200 pm)?

5.5 QUANTUM MECHANICS AND THE HEISENBERG UNCERTAINTY PRINCIPLE

With the particlelike nature of energy and the wavelike nature of matter established, let's return to the problem of atomic structure. Several models of atomic structure were proposed in the late nineteenth and early twentieth centuries, such as the Bohr model described in Section 5.3. The Bohr model was important historically because of its conclusion that electrons have only specific energy levels available to them, but the model fails for atoms with more than one electron.

The breakthrough in understanding atomic structure came in 1926, when the Austrian physicist Erwin Schrödinger (1887–1961) proposed what has come to be called the **quantum mechanical model** of the atom. The fundamental idea behind the model is that it's best to abandon the notion of an electron as a small particle moving around the nucleus in a defined path and to concentrate instead on the electron's wavelike properties. In fact, it was shown in 1927 by Werner Heisenberg (1901–1976) that it is *impossible* to know precisely where an electron is and what path it follows—a statement called the **Heisenberg uncertainty principle**.

The Heisenberg uncertainty principle can be understood by imagining what would happen if we tried to determine the position of an electron at a given moment. For us to "see" the electron, light photons of an appropriate frequency would have to interact with and bounce off the electron. But such an interaction would transfer energy from the photon to the electron, thereby increasing the energy of the electron and making it move faster. Thus, the very act of determining the electron's position would make that position change.

In mathematical terms, Heisenberg's principle states that the uncertainty in the electron's position, Δx, times the uncertainty in its momentum, Δmv, is equal to or greater than the quantity $h/4\pi$:

◀▬▬ **Heisenberg uncertainty principle** $(\Delta x)(\Delta mv) \geq \dfrac{h}{4\pi}$

According to this equation, we can never know both the position and the velocity of an electron (or of any other object) beyond a certain level of precision. If we know the *velocity* with a high degree of certainty (Δmv is small), then the *position* of the electron must be uncertain (Δx must be large). Conversely, if we know the position of the electron exactly (Δx is small), then we can't know its velocity (Δmv must be large). As a result, an electron will always appear as something of a blur whenever we attempt to make any physical measurements of its position and velocity.

A brief calculation can help make the conclusions of the uncertainty principle clearer. As mentioned in the previous section, the mass m of an electron is 9.11×10^{-31} kg and the velocity v of an electron in a hydrogen atom is 2.2×10^6 m/s. If we assume that the velocity is known to within 10%, or 0.2×10^6 m/s, then the uncertainty in the electron's position in a hydrogen atom is greater than 3×10^{-10} m, or 300 pm. But since the diameter of a hydrogen atom is only 240 pm, *the uncertainty in the electron's position is similar in size to the atom itself!*

▲ Even the motion of very fast objects such as bullets can be captured in daily life. On the atomic scale, however, velocity and position can't both be known precisely.

$$\text{If } (\Delta x)(\Delta mv) \geq \frac{h}{4\pi} \quad \text{then } (\Delta x) \geq \frac{h}{(4\pi)(\Delta mv)}$$

$$\Delta x \geq \frac{6.626 \times 10^{-34}\ \frac{\cancel{\text{kg}} \cdot \text{m}^2}{\cancel{\text{s}}}}{(4)(3.1416)(9.11 \times 10^{-31}\ \cancel{\text{kg}})\left(0.2 \times 10^6\ \frac{\text{m}}{\cancel{\text{s}}}\right)}$$

$$\Delta x \geq 3 \times 10^{-10}\ \text{m} \quad \text{or} \quad 300\ \text{pm}$$

When the mass m of an object is relatively large, as in daily life, then both Δx and Δv in the Heisenberg relationship are very small, so we have no problem in measuring both position and velocity for visible objects. The problem arises only on the atomic scale.

5.6 WAVE FUNCTIONS AND QUANTUM NUMBERS

Schrödinger's quantum mechanical model of atomic structure is framed in the form of a mathematical expression called a *wave equation* because it is similar in form to the equation used to describe the motion of ordinary waves in fluids. The solutions to the wave equation are called **wave functions**, or **orbitals**, and are represented by the symbol ψ (Greek psi). The best way to think about an electron's wave function is to regard it as an expression whose square, ψ^2, defines the probability of finding the electron within a given volume of space around the nucleus. As Heisenberg showed, we can never be completely certain about an electron's position. A wave function, however, tells where the electron will most probably be found.

$$\text{Wave equation} \xrightarrow{\text{Solve}} \text{Wave function or orbital } (\psi) \longrightarrow \text{Probability of finding electron in a region of space } (\psi^2)$$

A wave function is characterized by three parameters called **quantum numbers**, represented as n, l, and m_l, which describe the energy level of the orbital and the three-dimensional shape of the region in space occupied by a given electron.

- **The principal quantum number (n)** is a positive integer ($n = 1, 2, 3, 4, \dots$) on which the size and energy level of the orbital primarily depend. For hydrogen and other one-electron atoms, such as He^+, the energy of an orbital depends only on n. For atoms with more than one electron, the energy level of an orbital depends both on n and on the l quantum number.

  As the value of n increases, the number of allowed orbitals increases and the size of those orbitals becomes larger, thus allowing an electron to be farther from the nucleus. Because it takes energy to separate a negative charge from a positive charge, this increased distance between the electron and the nucleus means that the energy of the electron in the orbital increases as the quantum number n increases.

  We often speak of orbitals as being grouped according to the principal quantum number n into successive layers, or **shells**, around the nucleus. Those orbitals with $n = 3$, for example, are said to be in the third shell.

- **The angular-momentum quantum number (l)** defines the three-dimensional shape of the orbital. For an orbital whose principal quantum number is n, the angular-momentum quantum number l can have any integral value from 0 to $n - 1$. Thus, within each shell, there are n different shapes for orbitals.

$$\text{If } n = 1, \text{ then } l = 0$$
$$\text{If } n = 2, \text{ then } l = 0 \text{ or } 1$$
$$\text{If } n = 3, \text{ then } l = 0, 1, \text{ or } 2$$
$$\dots \text{and so forth}$$

Just as it's convenient to think of orbitals as being grouped into shells according to the principal quantum number n, we often speak of orbitals within a shell as being further grouped into **subshells** according to the angular-momentum quantum number l. Different subshells are usually designated by letters rather than by numbers, following the order s, p, d, f, g. (Historically, the letters $s, p, d,$ and f arose from the use of the words *sharp, principal, diffuse,* and *fundamental* to describe various lines in atomic spectra.) After f, successive subshells are designated alphabetically: g, h, and so on.

Quantum number l:	0	1	2	3	4	$\dots$
Subshell notation:	s	p	d	f	g	$\dots$

As an example, an orbital with $n = 3$ and $l = 2$ is a $3d$ orbital: 3 to represent the third shell and d to represent the $l = 2$ subshell.

- **The magnetic quantum number (m_l)** defines the spatial orientation of the orbital with respect to a standard set of coordinate axes. For an orbital whose angular-momentum quantum number is l, the magnetic quantum number m_l can have any integral value from $-l$ to $+l$. Thus, within each subshell—orbitals with the same shape, or value of l—there are $2l + 1$ different spatial orientations for those orbitals. We'll explore this point further in the next section.

$$\text{If } l = 0, \text{ then } m_l = 0$$
$$\text{If } l = 1, \text{ then } m_l = -1, 0, \text{ or } +1$$
$$\text{If } l = 2, \text{ then } m_l = -2, -1, 0, +1, \text{ or } +2$$
$$\dots \text{and so forth}$$

A summary of the allowed combinations of quantum numbers for the first four shells is given in Table 5.1.

TABLE 5.1 Allowed Combinations of Quantum Numbers n, l, and m_l for the First Four Shells

n	l	m_l	Orbital Notation	Number of Orbitals in Subshell	Number of Orbitals in Shell
1	0	0	$1s$	1	1
2	0	0	$2s$	1	4
	1	$-1, 0, +1$	$2p$	3	
3	0	0	$3s$	1	
	1	$-1, 0, +1$	$3p$	3	9
	2	$-2, -1, 0, +1, +2$	$3d$	5	
4	0	0	$4s$	1	
	1	$-1, 0, +1$	$4p$	3	
	2	$-2, -1, 0, +1, +2$	$4d$	5	16
	3	$-3, -2, -1, 0, +1, +2, +3$	$4f$	7	

The energy levels of various orbitals are shown in **Figure 5.8**. As noted earlier in this section, the energy levels of different orbitals in a hydrogen atom depend only on the principal quantum number n, but the energy levels of orbitals in multielectron atoms depend on both n and l. In other words, the orbitals in a given shell all have the same energy for hydrogen but have slightly different energies for other atoms, depending on their subshell. In fact, there is even some crossover of energies between one shell and another. A 3d orbital in some multielectron atoms has a higher energy than a 4s orbital, for instance.

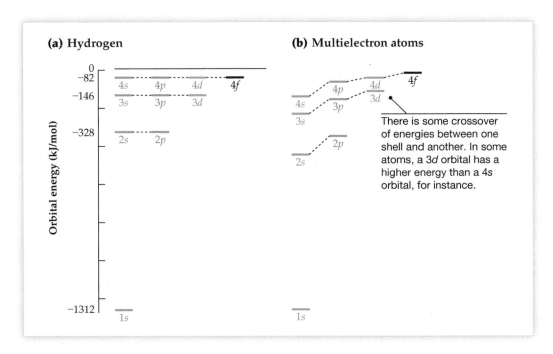

Figure 5.8

Energy levels of atomic orbitals: (a) hydrogen and (b) a typical multielectron atom. The differences between energies of various subshells in **(b)** are exaggerated for clarity.

WORKED EXAMPLE 5.5

USING QUANTUM NUMBERS TO IDENTIFY AN ORBITAL

Identify the shell and subshell of an orbital with the quantum numbers $n = 3$, $l = 1$, $m_l = 1$.

STRATEGY

The principal quantum number n gives the shell number, and the angular-momentum quantum number l gives the subshell designation. The magnetic quantum number m_l is related to the spatial orientation of the orbital.

SOLUTION

A value of $n = 3$ indicates that the orbital is in the third shell, and a value of $l = 1$ indicates that the orbital is of the p type. Thus, the orbital has the designation 3p.

WORKED EXAMPLE 5.6

ASSIGNING QUANTUM NUMBERS TO AN ORBITAL

Give the possible combinations of quantum numbers for a 4p orbital.

STRATEGY

The designation 4p indicates that the orbital has a principal quantum number $n = 4$ and an angular-momentum quantum number $l = 1$. The magnetic quantum number m_l can have any of the three values $-1, 0$, or $+1$.

SOLUTION

The allowable combinations are

$$n = 4, l = 1, m_l = -1 \qquad n = 4, l = 1, m_l = 0 \qquad n = 4, l = 1, m_l = +1$$

▶ **PROBLEM 5.10** Extend Table 5.1 to show allowed combinations of quantum numbers when $n = 5$. How many orbitals are in the fifth shell?

▶ **PROBLEM 5.11** Give orbital notations for electrons in orbitals with the following quantum numbers:

    (a) $n = 2, l = 1, m_l = 1$　　　**(b)** $n = 4, l = 3, m_l = -2$　　　**(c)** $n = 3, l = 2, m_l = -1$

▶ **PROBLEM 5.12** Give the allowed combinations of quantum numbers for the following orbitals:

    (a) A 3s orbital　　　　　　　　**(b)** A 2p orbital　　　　　　　　**(c)** A 4d orbital

5.7 THE SHAPES OF ORBITALS

We said in the previous section that the square of a wave function, or orbital, describes the probability of finding the electron within a specific region of space. The shape of that spatial region is defined by the angular-momentum quantum number l, with $l = 0$ called an s orbital, $l = 1$ a p orbital, $l = 2$ a d orbital, and so forth. Of the various possibilities, $s, p, d,$ and f orbitals are the most important because these are the only ones actually occupied in known elements. Let's look at each of the four individually.

s Orbitals

All s orbitals are spherical, meaning that the probability of finding an s electron depends only on distance from the nucleus, not on direction. Furthermore, because there is only one possible orientation of a sphere in space, an s orbital has $m_l = 0$ and there is only one s orbital per shell.

As shown in **Figure 5.9**, the value of ψ^2 for an s orbital is greatest near the nucleus and then drops off rapidly as distance from the nucleus increases, although it never

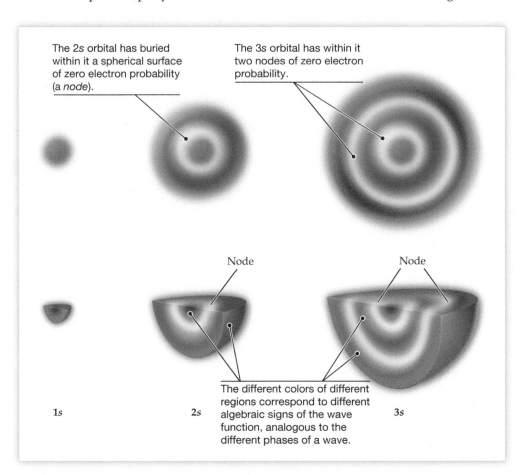

The 2s orbital has buried within it a spherical surface of zero electron probability (a *node*).

The 3s orbital has within it two nodes of zero electron probability.

Node

Node

The different colors of different regions correspond to different algebraic signs of the wave function, analogous to the different phases of a wave.

1s   2s   3s

Figure 5.9

Representations of 1s, 2s, and 3s orbitals. Slices through these spherical orbitals are shown on the top and cutaway views on the bottom, with the probability of finding an electron represented by the density of the shading.

goes all the way to zero, even at a large distance. As a result, there is no definite boundary to the atom and no definite size. For purposes like that of Figure 5.9, however, we usually imagine a boundary surface enclosing the volume where an electron spends most (say, 95%) of its time.

Although all s orbitals are spherical, there are significant differences among the s orbitals in different shells. For one thing, the size of the s orbital increases in successively higher shells, implying that an electron in an outer-shell s orbital is farther from the nucleus on average than an electron in an inner-shell s orbital. For another thing, the electron distribution in an outer-shell s orbital has more than one region of high probability. As shown in Figure 5.9, a 2s orbital is essentially a sphere within a sphere and has two regions of high probability, separated by a surface of zero probability called a **node**. Similarly, a 3s orbital has three regions of high probability and two spherical nodes.

The concept of an orbital node—a surface of zero electron probability separating regions of nonzero probability—is difficult to grasp because it raises the question "How does an electron get from one region of the orbital to another if it's not allowed to be at the node?" The question is misleading, though, because it assumes particle-like behavior for the electron rather than wavelike behavior.

In fact, nodes are an intrinsic property of waves, from moving waves of water in the ocean to the stationary, or standing, wave generated by vibrating a rope or guitar string (Figure 5.10). A node simply corresponds to the zero-amplitude part of the wave. On either side of the node is a nonzero wave amplitude. Note that a wave has two **phases**—peaks above the zero line and troughs below—corresponding to different algebraic signs, + and −. Similarly, the different regions of 2s and 3s orbitals have different phases, + and −, as indicated in Figure 5.9 by different colors.

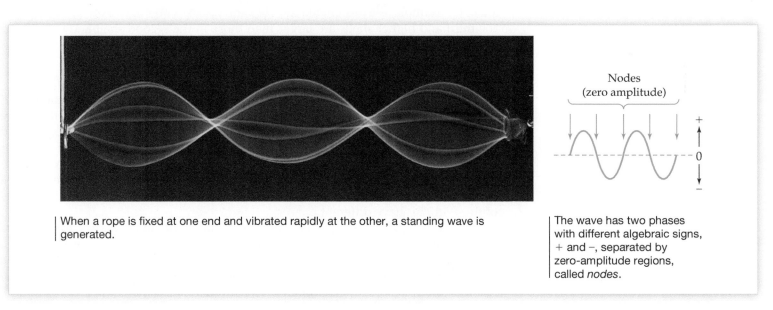

When a rope is fixed at one end and vibrated rapidly at the other, a standing wave is generated.

The wave has two phases with different algebraic signs, + and −, separated by zero-amplitude regions, called *nodes*.

Figure 5.10
A standing wave in a vibrating rope.

p Orbitals

The p orbitals are dumbbell-shaped rather than spherical, with their electron distribution concentrated in identical lobes on either side of the nucleus and separated by a planar node cutting through the nucleus. As a result, the probability of finding a p electron near the nucleus is zero. The two lobes of a p orbital have different phases, as indicated in **Figure 5.11** by different colors. We'll see in Chapter 7 that these phases are crucial for bonding because only lobes of the same phase can interact in forming covalent chemical bonds.

Figure 5.11

Representations of the three 2p orbitals. Each orbital is dumbbell-shaped and oriented in space along one of the three coordinate axes x, y, or z.

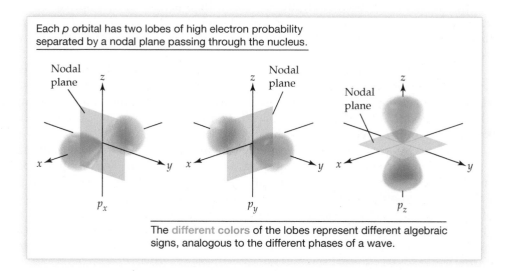

Each p orbital has two lobes of high electron probability separated by a nodal plane passing through the nucleus.

p_x p_y p_z

The different colors of the lobes represent different algebraic signs, analogous to the different phases of a wave.

There are three allowable values of m_l when $l = 1$, so each shell beginning with the second has three p orbitals, which are oriented in space at 90° angles to one another along the three coordinate axes x, y, and z. The three p orbitals in the second shell, for example, are designated $2p_x$, $2p_y$, and $2p_z$. As you might expect, p orbitals in the third and higher shells are larger than those in the second shell and extend farther from the nucleus. Their shape is roughly the same, however.

d and f Orbitals

The third and higher shells each contain five d orbitals, which differ from their s and p counterparts because they have two different shapes. Four of the five d orbitals are cloverleaf-shaped and have four lobes of maximum electron probability separated by two nodal planes through the nucleus (**Figure 5.12a–d**). The fifth d orbital is similar in shape to a p_z orbital but has an additional donut-shaped region of electron probability centered in the xy plane (**Figure 5.12e**). In spite of their different shapes, all five d orbitals in a given shell have the same energy. As with p orbitals, alternating lobes of the d orbitals have different phases.

You've probably noticed that both the number of nodal planes through the nucleus and the overall geometric complexity of the orbitals increases with the l quantum number of the subshell: An s orbital has one lobe and no nodal plane through the nucleus; a p orbital has two lobes and one nodal plane; and a d orbital has four lobes and two nodal planes. The seven f orbitals are more complex still, having eight lobes of maximum electron probability separated by three nodal planes through the nucleus. (Figure 5.12f shows one of the seven 4f orbitals.) Most of the elements we'll deal with in the following chapters don't use f orbitals in bonding, however, so we won't spend time on them.

▶ **PROBLEM 5.13** How many nodal planes through the nucleus do you think a g orbital has?

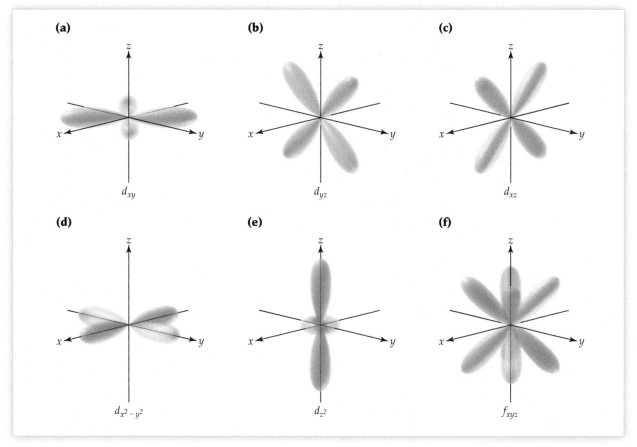

Figure 5.12
Representations of the five 3*d* orbitals. Four of the orbitals are shaped like a cloverleaf (**a–d**), and the fifth is shaped like an elongated dumbbell inside a donut (**e**). Also shown is one of the seven 4*f* orbitals (**f**). As with *p* orbitals in Figure 5.11, the different colors of the lobes reflect different phases.

CONCEPTUAL PROBLEM 5.14   Give a possible combination of *n* and *l* quantum numbers for the following fourth-shell orbital:

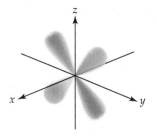

5.8 QUANTUM MECHANICS AND ATOMIC LINE SPECTRA

Now that we've seen how atomic structure is described according to the quantum mechanical model, let's return briefly to the subject of atomic line spectra first mentioned in Section 5.2. How does the quantum mechanical model account for the discrete wavelengths of light found in a line spectrum and for the Balmer–Rydberg equation that gives the values of those wavelengths?

Each electron in an atom occupies an orbital, and each orbital has a specific energy level. Thus, the energies available to electrons are quantized and can have only the specific values associated with the orbitals they occupy. When an atom is heated in a flame or electric discharge, the added thermal energy causes an electron to jump from a lower-energy orbital to a higher-energy orbital. In a hydrogen atom, for instance, the electron might jump from the 1s orbital to a second-shell orbital, to a third-shell orbital, or to an orbital in any higher shell, depending on the amount of energy added.

But the energetically excited atom is relatively unstable, and the electron rapidly returns to a lower-energy level accompanied by *emission* of energy equal to the difference between the higher and lower orbitals. Because the energies of the orbitals are quantized, the amount of energy emitted is also quantized. Thus, we observe the emission of only specific frequencies of radiation (Figure 5.13). By measuring the frequencies emitted by excited hydrogen atoms, we can calculate the energy differences between orbitals.

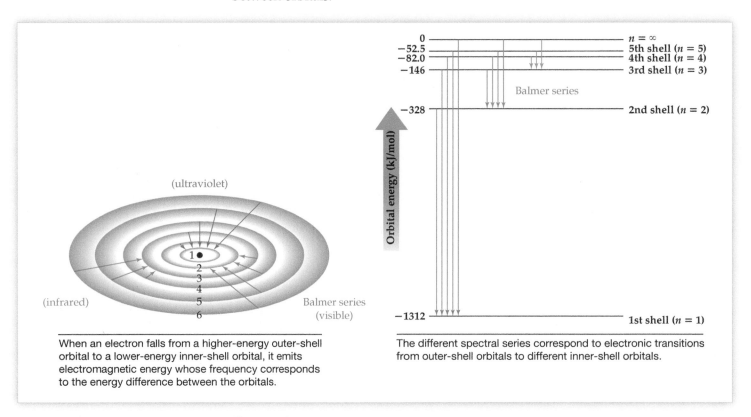

When an electron falls from a higher-energy outer-shell orbital to a lower-energy inner-shell orbital, it emits electromagnetic energy whose frequency corresponds to the energy difference between the orbitals.

The different spectral series correspond to electronic transitions from outer-shell orbitals to different inner-shell orbitals.

Figure 5.13
The origin of atomic line spectra.

The variables m and n in the Balmer–Rydberg equation for hydrogen (Section 5.2) represent the principal quantum numbers of the two orbitals involved in the electronic transition. The variable n corresponds to the principal quantum number of the higher-energy, outer-shell orbital that the transition is *from*, and the variable m corresponds to the principal quantum number of the lower-energy, inner-shell orbital that the transition is *to*. When $m = 1$, for example, the frequencies of emitted light correspond to energy differences between various outer-shell orbitals and the first-shell orbital. When $m = 2$ (now called the Balmer series), the frequencies correspond to energy differences between outer-shell orbitals and the second-shell orbitals.

$$\frac{1}{\lambda} = R_\infty \left(\frac{1}{m^2} - \frac{1}{n^2} \right)$$

Shell the transition is *to* (inner-shell)

Shell the transition is *from* (outer-shell)

Notice in Figure 5.13 that as n becomes larger and approaches infinity, the energy difference between the n shell and the first shell converges to a value of 1312 kJ/mol. That is, 1312 kJ is released when electrons come from a great distance (the "infinite" shell) and add to H^+ to give a mole of hydrogen atoms, each with an electron in its first shell:

$$H^+ + e^- \longrightarrow H + \text{Energy} \qquad (1312 \text{ kJ/mol})$$

Because the energy released on adding an electron to H^+ is equal to the energy absorbed on removing an electron from a hydrogen atom, we can also say that 1312 kJ/mol is required to remove the electron from a hydrogen atom. We'll see in the next chapter that the amount of energy necessary to remove an electron from a given atom provides an important clue about that element's chemical reactivity.

What is true for hydrogen is also true for all other atoms: All atoms show atomic line spectra when energetically excited electrons fall from higher-energy orbitals in outer shells to lower-energy orbitals in inner shells. As you might expect, though, these spectra become very complex for multielectron atoms in which different orbitals within a shell no longer have identical energies and in which a large number of electronic transitions are possible.

WORKED EXAMPLE 5.7

CALCULATING THE ENERGY DIFFERENCE BETWEEN TWO ORBITALS

What is the energy difference in kilojoules per mole between the first and second shells of the hydrogen atom if the lowest-energy emission in the spectral series with $m = 1$ and $n = 2$ occurs at $\lambda = 121.5$ nm?

STRATEGY

The lowest-energy emission line in the spectral series with $m = 1$ and $n = 2$ corresponds to the emission of light as an electron falls from the second shell to the first shell, with the energy of that light equal to the energy difference between shells. Knowing the wavelength of the light, we can calculate the energy of one photon using the equation, $E = hc/\lambda$, and then multiply by Avogadro's number to find the answer in joules (or kilojoules) per mole:

SOLUTION

$$E = \frac{hcN_A}{\lambda} = \frac{(6.626 \times 10^{-34} \text{ J} \cdot \cancel{s})\left(3.00 \times 10^8 \frac{\cancel{m}}{\cancel{s}}\right)\left(10^9 \frac{\cancel{nm}}{\cancel{m}}\right)(6.022 \times 10^{23} \text{ mol}^{-1})}{121.5 \cancel{nm}}$$

$$= 9.85 \times 10^5 \text{ J/mol} = 985 \text{ kJ/mol}$$

The energy difference between the first and second shells of the hydrogen atom is 985 kJ/mol.

▶ **PROBLEM 5.15** Calculate in kilojoules per mole the energy necessary to completely remove an electron from the first shell of a hydrogen atom ($R_\infty = 1.097 \times 10^{-2}$ nm^{-1}).

5.9 ELECTRON SPIN AND THE PAULI EXCLUSION PRINCIPLE

The three quantum numbers n, l, and m_l discussed in Section 5.6 define the energy, shape, and spatial orientation of orbitals, but they don't quite tell the whole story. When the line spectra of many multielectron atoms are studied in detail, it turns out that some lines actually occur as very closely spaced pairs. (You can see this pairing if you look closely at the visible spectrum of sodium in Figure 5.5.) Thus, there are more energy levels than simple quantum mechanics predicts, and a fourth quantum number is required. Denoted m_s, this fourth quantum number is related to a property called *electron spin*.

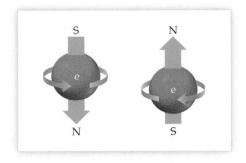

Figure 5.14

Electron spin. Electrons behave in some ways as if they were tiny charged spheres spinning around an axis. This spin (blue arrow) gives rise to a tiny magnetic field (green arrow) and to a fourth quantum number, m_s, which can have a value of either $+1/2$ or $-1/2$.

In some ways, electrons behave as if they were spinning around an axis, somewhat as the Earth spins daily. This spinning charge gives rise to a tiny magnetic field and to a **spin quantum number (m_s)**, which can have either of two values, $+1/2$ or $-1/2$ (Figure 5.14). A spin of $+1/2$ is usually represented by an up arrow ($\uparrow$), and a spin of $-1/2$ by a down arrow ($\downarrow$). Note that the value of m_s is independent of the other three quantum numbers, unlike the values of n, l, and m_l, which are interrelated.

The importance of the spin quantum number comes when electrons occupy specific orbitals in multielectron atoms. According to the **Pauli exclusion principle**, proposed in 1925 by the Austrian physicist Wolfgang Pauli (1900–1958), no two electrons in an atom can have the same four quantum numbers. In other words, the set of four quantum numbers associated with an electron acts as a unique "address" for that electron in an atom, and no two electrons can have the same address.

> **Pauli exclusion principle**   No two electrons in an atom can have the same four quantum numbers.

Think about the consequences of the Pauli exclusion principle. Electrons that occupy the same orbital have the same three quantum numbers, n, l, and m_l. But if they have the same values for n, l, and m_l, they must have different values for the fourth quantum number: either $m_s = +1/2$ or $m_s = -1/2$. Thus, an orbital can hold only two electrons, which must have opposite spins. An atom with x number of electrons therefore has at least $x/2$ occupied orbitals (although it might have more if some of its orbitals are only half-filled).

5.10 ORBITAL ENERGY LEVELS IN MULTIELECTRON ATOMS

As we said in Section 5.6, the energy level of an orbital in a hydrogen atom, which has only one electron, is determined by its principal quantum number n. Within a shell, all hydrogen orbitals have the same energy, independent of their other quantum numbers. The situation is different in multielectron atoms, however, where the energy level of a given orbital depends not only on the shell but also on the subshell. The s, p, d, and f orbitals within a given shell have slightly different energies in a multielectron atom, as shown previously in Figure 5.8, and there is even some crossover of energies between orbitals in different shells.

The difference in energy between subshells in multielectron atoms results from electron–electron repulsions. In hydrogen, the only electrical interaction is the attraction of the positive nucleus for the negative electron, but in multielectron atoms there are many different interactions. Not only are there the attractions of the nucleus for each electron, there are also the repulsions between every electron and each of its neighbors.

The repulsion of outer-shell electrons by inner-shell electrons is particularly important because the outer-shell electrons are pushed farther away from the nucleus and are thus held less tightly. Part of the attraction of the nucleus for an outer electron is thereby canceled, an effect we describe by saying that the outer electrons are *shielded* from the nucleus by the inner electrons (Figure 5.15). The nuclear charge actually felt by an electron, called the **effective nuclear charge, Z_{eff}**, is often substantially lower than the actual nuclear charge Z.

> **Effective nuclear charge** $Z_{eff} = Z_{actual} -$ Electron shielding

How does electron shielding lead to energy differences among orbitals within a shell? The answer is a consequence of the differences in orbital shapes. Compare a $2s$ orbital with a $2p$ orbital, for instance. The $2s$ orbital is spherical and has a large probability density near the nucleus, while the $2p$ orbitals are dumbbell-shaped and have a node at the nucleus (Section 5.7). An electron in a $2s$ orbital therefore spends more time closer to the nucleus than an electron in a $2p$ orbital does and is less

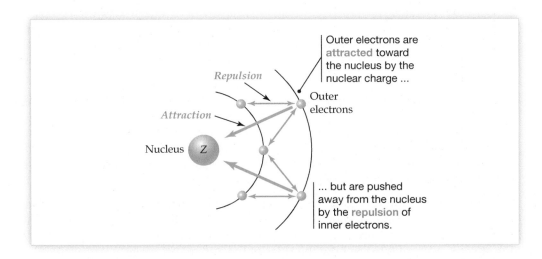

Figure 5.15
The origin of electron shielding and Z_{eff}.
The outer electrons feel a diminished nuclear attraction because inner electrons shield them from the full charge of the nucleus.

shielded. A $2s$ electron thus feels a higher Z_{eff}, is more tightly held by the nucleus, and is lower in energy than a $2p$ electron. In the same way, a $3p$ electron spends more time closer to the nucleus, feels a higher Z_{eff}, and has a lower energy than a $3d$ electron. More generally, within any given shell, a lower value of the angular-momentum quantum number l corresponds to a higher Z_{eff} and to a lower energy for the electron.

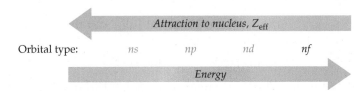

The idea that electrons in different orbitals are shielded differently and feel different values of Z_{eff} is a very useful one that we'll return to on several occasions to explain various chemical phenomena.

5.11 ELECTRON CONFIGURATIONS OF MULTIELECTRON ATOMS

All the parts are now in place to provide an electronic description for every element. Knowing the relative energies of the various orbitals, we can predict for each element which orbitals are occupied by electrons—the element's **electron configuration**.

A set of three rules called the **aufbau principle**, from the German word for "building up," guides the filling order of orbitals. In general, each successive electron added to an atom occupies the lowest-energy orbital available. The resultant lowest-energy configuration is called the **ground-state electron configuration** of the atom. Often, several orbitals will have the same energy level—for example, the three p orbitals or the five d orbitals in a given subshell. Orbitals that have the same energy level are said to be **degenerate**.

Rules of the aufbau principle:

1. **Lower-energy orbitals fill before higher-energy orbitals.** The ordering of energy levels for orbitals was shown in Figure 5.8 on page 163.

2. **An orbital can hold only two electrons, which must have opposite spins.** This is just a restatement of the Pauli exclusion principle (Section 5.9), emphasizing that no two electrons in an atom can have the same four quantum numbers.

3. **If two or more degenerate orbitals are available, one electron goes into each until all are half-full,** a statement called **Hund's rule.** Only then does a second electron fill one of the orbitals. Furthermore, the electrons in each of the singly occupied orbitals must have the same value for their spin quantum number.

◁▦▶ **Hund's rule**   If two or more orbitals with the same energy are available, one electron goes in each until all are half full. The electrons in the half-filled orbitals all have the same value of their spin quantum number.

Hund's rule derives from the fact that electrons repel one another and therefore remain as far apart as possible. Not surprisingly, they can remain farther apart and be lower in energy if they are in different orbitals describing different spatial regions than if they are in the same orbital occupying the same region. It also turns out that electrons in half-filled orbitals stay farther apart on average if they have the same spin rather than opposite spins.

Electron configurations are normally represented by listing the n quantum number and the s, p, d, or f designation of the occupied orbitals, beginning with the lowest energy one, and showing the occupancy of each orbital as a superscript. Let's look at some examples to see how the rules of the aufbau principle are applied.

• Hydrogen: Hydrogen has only one electron, which must go into the lowest-energy, $1s$ orbital. Thus, the ground-state electron configuration of hydrogen is $1s^1$.

$$\textbf{H: } 1s^1$$

• Helium: Helium has two electrons, both of which fit into the lowest-energy, $1s$ orbital. The two electrons have opposite spins.

$$\textbf{He: } 1s^2$$

• Lithium and beryllium: With the $1s$ orbital full, both the third and fourth electrons go into the next available orbital, $2s$.

$$\textbf{Li: } 1s^2\,2s^1 \qquad \textbf{Be: } 1s^2\,2s^2$$

• Boron through neon: The six elements from boron through neon have their three $2p$ orbitals filled successively. Because these three $2p$ orbitals have the same energy, they are degenerate and are filled according to Hund's rule. In carbon, for instance, the two $2p$ electrons are in different orbitals, which can be arbitrarily specified as $2p_x$, $2p_y$, or $2p_z$ when writing the electron configuration. The same is true of nitrogen, whose three $2p$ electrons must be in three different orbitals. Although not usually noted in the written electron configuration, the electrons in each of the singly occupied carbon and nitrogen $2p$ orbitals must have the same value of the spin quantum number—either $+1/2$ or $-1/2$.

For clarity, we sometimes specify electron configurations using orbital-filling diagrams, in which electrons are represented by arrows. The two values of the spin quantum numbers are indicated by having the arrow point either up or down. An up–down pair indicates that an orbital is filled, while a single up (or down) arrow indicates that an orbital is half filled. Note in the diagrams for carbon and nitrogen that the degenerate $2p$ orbitals are half filled rather than filled, according to Hund's rule, and that the electron spin is the same in each.

B: $1s^2\,2s^2\,2p^1$ or

C: $1s^2\,2s^2\,2p_x^{\ 1}\,2p_y^{\ 1}$ or

N: $1s^2\,2s^2\,2p_x^{\ 1}\,2p_y^{\ 1}\,2p_z^{\ 1}$ or

From oxygen through neon, the three $2p$ orbitals are successively filled. For fluorine and neon, it's no longer necessary to distinguish among the different $2p$ orbitals, so we can simply write $2p^5$ and $2p^6$.

O: $1s^2\,2s^2\,2p_x^{\,2}\,2p_y^{\,1}\,2p_z^{\,1}$ or $\underset{1s}{\uparrow\downarrow}\quad\underset{2s}{\uparrow\downarrow}\quad\underset{2p}{\uparrow\downarrow\quad\uparrow\quad\uparrow}$

F: $1s^2\,2s^2\,2p^5$ or $\underset{1s}{\uparrow\downarrow}\quad\underset{2s}{\uparrow\downarrow}\quad\underset{2p}{\uparrow\downarrow\quad\uparrow\downarrow\quad\uparrow}$

Ne: $1s^2\,2s^2\,2p^6$ or $\underset{1s}{\uparrow\downarrow}\quad\underset{2s}{\uparrow\downarrow}\quad\underset{2p}{\uparrow\downarrow\quad\uparrow\downarrow\quad\uparrow\downarrow}$

- **Sodium and magnesium:** The $3s$ orbital is filled next, giving sodium and magnesium the ground-state electron configurations shown. Note that we often write the configurations in a shorthand version by giving the symbol of the noble gas in the previous row to indicate electrons in filled shells and then specifying only those electrons in partially filled shells.

Neon configuration

Na: $1s^2\,2s^2\,2p^6\,3s^1$ or   [Ne] $3s^1$

Mg: $1s^2\,2s^2\,2p^6\,3s^2$ or   [Ne] $3s^2$

- **Aluminum through argon:** The $3p$ orbitals are now filled according to the same rules used previously for filling the $2p$ orbitals of boron through neon. Rather than explicitly identify which of the degenerate $3p$ orbitals are occupied in Si, P, and S, we'll simplify the writing by giving just the total number of electrons in the subshell. For example, we'll write $3p^2$ for silicon rather than $3p_x^{\,1}\,3p_y^{\,1}$.

Al: [Ne] $3s^2\,3p^1$	**Si:** [Ne] $3s^2\,3p^2$	**P:** [Ne] $3s^2\,3p^3$
S: [Ne] $3s^2\,3p^4$	**Cl:** [Ne] $3s^2\,3p^5$	**Ar:** [Ne] $3s^2\,3p^6$

- **Elements past argon:** Following the filling of the $3p$ subshell in argon, the first crossover in the orbital filling order is encountered. Rather than continue filling the third shell by populating the $3d$ orbitals, the next two electrons in potassium and calcium go into the $4s$ subshell. Only then does filling of the $3d$ subshell occur to give the first transition metal series from scandium through zinc.

K: [Ar] $4s^1$ **Ca:** [Ar] $4s^2$ **Sc:** [Ar] $4s^2\,3d^1 \longrightarrow$ **Zn:** [Ar] $4s^2\,3d^{10}$

The experimentally determined ground-state electron configurations of the elements are shown in **Figure 5.16**.

5.12 SOME ANOMALOUS ELECTRON CONFIGURATIONS

The guidelines discussed in the previous section for determining ground-state electron configurations work well but are not completely accurate. A careful look at Figure 5.16 shows that 90 electron configurations are correctly accounted for by the rules but that 21 of the predicted configurations are incorrect.

The reasons for the anomalies often have to do with the unusual stability of both half-filled and fully filled subshells. Chromium, for example, which we would predict to have the configuration [Ar] $4s^2\,3d^4$, actually has the configuration [Ar] $4s^1\,3d^5$. By moving an electron from the $4s$ orbital to an energetically similar $3d$ orbital, chromium trades one filled subshell ($4s^2$) for two half-filled subshells ($4s^1\,3d^5$), thereby allowing the two electrons to be farther apart. In the same way, copper, which we would predict to have the configuration [Ar] $4s^2\,3d^9$, actually has the configuration [Ar] $4s^1\,3d^{10}$. By transferring an electron from the $4s$ orbital to a $3d$ orbital, copper trades one filled subshell ($4s^2$) for a different filled subshell ($3d^{10}$) and gains a half-filled subshell ($4s^1$).

Periodic Table — Outer-shell, ground-state electron configurations of the elements

1 / 1A	2 / 2A	3 / 3B	4 / 4B	5 / 5B	6 / 6B	7 / 7B	8	9 / 8B	10	11 / 1B	12 / 2B	13 / 3A	14 / 4A	15 / 5A	16 / 6A	17 / 7A	18 / 8A
1 H $1s^1$																	2 He $1s^2$
3 Li $2s^1$	4 Be $2s^2$											5 B $2s^22p^1$	6 C $2s^22p^2$	7 N $2s^22p^3$	8 O $2s^22p^4$	9 F $2s^22p^5$	10 Ne $2s^22p^6$
11 Na $3s^1$	12 Mg $3s^2$											13 Al $3s^23p^1$	14 Si $3s^23p^2$	15 P $3s^23p^3$	16 S $3s^23p^4$	17 Cl $3s^23p^5$	18 Ar $3s^23p^6$
19 K $4s^1$	20 Ca $4s^2$	21 Sc $4s^23d^1$	22 Ti $4s^23d^2$	23 V $4s^23d^3$	24 Cr $4s^13d^5$	25 Mn $4s^23d^5$	26 Fe $4s^23d^6$	27 Co $4s^23d^7$	28 Ni $4s^23d^8$	29 Cu $4s^13d^{10}$	30 Zn $4s^23d^{10}$	31 Ga $4s^23d^{10}4p^1$	32 Ge $4s^23d^{10}4p^2$	33 As $4s^23d^{10}4p^3$	34 Se $4s^23d^{10}4p^4$	35 Br $4s^23d^{10}4p^5$	36 Kr $4s^23d^{10}4p^6$
37 Rb $5s^1$	38 Sr $5s^2$	39 Y $5s^24d^1$	40 Zr $5s^24d^2$	41 Nb $5s^14d^4$	42 Mo $5s^14d^5$	43 Tc $5s^24d^5$	44 Ru $5s^14d^7$	45 Rh $5s^14d^8$	46 Pd $4d^{10}$	47 Ag $5s^14d^{10}$	48 Cd $5s^24d^{10}$	49 In $5s^24d^{10}5p^1$	50 Sn $5s^24d^{10}5p^2$	51 Sb $5s^24d^{10}5p^3$	52 Te $5s^24d^{10}5p^4$	53 I $5s^24d^{10}5p^5$	54 Xe $5s^24d^{10}5p^6$
55 Cs $6s^1$	56 Ba $6s^2$	71 Lu $6s^24f^{14}5d^1$	72 Hf $6s^24f^{14}5d^2$	73 Ta $6s^24f^{14}5d^3$	74 W $6s^24f^{14}5d^4$	75 Re $6s^24f^{14}5d^5$	76 Os $6s^24f^{14}5d^6$	77 Ir $6s^24f^{14}5d^7$	78 Pt $6s^14f^{14}5d^9$	79 Au $6s^14f^{14}5d^{10}$	80 Hg $6s^24f^{14}5d^{10}$	81 Tl $6s^24f^{14}5d^{10}6p^1$	82 Pb $6s^24f^{14}5d^{10}6p^2$	83 Bi $6s^24f^{14}5d^{10}6p^3$	84 Po $6s^24f^{14}5d^{10}6p^4$	85 At $6s^24f^{14}5d^{10}6p^5$	86 Rn $6s^24f^{14}5d^{10}6p^6$
87 Fr $7s^1$	88 Ra $7s^2$	103 Lr $7s^25f^{14}6d^1$	104 Rf $7s^25f^{14}6d^2$	105 Db $7s^25f^{14}6d^3$	106 Sg $7s^25f^{14}6d^4$	107 Bh $7s^25f^{14}6d^5$	108 Hs $7s^25f^{14}6d^6$	109 Mt $7s^25f^{14}6d^7$	110 Ds $7s^15f^{14}6d^9$	111 Rg $7s^15f^{14}6d^{10}$	112 Cn $7s^25f^{14}6d^{10}$	113 —	114 —	115 —	116 —	117 —	118 —

Lanthanides:

57 La $6s^25d^1$	58 Ce $6s^24f^15d^1$	59 Pr $6s^24f^3$	60 Nd $6s^24f^4$	61 Pm $6s^24f^5$	62 Sm $6s^24f^6$	63 Eu $6s^24f^7$	64 Gd $6s^24f^75d^1$	65 Tb $6s^24f^9$	66 Dy $6s^24f^{10}$	67 Ho $6s^24f^{11}$	68 Er $6s^24f^{12}$	69 Tm $6s^24f^{13}$	70 Yb $6s^24f^{14}$

Actinides:

89 Ac $7s^26d^1$	90 Th $7s^26d^2$	91 Pa $7s^25f^26d^1$	92 U $7s^25f^36d^1$	93 Np $7s^25f^46d^1$	94 Pu $7s^25f^6$	95 Am $7s^25f^7$	96 Cm $7s^25f^76d^1$	97 Bk $7s^25f^9$	98 Cf $7s^25f^{10}$	99 Es $7s^25f^{11}$	100 Fm $7s^25f^{12}$	101 Md $7s^25f^{13}$	102 No $7s^25f^{14}$

Figure 5.16
Outer-shell, ground-state electron configurations of the elements.

Most of the anomalous electron configurations shown in Figure 5.16 occur in elements with atomic numbers greater than $Z = 40$, where the energy differences between subshells are small. In all cases, the transfer of an electron from one subshell to another lowers the total energy of the atom because of a decrease in electron–electron repulsions.

▶ **PROBLEM 5.16** Look at the electron configurations in Figure 5.16, and identify the 21 anomalous ones.

5.13 ELECTRON CONFIGURATIONS AND THE PERIODIC TABLE

Why are electron configurations so important, and what do they have to do with the periodic table? The answers emerge when you look closely at Figure 5.16. Focusing only on the electrons in the outermost shell, called the **valence shell**, all the elements in a given group of the periodic table have similar valence-shell electron configurations (Table 5.2). The group 1A elements, for example, all have an s^1 valence-shell configuration; the group 2A elements have an s^2 valence-shell configuration; the group 3A elements have an $s^2 p^1$ valence-shell configuration; and so on across every group of the periodic table (except for the small number of anomalies). Furthermore, because the valence-shell electrons are outermost and least tightly held, they are the most important for determining an element's properties, thus explaining why the elements in a given group of the periodic table have similar chemical behavior.

The periodic table can be divided into four regions, or blocks, of elements according to the orbitals being filled (Figure 5.17). The group 1A and 2A elements on the left side of the table are called the *s-block elements* because they result from the filling of an s orbital; the group 3A–8A elements on the right side of the table are the *p-block elements* because they result from the filling of p orbitals; the transition metal *d-block elements* in the middle of the table result from the filling of d orbitals; and the lanthanide/actinide *f-block elements* detached at the bottom of the table result from the filling of f orbitals.

TABLE 5.2 Valence-Shell Electron Configurations of Main-Group Elements

Group	Valence-Shell Electron Configuration	
1A	ns^1	(1 total)
2A	ns^2	(2 total)
3A	$ns^2 np^1$	(3 total)
4A	$ns^2 np^2$	(4 total)
5A	$ns^2 np^3$	(5 total)
6A	$ns^2 np^4$	(6 total)
7A	$ns^2 np^5$	(7 total)
8A	$ns^2 np^6$	(8 total)

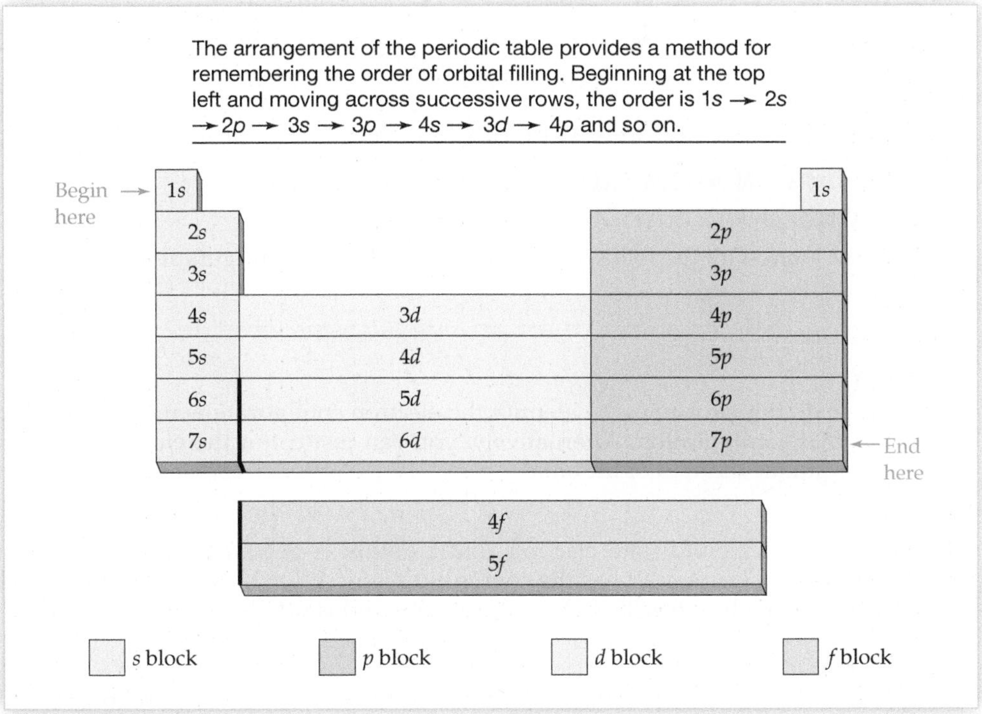

The arrangement of the periodic table provides a method for remembering the order of orbital filling. Beginning at the top left and moving across successive rows, the order is $1s \rightarrow 2s \rightarrow 2p \rightarrow 3s \rightarrow 3p \rightarrow 4s \rightarrow 3d \rightarrow 4p$ and so on.

Begin here → 1s   1s
2s   2p
3s   3p
4s   3d   4p
5s   4d   5p
6s   5d   6p
7s   6d   7p ← End here

4f
5f

☐ s block   ☐ p block   ☐ d block   ☐ f block

Figure 5.17
Blocks of the periodic table. Each block corresponds to the filling of a different kind of orbital.

Thinking of the periodic table as outlined in Figure 5.17 provides a useful way to remember the order of orbital filling. Beginning at the top left corner of the periodic table and going across successive rows gives the correct orbital-filling order. The first row of the periodic table, for instance, contains only the two s-block elements H and He, so the first available s orbital ($1s$) is filled first. The second row begins with two s-block elements (Li and Be) and continues with six p-block elements (B through Ne), so the next available s orbital ($2s$) and then the first available p orbitals ($2p$) are filled. Moving similarly across the third row, the $3s$ and $3p$ orbitals are filled. The fourth row again starts with two s-block elements (K and Ca) but is then followed by 10 d-block elements (Sc through Zn) and six p-block elements (Ga through Kr). Thus, the order of orbital filling is $4s$ followed by the first available d orbitals ($3d$) followed by $4p$. Continuing through successive rows of the periodic table gives the entire filling order:

$$1s \rightarrow 2s \rightarrow 2p \rightarrow 3s \rightarrow 3p \rightarrow 4s \rightarrow 3d \rightarrow 4p \rightarrow 5s \rightarrow 4d \rightarrow$$
$$5p \rightarrow 6s \rightarrow 4f \rightarrow 5d \rightarrow 6p \rightarrow 7s \rightarrow 5f \rightarrow 6d \rightarrow 7p$$

WORKED EXAMPLE 5.8

ASSIGNING A GROUND-STATE ELECTRON CONFIGURATION TO AN ATOM

Give the ground-state electron configuration of arsenic, $Z = 33$, and draw an orbital-filling diagram, indicating the electrons as up or down arrows.

STRATEGY

Think of the periodic table as having s, p, d, and f blocks of elements, as shown in Figure 5.17. Start with hydrogen at the upper left, and fill orbitals until 33 electrons have been added. Remember that only 2 electrons can go into an orbital and that each one of a set of degenerate orbitals must be half filled before any one can be completely filled.

SOLUTION

As: $1s^2\, 2s^2\, 2p^6\, 3s^2\, 3p^6\, 4s^2\, 3d^{10}\, 4p^3$ or $[Ar]\, 4s^2\, 3d^{10}\, 4p^3$

An orbital-filling diagram indicates the electrons in each orbital as arrows. Note that the three $4p$ electrons all have the same spin:

As: [Ar] $\underset{4s}{\underline{\uparrow\downarrow}}$ $\underset{3d}{\underline{\uparrow\downarrow}\;\underline{\uparrow\downarrow}\;\underline{\uparrow\downarrow}\;\underline{\uparrow\downarrow}\;\underline{\uparrow\downarrow}}$ $\underset{4p}{\underline{\uparrow}\;\underline{\uparrow}\;\underline{\uparrow}}$

WORKED CONCEPTUAL EXAMPLE 5.9

IDENTIFYING AN ATOM FROM ITS GROUND-STATE ELECTRON CONFIGURATION

Identify the atom with the following ground-state electron configuration:

[Kr] $\underline{\uparrow\downarrow}$ $\underline{\uparrow}\;\underline{\uparrow}\;\underline{\uparrow}\;\underline{\uparrow}\;\underline{\uparrow}$ $\underline{}\;\underline{}\;\underline{}$

STRATEGY

One way to do this problem is to identify the electron configuration and decide which atom has that configuration. Alternatively, you can just count the electrons, thereby finding the atomic number of the atom.

SOLUTION

The atom whose ground-state electron configuration is depicted is in the fifth row because it follows krypton. It has the configuration $5s^2\, 4d^5$, which identifies it as technetium. Alternatively, it has $36 + 7 = 43$ electrons and is the element with $Z = 43$.

▶ PROBLEM 5.17   Give expected ground-state electron configurations for the following atoms, and draw orbital-filling diagrams for parts (a)–(c).

(a) Ti ($Z = 22$)   (b) Zn ($Z = 30$)   (c) Sn ($Z = 50$)   (d) Pb ($Z = 82$)

▶ **PROBLEM 5.18** Take a guess. What do you think is a likely ground-state electron configuration for the sodium *ion*, Na^+, formed by loss of an electron from a neutral sodium atom? What is a likely ground-state electron configuration for the chloride ion, Cl^-, formed by adding an electron to a neutral chlorine atom?

CONCEPTUAL PROBLEM 5.19 Identify the atom with the following ground-state electron configuration:

[Ar] ⇅   ⇅ ⇅ ⇅ ↑ ↑   _ _ _

5.14 ELECTRON CONFIGURATIONS AND PERIODIC PROPERTIES: ATOMIC RADII

We began this chapter by saying that atomic radius is one of many elemental properties to show periodic behavior. You might wonder, though, how we can talk about a definite size for an atom, having said in Section 5.7 that the electron clouds around atoms have no specific boundaries. What's usually done is to define an atom's radius as being half the distance between the nuclei of two identical atoms when they are bonded together. In Cl_2, for example, the distance between the two chlorine nuclei is 198 pm; in diamond (elemental carbon), the distance between two carbon nuclei is 154 pm. Thus, we say that the atomic radius of chlorine is half the Cl—Cl distance, or 99 pm, and the atomic radius of carbon is half the C—C distance, or 77 pm.

It's possible to check the accuracy of atomic radii by making sure that the assigned values are additive. For instance, since the atomic radius of Cl is 99 pm and the atomic radius of C is 77 pm, the distance between Cl and C nuclei when those two atoms are bonded together ought to be roughly 99 pm + 77 pm, or 176 pm. In fact, the measured distance between chlorine and carbon in chloromethane (CH_3Cl) is 178 pm, remarkably close to the expected value.

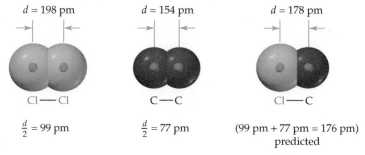

d = 198 pm d = 154 pm d = 178 pm

Cl — Cl   C — C   Cl — C

$\frac{d}{2}$ = 99 pm $\frac{d}{2}$ = 77 pm   (99 pm + 77 pm = 176 pm)
                                      predicted

As shown pictorially in Figure 5.18 and graphically in Figure 5.1 at the beginning of this chapter, a comparison of atomic radius versus atomic number shows a

Figure 5.18
Atomic radii of the elements in picometers.

Radius increases Radius decreases ⟶   Radius increases

H 37																	He
Li 152	Be 112											B 83	C 77	N 75	O 73	F 72	Ne
Na 186	Mg 160											Al 143	Si 117	P 110	S 104	Cl 99	Ar
K 227	Ca 197	Sc 162	Ti 147	V 134	Cr 128	Mn 127	Fe 126	Co 125	Ni 124	Cu 128	Zn 134	Ga 135	Ge 122	As 120	Se 116	Br 114	Kr
Rb 248	Sr 215	Y 180	Zr 160	Nb 146	Mo 139	Tc 136	Ru 134	Rh 134	Pd 137	Ag 144	Cd 151	In 167	Sn 140	Sb 140	Te 143	I 133	Xe
Cs 265	Ba 222	Lu 173	Hf 159	Ta 146	W 139	Re 137	Os 135	Ir 136	Pt 138	Au 144	Hg 151	Tl 170	Pb 175	Bi 150	Po 167	At	Rn

periodic rise-and-fall pattern. Atomic radii increase going down a group of the periodic table (Li < Na < K < Rb < Cs, for instance) but decrease going across a row from left to right (Na > Mg > Al > Si > P > S > Cl, for instance). How can this behavior be explained?

The increase in radius going down a group of the periodic table occurs because successively larger valence-shell orbitals are occupied. In Li, for example, the outermost occupied shell is the second one ($2s^1$); in Na it's the third one ($3s^1$); in K it's the fourth one ($4s^1$); and so on through Rb ($5s^1$), Cs ($6s^1$), and Fr ($7s^1$). Because larger shells are occupied, the atomic radii are also larger.

The decrease in radius from left to right across the periodic table occurs because of an increase in effective nuclear charge caused by the increasing number of protons in the nucleus. As we saw in Section 5.10, Z_{eff}, the effective nuclear charge actually felt by an electron, is lower than the true nuclear charge Z because of shielding by other electrons in the atom. The amount of shielding felt by an electron depends on both the shell and subshell of the other electrons with which it is interacting.

As a general rule, a valence-shell electron is . . .

- . . . strongly shielded by electrons in inner shells, which are closer to the nucleus.
- . . . less strongly shielded by other electrons in the same shell, according to the order $s > p > d > f$.
- . . . only weakly shielded by other electrons in the same subshell, which are at the same distance from the nucleus.

Going across the third period from Na to Ar, for example, each additional electron adds to the same shell (from $3s^1$ for Na to $3s^2 3p^6$ for Ar). Because electrons in the same shell are at approximately the same distance from the nucleus, they are relatively ineffective at shielding one another. At the same time, though, the nuclear charge Z increases from +11 for Na to +18 for Ar. Thus, the *effective* nuclear charge for the valence-shell electrons increases across the period, drawing all the valence-shell electrons closer to the nucleus and progressively shrinking the atomic radii (Figure 5.19).

Figure 5.19
Plots of atomic radius and calculated Z_{eff} for the highest-energy electron versus atomic number.

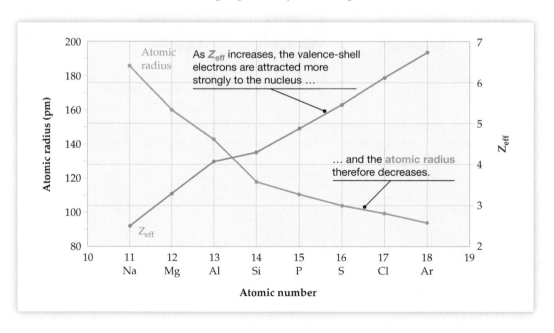

What is true of atomic radius is also true of other atomic properties, whose periodicity can be explained by electron configurations. We'll continue the subject in the next chapter.

▶ **PROBLEM 5.20** Which atom in each of the following pairs would you expect to be larger? Explain.

    (a) Mg or Ba   **(b)** W or Hf   **(c)** Si or Sn   **(d)** Os or Lu

INQUIRY WHAT DO COMPACT FLUORESCENT LIGHTS HAVE TO DO WITH ATOMIC LINE SPECTRA?

In the standard incandescent lightbulb that has been used for more than a century, an electrical current passes through a thin tungsten filament, which is thereby heated and begins to glow. The wavelengths and intensity of the light emitted depend on the temperature of the glowing filament—typically about 2500 °C—and cover the range from ultraviolet (200–400 nm, through the visible (400–800 nm), to the infrared 800–2000 nm. The ultraviolet frequencies are blocked by the glass of the bulb, the visible frequencies pass through (the whole point of the lightbulb, after all), and the infrared frequencies warm the bulb and its surroundings.

Despite its long history, an incandescent bulb is actually an extremely inefficient device. In fact, only about 5% of the electrical energy consumed by the bulb is converted into visible light, with most of the remaining 95% converted into heat. Thus, many households and businesses are replacing their incandescent lightbulbs with modern compact fluorescent bulbs in an effort to use less energy. (Not that fluorescent bulbs are terribly efficient themselves—only about 20% of the energy they consume is converted into light—but that still makes them about four times better than incandescents.)

A fluorescent bulb is, in essence, a variation of the cathode-ray tube described in Section 2.3. The bulb has two main parts, an argon-filled glass tube (either straight or coiled) containing a small amount of mercury vapor, and electronic circuitry that provides a controlled high-voltage current. The current passes through a filament, which heats up and emits a flow of electrons through the tube. In the tube, some of the flowing electrons collide with mercury atoms, transferring their kinetic energy and exciting mercury electrons to higher-energy orbitals. Photons are then released when the excited mercury electrons fall back to the ground state, generating an atomic line spectrum.

Some photons emitted by the excited mercury atoms are in the visible range and contribute to the light we observe, but most are in the ultraviolet range at 185 nm and 254 nm and are invisible to our eyes. To capture this ultraviolet energy, fluorescent bulbs are coated on the inside with a *phosphor*, a substance that absorbs the ultraviolet light and re-emits the energy as visible light. As a result, fluorescent lights waste much less energy than incandescent bulbs.

Many different phosphors are used in fluorescent lights, each emitting its own line spectrum with visible light of various colors. Typically, a so-called *triphosphor* mixture is used, consisting of several complex metal oxides and rare-earth ions: $Y_2O_3:Eu^{3+}$ (red emitting), $CeMgAl_{11}O_{19}:Tb^{3+}$ (green emitting), and $BaMgAl_{10}O_{17}:Eu^{2+}$ (blue emitting). The final color that results can be tuned as desired by the manufacturer, but typically the three emissions together are distributed fairly evenly over the visible spectrum and provide a color reproduction that our eyes perceive as natural white light (Figure 5.20).

▶ **PROBLEM 5.21** How do atomic line spectra give rise to the light emitted from fluorescent bulbs?

▲ Compact fluorescent bulbs like those shown here are a much more energy-efficient way to light a home than typical incandescent lightbulbs.

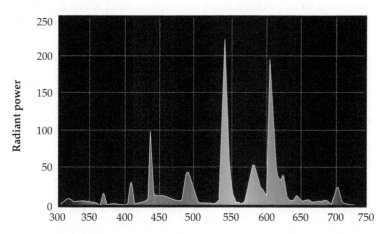

Figure 5.20

The triphosphor spectrum emitted from a typical fluorescent bulb. The triphosphor spectrum is distributed over the visible spectrum and is perceived by our eyes as white light.

SUMMARY

Understanding the nature of atoms and molecules begins with an understanding of light and other kinds of **electromagnetic energy** that make up the **electromagnetic spectrum**. An electromagnetic wave travels through a vacuum at the speed of light (c) and is characterized by its **frequency (ν)**, **wavelength (λ)**, and **amplitude**. Unlike the white light of the sun, which consists of a nearly continuous distribution of wavelengths, the light emitted by an excited atom consists of only a few discrete wavelengths, a so-called **line spectrum**. The observed wavelengths correspond to the specific energy differences between energies of different orbitals.

Atomic line spectra arise because electromagnetic energy occurs only in discrete amounts, or **quanta**. Just as light behaves in some respects like a stream of small particles (**photons**), so electrons and other tiny units of matter behave in some respects like waves. The wavelength of a particle of mass m traveling at a velocity v is given by the **de Broglie equation**, $\lambda = h/mv$, where h is Planck's constant.

The **quantum mechanical model** proposed in 1926 by Erwin Schrödinger describes an atom by a mathematical equation similar to that used to describe wave motion. The behavior of each electron in an atom is characterized by a **wave function**, or **orbital**, whose square defines the probability of finding the electron in a given volume of space. Each wave function has a set of three parameters called **quantum numbers**. The **principal quantum number n** defines the size of the orbital; the **angular-momentum quantum number l** defines the shape of the orbital; and the **magnetic quantum number m_l** defines the spatial orientation of the orbital. In a hydrogen atom, which contains only one electron, the energy of an orbital depends only on n. In a multielectron atom, the energy of an orbital depends on both n and l. In addition, the **spin quantum number m_s** specifies the electron spin as either $+1/2$ or $-1/2$.

Orbitals can be grouped into successive layers, or **shells**, according to their principal quantum number n. Within a shell, orbitals are grouped into s, p, d, and f **subshells** according to their angular-momentum quantum numbers l. An orbital in an s subshell is spherical, an orbital in a p subshell is dumbbell-shaped, and four of the five orbitals in a d subshell are cloverleaf-shaped.

The **ground-state electron configuration** of a multielectron atom is arrived at by following a series of rules called the **aufbau principle**.

1. The lowest-energy orbitals fill first.
2. Only two electrons of opposite spin go into any one orbital (the **Pauli exclusion principle**).
3. If two or more orbitals are equal in energy (**degenerate**), each is half filled before any one of them is completely filled (**Hund's rule**).

The periodic table is the most important organizing principle of chemistry. It is successful because elements in each group of the periodic table have similar **valence-shell electron configurations** and therefore have similar properties. For example, atomic radii of elements show a periodic rise-and-fall pattern according to the positions of the elements in the table. Atomic radii increase going down a group because n increases, and they decrease from left to right across a period because the **effective nuclear charge (Z_{eff})** increases.

KEY WORDS

amplitude *153*
angular-momentum
   quantum number (*l*) *162*
aufbau principle *171*
Balmer–Rydberg
   equation *155*
d-block element *175*
de Broglie equation *159*
degenerate *171*
effective nuclear
   charge (*Z*$_{eff}$) *170*
electromagnetic energy *151*

electromagnetic
   spectrum *151*
electron configuration *171*
f-block element *175*
frequency (*ν*) *153*
ground-state electron
   configuration *171*
Heisenberg uncertainty
   principle *160*
hertz (Hz) *153*
Hund's rule *171*
line spectrum *154*

magnetic quantum
   number (*m*$_l$) *162*
node *165*
orbital *161*
p-block element *175*
Pauli exclusion
   principle *170*
phase *165*
photon *157*
principal quantum
   number (*n*) *161*
quantum *158*

quantum mechanical
   model *160*
quantum number *161*
s-block element *175*
shell *161*
spin quantum
   number (*m*$_s$) *170*
subshell *162*
valence shell *175*
wave function *161*
wavelength (*λ*) *153*

CONCEPTUAL PROBLEMS

Problems 5.1–5.21 appear within the chapter.

5.22 Where on the blank outline of the periodic table do elements that meet the following descriptions appear?

    (a) Elements with the valence-shell ground-state electron configuration $ns^2\,np^5$

    (b) An element whose fourth shell contains two p electrons

    (c) An element with the ground-state electron configuration [Ar] $4s^2 3d^{10} 4p^5$

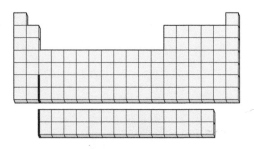

5.23 Where on the periodic table do elements that meet the following descriptions appear?

(a) Elements with electrons whose largest principal quantum number is $n = 4$

(b) Elements with the valence-shell ground-state electron configuration $ns^2 np^3$

(c) Elements that have only one unpaired p electron

(d) The d-block elements

(e) The p-block elements

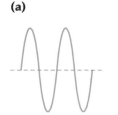

5.24 One of the elements shown on the following periodic table has an anomalous ground-state electron configuration. Which is it —red, blue, or green—and why?

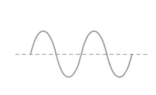

5.25 Two electromagnetic waves are represented below.

(a) Which wave has the greater intensity?

(b) Which wave corresponds to higher-energy radiation?

(c) Which wave represents yellow light, and which represents infrared radiation?

(a)   **(b)**

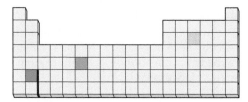

5.26 What atom has the following orbital-filling diagram?

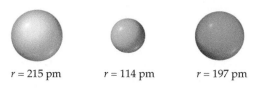

5.27 The following orbital-filling diagram represents an excited state rather than the ground state of an atom. Identify the atom, and give its ground-state electron configuration.

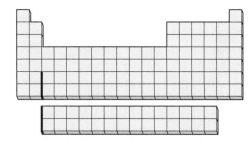

5.28 Which of the following three spheres represents a Ca atom, which an Sr atom, and which a Br atom?

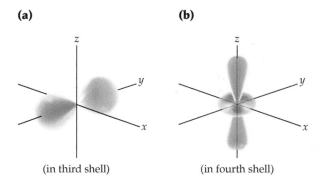

$r = 215$ pm $r = 114$ pm $r = 197$ pm

5.29 Identify each of the following orbitals, and give n and l quantum numbers for each.

(a)   **(b)**

(in third shell)   (in fourth shell)

SECTION PROBLEMS

Electromagnetic Energy and Atomic Spectra (Sections 5.1–5.3)

5.30 Which has the higher frequency, red light or violet light? Which has the longer wavelength? Which has the greater energy?

5.31 Which has the higher frequency, infrared light or ultraviolet light? Which has the longer wavelength? Which has the greater energy?

5.32 The Hubble Space Telescope detects electromagnetic energy in the wavelength range 1.15×10^{-7} m to 2.0×10^{-6} m. What region of the electromagnetic spectrum is found completely within this range? What regions fall partially in this range?

5.33 The Green Bank Telescope in West Virginia—the world's largest steerable radio telescope—detects frequencies from 290 MHz to 90 GHz. What region or regions of the electromagnetic spectrum are found completely or partially within its detection range?

5.34 What is the wavelength in meters of ultraviolet light with $\nu = 5.5 \times 10^{15}$ s^{-1}?

5.35 What is the frequency of a microwave with $\lambda = 4.33 \times 10^{-3}$ m?

5.36 Calculate the energies of the following waves in kilojoules per mole, and tell which member of each pair has the higher value.

(a) An FM radio wave at 99.5 MHz and an AM radio wave at 1150 kHz

(b) An X ray with $\lambda = 3.44 \times 10^{-9}$ m and a microwave with $\lambda = 6.71 \times 10^{-2}$ m

5.37 The MRI (magnetic resonance imaging) body scanners used in hospitals operate with 400 MHz radiofrequency energy. How much energy does this correspond to in kilojoules per mole?

5.38 A certain cellular telephone transmits at a frequency of 825 MHz and receives at a frequency of 875 MHz.

(a) What is the wavelength of the transmitted signal in cm?

(b) What is the wavelength of the received signal in cm?

5.39 Optical fibers allow the fast transmission of vast amounts of data. In one type of fiber, the wavelength of transmitted light is 1.3×10^3 nm.

(a) What is the frequency of the light?

(b) Fiber optic cable is available in 12 km lengths. How long will it take for a signal to travel that distance assuming that the speed of light in the cable is the same as in a vacuum?

5.40 What is the wavelength in meters of photons with the following energies? In what region of the electromagnetic spectrum does each appear?

(a) 90.5 kJ/mol   **(b)** 8.05×10^{-4} kJ/mol

(c) 1.83×10^3 kJ/mol

5.41 What is the energy of each of the following photons in kilojoules per mole?

(a) $\nu = 5.97 \times 10^{19}$ s^{-1} **(b)** $\nu = 1.26 \times 10^6$ s^{-1}

(c) $\lambda = 2.57 \times 10^2$ m

5.42 The data encoded on CDs, DVDs, and Blu-ray discs is read by lasers. What is the wavelength in nanometers and the energy in joules of the following lasers?

(a) CD laser, $\nu = 3.85 \times 10^{14}$ s^{-1}

(b) DVD laser, $\nu = 4.62 \times 10^{14}$ s^{-1}

(c) Blu-ray laser, $\nu = 7.41 \times 10^{14}$ s^{-1}

5.43 The semimetal germanium is used as a component in photodetectors, which generate electric current when exposed to light. If a germanium photodetector responds to photons in the range $\lambda = 400 - 1700$ nm, will the following light sources be detected?

(a) a laser with $\nu = 4.35 \times 10^{14}$ s^{-1}

(b) photons with $E = 43$ kJ/mol

(c) electromagnetic radiation with $\nu = 706$ THz

5.44 According to the equation for the Balmer line spectrum of hydrogen, a value of $n = 3$ gives a red spectral line at 656.3 nm, a value of $n = 4$ gives a green line at 486.1 nm, and a value of $n = 5$ gives a blue line at 434.0 nm. Calculate the energy in kilojoules per mole of the radiation corresponding to each of these spectral lines.

5.45 According to the values cited in Problem 5.44, the wavelength differences between lines in the Balmer series become smaller as n becomes larger. In other words, the wavelengths converge toward a minimum value as n becomes very large. At what wavelength in nanometers do the lines converge?

Particles and Waves (Section 5.4–5.5)

5.46 Protons and electrons can be given very high energies in particle accelerators. What is the wavelength in meters of an electron (mass = 9.11×10^{-31} kg) that has been accelerated to 99% of the speed of light? In what region of the electromagnetic spectrum is this wavelength?

5.47 What is the wavelength in meters of a proton (mass = 1.673×10^{-24} g) that has been accelerated to 25% of the speed of light? In what region of the electromagnetic spectrum is this wavelength?

5.48 What is the de Broglie wavelength in meters of a baseball weighing 145 g and traveling at 156 km/h?

5.49 What is the de Broglie wavelength in meters of a mosquito weighing 1.55 mg and flying at 1.38 m/s?

5.50 At what speed in meters per second must a 145 g baseball be traveling to have a de Broglie wavelength of 0.500 nm?

5.51 What velocity would an electron (mass = 9.11×10^{-31} kg) need for its de Broglie wavelength to be that of red light (750 nm)?

5.52 Use the Heisenberg uncertainty principle to calculate the uncertainty in meters in the position of a honeybee weighing 0.68 g and traveling at a velocity of 0.85 m/s. Assume that the uncertainty in the velocity is 0.1 m/s.

5.53 The mass of a helium atom is 4.0026 amu, and its average velocity at 25 °C is 1.36×10^3 m/s. What is the uncertainty in meters in the position of a helium atom if the uncertainty in its velocity is 1%?

Orbitals and Quantum Mechanics (Sections 5.6–5.9)

5.54 What are the four quantum numbers, and what does each specify?

5.55 What is the Heisenberg uncertainty principle, and how does it affect our description of atomic structure?

5.56 Why do we have to use an arbitrary value such as 95% to determine the spatial limitations of an orbital?

5.57 How many nodal surfaces does a $4s$ orbital have? Draw a cutaway representation of a $4s$ orbital showing the nodes and the regions of maximum electron probability.

5.58 What is meant by the term effective nuclear charge, Z_{eff}, and what causes it?

5.59 How does electron shielding in multielectron atoms give rise to energy differences among $3s$, $3p$, and $3d$ orbitals?

5.60 Give the allowable combinations of quantum numbers for each of the following electrons:

(a) A $4s$ electron   **(b)** A $3p$ electron

(c) A $5f$ electron   **(d)** A $5d$ electron

5.61 Give the orbital designations of electrons with the following quantum numbers:

(a) $n = 3, l = 0, m_l = 0$ **(b)** $n = 2, \ l = 1, \ m_l = -1$

(c) $n = 4, l = 3, m_l = -2$ **(d)** $n = 4, \ l = 2, \ m_l = 0$

5.62 Tell which of the following combinations of quantum numbers are not allowed. Explain your answers.

(a) $n = 3, l = 0, m_l = -1$

(b) $n = 3, l = 1, m_l = 1$

(c) $n = 4, l = 4, m_l = 0$

5.63 Which of the following combinations of quantum numbers can refer to an electron in a ground-state cobalt atom ($Z = 27$)?

(a) $n = 3, l = 0, m_l = 2$

(b) $n = 4, l = 2, m_l = -2$

(c) $n = 3, l = 1, m_l = 0$

5.64 What is the maximum number of electrons in an atom whose highest-energy electrons have the principal quantum number $n = 5$?

5.65 What is the maximum number of electrons in an atom whose highest-energy electrons have the principal quantum number $n = 4$ and the angular-momentum quantum number $l = 0$?

5.66 The wavelength of light at which the Balmer series converges (Problem 5.45) corresponds to the amount of energy required to completely remove an electron from the second shell of a hydrogen atom. Calculate this energy in kilojoules per mole.

5.67 One series of lines of the hydrogen spectrum is caused by emission of energy accompanying the fall of an electron from outer shells to the fourth shell. The lines can be calculated using the Balmer–Rydberg equation:

$$\frac{1}{\lambda} = R_\infty \left[\frac{1}{m^2} - \frac{1}{n^2} \right]$$

where $m = 4$, $R_\infty = 1.097 \times 10^{-2}$ nm^{-1}, and n is an integer greater than 4. Calculate the wavelengths in nanometers and energies in kilojoules per mole of the first two lines in the series. In what region of the electromagnetic spectrum do they fall?

5.68 Sodium atoms emit light with a wavelength of 330 nm when an electron moves from a $4p$ orbital to a $3s$ orbital. What is the energy difference between the orbitals in kilojoules per mole?

5.69 Excited rubidium atoms emit red light with $\lambda = 795$ nm. What is the energy difference in kilojoules per mole between orbitals that give rise to this emission?

Electron Configurations (Sections 5.10–5.13)

5.70 Why does the number of elements in successive periods of the periodic table increase by the progression 2, 8, 18, 32?

5.71 Which two of the four quantum numbers determine the energy level of an orbital in a multielectron atom?

5.72 Which orbital in each of the following pairs is higher in energy?

(a) $5p$ or $5d$ (b) $4s$ or $3p$ (c) $6s$ or $4d$

5.73 Order the orbitals for a multielectron atom in each of the following lists according to increasing energy:

(a) $4d, 3p, 2p, 5s$ (b) $2s, 4s, 3d, 4p$ (c) $6s, 5p, 3d, 4p$

5.74 According to the aufbau principle, which orbital is filled immediately *after* each of the following in a multielectron atom?

(a) $4s$ (b) $3d$ (c) $5f$ (d) $5p$

5.75 According to the aufbau principle, which orbital is filled immediately *before* each of the following?

(a) $3p$ (b) $4p$ (c) $4f$ (d) $5d$

5.76 Give the expected ground-state electron configurations for the following elements:

(a) Ti   (b) Ru   (c) Sn   (d) Sr   (e) Se

5.77 Give the expected ground-state electron configurations for atoms with the following atomic numbers:

(a) $Z = 55$ (b) $Z = 40$ (c) $Z = 80$ (d) $Z = 62$

5.78 Draw orbital-filling diagrams for the following atoms. Show each electron as an up or down arrow, and use the abbreviation of the preceding noble gas to represent inner-shell electrons.

(a) Rb   (b) W   (c) Ge   (d) Zr

5.79 Draw orbital-filling diagrams for atoms with the following atomic numbers. Show each electron as an up or down arrow, and use the abbreviation of the preceding noble gas to represent inner-shell electrons.

(a) $Z = 25$ (b) $Z = 56$ (c) $Z = 28$ (d) $Z = 47$

5.80 Order the electrons in the following orbitals according to their shielding ability: $4s$, $4d$, $4f$.

5.81 Order the following elements according to increasing Z_{eff}: Ca, Se, Kr, K.

5.82 How many unpaired electrons are present in each of the following ground-state atoms?

(a) O   (b) Si   (c) K   (d) As

5.83 Identify the following atoms:

(a) It has the ground-state electron configuration [Ar] $4s^2 3d^{10} 4p^1$.

(b) It has the ground-state electron configuration [Kr] $4d^{10}$.

5.84 At what atomic number is the filling of a g orbital likely to begin?

5.85 Assuming that g orbitals fill according to Hund's rule, what is the atomic number of the first element to have a filled g orbital?

Electron Configurations and Periodic Properties (Section 5.14)

5.86 Why do atomic radii increase going down a group of the periodic table?

5.87 Why do atomic radii decrease from left to right across a period of the periodic table?

5.88 Order the following atoms according to increasing atomic radius: S, F, O.

5.89 Which atom in each of the following pairs has a larger radius?

(a) Na or K   (b) V or Ta

(c) V or Zn   (d) Li or Ba

5.90 The amount of energy that must be added to remove an electron from a neutral atom to give a positive ion is called the atom's *ionization energy*. Which would you expect to have the larger ionization energy, Na or Mg? Explain.

5.91 The amount of energy released when an electron adds to a neutral atom to give a negative ion is called the atom's *electron affinity*. Which would you expect to have the larger electron affinity, C or F? Explain.

5.92 What is the expected ground-state electron configuration of the recently discovered element with $Z = 116$?

5.93 What is the atomic number and expected ground-state electron configuration of the yet undiscovered element directly below Fr in the periodic table?

CHAPTER PROBLEMS

5.94 Orbital energies in single-electron atoms or ions, such as He^+, can be described with an equation similar to the Balmer–Rydberg equation:

$$\frac{1}{\lambda} = Z^2 R \left[\frac{1}{m^2} - \frac{1}{n^2} \right]$$

where Z is the atomic number. What wavelength of light in nm is emitted when the electron in He^+ falls from $n = 3$ to $n = 2$?

5.95 Like He^+, the Li^{2+} ion is a single-electron system (Problem 5.94). What wavelength of light in nm must be absorbed to promote the electron in Li^{2+} from $n = 1$ to $n = 4$?

5.96 Use the Balmer equation to calculate the wavelength in nanometers of the spectral line for hydrogen when $n = 6$. What is the energy in kilojoules per mole of the radiation corresponding to this line?

5.97 Lines in a certain series of the hydrogen spectrum are caused by emission of energy accompanying the fall of an electron from outer shells to the fifth shell. Use the Balmer–Rydberg equation to calculate the wavelengths in nanometers and energies in kilojoules per mole of the two longest-wavelength lines in the series. In what region of the electromagnetic spectrum do they fall?

5.98 What is the shortest wavelength in nanometers in the series you calculated in Problem 5.97?

5.99 What is the wavelength in meters of photons with the following energies? In what region of the electromagnetic spectrum does each appear?
(a) 142 kJ/mol   (b) 4.55×10^{-2} kJ/mol
(c) 4.81×10^4 kJ/mol

5.100 What is the energy of each of the following photons in kilojoules per mole?
(a) $\nu = 3.79 \times 10^{11} \, s^{-1}$ (b) $\nu = 5.45 \times 10^4 \, s^{-1}$
(c) $\lambda = 4.11 \times 10^{-5}$ m

5.101 The *second* in the SI system is defined as the duration of 9,192,631,770 periods of radiation corresponding to the transition between two energy levels of a cesium-133 atom. What is the energy difference between the two levels in kilojoules per mole?

5.102 Write the symbol, give the ground-state electron configuration, and draw an orbital-filling diagram for each of the following atoms. Use the abbreviation of the preceding noble gas to represent the inner-shell electrons.
(a) The heaviest alkaline earth metal
(b) The lightest transition metal
(c) The heaviest actinide metal
(d) The lightest semimetal
(e) The group 6A element in the fifth period

5.103 Imagine a universe in which the four quantum numbers can have the same possible values as in our universe except that the angular-momentum quantum number l can have integral values of $0, 1, 2, \ldots , n + 1$ (instead of $0, 1, 2, \ldots , n - 1$).
(a) How many elements would be in the first two rows of the periodic table in this universe?
(b) What would be the atomic number of the element in the second row and fifth column?

(c) Draw an orbital-filling diagram for the element with atomic number 12.

5.104 Cesium metal is frequently used in photoelectric cells because the amount of energy necessary to eject electrons from a cesium surface is relatively small—only 206.5 kJ/mol. What wavelength of light in nanometers does this correspond to?

5.105 The laser light used in compact disc players has $\lambda = 780$ nm. In what region of the electromagnetic spectrum does this light appear? What is the energy of this light in kilojoules per mole?

5.106 Draw orbital-filling diagrams for the following atoms. Show each electron as an up or down arrow, and use the abbreviation of the preceding noble gas to represent inner-shell electrons.
(a) Sr   (b) Cd   (c) has $Z = 22$ (d) has $Z = 34$

5.107 The atomic radii of Y (180 pm) and La (187 pm) are significantly different, but the radii of Zr (160 pm) and Hf (159 pm) are essentially identical. Explain.

5.108 You're probably familiar with using Scotch Tape for wrapping presents but may not know that it can also generate electromagnetic radiation. When Scotch Tape is unrolled in a vacuum (but not in air), photons with a range of frequencies around $\nu = 2.9 \times 10^{18} \, s^{-1}$ are emitted in nanosecond bursts.
(a) What is the wavelength in meters of photons with $\nu = 2.9 \times 10^{18} \, s^{-1}$?
(b) What is the energy in kJ/mol of photons with $\nu = 2.9 \times 10^{18} \, s^{-1}$?
(c) What type of electromagnetic radiation are these photons?

5.109 Hard wintergreen-flavored candies are *triboluminescent*, meaning that they emit flashes of light when crushed. (You can see it for yourself if you look in a mirror while crunching a wintergreen Life Saver in your mouth in a dark room.) The strongest emission is around $\lambda = 450$ nm.
(a) What is the frequency in s^{-1} of photons with $\lambda = 450$ nm?
(b) What is the energy in kJ/mol of photons with $\lambda = 450$ nm?
(c) What is the color of the light with $\lambda = 450$ nm?

5.110 One method for calculating Z_{eff} is to use the equation

$$Z_{eff} = \sqrt{\frac{(E)(n^2)}{1312 \text{ kJ/mol}}}$$

where E is the energy necessary to remove an electron from an atom and n is the principal quantum number of the electron. Use this equation to calculate Z_{eff} values for the highest-energy electrons in potassium ($E = 418.8$ kJ/mol) and krypton ($E = 1350.7$ kJ/mol).

5.111 One watt (W) is equal to 1 J/s. Assuming that 5.0% of the energy output of a 75 W lightbulb is visible light and that the average wavelength of the light is 550 nm, how many photons are emitted by the lightbulb each second?

5.112 Microwave ovens work by irradiating food with microwave radiation, which is absorbed and converted into heat. Assuming that radiation with $\lambda = 15.0$ cm is used, that all the energy is converted to heat, and that

4.184 J is needed to raise the temperature of 1.00 g of water by 1.00 °C, how many photons are necessary to raise the temperature of a 350 mL cup of water from 20 °C to 95 °C?

5.113 Photochromic sunglasses, which darken when exposed to light, contain a small amount of colorless AgCl embedded in the glass. When irradiated with light, metallic silver atoms are produced and the glass darkens: AgCl $\longrightarrow$ Ag + Cl. Escape of the chlorine atoms is prevented by the rigid structure of the glass, and the reaction therefore reverses as soon as the light is removed. If 310 kJ/mol of energy is required to make the reaction proceed, what wavelength of light is necessary?

5.114 The amount of energy necessary to remove an electron from an atom is a quantity called the *ionization energy*, E_i. This energy can be measured by a technique called *photoelectron spectroscopy*, in which light of wavelength λ is directed at an atom, causing an electron to be ejected. The kinetic energy of the ejected electron (E_k) is measured by determining its velocity, v ($E_k = mv^2/2$), and E_i is then calculated using the conservation of energy principle. That is, the energy of the incident light equals E_i plus E_k. What is the ionization energy of selenium atoms in kilojoules per mole if light with $\lambda = 48.2$ nm produces electrons with a velocity of 2.371×10^6 m/s? The mass, m, of an electron is 9.109×10^{-31} kg.

5.115 X rays with a wavelength of 1.54×10^{-10} m are produced when a copper metal target is bombarded with high-energy electrons that have been accelerated by a voltage difference of 30,000 V. The kinetic energy of the electrons equals the product of the voltage difference and the electronic charge in coulombs, where 1 volt-coulomb = 1 J.

(a) What is the kinetic energy in joules and the de Broglie wavelength in meters of an electron that has been accelerated by a voltage difference of 30,000 V?

(b) What is the energy in joules of the X rays emitted by the copper target?

5.116 In the Bohr model of atomic structure, electrons are constrained to orbit a nucleus at specific distances, given by the equation

$$r = \frac{n^2 a_0}{Z}$$

where r is the radius of the orbit, Z is the charge on the nucleus, a_0 is the *Bohr radius* and has a value of 5.292×10^{-11} m, and n is a positive integer ($n = 1, 2, 3, \ldots$)

like a principal quantum number. Furthermore, Bohr concluded that the energy level E of an electron in a given orbit is

$$E = \frac{-Ze^2}{2r}$$

where e is the charge on an electron. Derive an equation that will let you calculate the difference ΔE between any two energy levels. What relation does your equation have to the Balmer–Rydberg equation?

5.117 Assume that the rules for quantum numbers are different and that the spin quantum number m_s can have any of three values, $m_s = -1/2, 0, +1/2$, while all other rules remain the same.

(a) Draw an orbital-filling diagram for the element with $Z = 25$, showing the individual electrons in the outermost subshell as up arrows, down arrows, or 0. How many partially filled orbitals does the element have?

(b) What is the atomic number of the element in the 3rd column of the 4th row under these new rules? What block does it belong to ($s, p, d,$ or f)?

5.118 Given the subshells 1s, 2s, 2p, 3s, 3p, and 3d, identify those that meet the following descriptions:

(a) Has $l = 2$

(b) Can have $m_l = -1$

(c) Is empty in a nitrogen atom

(d) Is full in a carbon atom

(e) Contains the outermost electrons in a beryllium atom

(f) Can contain two electrons, both with spin $m_s = +1/2$

5.119 A hydrogen atom with an electron in the first shell ($n = 1$) absorbs ultraviolet light with a wavelength of 1.03×10^{-7} m. To what shell does the electron jump?

5.120 A minimum energy of 7.21×10^{-19} J is required to produce the photoelectric effect in chromium metal.

(a) What is the minimum frequency of light needed to remove an electron from chromium?

(b) Light with a wavelength of 2.50×10^{-7} m falls on a piece of chromium in an evacuated glass tube. What is the minimum de Broglie wavelength of the emitted electrons? (Note that the energy of the incident light must be conserved; that is, the photon's energy must equal the sum of the energy needed to eject the electron plus the kinetic energy of the electron.)

MULTICONCEPT PROBLEMS

5.121 A photon produced by an X-ray machine has an energy of 4.70×10^{-16} J.

(a) What is the frequency of the photon?

(b) What is the wavelength of radiation of frequency (a)?

(c) What is the velocity of an electron with a de Broglie wavelength equal to (b)?

(d) What is the kinetic energy of an electron traveling at velocity (c)?

5.122 An energetically excited hydrogen atom has its electron in a 5f subshell. The electron drops down to the 3d subshell, releasing a photon in the process.

(a) Give the n and l quantum numbers for both subshells, and give the range of possible m_l quantum numbers.

(b) What wavelength of light is emitted by the process?

(c) The hydrogen atom now has a single electron in the 3d subshell. What is the energy in kJ/mol required to remove this electron?

5.123 Consider the noble gas xenon.

(a) Write the electron configuration of xenon using the abbreviation of the previous noble gas.

(b) When xenon absorbs 801 kJ/mol of energy, it is excited into a higher-energy state in which the outermost electron has been promoted to the next available subshell. Write the electron configuration for this excited xenon.

(c) The energy required to completely remove the outermost electron from the excited xenon atom is 369 kJ/mol, almost identical to that of cesium (376 kJ/mol). Explain.

CHAPTER 6

Ionic Bonds and Some Main-Group Chemistry

This statue at the 700 year old Wieliczka salt mine in Poland was carved entirely out of salt.

CONTENTS

Now that we have a description of the electronic structure of isolated atoms, let's extend that description to atoms in chemical compounds. What is the force that holds atoms together in chemical compounds? Certainly there must be *some* force holding atoms together; otherwise, they would simply fly apart and no chemical compounds could exist. As we saw in Section 2.10, the forces that hold atoms together are called chemical bonds and are of two types: covalent bonds and ionic bonds. In this and the next chapter, we'll look at the nature of chemical bonds and at the energy changes that accompany their formation and breakage. We'll begin in the present chapter with a look at ions and at the ionic bonds formed between halogens and main-group metals.

6.1 ELECTRON CONFIGURATIONS OF IONS

We've seen on several occasions, particularly during the discussion of redox reactions in Sections 4.7 and 4.8, that metals (left side of the periodic table) tend to give up electrons in their chemical reactions and form cations. Conversely, halogens and some other nonmetals (right side of the table) tend to accept electrons in their chemical reactions and form anions. What are the ground-state electron configurations of the resultant ions?

For main-group elements, the electrons given up by a metal in forming a cation come from the highest-energy occupied orbital, while the electrons that are accepted by a nonmetal in forming an anion go into the lowest-energy unoccupied orbital according to the aufbau principle (Section 5.11). When a sodium atom ($1s^2 2s^2 2p^6 3s^1$) reacts with a chlorine atom and gives up an electron, for example, the valence-shell $3s$ electron of sodium is lost, giving an Na^+ ion with the noble-gas electron configuration of neon ($1s^2 2s^2 2p^6$). At the same time, when the chlorine atom ($1s^2 2s^2 2p^6 3s^2 3p^5$) accepts an electron from sodium, the electron fills the remaining vacancy in the $3p$ subshell to give a Cl^- ion with the noble-gas electron configuration of argon ($1s^2 2s^2 2p^6 3s^2 3p^6$).

$$\textbf{Na: } 1s^2 2s^2 2p^6 3s^1 \xrightarrow{-e^-} \textbf{Na}^+\text{: } 1s^2 2s^2 2p^6$$

$$\textbf{Cl: } 1s^2 2s^2 2p^6 3s^2 3p^5 \xrightarrow{+e^-} \textbf{Cl}^-\text{: } 1s^2 2s^2 2p^6 3s^2 3p^6$$

What is true for sodium is also true for the other elements in group 1A: All form positive ions by losing their valence-shell s electron when they undergo reaction, and all the resultant ions have noble-gas electron configurations. Similarly for the elements in group 2A: All form a doubly positive ion when they react, losing both their valence-shell s electrons. An Mg atom ($1s^2 2s^2 2p^6 3s^2$), for example, goes to an Mg^{2+} ion with the neon configuration $1s^2 2s^2 2p^6$ by loss of its two $3s$ electrons.

$$\textbf{Group 1A atom: } [\text{Noble gas}]\, ns^1 \xrightarrow{-e^-} \textbf{Group 1A ion}^+\text{: } [\text{Noble gas}]$$

$$\textbf{Group 2A atom: } [\text{Noble gas}]\, ns^2 \xrightarrow{-2\,e^-} \textbf{Group 2A ion}^{2+}\text{: } [\text{Noble gas}]$$

Just as the group 1A and 2A metals *lose* the appropriate number of electrons to yield ions with noble-gas configurations, the group 6A and group 7A nonmetals *gain* the appropriate number of electrons when they react with metals. The halogens in group 7A gain one electron to form singly charged anions with noble-gas configurations, and the elements in group 6A gain two electrons to form doubly charged anions with noble-gas configurations. Oxygen ($1s^2 2s^2 2p^4$), for example, becomes the O^{2-} ion with the neon configuration ($1s^2 2s^2 2p^6$) when it reacts with a metal:

$$\textbf{Group 6A atom: } [\text{Noble gas}]\, ns^2 np^4 \xrightarrow{+2\,e^-} \textbf{Group 6A ion}^{2-}\text{: } [\text{Noble gas}]\, ns^2 np^6$$

$$\textbf{Group 7A atom: } [\text{Noble gas}]\, ns^2 np^5 \xrightarrow{+e^-} \textbf{Group 7A ion}^-\text{: } [\text{Noble gas}]\, ns^2 np^6$$

The formulas and electron configurations of the most common main-group ions are listed in Table 6.1.

Remember...

The ground-state electron configuration of an atom or ion is a description of the atomic orbitals that are occupied in the lowest-energy state of the atom or ion. (Section 5.11)

Remember...

According to the aufbau principle, lower-energy orbitals fill before higher-energy ones and an orbital can hold only two electrons, which have opposite spins. (Section 5.11)

TABLE 6.1   Some Common Main-Group Ions and Their Noble-Gas Electron Configurations

Group 1A	Group 2A	Group 3A	Group 6A	Group 7A	Electron Configuration
H^+					[None]
H^-					[He]
Li^+	Be^{2+}				[He]
Na^+	Mg^{2+}	Al^{3+}	O^{2-}	F^-	[Ne]
K^+	Ca^{2+}	$*Ga^{3+}$	S^{2-}	Cl^-	[Ar]
Rb^+	Sr^{2+}	$*In^{3+}$	Se^{2-}	Br^-	[Kr]
Cs^+	Ba^{2+}	$*Tl^{3+}$	Te^{2-}	I^-	[Xe]

* These ions don't have a true noble-gas electron configuration because they have an additional filled d subshell.

The situation is a bit different for ion formation from the transition-metal elements than it is for the main-group elements. Transition metals react with nonmetals to form cations by first losing their valence-shell s electrons and then losing one or more d electrons. As a result, all the remaining valence electrons in transition-metal cations occupy d orbitals. Iron, for instance, forms the Fe^{2+} ion by losing its two $4s$ electrons and forms the Fe^{3+} ion by losing two $4s$ electrons and one $3d$ electron:

$$\textbf{Fe: } [Ar]\, 4s^2\, 3d^6 \xrightarrow{-2\,e^-} \textbf{Fe}^{2+}\textbf{: } [Ar]\, 3d^6$$

$$\textbf{Fe: } [Ar]\, 4s^2\, 3d^6 \xrightarrow{-3\,e^-} \textbf{Fe}^{3+}\textbf{: } [Ar]\, 3d^5$$

It may seem strange that building up the periodic table adds the $3d$ electrons *after* the $4s$ electrons, whereas ion formation from a transition metal removes the $4s$ electrons *before* the $3d$ electrons. Note, though, that the two processes are not the reverse of one another, so they can't be compared directly. Building up the periodic table adds one electron to the valence shell and also adds one positive charge to the nucleus, but ion formation removes an electron from the valence shell without altering the nucleus.

▶ PROBLEM 6.1   Predict the ground-state electron configuration for each of the following ions, and explain your answers.
(a) Ra^{2+} (b) Y^{3+} (c) Ti^{4+} (d) N^{3-}

▶ PROBLEM 6.2   What doubly positive ion has the following ground-state electron configuration? $1s^2\, 2s^2\, 2p^6\, 3s^2\, 3p^6\, 3d^{10}$

6.2   IONIC RADII

Remember...

Atomic radii increase down a column of the periodic table because successively larger valence-shell orbitals are occupied, and radii decrease from left to right across a row of the periodic table because the effective nuclear charge increases across the row. (Section 5.14)

Just as there are systematic differences in the radii of atoms (Section 5.14), there are also systematic differences in the radii of ions. As shown in Figure 6.1 for the elements of groups 1A and 2A, atoms shrink dramatically when an electron is removed to form a cation. The radius of an Na atom, for example, is 186 pm, but that of an Na^+ cation is 102 pm. Similarly, the radius of an Mg atom is 160 pm and that of an Mg^{2+} cation is 72 pm.

The cation that results when an electron is removed from a neutral atom is smaller than the original atom both because the electron is removed from a large,

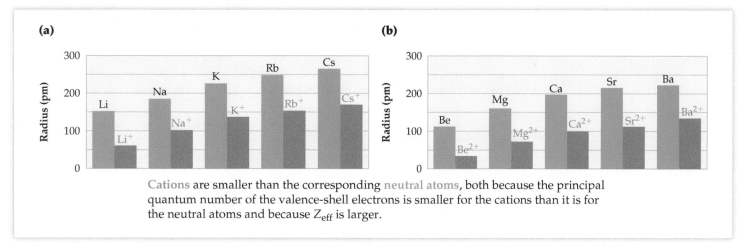

Cations are smaller than the corresponding neutral atoms, both because the principal quantum number of the valence-shell electrons is smaller for the cations than it is for the neutral atoms and because Z_{eff} is larger.

Figure 6.1
Radii of (a) group 1A atoms and their cations; (b) group 2A atoms and their cations.

valence-shell orbital and because there is an increase in the effective nuclear charge, Z_{eff} for the remaining electrons (Section 5.10). On going from a neutral Na atom to a charged Na^+ cation, for example, the electron configuration changes from $1s^2 2s^2 2p^6 3s^1$ to $1s^2 2s^2 2p^6$. The valence shell of the Na *atom* is the *third* shell, but the valence shell of the Na^+ *cation* is the *second* shell. Thus, the Na^+ ion has a smaller valence shell than the Na atom and therefore a smaller size. In addition, the effective nuclear charge felt by the valence-shell electrons is greater in the Na^+ cation than in the neutral atom. The Na atom has 11 protons and 11 electrons, but the Na^+ cation has 11 protons and only 10 electrons. The smaller number of electrons in the cation means that they shield one another to a lesser extent and therefore are pulled in more strongly toward the nucleus.

The same effects felt by the group 1A elements when a single electron is lost are felt by the group 2A elements when two electrons are lost. For example, loss of two valence-shell electrons from an Mg atom ($1s^2 2s^2 2p^6 3s^2$) gives the Mg^{2+} cation ($1s^2 2s^2 2p^6$). The smaller valence shell of the Mg^{2+} cation and the increase in effective nuclear charge combine to cause a dramatic shrinkage. A similar shrinkage occurs whenever any of the metal atoms on the left-hand two-thirds of the periodic table is converted into a cation.

Just as neutral atoms shrink when converted to cations by loss of one or more electrons, they expand when converted to anions by gain of one or more electrons. As shown in Figure 6.2 for the group 7A elements (halogens), the expansion is dramatic. Chlorine, for example, nearly doubles in radius, from 99 pm for the neutral atom to 184 pm for the chloride anion.

Remember...
The **effective nuclear charge (Z_{eff})** felt by an electron is due to electron shielding of outer electrons by inner electrons and may be substantially lower than the actual nuclear charge:

$$Z_{eff} = Z_{actual} - \text{electron shielding.}$$

(Section 5.10)

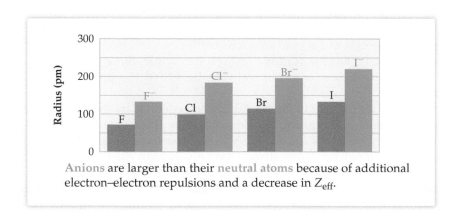

Anions are larger than their neutral atoms because of additional electron–electron repulsions and a decrease in Z_{eff}.

Figure 6.2
Radii of the group 7A atoms (halogens) and their anions.

The expansion that occurs when a group 7A atom gains an electron to yield an anion can't be accounted for by a change in the quantum number of the valence shell, because the added electron simply completes an already occupied p subshell: [Ne] $3s^2 3p^5$ for a Cl atom becomes [Ne] $3s^2 3p^6$ for a Cl^- anion, for instance. Thus, the expansion is due entirely to the decrease in effective nuclear charge and the increase in electron–electron repulsions that occurs when an extra electron is added.

▶ **PROBLEM 6.3**   Which atom or ion in each of the following pairs would you expect to be larger? Explain.

(a) O or O^{2-} (b) O or S   (c) Fe or Fe^{3+} (d) H or H^-

CONCEPTUAL PROBLEM 6.4   Which of the following spheres represents a K^+ ion, which a K atom, and which a Cl^- ion?

$r = 227$ pm $r = 184$ pm $r = 133$ pm

6.3   IONIZATION ENERGY

We saw in the previous chapter that the absorption of electromagnetic energy by an atom leads to a change in electron configuration. When energy is added, a valence-shell electron is promoted from a lower-energy orbital to a higher-energy one with a larger principal quantum number n. If enough energy is absorbed, the electron can even be removed completely from the atom, leaving behind a cation. The amount of energy necessary to remove the highest-energy electron from an isolated neutral atom in the gaseous state is called the atom's **ionization energy**, abbreviated E_i. For hydrogen, $E_i = 1312.0$ kJ/mol.

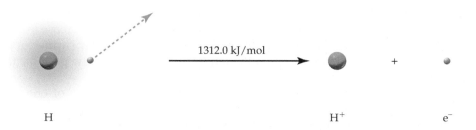

1312.0 kJ/mol

H H^+ + e^-

As shown by the plot in **Figure 6.3**, ionization energies differ widely, from a low of 375.7 kJ/mol for cesium to a high of 2372.3 kJ/mol for helium. Furthermore, the data show a clear periodicity. The minimum E_i values correspond to the group 1A elements (alkali metals), the maximum E_i values correspond to the group 8A elements (noble gases), and a gradual increase in E_i occurs from left to right across a row of the periodic table—from Na to Ar, for example. Note that all the values are positive, meaning that energy must always be added to remove an electron from an atom.

The periodicity evident in Figure 6.3 can be explained by looking at electron configurations. Atoms of the group 8A elements have filled valence subshells, either s for helium or both s and p for the other noble gases. As we saw in Section 5.14, an electron in a filled valence subshell feels a relatively high Z_{eff} because electrons in the same subshell don't shield one another very strongly. As a result, the electrons are held tightly to the nucleus, the radius of the atom is small, and the energy necessary to remove an electron is relatively large. Atoms of group 1A elements, by contrast,

Remember...

Valence electrons are strongly **shielded** by inner-shell (core) electrons, are less strongly shielded by other electrons in the same shell according to the order $s > p > d > f$, and are only weakly shielded by other electrons in the same subshell.   (Section 5.14)

Figure 6.3
Ionization energies of the first 92 elements.

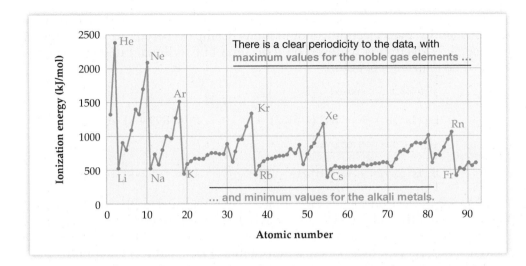

have only a single *s* electron in their valence shell. This single valence electron is shielded from the nucleus by all the inner-shell electrons, called the **core electrons**, resulting in a low Z_{eff}. The valence electron is thus held loosely, and the energy necessary to remove it is relatively small.

The plot of ionization energies in Figure 6.3 also shows other trends in the data beyond the obvious periodicity. One such trend is that ionization energies gradually decrease going down a group in the periodic table, from He to Rn and from Li to Fr, for instance. As the atomic number increases going down a group, both the principal quantum number of the valence-shell electrons and their average distance from the nucleus also increase. As a result, the valence-shell electrons are less tightly held and E_i is smaller.

Yet another point about the E_i data is that minor irregularities occur across a row of the periodic table. A close look at E_i values of the first 20 elements (**Figure 6.4**) shows that the E_i of beryllium is larger than that of its neighbor boron and the E_i of nitrogen is larger than that of its neighbor oxygen. Similarly, magnesium has a larger E_i than aluminum and phosphorus has a slightly larger E_i than sulfur.

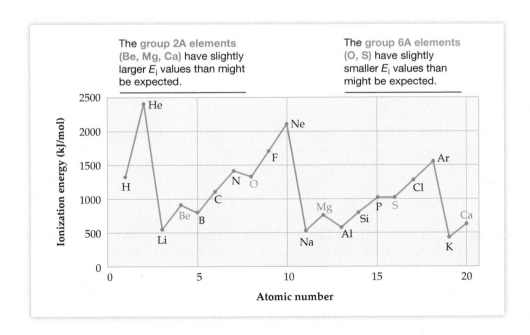

Figure 6.4
Ionization energies of the first 20 elements.

The slightly enlarged E_i values for the group 2A elements Be, Mg, and others can be explained by their electron configurations. Compare beryllium with boron, for instance. A $2s$ electron is removed on ionization of beryllium, but a $2p$ electron is removed on ionization of boron:

s electron removed

$$\text{Be } (1s^2\, 2s^2) \longrightarrow \text{Be}^+ (1s^2\, 2s^1) + e^- \qquad E_i = 899.4 \text{ kJ/mol}$$

p electron removed

$$\text{B } (1s^2\, 2s^2\, 2p^1) \longrightarrow \text{B}^+ (1s^2\, 2s^2) + e^- \qquad E_i = 800.6 \text{ kJ/mol}$$

Because a $2s$ electron spends more time closer to the nucleus than a $2p$ electron, it is held more tightly and is harder to remove. Thus, the E_i of beryllium is larger than that of boron. Put another way, the $2p$ electron of boron is shielded somewhat by the $2s$ electrons and is thus more easily removed than a $2s$ electron of beryllium.

The lowered E_i values for atoms of group 6A elements can be explained by their electron configurations as well. Comparing nitrogen with oxygen, for instance, the nitrogen electron is removed from a half-filled orbital, whereas the oxygen electron is removed from a filled orbital:

Half-filled orbital

$$\text{N } (1s^2\, 2s^2\, 2p_x^1\, 2p_y^1\, 2p_z^1) \longrightarrow \text{N}^+ (1s^2\, 2s^2\, 2p_x^1\, 2p_y^1) + e^- \qquad E_i = 1402.3 \text{ kJ/mol}$$

Filled orbital

$$\text{O } (1s^2\, 2s^2\, 2p_x^2\, 2p_y^1\, 2p_z^1) \longrightarrow \text{O}^+ (1s^2\, 2s^2\, 2p_x^1\, 2p_y^1\, 2p_z^1) + e^- \quad E_i = 1313.9 \text{ kJ/mol}$$

Because electrons repel one another and tend to stay as far apart as possible, electrons that are forced together in a filled orbital are slightly higher in energy than those in a half-filled orbital, so removing one is slightly easier. Thus, oxygen has a smaller E_i than nitrogen.

WORKED EXAMPLE 6.1

IONIZATION ENERGIES

Arrange the elements Se, Cl, and S in order of increasing ionization energy.

STRATEGY

Ionization energy generally increases from left to right across a row of the periodic table and decreases from top to bottom down a group. Chlorine should have a larger E_i than its neighbor sulfur, and selenium should have a smaller E_i than sulfur.

SOLUTION

The order is Se < S < Cl.

▶ **PROBLEM 6.5** Using the periodic table as your guide, predict which element in each of the following pairs has the larger ionization energy:

(a) K or Br   (b) S or Te   (c) Ga or Se   (d) Ne or Sr

6.4 HIGHER IONIZATION ENERGIES

Ionization is not limited to the loss of a single electron from an atom. Two, three, or even more electrons can be lost sequentially from an atom, and the amount of energy associated with each step can be measured.

$$\text{M + Energy} \longrightarrow \text{M}^+ + e^- \qquad \text{First ionization energy } (E_{i1})$$
$$\text{M}^+ + \text{Energy} \longrightarrow \text{M}^{2+} + e^- \qquad \text{Second ionization energy } (E_{i2})$$
$$\text{M}^{2+} + \text{Energy} \longrightarrow \text{M}^{3+} + e^- \qquad \text{Third ionization energy } (E_{i3})$$
$$\ldots \text{ and so forth}$$

Successively larger amounts of energy are required for each ionization step because it is much harder to pull a negatively charged electron away from a positively charged ion than from a neutral atom. Interestingly, though, the energy differences between successive steps vary dramatically from one element to another. Removing the second electron from sodium takes nearly 10 times as much energy as removing the first one (4562 versus 496 kJ/mol), but removing the second electron from magnesium takes only twice as much energy as removing the first one (1451 versus 738 kJ/mol).

Large jumps in successive ionization energies are also found for other elements, as can be seen by following the zigzag line in Table 6.2. Magnesium has a large jump between its second and third ionization energies, aluminum has a large jump between its third and fourth ionization energies, silicon has a large jump between its fourth and fifth ionization energies, and so on.

TABLE 6.2   Higher Ionization Energies (kJ/mol) for Main-Group Third-Row Elements

Group	1A	2A	3A	4A	5A	6A	7A	8A
E_i Number	Na	Mg	Al	Si	P	S	Cl	Ar
E_{i1}	496	738	578	787	1,012	1,000	1,251	1,520
E_{i2}	4,562	1,451	1,817	1,577	1,903	2,251	2,297	2,665
E_{i3}	6,912	7,733	2,745	3,231	2,912	3,361	3,822	3,931
E_{i4}	9,543	10,540	11,575	4,356	4,956	4,564	5,158	5,770
E_{i5}	13,353	13,630	14,830	16,091	6,273	7,013	6,540	7,238
E_{i6}	16,610	17,995	18,376	19,784	22,233	8,495	9,458	8,781
E_{i7}	20,114	21,703	23,293	23,783	25,397	27,106	11,020	11,995

The large increases in ionization energies highlighted by the zigzag line in Table 6.2 are yet another consequence of electron configurations. It's relatively easier to remove an electron from a *partially* filled valence shell because Z_{eff} is lower, but it's relatively harder to remove an electron from a *filled* valence shell because Z_{eff} is higher. In other words, ions formed by reaction of main-group elements usually have filled s and p subshells (a noble-gas electron configuration), which corresponds to having eight electrons (an *octet*) in the valence shell of an atom or ion. Sodium ([Ne] $3s^1$) loses only one electron easily, magnesium ([Ne] $3s^2$) loses only two electrons easily, aluminum ([Ne] $3s^2 3p^1$) loses only three electrons easily, and so on across the row. We'll further explore the stability of valence-shell electron octets in Section 6.6.

8 electrons in outer (2nd) shell

$$Na\ (1s^2\,2s^2\,2p^6\,3s^1) \longrightarrow Na^+\,(1s^2\,2s^2\,2p^6) + e^-$$
$$Mg\ (1s^2\,2s^2\,2p^6\,3s^2) \longrightarrow Mg^{2+}\,(1s^2\,2s^2\,2p^6) + 2\,e^-$$
$$Al\ (1s^2\,2s^2\,2p^6\,3s^2\,3p^1) \longrightarrow Al^{3+}\,(1s^2\,2s^2\,2p^6) + 3\,e^-$$
$$Cl\ (1s^2\,2s^2\,2p^6\,3s^2\,3p^5) \longrightarrow Cl^{7+}\,(1s^2\,2s^2\,2p^6) + 7\,e^-$$

WORKED EXAMPLE 6.2

HIGHER IONIZATION ENERGIES

Which has the larger fifth ionization energy, Ge or As?

STRATEGY

Look at their positions in the periodic table. The group 4A element germanium has four valence-shell electrons and thus has four relatively low ionization energies, whereas the group 5A element arsenic has five valence-shell electrons and has five low ionization energies.

SOLUTION

Germanium has a larger E_{i5} than arsenic.

▶ **PROBLEM 6.6**

(a) Which has the larger third ionization energy, Be or N?

(b) Which has the larger fourth ionization energy, Ga or Ge?

▶ **PROBLEM 6.7** Three atoms have the following electron configurations:

(a) $1s^2\,2s^2\,2p^6\,3s^2\,3p^1$

(b) $1s^2\,2s^2\,2p^6\,3s^2\,3p^5$

(c) $1s^2\,2s^2\,2p^6\,3s^2\,3p^6\,4s^1$

Which of the three has the largest E_{i1}? Which has the smallest E_{i4}?

CONCEPTUAL PROBLEM 6.8 Order the indicated three elements according to the ease with which each is likely to lose its third electron:

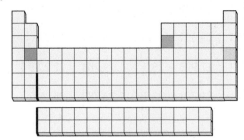

6.5 ELECTRON AFFINITY

Just as it's possible to measure the energy change on *removing* an electron from an atom to form a *cation*, it's also possible to measure the energy change on *adding* an electron to an atom to form an *anion*. An element's **electron affinity**, abbreviated E_{ea}, is the energy change that occurs when an electron is added to an isolated atom in the gaseous state.

Ionization energies (Section 6.3) are always positive because energy must always be added to separate a negatively charged electron from the resultant positively charged cation. Electron affinities, however, are generally negative because energy is usually released when a neutral atom adds an additional electron.* We'll see in Chapter 8 that this same convention is used throughout chemistry: A positive energy change means that energy is added, and a negative energy change means that energy is released.

---

*We have defined E_{ea} as the energy *released* when a neutral atom *gains* an electron to form an anion and have given it a negative sign. Some books and reference sources adopt the opposite point of view, defining E_{ea} as the energy *gained* when an anion *loses* an electron to form a neutral atom and giving it a positive value. The two definitions are simply the reverse of one another, so the sign of the energy change is also reversed.

The more negative the E_{ea}, the greater the tendency of the atom to accept an electron and the more stable the anion that results. In contrast, an atom that forms an unstable anion by addition of an electron has, in principle, a positive value of E_{ea}, but no experimental measurement can be made because the process does not take place. All we can say is that the E_{ea} for such an atom is greater than zero. The E_{ea} of hydrogen, for instance, is -72.8 kJ/mol, meaning that energy is released and the H^- anion is stable. The E_{ea} of neon, however, is greater than 0 kJ/mol, meaning that Ne does not add an electron and the Ne^- anion is not stable.

$$H\,(1s^1) + e^- \longrightarrow H^-\,(1s^2) + 72.8\ \text{kJ/mol} \qquad\qquad E_{ea} = -72.8\ \text{kJ/mol}$$

$$Ne\,(1s^2\,2s^2\,2p^6) + e^- + \text{Energy} \longrightarrow Ne^-\,(1s^2\,2s^2\,2p^6\,3s^1) \qquad E_{ea} > 0\ \text{kJ/mol}$$

As with ionization energies, electron affinities show a periodicity that is related to the electron configurations of the elements. The data in **Figure 6.5** indicate that group 7A elements have the most negative electron affinities, corresponding to the largest release of energy, while group 2A and group 8A elements have near-zero or positive electron affinities, corresponding to a small release or even an absorption of energy.

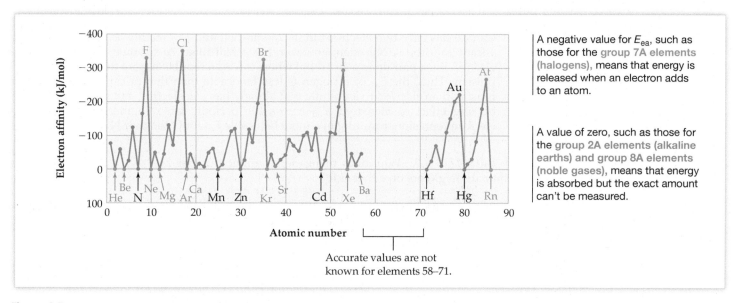

A negative value for E_{ea}, such as those for the group 7A elements (halogens), means that energy is released when an electron adds to an atom.

A value of zero, such as those for the group 2A elements (alkaline earths) and group 8A elements (noble gases), means that energy is absorbed but the exact amount can't be measured.

Figure 6.5
Electron affinities for elements 1–57 and 72–86.

The value of an element's electron affinity is due to an interplay of several offsetting factors. Attraction between the additional electron and the nucleus favors a negative E_{ea}, but the increase in electron–electron repulsions that results from addition of the extra electron favors a positive E_{ea}.

Large negative E_{ea}'s are found for the halogens (F, Cl, Br, I) because each of these elements has both a high Z_{eff} and room in its valence shell for an additional electron. Halide anions have a noble-gas electron configuration with filled s and p sublevels, and the attraction between the additional electron and the atomic nucleus is high. Positive E_{ea}'s are found for the noble-gas elements (He, Ne, Ar, Kr, Xe), however, because the s and p sublevels in these elements are already full, so the additional electron must go into the next higher shell, where it is shielded from the nucleus and feels a relatively low Z_{eff}. The attraction of the nucleus for the added electron is therefore small and is outweighed by the additional electron–electron repulsions.

A halogen: $Cl\,(\ldots 3s^2\,3p^5) + e^- \longrightarrow Cl^-\,(\ldots 3s^2\,3p^6) \qquad E_{ea} = -348.6\ \text{kJ/mol}$

A noble gas: $Ar\,(\ldots 3s^2\,3p^6) + e^- \longrightarrow Ar^-\,(\ldots 3s^2\,3p^6\,4s^1) \quad E_{ea} > 0\ \text{kJ/mol}$

In looking for other trends in the data of Figure 6.5, the near-zero E_{ea}'s of the alkaline-earth metals (Be, Mg, Ca, Sr, Ba) are particularly striking. Atoms of these elements have filled s subshells, which means that the additional electron must go into a p subshell. The higher energy of the p subshell, together with a relatively low Z_{eff} for elements on the left side of the periodic table, means that alkaline-earth atoms accept an electron reluctantly and have E_{ea} values near zero.

An alkaline earth: $\quad Mg\,(\dots 3s^2) + e^- \longrightarrow Mg^-\,(\dots 3s^2\,3p^1) \qquad E_{ea} \approx 0\ kJ/mol$

WORKED EXAMPLE 6.3

ELECTRON AFFINITIES

Why does nitrogen have a less favorable (more positive) E_{ea} than its neighbors on either side, C and O?

STRATEGY AND SOLUTION

The magnitude of an element's E_{ea} depends on the element's valence-shell electron configuration. The electron configurations of C, N, and O are

$$\text{Carbon: } 1s^2\,2s^2\,2p_x^{\,1}\,2p_y^{\,1} \qquad\qquad \text{Nitrogen: } 1s^2\,2s^2\,2p_x^{\,1}\,2p_y^{\,1}\,2p_z^{\,1}$$

$$\text{Oxygen: } 1s^2\,2s^2\,2p_x^{\,2}\,2p_y^{\,1}\,2p_z^{\,1}$$

Carbon has only two electrons in its $2p$ subshell and can readily accept another in its vacant $2p_z$ orbital. Nitrogen, however, has a half-filled $2p$ subshell, so the additional electron must pair up in a $2p$ orbital where it feels a repulsion from the electron already present. Thus, the E_{ea} of nitrogen is less favorable than that of carbon. Oxygen also must add an electron to an orbital that already has one electron, but the additional stabilizing effect of increased Z_{eff} across the periodic table counteracts the effect of electron repulsion, resulting in a more favorable E_{ea} for O than for N.

▶ **PROBLEM 6.9** Why does manganese, atomic number 25, have a less favorable E_{ea} than its neighbors on either side?

CONCEPTUAL PROBLEM 6.10 Which of the indicated three elements has the least favorable E_{ea}, and which has the most favorable E_{ea}?

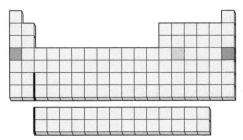

6.6 THE OCTET RULE

Let's list the important points discussed in the previous four sections and see if we can draw some general conclusions:

- **Group 1A elements** have a relatively low E_{i1}, so they tend to lose their ns^1 valence-shell electron easily when they react, thereby adopting the electron configuration of the noble gas in the previous row of the periodic table.
- **Group 2A elements** have relatively low E_{i1} and E_{i2}, so they tend to lose both their ns^2 valence-shell electrons easily when they react and adopt a noble-gas electron configuration.

- **Group 7A elements** have a relatively large negative E_{ea}, so they tend to gain one electron easily when they react, changing from ns^2np^5 to ns^2np^6 and thereby adopting the configuration of the neighboring noble gas in the same row.
- **Group 8A (noble gas) elements** are essentially inert and undergo very few reactions. They neither gain nor lose electrons easily.

All these observations can be gathered into a single statement called the **octet rule**:

> **Octet rule** Main-group elements tend to undergo reactions that leave them with eight outer-shell electrons. That is, main-group elements react so that they attain a noble-gas electron configuration with filled s and p sublevels in their valence electron shell.

As we'll see in the next chapter, there are exceptions to the octet rule, particularly for elements in the third and lower rows of the periodic table. Nevertheless, the rule is useful for making predictions and for providing insights about chemical bonding.

Why does the octet rule work? What factors determine how many electrons an atom is likely to gain or lose? Clearly, electrons are most likely to be lost if they are held loosely in the first place—that is, if they feel a relatively low effective nuclear charge, Z_{eff}, and have lower ionization energies. Valence-shell electrons in the group 1A, 2A, and 3A metals, for instance, are shielded from the nucleus by core electrons, feel a low Z_{eff}, and are therefore lost relatively easily. Once the next lower noble-gas configuration is reached, though, loss of an additional electron suddenly becomes much more difficult because it must come from an inner shell, where it feels a much higher Z_{eff}.

Conversely, electrons are most likely to be gained if they can be held tightly by a high Z_{eff}. Valence-shell electrons in the group 6A and 7A elements, for example, are poorly shielded, feel high values of Z_{eff}, and aren't lost easily. The high Z_{eff} thus makes possible the gain of one or more additional electrons into vacant valence-shell orbitals. Once the noble-gas configuration is reached, though, lower-energy orbitals are no longer available. An additional electron would have to be placed in a higher-energy orbital, where it would feel only a low Z_{eff}.

Eight is therefore the magic number for valence-shell electrons. Taking electrons *from* a filled octet is difficult because they are tightly held by a high Z_{eff}; adding more electrons *to* a filled octet is difficult because, with s and p sublevels full, no low-energy orbital is available.

WORKED EXAMPLE 6.4

CHEMICAL REACTIONS AND THE OCTET RULE

Lithium metal reacts with nitrogen to yield Li_3N. What noble-gas configuration does the nitrogen atom in Li_3N have?

STRATEGY AND SOLUTION

The compound Li_3N contains three Li^+ ions, each formed by loss of a $2s$ electron from lithium metal (group 1A). The nitrogen atom in Li_3N must therefore gain three electrons over the neutral atom, making it triply negative (N^{3-}) and giving it a valence-shell octet with the neon configuration:

$$\text{N configuration: } (1s^2\, 2s^2\, 2p^3) \qquad N^{3-} \text{ configuration: } (1s^2\, 2s^2\, 2p^6)$$

▶ **PROBLEM 6.11** What noble-gas configurations are the following elements likely to adopt in reactions when they form ions?

(a) Rb   (b) Ba   (c) Ga   (d) F

▶ **PROBLEM 6.12** What are group 6A elements likely to do when they form ions—gain electrons or lose them? How many?

6.7 IONIC BONDS AND THE FORMATION OF IONIC SOLIDS

When an element that gives up an electron relatively easily (that is, has a small positive ionization energy) comes in contact with an element that accepts an electron easily (that is, has a large negative electron affinity), the element with the small E_i can transfer an electron to the element with the negative E_{ea}, yielding a cation and an anion. Sodium, for example, reacts with chlorine to give Na^+ ions and Cl^- ions:

$$Na + Cl \longrightarrow Na^+ \; Cl^-$$

$$1s^2\, 2s^2\, 2p^6\, 3s^1 \quad 1s^2\, 2s^2\, 2p^6\, 3s^2\, 3p^5 \qquad\qquad 1s^2\, 2s^2\, 2p^6 \quad 1s^2\, 2s^2\, 2p^6\, 3s^2\, 3p^6$$

What about the overall energy change, ΔE, for the reaction of sodium with chlorine to yield Na^+ and Cl^- ions? (The Greek capital letter delta, Δ, is used to represent a change in the value of the indicated quantity, in this case an energy change ΔE.) It's apparent from E_i and E_{ea} values that the amount of energy released when a chlorine atom accepts an electron ($E_{ea} = -348.6$ kJ/mol) is insufficient to offset the amount absorbed when a sodium atom loses an electron ($E_i = +495.8$ kJ/mol):

E_i for Na	$= +495.8$ kJ/mol	(Unfavorable)
E_{ea} for Cl	$= -348.6$ kJ/mol	(Favorable)
ΔE	$= +147.2$ kJ/mol	(Unfavorable)

Remember...

In an **ionic solid**, oppositely charged ions are attracted to one another by ionic bonds and are packed together in a regular way. We can't specify which ions "belong" to each other, however, as we can with atoms in covalent molecules. (Section 2.11)

The net ΔE for the reaction of sodium and chlorine atoms would be unfavorable by $+147.2$ kJ/mol, and no reaction would occur, unless some other factor were involved. This additional factor, which is more than enough to overcome the unfavorable energy change of electron transfer, is the large gain in stability due to the electrostatic attractions between product anions and cations and the formation of an **ionic solid**.

The actual reaction of solid sodium metal with gaseous chlorine molecules to form solid sodium chloride occurs all at once rather than in a stepwise manner, but it's easier to make an energy calculation if we imagine a series of hypothetical steps for which exact energy changes can be measured experimentally. There are five steps to take into account to calculate the overall energy change.

Step 1. Solid Na metal is first converted into isolated, gaseous Na atoms, a process called *sublimation*. Because energy must be added to disrupt the forces holding atoms together in a solid, the heat of sublimation has a positive value: +107.3 kJ/mol for Na.

$$Na(s) \longrightarrow Na(g)$$
+107.3 kJ/mol

Step 2. Gaseous Cl_2 molecules are split into individual Cl atoms. Energy must be added to break molecules apart, and the energy required for bond breaking therefore has a positive value: +243 kJ/mol for Cl_2 (or 122 kJ/mol for $1/2$ Cl_2). We'll look further into bond dissociation energies in Section 7.2.

$$1/2\, Cl_2(g) \longrightarrow Cl(g)$$
+122 kJ/mol

Step 3. Isolated Na atoms are ionized into Na^+ ions plus electrons. The energy required is the first ionization energy of sodium (E_{i1}) and has a positive value: +495.8 kJ/mol.

$$Na(g) \longrightarrow Na^+(g) + e^-$$
+495.8 kJ/mol

Step 4. Cl^- ions are formed from Cl atoms by addition of an electron. The energy released is the electron affinity of chlorine (E_{ea}) and has a negative value: −348.6 kJ/mol.

$$Cl(g) + e^- \longrightarrow Cl^-(g)$$
−348.6 kJ/mol

Step 5. Lastly, solid NaCl is formed from isolated Na^+ and Cl^- ions. The energy change is a measure of the overall electrostatic interactions between ions in the solid. It is the amount of energy released when isolated ions condense to form a solid, and it has a negative value: −787 kJ/mol for NaCl.

$$Na^+(g) + Cl^-(g) \longrightarrow NaCl(s)$$
−787 kJ/mol

Net reaction: $Na(s) + 1/2\, Cl_2(g) \longrightarrow NaCl(s)$

Net energy change: −411 kJ/mol

The five hypothetical steps in the reaction between sodium metal and gaseous chlorine are depicted in **Figure 6.6** in a pictorial format called a **Born–Haber cycle**, which shows how each step contributes to the overall energy change and how the

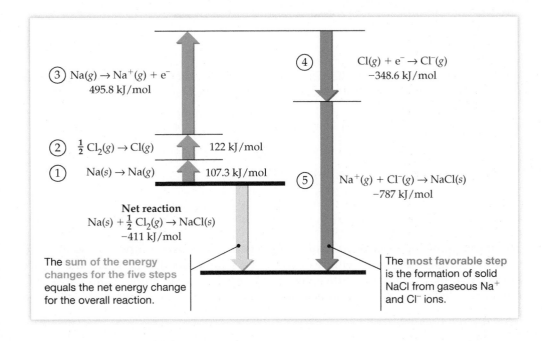

Figure 6.6

A Born–Haber cycle for the formation of NaCl(s) from Na(s) and $Cl_2(g)$.

net process is the sum of the individual steps. As indicated in the diagram, steps 1, 2, and 3 have positive values and absorb energy, while steps 4 and 5 have negative values and release energy. The largest contribution is step 5, which measures the electrostatic forces between ions in the solid product—that is, the strength of the ionic bonding. Were it not for this large amount of stabilization of the solid due to ionic bonding, no reaction would take place.

A similar Born–Haber cycle for the reaction of magnesium with chlorine shows the energy changes involved in the reaction of an alkaline-earth element (Figure 6.7). As in the reaction of sodium and chlorine to form NaCl, there are five contributions to the overall energy change. First, solid magnesium metal must be converted into isolated gaseous magnesium atoms (sublimation). Second, the bond in Cl_2 molecules must be broken to yield chlorine atoms. Third, the magnesium atoms must lose two electrons to form the dipositive Mg^{2+} ions. Fourth, the chlorine atoms formed in step 2 must accept electrons to form Cl^- ions. Fifth, the gaseous ions must combine to form the ionic solid, $MgCl_2$. As the Born–Haber cycle indicates, it is the large contribution from ionic bonding that releases enough energy to drive the entire process.

Figure 6.7
A Born–Haber cycle for the formation of $MgCl_2$ from the elements.

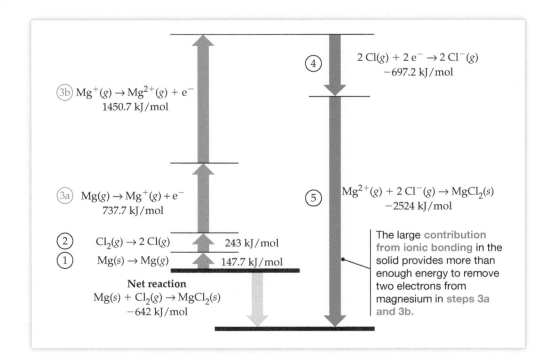

▶ **PROBLEM 6.13** Calculate the net energy change in kilojoules per mole that takes place on formation of KF(s) from the elements: $K(s) + 1/2\ F_2(g) \longrightarrow KF(s)$. The following information is needed:

Heat of sublimation for K(s) = 89.2 kJ/mol $\qquad$ E_{ea} for F(g) = −328 kJ/mol

Bond dissociation energy for $F_2(g)$ = 158 kJ/mol $\qquad$ E_i for K(g) = 418.8 kJ/mol

Electrostatic interactions in KF(s) = −821 kJ/mol

6.8 LATTICE ENERGIES IN IONIC SOLIDS

The measure of the electrostatic interaction energies between ions in a solid—and thus the measure of the strength of the solid's ionic bonds—is called the **lattice energy (*U*).** By convention, lattice energy is defined as the amount of energy that must be added to break up an ionic solid into its individual gaseous ions, so it has a positive value. The formation of a solid from ions is the reverse of the breakup, however, and step 5 in the Born–Haber cycle of Figure 6.6 therefore has a negative value, $-U$.

$$NaCl(s) \longrightarrow Na^+(g) + Cl^-(g) \qquad U = +787 \text{ kJ/mol} \quad \text{(Energy absorbed)}$$

$$Na^+(g) + Cl^-(g) \longrightarrow NaCl(s) \qquad -U = -787 \text{ kJ/mol} \quad \text{(Energy released)}$$

The force F that results from the interaction of electric charges is described by **Coulomb's law** and is equal to a constant k times the product of the charges on the ions, z_1 and z_2, divided by the square of the distance d between their centers (nuclei):

Coulomb's Law $F = k \times \dfrac{z_1 z_2}{d^2}$

Because energy is equal to force times distance, the negative of the lattice energy is

$$-U = F \times d = k \times \frac{z_1 z_2}{d}$$

The value of the constant k depends on the arrangement of the ions in the specific compound and is different for different substances.

Lattice energies are large when the distance d between ions is small and when the charges z_1 and z_2 are large. A small distance d means that the ions are close together, which implies that they have small ionic radii. Thus, if z_1 and z_2 are held constant, the largest lattice energies belong to compounds formed from the smallest ions, as listed in Table 6.3.

Within a series of compounds that have the same anion but different cations, lattice energy increases as the cation becomes smaller. Comparing LiF, NaF, and KF, for example, cation size follows the order $K^+ > Na^+ > Li^+$, so lattice energies follow the order LiF > NaF > KF. Similarly, within a series of compounds that have the same cation but different anions, lattice energy increases as anion size decreases. Comparing LiF, LiCl, LiBr, and LiI, for example, anion size follows the order $I^- > Br^- > Cl^- > F^-$, so lattice energies follow the reverse order LiF > LiCl > LiBr > LiI.

TABLE 6.3   Lattice Energies of Some Ionic Solids (kJ/mol)

Cation	Anion				
	F^-	Cl^-	Br^-	I^-	O^{2-}
Li^+	1036	853	807	757	2925
Na^+	923	787	747	704	2695
K^+	821	715	682	649	2360
Be^{2+}	3505	3020	2914	2800	4443
Mg^{2+}	2957	2524	2440	2327	3791
Ca^{2+}	2630	2258	2176	2074	3401
Al^{3+}	5215	5492	5361	5218	15,916

Table 6.3 also shows that compounds of ions with higher charges have larger lattice energies than compounds of ions with lower charges. In comparing NaI, MgI$_2$, and AlI$_3$, for example, the order of charges on the cations is $Al^{3+} > Mg^{2+} > Na^+$, and the order of lattice energies is AlI$_3$ > MgI$_2$ > NaI.

WORKED EXAMPLE 6.5

LATTICE ENERGIES

Which has the larger lattice energy, NaCl or CsI?

STRATEGY

The magnitude of a substance's lattice energy is affected both by the charges on its constituent ions and by the sizes of those ions. The higher the charges on the ions and the smaller the sizes of the ions, the larger the lattice energy. In this case, all four ions—Na^+, Cs^+, Cl^-, and I^-—are singly charged, so they differ only in size.

SOLUTION

Because Na^+ is smaller than Cs^+ and Cl^- is smaller than I^-, the distance between ions is smaller in NaCl than in CsI. Thus, NaCl has the larger lattice energy.

WORKED CONCEPTUAL EXAMPLE 6.6

LATTICE ENERGIES

Which of the following alkali metal halides has the larger lattice energy, and which has the smaller lattice energy? Explain.

(a)   **(b)**

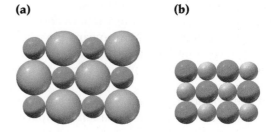

STRATEGY

The magnitude of a lattice energy depends directly on the charge on the ions and inversely on the distance between ions (that is, on the radii of the ions). In this instance, all the ions in both drawings are singly charged, so only the size of the ions is important.

SOLUTION

The ions in drawing **(b)** are smaller than those in drawing **(a)**, so **(b)** has the larger lattice energy.

▶ PROBLEM 6.14   Which substance in each of the following pairs has the larger lattice energy?

(a) KCl or RbCl   (b) CaF_2 or BaF_2 (c) CaO or KI

CONCEPTUAL PROBLEM 6.15   One of the following pictures represents NaCl and one represents MgO. Which is which, and which has the larger lattice energy?

(a)   **(b)**

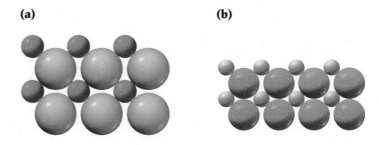

6.9 SOME CHEMISTRY OF THE ALKALI METALS

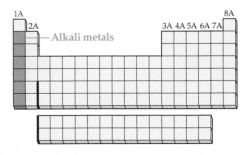

Now that we know something about ionization energies, electron affinities, lattice energies, and the octet rule, let's look briefly at the chemistry of some elements that form ionic bonds. The alkali metals of group 1A—Li, Na, K, Rb, Cs, and Fr—have the smallest ionization energies of all the elements because of their valence-shell ns^1 electron configurations (Figure 6.3). They therefore lose this ns^1 electron easily in chemical reactions to yield 1+ ions and are thus among the most powerful reducing agents in the periodic table (Sections 4.6–4.8). In fact, the chemistry of the alkali metals is dominated by their ability to donate an electron to another element or compound.

As their group name implies, the alkali metals are *metallic*. They have a bright, silvery appearance, are malleable, and are good conductors of electricity. Unlike the more common metals such as iron, though, the alkali metals are all soft enough to cut with a dull knife, have low melting points and densities, and are so reactive that they must be stored under oil to prevent their instantaneous reaction with oxygen and moisture. None are found in the elemental state in nature; they occur only in salts. Their properties are summarized in Table 6.4.

Remember...

A **reducing agent** is a substance that loses one or more electrons and is itself oxidized. An oxidizing agent is a substance that gains one or more electrons and is itself reduced. (Sections 4.6–4.8)

TABLE 6.4 Properties of Alkali Metals

Name	Melting Point (°C)	Boiling Point (°C)	Density (g/cm³)	First Ionization Energy (kJ/mol)	Abundance on Earth (%)	Atomic Radius (pm)	Ionic (M⁺) Radius (pm)
Lithium	180.5	1342	0.534	520.2	0.0020	152	68
Sodium	97.7	883	0.971	495.8	2.36	186	102
Potassium	63.3	759	0.862	418.8	2.09	227	138
Rubidium	39.3	688	1.532	403.0	0.009 0	248	152
Cesium	28.4	671	1.873	375.7	0.000 10	265	167
Francium	—	—	—	~400	Trace	—	—

Production of Alkali Metals

Alkali metals are produced commercially by reduction of their chloride salts, although the exact procedure differs for each element. Both lithium metal and sodium metal are produced by *electrolysis*, a process in which an electric current is passed through the molten salt. The details of the process won't be discussed until Sections 17.12 and 17.13, but the fundamental idea is to use electrical energy to break down an ionic compound into its elements. A high reaction temperature is necessary to keep the salt liquid.

$$2\,\text{LiCl}(l) \xrightarrow[\text{450 °C}]{\text{Electrolysis in KCl}} 2\,\text{Li}(l) + \text{Cl}_2(g)$$

$$2\,\text{NaCl}(l) \xrightarrow[\text{580 °C}]{\text{Electrolysis in CaCl}_2} 2\,\text{Na}(l) + \text{Cl}_2(g)$$

Potassium, rubidium, and cesium metals are produced by chemical reduction rather than by electrolysis. Sodium is the reducing agent used in potassium production, and calcium is the reducing agent used for preparing rubidium and cesium.

$$\text{KCl}(l) + \text{Na}(l) \underset{\text{850 °C}}{\rightleftarrows} \text{K}(g) + \text{NaCl}(l)$$

$$2\,\text{RbCl}(l) + \text{Ca}(l) \underset{\text{750 °C}}{\rightleftarrows} 2\,\text{Rb}(g) + \text{CaCl}_2(l)$$

$$2\,\text{CsCl}(l) + \text{Ca}(l) \underset{\text{750 °C}}{\rightleftarrows} 2\,\text{Cs}(g) + \text{CaCl}_2(l)$$

All three of the above reductions appear contrary to the activity series, described in Section 4.8, according to which sodium is not a strong enough reducing agent to react with K^+ and calcium is not a strong enough reducing agent to react with either Rb^+ or Cs^+. At high reaction temperatures, however, equilibria are established in which

▲ A sample of sodium metal.

Remember...

The **activity series**, shown in Table 4.5 on page 130, ranks the elements in order of their reducing ability. Elements at the top of the activity series, such as Li and Na, are stronger reducing agents, while elements at the bottom, such as Au and Hg, are weaker reducing agents. (Section 4.8)

small amounts of the products are formed. These products are then removed from the reaction mixture by distillation, thereby driving the reactions toward more product formation. We'll explore the general nature of such chemical equilibria in Chapter 13.

Reactions of Alkali Metals

Alkali metals react rapidly with group 7A elements (halogens) to yield colorless, crystalline ionic salts called *halides*. The reactivity of an alkali metal increases as its ionization energy decreases, giving a reactivity order $Cs > Rb > K > Na > Li$. Cesium is the most reactive, combining almost explosively with the halogens.

$$2\,M(s) + X_2 \longrightarrow 2\,MX(s)$$
A metal halide

where M = Alkali metal (Li, Na, K, Rb, or Cs)

X = Halogen (F, Cl, Br, or I)

All the alkali metals also react rapidly with oxygen, but different metals give different kinds of products. Lithium reacts with O_2 to yield the *oxide*, Li_2O; sodium reacts to yield the *peroxide*, Na_2O_2; and the remaining alkali metals, K, Rb, and Cs, form either peroxides or *superoxides*, MO_2, depending on the reaction conditions and on how much oxygen is present. The reasons for the differences have to do largely with the differences in stability of the various products and with how the ions pack together in crystals. The alkali metal cations have a +1 charge in all cases, but the oxygen anions might be either O^{2-}, O_2^{2-}, or O_2^{-}.

$$4\,Li(s) + O_2(g) \longrightarrow 2\,Li_2O(s) \qquad \text{An } oxide; \text{ the anion is } O^{2-}$$
$$2\,Na(s) + O_2(g) \longrightarrow Na_2O_2(s) \qquad \text{A } peroxide; \text{ the anion is } O_2^{2-}$$
$$K(s) + O_2(g) \longrightarrow KO_2(s) \qquad \text{A } superoxide; \text{ the anion is } O_2^{-}$$

Potassium superoxide, KO_2, is a particularly valuable compound because of its use in spacecraft and in self-contained breathing devices to remove moisture and CO_2 from exhaled air, generating oxygen in the process:

$$2\,KO_2(s) + H_2O(g) \longrightarrow KOH(s) + KO_2H(s) + O_2(g)$$
$$4\,KO_2(s) + 2\,CO_2(g) \longrightarrow 2\,K_2CO_3(s) + 3\,O_2(g)$$

Perhaps the most well-known and dramatic reaction of the alkali metals is with water to yield hydrogen gas and an alkali metal hydroxide, MOH. In fact, it's this reaction that gives the elements their group name because the solution of metal hydroxide that results from adding an alkali metal to water is *alkaline*, or basic. Lithium undergoes the reaction with vigorous bubbling as hydrogen is released, sodium reacts rapidly with evolution of heat, and potassium reacts so violently that

Lithium reacts vigorously, with bubbling.

Sodium reacts violently.

Potassium reacts almost explosively.

▲ All the alkali metals react with water to generate H_2 gas.

the hydrogen produced bursts instantly into flame. Rubidium and cesium react almost explosively.

$$2 M(s) + 2 H_2O(l) \longrightarrow 2 M^+(aq) + 2 OH^-(aq) + H_2(g)$$
$$\text{where} \quad M = \text{Li, Na, K, Rb, or Cs}$$

Finally, the alkali metals also react with ammonia to yield H_2 gas plus a metal *amide*, MNH_2, a reaction analogous to that between an alkali metal and water.

$$2 M(s) + 2 NH_3(l) \longrightarrow 2 M^+(soln) + 2 NH_2{}^-(soln) + H_2(g)$$
$$\text{where} \quad M = \text{Li, Na, K, Rb, or Cs}$$

The reaction is sufficiently slow at lower temperatures that it's possible for the alkali metals to dissolve in liquid ammonia at $-33\,°C$, forming deep blue solutions of metal cations and dissolved electrons. These solutions are extremely powerful reducing agents.

$$M(s) \xrightarrow[\text{solvent}]{\text{Liquid } NH_3} M^+(soln) + e^-(soln)$$
$$\text{where} \quad M = \text{Li, Na, K, Rb, or Cs}$$

▲ Sodium metal dissolves in liquid ammonia at low temperature to yield a blue solution of Na^+ ions and solvent-surrounded electrons.

▶ **PROBLEM 6.16** Assign charges to the oxygen-containing anions in the following compounds:

(a) Li_2O (b) K_2O_2 (c) CsO_2

▶ **PROBLEM 6.17** Complete the following equations so that the same numbers and kinds of atoms appear on both sides of the reaction arrow. If no reaction takes place, write N.R.

(a) $Cs(s) + H_2O(l) \longrightarrow$?   (b) $Rb(s) + O_2(g) \longrightarrow$?   (c) $K(s) + NH_3(g) \longrightarrow$?

6.10 SOME CHEMISTRY OF THE ALKALINE-EARTH METALS

The alkaline-earth elements of group 2A—Be, Mg, Ca, Sr, Ba, and Ra—are similar to the alkali metals in many respects. They differ, however, in that they have ns^2 valence-shell electron configurations and can therefore lose two electrons in forming doubly positive ions, M^{2+}. Because their first ionization energy is larger than that of alkali metals (Figure 6.3), the group 2A metals are somewhat less reactive than alkali metals. The general reactivity trend is Ba > Sr > Ca > Mg > Be.

Although harder than their neighbors in group 1A, the alkaline-earth elements are still relatively soft, silvery metals. They tend, however, to have higher melting points and densities than alkali metals, as listed in Table 6.5. Alkaline-earth elements are less reactive toward oxygen and water than alkali metals but are nevertheless found in nature only in salts, not in the elemental state.

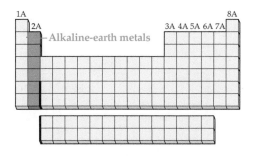

TABLE 6.5 Properties of Alkaline-Earth Metals

Name	Melting Point (°C)	Boiling Point (°C)	Density (g/cm³)	First Ionization Energy (kJ/mol)	Abundance on Earth (%)	Atomic Radius (pm)	Ionic (M^{2+}) Radius (pm)
Beryllium	1287	2471	1.848	899.4	0.000 28	112	44
Magnesium	650	1090	1.738	737.7	2.33	160	66
Calcium	842	1484	1.55	589.8	4.15	197	99
Strontium	777	1382	2.54	549.5	0.038	215	112
Barium	727	1897	3.62	502.9	0.042	222	134
Radium	700	1140	~5.0	509.3	Trace	223	143

Production of Alkaline-Earth Metals

Pure alkaline-earth metals, like alkali metals, are produced commercially by reduction of their salts, either chemically or through electrolysis. Beryllium is prepared by reduction of BeF_2 with magnesium, and magnesium is prepared by electrolysis of its molten chloride.

$$BeF_2(l) + Mg(l) \xrightarrow{1300\,°C} Be(l) + MgF_2(l)$$

$$MgCl_2(l) \xrightarrow[750\,°C]{Electrolysis} Mg(l) + Cl_2(g)$$

Calcium, strontium, and barium are all made by high-temperature reduction of their oxides with aluminum metal.

$$3\,MO(l) + 2\,Al(l) \xrightarrow{High\ temp} 3\,M(l) + Al_2O_3(s)$$

$$\text{where} \quad M = Ca, Sr, \text{ or } Ba$$

Reactions of Alkaline-Earth Metals

Alkaline-earth metals react with halogens to yield ionic halide salts, MX_2, and with oxygen to form oxides, MO:

$$M + X_2 \longrightarrow MX_2 \quad \text{where} \quad M = Be, Mg, Ca, Sr, \text{ or } Ba$$

$$2\,M + O_2 \longrightarrow 2\,MO \qquad\qquad X = F, Cl, Br, \text{ or } I$$

Beryllium and magnesium are relatively unreactive toward oxygen at room temperature, but both burn with a brilliant white glare when ignited by a flame. Calcium, strontium, and barium are so reactive that they are best stored under oil to keep them from contact with air. Like the heavier alkali metals, strontium and barium form peroxides, MO_2.

With the exception of beryllium, the alkaline-earth elements react with water to yield metal hydroxides, $M(OH)_2$. Magnesium undergoes reaction only at temperatures above 100 °C, while calcium and strontium react slowly with liquid water at room temperature. Only barium reacts vigorously at room temperature.

$$M(s) + 2\,H_2O(l) \longrightarrow M(OH)_2 + H_2(g)$$

$$\text{where} \quad M = Mg, Ca, Sr, \text{ or } Ba$$

▲ Calcium metal reacts very slowly with water at room temperature.

▶ PROBLEM 6.18 Predict the products of the following reactions, and balance the equations so that the numbers and kinds of atoms are the same on both sides of the reaction arrows:

(a) $Be(s) + Br_2(l) \longrightarrow$?   (b) $Sr(s) + H_2O(l) \longrightarrow$?   (c) $Mg(s) + O_2(g) \longrightarrow$?

▶ PROBLEM 6.19 What product do you think is formed by reaction of magnesium with sulfur, a group 6A element? What is the charge on the sulfide ion in the product?

6.11 SOME CHEMISTRY OF THE HALOGENS

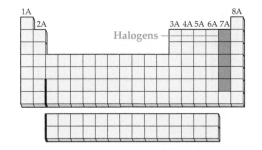

The halogens of group 7A—F, Cl, Br, I, and At—are completely different from the main-group metals we've been discussing up to this point. The halogens are non-metals rather than metals, they exist as diatomic molecules rather than as individual atoms, and they tend to gain rather than lose electrons when they enter into reactions because of their ns^2np^5 electron configurations. In other words, the halogens are characterized by large negative electron affinities and large positive ionization energies. Some of their properties are listed in Table 6.6.

TABLE 6.6   Properties of Halogens

Name	Melting Point (°C)	Boiling Point (°C)	Density (g/cm³)	Electron Affinity (kJ/mol)	Abundance on Earth (%)	Atomic Radius (pm)	Ionic (X^-) Radius (pm)
Fluorine	−220	−188	1.50 (*l*)	−328	0.062	72	133
Chlorine	−101	−34	2.03 (*l*)	−349	0.013	99	181
Bromine	−7	59	3.12 (*l*)	−325	0.000 3	114	196
Iodine	114	184	4.930(*s*)	−295	0.000 05	133	220
Astatine	—	—	—	−270	Trace	—	—

Halogens are too reactive to occur in nature as free elements. Instead, they are found only as their anions in various salts and minerals. Even the name *halogen* implies reactivity, since it comes from the Greek words *hals* (salt) and *gennan* (to form). Thus, a halogen is literally a salt former.

Production of Halogens

All the free halogens are produced commercially by oxidation of their anions. Fluorine and chlorine are both produced by electrolysis: fluorine from a molten 1:2 molar mixture of KF and HF, and chlorine from molten NaCl.

$$2\,HF(l) \xrightarrow[\text{100 °C}]{\text{Electrolysis}} H_2(g) + F_2(g)$$

$$2\,NaCl(l) \xrightarrow[\text{580 °C}]{\text{Electrolysis}} 2\,Na(l) + Cl_2(g)$$

Bromine and iodine are both prepared by oxidation of the corresponding halide ion with chlorine. Naturally occurring aqueous solutions of bromide ion with concentrations of up to 5000 ppm are found in Arkansas and in the Dead Sea in Israel. Iodide ion solutions of up to 100 ppm concentration are found in Oklahoma and Michigan.

$$2\,Br^-(aq) + Cl_2(g) \longrightarrow Br_2(l) + 2\,Cl^-(aq)$$
$$2\,I^-(aq) + Cl_2(g) \longrightarrow I_2(s) + 2\,Cl^-(aq)$$

▲ The Dead Sea in Israel has a particularly high concentration of bromide ion.

Reactions of Halogens

Halogens are among the most reactive elements in the periodic table. Fluorine, in fact, forms compounds with every other element except the three noble gases He, Ne, and Ar. As noted previously, their large negative electron affinities allow halogens to accept electrons from other atoms to yield halide anions, X^-.

Halogens react with every metal in the periodic table to yield metal halides. With alkali and alkaline-earth metals, the formula of the halide product is easily predictable. With transition metals, though, more than one product can sometimes form depending on the reaction conditions and the amounts of reactants present. Iron, for instance, can react with Cl_2 to form either $FeCl_2$ or $FeCl_3$. Without knowing a good deal more about transition-metal chemistry, it's not possible to make predictions at this point. The reaction can be generalized as

$$2\,M + n\,X_2 \longrightarrow 2\,MX_n \quad \text{where} \quad M = \text{Metal}$$
$$X = \text{F, Cl, Br, or I}$$

▲ This beautiful piece of glass was etched with gaseous HF, one of the few substances that reacts with and etches glass (SiO_2), according to the equation $SiO_2(s) + 4 HF(g) \rightarrow SiF_4(g) + 2 H_2O(l)$.

Remember...

An **acid** is a substance that dissociates in water to give hydrogen ions (H^+), and a base is a substance that dissociates in water to give hydroxide ions (OH^-).   (Section 4.5)

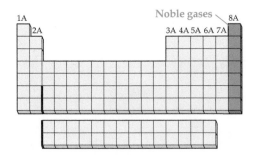

XeF$_2$

XeF$_4$

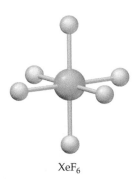

XeF$_6$

Unlike the metallic elements, halogens become less rather than more reactive going down the periodic table because of their generally decreasing electron affinity. Thus, their reactivity order is $F_2 > Cl_2 > Br_2 > I_2$. Fluorine often reacts violently, chlorine and bromine somewhat less so, and iodine often sluggishly.

In addition to their reaction with metals, halogens also react with hydrogen gas to yield hydrogen halides, HX. Fluorine reacts explosively with hydrogen as soon as the two gases come in contact. Chlorine also reacts explosively once the reaction is initiated by a spark or by ultraviolet light, but the mixture of gases is stable in the dark. Bromine and iodine react more slowly.

$$H_2(g) + X_2 \longrightarrow 2 HX(g) \qquad \text{where} \qquad X = F, Cl, Br, \text{ or } I$$

Hydrogen halides are useful because they are **acids**—compounds that produce H^+ ions when dissolved in water. An aqueous solution of HCl, for instance, is used throughout the chemical industry in a vast number of processes, from pickling steel (removing its iron oxide coating) to dissolving animal bones for producing gelatin.

$$HX \xrightarrow[\text{in } H_2O]{\text{Dissolve}} H^+(aq) + X^-(aq)$$

Hydrogen fluoride (HF) is used frequently for etching glass because it is one of the few substances that reacts with glass.

6.12 SOME CHEMISTRY OF THE NOBLE GASES

The noble gases of group 8A—He, Ne, Ar, Kr, Xe, and Rn—are neither metals nor reactive nonmetals. Rather, they are colorless, odorless, unreactive gases. The $1s^2$ valence-shell electron configuration for He and ns^2np^6 for the others already contain octets and thus make it difficult for the noble gases to either gain or lose electrons.

Although sometimes referred to as rare gases or inert gases, these older names are not really accurate because the group 8A elements are neither rare nor completely inert. Argon, for instance, makes up nearly 1% by volume of dry air, and there are several dozen known compounds of krypton and xenon, although none occur naturally. Some properties of the noble gases are listed in Table 6.7.

TABLE 6.7   Properties of Noble Gases

Name	Melting Point (°C)	Boiling Point (°C)	First Ionization Energy (kJ/mol)	Abundance in Dry Air (vol %)
Helium	−272.2	−268.9	2372.3	5.2×10^{-4}
Neon	−248.6	−246.1	2080.6	1.8×10^{-3}
Argon	−189.3	−185.9	1520.4	0.93
Krypton	−157.4	−153.2	1350.7	1.1×10^{-4}
Xenon	−111.8	−108.0	1170.4	9×10^{-6}
Radon	−71	−61.7	1037	Trace

Helium and neon undergo no chemical reactions and form no known compounds. Argon forms only HArF, and krypton and xenon react only with fluorine. Depending on the reaction conditions and on the amounts of reactants present, xenon can form three different fluorides: XeF_2, XeF_4, and XeF_6.

$$Xe(g) + F_2(g) \longrightarrow XeF_2(s)$$
$$Xe(g) + 2 F_2(g) \longrightarrow XeF_4(s)$$
$$Xe(g) + 3 F_2(g) \longrightarrow XeF_6(s)$$

The lack of reactivity of the noble gases is a consequence of their unusually large ionization energies (Figure 6.3) and their unusually small electron affinities (Figure 6.5), which result from their valence-shell electron configurations.

INQUIRY IS EATING SALT UNHEALTHY?

▲ Harvesting salt.

If you're like most people, you probably feel a little guilty about reaching for the salt-shaker at mealtime. The notion that high salt intake and high blood pressure go hand in hand is surely among the most highly publicized pieces of nutritional advice to appear in recent decades.

Salt has not always been held in such disrepute. Historically, salt has been prized since the earliest recorded times as a seasoning and a food preservative. Words and phrases in many languages reflect the importance of salt as a life-giving and life-sustaining substance. We refer to a kind and generous person as "the salt of the earth," for instance, and we speak of being "worth one's salt." In Roman times, soldiers were paid in salt; the English word salary is derived from the Latin word for paying salt wages (*salarium*).

Salt is perhaps the easiest of all minerals to obtain and purify. The simplest method, used for thousands of years throughout the world in coastal climates where sunshine is abundant and rainfall is scarce, is to evaporate seawater. Although the exact amount varies depending on the source, seawater contains an average of about 3.5% by mass of dissolved substances, most of which is sodium chloride. It has been estimated that evaporation of all the world's oceans would yield approximately *4.5 million cubic miles* of NaCl.

Only about 10% of current world salt production comes from evaporation of seawater. Most salt is obtained by mining the vast deposits of halite, or rock salt, formed by evaporation of ancient inland seas. These salt beds vary in thickness up to hundreds of meters and vary in depth from a few meters to thousands of meters below the Earth's surface. Salt mining has gone on for at least 3400 years, and the Wieliczka mine in Galicia, Poland (shown on the chapter-opening page), was worked continuously for more than 700 years until its closure in 1996.

Let's get back now to the dinner table. What about the link between dietary salt intake and high blood pressure? There's no doubt that most people in industrialized nations have a relatively high salt intake, and there's no doubt that high blood pressure among industrialized populations is on the rise. What's not so clear is exactly how the two observations are related.

The case against salt has been made largely by comparing widely diverse populations with different dietary salt intakes—by comparing the health of modern Americans with that of inhabitants of the Amazon rain forest, for example. Obviously, though, industrialization brings with it far more changes than simply an increase in dietary salt intake, and many of these other changes may be much more important than salt in contributing to hypertension.

In a study called the DASH-Sodium study, published in 2001, a strong correlation was found between a change in salt intake and a change in blood pressure. When volunteers cut back their salt intake from 8.3 g per day—roughly what Americans typically consume—to 3.8 g per day, significant drops in blood pressure were found. The largest reduction in blood pressure was seen in people already diagnosed with hypertension, but even subjects with normal blood pressure lowered their readings by several percentage points.

What should an individual do? The best answer, as in so many things, is to use moderation and common sense. People with hypertension should make a strong effort to lower their sodium intake; others might be well advised to choose unsalted snacks, use less salt in preparing food, and read nutrition labels for sodium content.

But one further point: Nutritional advice is never one-size-fits-all. Atheletes, construction workers, farm workers, and others who sweat profusely, may well need to *increase* their salt intake to avoid problems with low sodium and potassium levels.

▸ **PROBLEM 6.20**   How is salt obtained commercially?

SUMMARY

Metallic elements, on the left side of the periodic table, tend to give up electrons to form cations, while the halogens and a few other non-metallic elements, on the right side of the table, tend to accept electrons to form anions. The electrons given up by a main-group metal in forming a cation come from the highest-energy occupied orbital, while the electrons that are accepted by a nonmetal in forming an anion go into the lowest-energy unoccupied orbital. Sodium metal, for instance, loses its valence-shell 3s electron to form an Na^+ ion with the electron configuration of neon, while chlorine gains a 3p electron to form a Cl^- anion with the electron configuration of argon.

The amount of energy necessary to remove a valence electron from an isolated neutral atom is called the atom's **ionization energy** (E_i). Ionization energies are smallest for metallic elements on the left side of the periodic table and largest for nonmetallic elements on the right side. As a result, metals usually give up electrons and act as reducing agents in chemical reactions.

Ionization is not limited to the removal of a single electron from an atom. Two, three, or even more electrons can be removed sequentially from an atom, although larger amounts of energy are required for each successive ionization step. In general, valence-shell electrons are much more easily removed than **core electrons**.

The amount of energy released or absorbed when an electron adds to an isolated neutral atom is called the atom's **electron affinity** (E_{ea}). By convention, a negative E_{ea} corresponds to a release of energy and a positive E_{ea} corresponds to an absorption of energy. Electron affinities are most negative for group 7A elements and most positive for group 2A and 8A elements. As a result, the group 7A elements usually accept electrons and act as oxidizing agents in chemical reactions.

In general, reactions of main-group elements can be described by the **octet rule**, which states that these elements tend to undergo reactions so as to attain a noble-gas electron configuration with filled s and p sublevels in their valence shell. Elements on the left side of the periodic table tend to give up electrons until a noble-gas configuration is reached; elements on the right side of the table tend to accept electrons until a noble-gas configuration is reached; and the noble gases themselves are essentially unreactive.

Main-group metals in groups 1A and 2A react with halogens in group 7A, during which the metal loses one or more electrons to the halogen. The product, a metal halide such as NaCl, is an ionic solid that consists of metal cations and halide anions electrostatically attracted to one another by ionic bonds. The sum of the interaction energies among all ions in a crystal is called the crystal's **lattice energy** (U).

KEY WORDS

Born–Haber cycle 199
core electron 191
Coulomb's law 201
electron affinity (E_{ea}) 194
ionization energy (E_i) 190
lattice energy (U) 200
octet rule 197

CONCEPTUAL PROBLEMS

Problems 6.1–6.20 appear within the chapter.

6.21 In the following drawings, red spheres represent cations and blue spheres represent anions. Match each of the drawings (a)–(d) with the following ionic compounds:

(i) $Ca_3(PO_4)_2$ (ii) Li_2CO_3 (iii) $FeCl_2$ (iv) $MgSO_4$

(a)

(b)

(c)

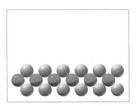

(d)

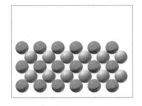

6.22 Which of the following drawings is more likely to represent an ionic compound, and which a covalent compound?

(a) **(b)**

6.23 Circle the approximate part or parts of the periodic table where the following elements appear:

(a) Elements with the smallest values of E_{i1}
(b) Elements with the largest atomic radii
(c) Elements with the most negative values of E_{ea}

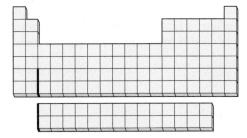

6.24 Where on the periodic table would you find the element that has an ion with each of the following electron configurations? Identify each ion.

(a) 3+ ion: $1s^2 2s^2 2p^6$ (b) 3+ ion: $[Ar] 3d^3$

(c) 2+ ion: $[Kr] 5s^2 4d^{10}$ (d) 1+ ion: $[Kr] 4d^{10}$

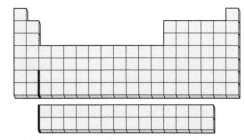

6.25 Which of the following spheres is likely to represent a metal atom, and which a nonmetal atom? Which sphere in the products represents a cation, and which an anion?

 +  ⟶  +

6.26 Each of the pictures (a)–(d) represents one of the following substances at 25 °C: sodium, chlorine, iodine, sodium chloride. Which picture corresponds to which substance?

(a) (b) (c) (d)

6.27 Which of the following alkali metal halides has the largest lattice energy, and which has the smallest lattice energy? Explain.

(a) (b) (c)

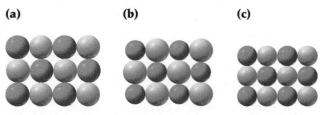

6.28 Three binary compounds are represented on the following drawing: red with red, blue with blue, and green with green. Give a likely formula for each compound.

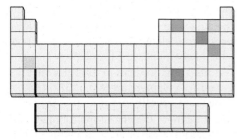

6.29 Given the following values for the formation of LiCl(s) from its elements, draw a Born–Haber cycle similar to that shown in Figure 6.6 on page 199.

E_{ea} for Cl(g) = −348.6 kJ/mol

Heat of sublimation for Li(s) = +159.4 kJ/mol

E_{i1} for Li(g) = +520 kJ/mol

Bond dissociation energy for Cl$_2$(g) = +243 kJ/mol

Lattice energy for LiCl(s) = +853 kJ/mol

SECTION PROBLEMS

Ions, Ionization Energy, and Electron Affinity (Sections 6.1–6.5)

6.30 What is the difference between a covalent bond and an ionic bond? Give an example of each.

6.31 What is the difference between a molecule and an ion? Give an example of each.

6.32 How many protons and electrons are in each of the following ions?

(a) Be^{2+} (b) Rb^+ (c) Se^{2-} (d) Au^{3+}

6.33 What is the identity of the element X in the following ions?

(a) X^{2+}, a cation that has 36 electrons

(b) X^-, an anion that has 36 electrons

6.34 What are the likely ground-state electron configurations of the following cations?

(a) La^{3+} (b) Ag^+ (c) Sn^{2+}

6.35 What are the likely ground-state electron configurations of the following anions?

(a) Se^{2-} (b) N^{3-}

6.36 What is the electron configuration of Ca^{2+}? What is the electron configuration of Ti^{2+}?

6.37 What tripositive ion has the electron configuration $[Kr] 4d^3$? What neutral atom has the electron configuration $[Kr] 5s^2 4d^2$?

6.38 There are two elements in the transition-metal series Sc through Zn that have four unpaired electrons in their 2+ ions. Identify them.

6.39 Identify the element whose 2+ ion has the ground-state electron configuration $[Ar] 3d^{10}$.

6.40 Which group of elements in the periodic table has the largest E_{i1}, and which group has the smallest? Explain.

6.41 Which element in the periodic table has the smallest ionization energy? Which has the largest?

6.42 **(a)** Which has the smaller second ionization energy, K or Ca?

(b) Which has the larger third ionization energy, Ga or Ca?

6.43 **(a)** Which has the smaller fourth ionization energy, Sn or Sb?

(b) Which has the larger sixth ionization energy, Se or Br?

6.44 Three atoms have the following electron configurations:

(a) $1s^2\,2s^2\,2p^6\,3s^2\,3p^3$

(b) $1s^2\,2s^2\,2p^6\,3s^2\,3p^6$

(c) $1s^2\,2s^2\,2p^6\,3s^2\,3p^6\,4s^2$

Which of the three has the largest E_{i2}? Which has the smallest E_{i7}?

6.45 Write the electron configuration of the atom in the third row of the periodic table that has the smallest E_{i4}.

6.46 The first four ionization energies in kJ/mol of a certain second-row element are 801, 2427, 3660, and 25,025. What is the likely identity of the element?

6.47 The first four ionization energies in kJ/mol of a certain second-row element are 900, 1757, 14,849, and 21,007. What is the likely identity of the element?

6.48 Which element in each of the following sets has the smallest first ionization energy, and which has the largest?

(a) Li, Ba, K   **(b)** B, Be, Cl   **(c)** Ca, C, Cl

6.49 What elements meet the following descriptions? **(a)** Has largest E_{i3} **(b)** Has largest E_{i7}

6.50 What is the relationship between the electron affinity of a singly charged cation such as Na^+ and the ionization energy of the neutral atom?

6.51 What is the relationship between the ionization energy of a singly charged anion such as Cl^- and the electron affinity of the neutral atom?

6.52 Which has the more negative electron affinity, Na^+ or Na? Na^+ or Cl?

6.53 Which has the more negative electron affinity, Br or Br^-?

6.54 Why is energy usually released when an electron is added to a neutral atom but absorbed when an electron is removed from a neutral atom?

6.55 Why does ionization energy increase regularly across the periodic table from group 1A to group 8A, whereas electron affinity increases irregularly from group 1A to group 7A and then falls dramatically for group 8A?

6.56 No element has a negative second electron affinity. That is, the process $A^-(g) + e^- \longrightarrow A^{2-}(g)$ is unfavorable for every element. Suggest a reason.

6.57 Why does phosphorus have a less-negative electron affinity than its neighbors silicon and sulfur?

Ionic Bonds and Lattice Energy (Sections 6.7 and 6.8)

6.58 Order the following compounds according to their expected lattice energies: LiCl, KCl, KBr, $MgCl_2$.

6.59 Order the following compounds according to their expected lattice energies: $AlBr_3$, $MgBr_2$, LiBr, CaO.

6.60 Calculate the energy change in kilojoules per mole when lithium atoms lose an electron to bromine atoms to form isolated Li^+ and Br^- ions. [The E_i for Li(g) is 520 kJ/mol; the E_{ea} for Br(g) is −325 kJ/mol.]

6.61 Cesium has the smallest ionization energy of all elements (376 kJ/mol), and chlorine has the most negative electron affinity (−349 kJ/mol). Will a cesium atom transfer an electron to a chlorine atom to form isolated $Cs^+(g)$ and $Cl^-(g)$ ions? Explain.

6.62 Find the lattice energy of LiBr(s) in Table 6.3, and calculate the energy change in kilojoules per mole for the formation of solid LiBr from the elements. [The sublimation energy for Li(s) is +159.4 kJ/mol, the bond dissociation energy of $Br_2(g)$ is +224 kJ/mol, and the energy necessary to convert $Br_2(l)$ to $Br_2(g)$ is 30.9 kJ/mol.]

6.63 Look up the lattice energies in Table 6.3, and calculate the energy change in kilojoules per mole for the formation of the following substances from their elements:

(a) LiF(s) [The sublimation energy for Li(s) is +159.4 kJ/mol, the E_i for Li(g) is 520 kJ/mol, the E_{ea} for F(g) is −328 kJ/mol, and the bond dissociation energy of $F_2(g)$ is +158 kJ/mol.]

(b) $CaF_2(s)$ [The sublimation energy for Ca(s) is +178.2 kJ/mol, E_{i1} = +589.8 kJ/mol, and E_{i2} = +1145 kJ/mol.]

6.64 Born–Haber cycles, such as those shown in Figures 6.6 and 6.7, are called *cycles* because they form closed loops. If any five of the six energy changes in the cycle are known, the value of the sixth can be calculated. Use the following five values to calculate the lattice energy in kilojoules per mole for sodium hydride, NaH(s):

E_{ea} for H(g) = −72.8 kJ/mol

E_{i1} for Na(g) = +495.8 kJ/mol

Heat of sublimation for Na(s) = +107.3 kJ/mol

Bond dissociation energy for $H_2(g)$ = +435.9 kJ/mol

Net energy change for the formation of NaH(s) from its elements = −60 kJ/mol

6.65 Calculate a lattice energy for $CaH_2(s)$ in kilojoules per mole using the following information:

E_{ea} for H(g) = −72.8 kJ/mol

E_{i1} for Ca(g) = +589.8 kJ/mol

E_{i2} for Ca(g) = +1145 kJ/mol

Heat of sublimation for Ca(s) = +178.2 kJ/mol

Bond dissociation energy for $H_2(g)$ = +435.9 kJ/mol

Net energy change for the formation of $CaH_2(s)$ from its elements = −186.2 kJ/mol

6.66 Calculate the overall energy change in kilojoules per mole for the formation of CsF(s) from its elements using the following data:

E_{ea} for F(g) = −328 kJ/mol

E_{i1} for Cs(g) = +375.7 kJ/mol

E_{i2} for Cs(g) = +2422 kJ/mol

Heat of sublimation for Cs(s) = +76.1 kJ/mol

Bond dissociation energy for $F_2(g)$ = +158 kJ/mol

Lattice energy for CsF(s) = +740 kJ/mol

6.67 The estimated lattice energy for $CsF_2(s)$ is +2347 kJ/mol. Use the data given in Problem 6.66 to calculate an overall energy change in kilojoules per mole for the formation of $CsF_2(s)$ from its elements. Does the overall reaction absorb energy or release it? In light of your answer to Problem 6.66, which compound is more likely to form in the reaction of cesium with fluorine, CsF or CsF_2?

6.68 Calculate the overall energy change in kilojoules per mole for the formation of CaCl(*s*) from the elements. The following data are needed:

E_{ea} for Cl(*g*) = −348.6 kJ/mol

E_{i1} for Ca(*g*) = +589.8 kJ/mol

E_{i2} for Ca(*g*) = +1145 kJ/mol

Heat of sublimation for Ca(*s*) = +178.2 kJ/mol

Bond dissociation energy for Cl_2(*g*) = +243 kJ/mol

Lattice energy for $CaCl_2$(*s*) = +2258 kJ/mol

Lattice energy for CaCl(*s*) = +717 kJ/mol (estimated)

6.69 Use the data in Problem 6.68 to calculate an overall energy change for the formation of $CaCl_2$(*s*) from the elements. Which is more likely to form, CaCl or $CaCl_2$?

6.70 Use the data and the result in Problem 6.64 to draw a Born–Haber cycle for the formation of NaH(*s*) from its elements.

6.71 Use the data and the result in Problem 6.63(a) to draw a Born–Haber cycle for the formation of LiF(*s*) from its elements.

Main-Group Chemistry (Sections 6.9–6.12)

6.72 Little is known about the chemistry of astatine (At) from direct observation, but reasonable predictions can be made.

(a) Is astatine likely to be a gas, a liquid, or a solid?

(b) Is astatine likely to react with sodium? If so, what is the formula of the product?

6.73 Look at the properties of the alkali metals summarized in Table 6.4, and predict reasonable values for the melting point, boiling point, density, and atomic radius of francium.

6.74 Why does chemical reactivity increase from top to bottom in groups 1A and 2A?

6.75 Why does chemical reactivity decrease from top to bottom in group 7A?

6.76 Write chemical equations for the reaction of potassium with the following substances, making sure that the numbers and kinds of atoms are the same on both sides of the equations. If no reaction occurs, write N.R.

(a) H_2O (b) NH_3 (c) Br_2 (d) O_2

6.77 Write chemical equations for the reaction of calcium with the following substances, making sure that the numbers and kinds of atoms are the same on both sides of the equations. If no reaction occurs, write N.R.

(a) H_2O (b) He   (c) Br_2 (d) O_2

6.78 Write chemical equations for the reaction of chlorine with the following substances, making sure that the numbers and kinds of atoms are the same on both sides of the equations. If no reaction occurs, write N.R.

(a) H_2 (b) Ar   (c) Rb

6.79 Milk of magnesia, a widely used antacid, is an aqueous suspension of $Mg(OH)_2$. How would you prepare $Mg(OH)_2$ from magnesium metal?

6.80 The element bromine was first prepared by oxidation of aqueous potassium bromide with solid manganese(IV) oxide. Write a balanced net ionic equation for the reaction in aqueous acidic solution. (Mn^{2+} is also formed.)

6.81 The first preparation of chlorine was similar to the synthesis of elemental bromine (Problem 6.80). A later method entailed the reaction of hydrogen chloride and oxygen at 400 °C. Write a balanced equation for the reaction. (Water is also formed.)

6.82 Passing an electric current (*electrolysis*) through a solution of Al_2O_3 in molten cryolite (Na_3AlF_6) around 1000 °C produces aluminum metal, which separates from the solution as a liquid. Write a balanced equation for the reaction. (Oxygen is also formed.)

6.83 Barium metal can be prepared from its oxide by heating with aluminum at 1200 °C. (Aluminum oxide is also formed.) At the reaction temperature, the oxides are solids, aluminum is a liquid, and barium is a gas. Write a balanced equation for the reaction.

6.84 Reaction of titanium and chlorine at 300 °C yields a metal halide that is 25.25% Ti by mass. The melting point (−24 °C) and boiling point (136 °C) of the halide suggest it is a molecular compound rather than an ionic one.

(a) What are the formula and name of the compound, assuming the molecular formula is the same as the empirical formula?

(b) Write the balanced equation for the reaction.

(c) When treated with magnesium, the compound yields high-purity titanium metal. Write a balanced equation for the reaction.

6.85 Niobium reacts with fluorine at room temperature to give a solid binary compound that is 49.44% Nb by mass.

(a) What is the empirical formula of the compound?

(b) Write a balanced equation for the reaction.

(c) The compound reacts with hydrogen to regenerate metallic niobium. Write a balanced equation for the reaction.

CHAPTER PROBLEMS

6.86 Cu^+ has an ionic radius of 77 pm, but Cu^{2+} has an ionic radius of 73 pm. Explain.

6.87 The following ions all have the same number of electrons: Ti^{4+}, Sc^{3+}, Ca^{2+}, S^{2-}. Order them according to their expected sizes, and explain your answer.

6.88 Calculate overall energy changes in kilojoules per mole for the formation of MgF(*s*) and MgF_2(*s*) from their elements. In light of your answers, which compound is more likely to form in the reaction of magnesium with fluorine, MgF or MgF_2? The following data are needed:

E_{ea} for F(*g*) = −328 kJ/mol

E_{i1} for Mg(*g*) = +737.7 kJ/mol

E_{i2} for Mg(*g*) = +1450.7 kJ/mol

Heat of sublimation for Mg(*s*) = +147.7 kJ/mol

Bond dissociation energy for F_2(*g*) = +158 kJ/mol

Lattice energy for MgF_2(*s*) = +2952 kJ/mol

Lattice energy for MgF(*s*) = 930 kJ/mol (estimated)

6.89 Draw Born–Haber cycles for the formation of both MgF and MgF_2 (Problem 6.88).

6.90 We saw in Section 6.7 that the reaction of solid sodium with gaseous chlorine to yield solid sodium chloride (Na^+Cl^-) is favorable by 411 kJ/mol. Calculate the energy change for the alternative reaction that yields chlorine sodide (Cl^+Na^-), and then explain why sodium chloride formation is preferred.

$$2\,Na(s) + Cl_2(g) \longrightarrow 2\,Cl^+Na^-(s)$$

Assume that the lattice energy for Cl^+Na^- is the same as that for Na^+Cl^-. The following data are needed in addition to that found in Section 6.7:

E_{ea} for Na(g) = −52.9 kJ/mol

E_{i1} for Cl(g) = +1251 kJ/mol

6.91 Draw a Born–Haber cycle for the reaction of sodium with chlorine to yield chlorine sodide (Problem 6.90).

6.92 Write chemical equations for the reaction of lithium with the following substances, making sure that the numbers and kinds of atoms are the same on both sides of the equations. If no reaction occurs, write N.R.

(a) H_2O (b) NH_3 (c) Br_2

(d) N_2 (e) O_2

6.93 Write chemical equations for the reaction of fluorine with the following substances, making sure that the numbers and kinds of atoms are the same on both sides of the equations. If no reaction occurs, write N.R.

(a) H_2 (b) Na   (c) Sr

6.94 Each of the following pairs of elements will react to form a binary ionic compound. Write the formula of each compound formed, and give its name.

(a) Magnesium and chlorine

(b) Calcium and oxygen

(c) Lithium and nitrogen

(d) Aluminum and oxygen

6.95 Element X reacts with element Y to give a product containing X^{3+} ions and Y^{2-} ions.

(a) Is element X likely to be a metal or a nonmetal? Explain.

(b) Is element Y likely to be a metal or a nonmetal? Explain.

(c) What is the formula of the product?

(d) In what groups of the periodic table are elements X and Y likely to be found?

6.96 Many early chemists noted a diagonal relationship among elements in the periodic table, whereby a given element is sometimes more similar to the element below and to the right than it is to the element directly below. Lithium is more similar to magnesium than to sodium, for example, and boron is more similar to silicon than to aluminum. Use your knowledge about the periodic trends of such properties as atomic radii and Z_{eff} to explain the existence of diagonal relationships.

6.97 Heating elemental cesium and platinum together for two days at 973 K gives a dark red ionic compound that is 57.67% Cs and 42.33% Pt.

(a) What is the empirical formula of the compound?

(b) What are the charge and electron configuration of the cesium ion?

(c) What are the charge and electron configuration of the platinum ion?

6.98 Use the following information plus the data given in Tables 6.2 and 6.3 to calculate the second electron affinity, E_{ea2}, of oxygen. Is the O^{2-} ion stable in the gas phase? Why is it stable in solid MgO?

Heat of sublimation for Mg(s) = +147.7 kJ/mol

Bond dissociation energy for $O_2(g)$ = +498.4 kJ/mol

E_{ea1} for O(g) = −141.0 kJ/mol

Net energy change for formation of MgO(s) from its elements = −601.7 kJ/mol

6.99 (a) Which element from each set has the largest atomic radius? Explain.

(i) Ba, Ti, Ra, Li   (ii) F, Al, In, As

(b) Which element from each set has the smallest ionization energy? Explain.

(i) Tl, Po, Se, Ga   (ii) Cs, Ga, Bi, Se

6.100 (a) Which of the elements Be, N, O, and F has the most negative electron affinity? Explain.

(b) Which of the ions Se^{2-}, F^-, O^{2-}, and Rb^+ has the largest radius? Explain.

6.101 Given the following information, construct a Born–Haber cycle to calculate the lattice energy of $CaC_2(s)$:

Net energy change for the formation of $CaC_2(s)$ = −60 kJ/mol

Heat of sublimation for Ca(s) = +178 kJ/mol

E_{i1} for Ca(g) = +590 kJ/mol

E_{i2} for Ca(g) = +1145 kJ/mol

Heat of sublimation for C(s) = +717 kJ/mol

Bond dissociation energy for $C_2(g)$ = +614 kJ/mol

E_{ea1} for $C_2(g)$ = −315 kJ/mol

E_{ea2} for $C_2(g)$ = +410 kJ/mol

6.102 Given the following information, construct a Born–Haber cycle to calculate the lattice energy of $CrCl_2I(s)$:

Net energy change for the formation of $CrCl_2I(s)$ = −420 kJ/mol

Bond dissociation energy for $Cl_2(g)$ = +243 kJ/mol

Bond dissociation energy for $I_2(s)$ = +151 kJ/mol

Heat of sublimation for $I_2(s)$ = +62 kJ/mol

Heat of sublimation for Cr(s) = +397 kJ/mol

E_{i1} for Cr(g) = 652 kJ/mol

E_{i2} for Cr(g) = 1588 kJ/mol

E_{i3} for Cr(g) = 2882 kJ/mol

E_{ea} for Cl(g) = −349 kJ/mol

E_{ea} for I(g) = −295 kJ/mol

MULTICONCEPT PROBLEMS

6.103 Consider the electronic structure of the element bismuth.

    (a) The first ionization energy of bismuth is $E_{i1} = +703$ kJ/mol. What is the longest possible wavelength of light that could ionize an atom of bismuth?

    (b) Write the electron configurations of neutral Bi and the Bi^+ cation.

    (c) What are the n and l quantum numbers of the electron removed when Bi is ionized to Bi^+?

    (d) Would you expect element 115 to have an ionization energy greater than, equal to, or less than that of bismuth? Explain.

6.104 Iron is commonly found as Fe, Fe^{2+}, and Fe^{3+}.

    (a) Write electron configurations for each of the three.

    (b) What are the n and l quantum numbers of the electron removed on going from Fe^{2+} to Fe^{3+}?

    (c) The third ionization energy of Fe is $E_{i3} = +2952$ kJ/mol. What is the longest wavelength of light that could ionize $Fe^{2+}(g)$ to $Fe^{3+}(g)$?

    (d) The third ionization energy of Ru is less than the third ionization energy of Fe. Explain.

6.105 The ionization energy of an atom can be measured by photoelectron spectroscopy, in which light of wavelength λ is directed at an atom, causing an electron to be ejected. The kinetic energy of the ejected electron (E_K) is measured by determining its velocity, v, since $E_K = 1/2 \, mv^2$. The E_i is then calculated using the relationship that the energy of the incident light equals the sum of E_i plus E_K.

    (a) What is the ionization energy of rubidium atoms in kilojoules per mole if light with $\lambda = 58.4$ nm produces electrons with a velocity of 2.450×10^6 m/s? (The mass of an electron is 9.109×10^{-31} kg.)

    (b) What is the ionization energy of potassium in kilojoules per mole if light with $\lambda = 142$ nm produces electrons with a velocity of 1.240×10^6 m/s?

Covalent Bonds and Molecular Structure

Shape is important, both in architecture and in chemistry.

CONTENTS

We saw in the previous chapter that a bond between a metal and a reactive nonmetal is typically formed by the transfer of electrons between atoms. The metal atom loses one or more electrons and becomes a cation, while the reactive nonmetal atom gains one or more electrons and becomes an anion. The oppositely charged ions are held together by the electrostatic attractions that we call ionic bonds.

How, though, do bonds form between atoms of the same or similar elements? How can we describe the bonds in such substances as H_2, Cl_2, CO_2, and the tens of millions of other nonionic compounds? Simply put, the answer is that the bonds in such compounds are formed by the *sharing* of electrons between atoms rather than by the transfer of electrons from one atom to another. As we saw in Section 2.10, a bond formed by the sharing of electrons is called a *covalent bond*, and the unit of matter held together by one or more covalent bonds is called a *molecule*. We'll explore the nature of covalent bonding in this chapter.

7.1   COVALENT BONDING IN MOLECULES

To see how the formation of a covalent, shared-electron bond between atoms can be described, let's look at the H—H bond in the H_2 molecule as the simplest example. When two hydrogen atoms come close together, electrostatic interactions begin to develop between them. The two positively charged nuclei repel each other, and the two negatively charged electrons repel each other, but each nucleus attracts both electrons (Figure 7.1). If the attractive forces are stronger than the repulsive forces, a covalent bond is formed, with the two atoms held together and the two shared electrons occupying the region between the nuclei.

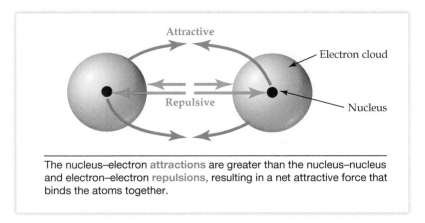

The nucleus–electron **attractions** are greater than the nucleus–nucleus and electron–electron **repulsions**, resulting in a net attractive force that binds the atoms together.

Figure 7.1
A covalent H—H bond. The bond is the net result of attractive and repulsive electrostatic forces.

In essence, the shared electrons act as a kind of "glue" to bind the two atoms into an H_2 molecule. Both nuclei are simultaneously attracted to the same electrons and are therefore held together, much as two tug-of-war teams pulling on the same rope are held together.

The magnitudes of the various attractive and repulsive forces between nuclei and electrons in a covalent bond depend on how close the atoms are. If the hydrogen atoms are too far apart, the attractive forces are small and no bond exists. If the hydrogen atoms are too close together, the repulsive interaction between the nuclei becomes so strong that it pushes the atoms apart. Thus, there is an optimum distance between nuclei called the **bond length** where net attractive forces are maximized and the H—H molecule is most stable. In the H_2 molecule, the bond length is 74 pm. On a graph of energy versus internuclear distance, the bond length is the H—H distance in the minimum-energy, most stable arrangement (Figure 7.2).

Every covalent bond has its own characteristic length that leads to maximum stability and that is roughly predictable from a knowledge of atomic radii (Section 5.14). For example, because the atomic radius of hydrogen is 37 pm and the atomic radius of chlorine is 99 pm, the H—Cl bond length in a hydrogen chloride molecule should be approximately 37 pm + 99 pm = 136 pm. The actual value is 127 pm.

Figure 7.2
A graph of potential energy versus internuclear distance for the H$_2$ molecule.

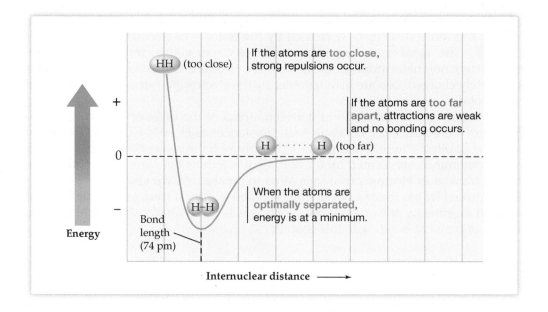

7.2   STRENGTHS OF COVALENT BONDS

Look again at Figure 7.2, the graph of energy versus internuclear distance for the H$_2$ molecule, and note how the H$_2$ molecule is lower in energy than two separate hydrogen atoms. When pairs of hydrogen atoms bond together, they form lower-energy H$_2$ molecules and release 436 kJ/mol. Looked at from the other direction, 436 kJ must be *added* to split 1 mol of H$_2$ molecules apart into 2 mol of hydrogen atoms.

The amount of energy that must be supplied to break a chemical bond in an isolated molecule in the gaseous state—and thus the amount of energy released when the bond forms—is called the **bond dissociation energy (D).** Bond dissociation energies are always positive because energy must always be supplied to break a bond. Conversely, the amount of energy released on forming a bond always has a negative value.

Every bond in every molecule has its own specific bond dissociation energy. Not surprisingly, though, bonds between the same pairs of atoms usually have similar dissociation energies. For example, carbon–carbon bonds usually have D values of approximately 350–380 kJ/mol regardless of the exact structure of the molecule. Note in the following examples that covalent bonds are indicated by lines between atoms, as described in Section 2.10.

Remember...

The structural formula of a molecule uses lines between the atoms to indicate the shared electrons in covalent bonds. (Section 2.10)

Ethane
D = 377 kJ/mol

Propane
D = 370 kJ/mol

Butane
D = 372 kJ/mol

Because similar bonds have similar bond dissociation energies, it's possible to construct a table of average values to compare different kinds of bonds (Table 7.1). Keep in mind, though, that the actual value in a specific molecule might vary by ±10% from the average.

TABLE 7.1 Average Bond Dissociation Energies, *D* (kJ/mol)

H—H	436[a]	C—H	410	N—H	390	O—F	180	I—I	151[a]
H—C	410	C—C	350	N—C	300	O—Cl	200	S—F	310
H—F	570[a]	C—F	450	N—F	270	O—Br	210	S—Cl	250
H—Cl	432[a]	C—Cl	330	N—Cl	200	O—I	220	S—Br	210
H—Br	366[a]	C—Br	270	N—Br	240	O—N	200	S—S	225
H—I	298[a]	C—I	240	N—N	240	O—O	180		
H—N	390	C—N	300	N—O	200	F—F	159a		
H—O	460	C—O	350	O—H	460	Cl—Cl	243[a]		
H—S	340	C—S	260	O—C	350	Br—Br	193[a]		

Multiple covalent bonds[b]

C=C	728	C≡C	965	C=O	732	O=O	498[a]	N≡N	945[a]

[a] Exact value
[b] We'll discuss multiple covalent bonds in Section 7.5.

The bond dissociation energies listed in Table 7.1 cover a wide range, from a low of 151 kJ/mol for the I—I bond to a high of 570 kJ/mol for the H—F bond. As a rule of thumb, though, most of the bonds commonly encountered in naturally occurring molecules (C—H, C—C, C—O) have values in the range 350–400 kJ/mol.

7.3 A COMPARISON OF IONIC AND COVALENT COMPOUNDS

Look at the comparison between NaCl and HCl in Table 7.2 to get an idea of the difference between ionic and covalent compounds. Sodium chloride, an ionic compound, is a white solid with a melting point of 801 °C and a boiling point of 1465 °C. Hydrogen chloride, a covalent compound, is a colorless gas with a melting point of −115 °C and a boiling point of −84.9 °C. What accounts for such large differences in properties between ionic compounds and covalent compounds?

TABLE 7.2 Some Physical Properties of NaCl and HCl

Property	NaCl	HCl
Formula mass	58.44 amu	36.46 amu
Physical appearance	White solid	Colorless gas
Type of bond	Ionic	Covalent
Melting point	801 °C	−115 °C
Boiling point	1465 °C	−84.9 °C

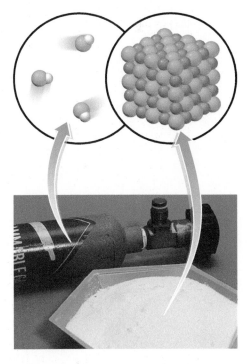

▲ Sodium chloride, an ionic compound, is a white, crystalline solid that melts at 801 °C. Hydrogen chloride, a molecular compound, is a gas at room temperature.

Ionic compounds are high-melting solids because of their ionic bonds. As discussed previously in Section 2.11, a visible sample of sodium chloride consists not of NaCl molecules but of a vast three-dimensional network of ions in which each Na$^+$ cation is attracted to many surrounding Cl$^-$ anions and each Cl$^-$ ion is attracted to many surrounding Na$^+$ ions. For sodium chloride to melt or boil so that the ions break free of one another, every ionic attraction in the entire crystal—the lattice energy—must be overcome, a process that requires a large amount of energy.

Covalent compounds, by contrast, are low-melting solids, liquids, or even gases. A sample of a covalent compound, such as hydrogen chloride, consists of discrete HCl molecules. The covalent bond within an individual molecule may be very strong, but the attractive forces between the different molecules are fairly weak. As a

Remember...

Lattice energy (*U*) is the amount of energy that must be supplied to break an ionic solid into its individual gaseous ions and is thus a measure of the strength of the crystal's ionic bonds. (Section 6.8)

result, relatively little energy is required to overcome the forces between molecules and cause a covalent compound to melt or boil. We'll look at the nature of intermolecular forces and the boiling process in Chapter 10.

7.4 POLAR COVALENT BONDS: ELECTRONEGATIVITY

We've given the impression up to this point that a given bond is either purely ionic, with electrons completely transferred, or purely covalent, with electrons shared equally. In fact, though, ionic and covalent bonds represent only the two extremes of a continuous range of possibilities. Between these two extremes are the large majority of bonds in which the bonding electrons are shared unequally between two atoms but are not completely transferred. Such bonds are said to be **polar covalent bonds** (Figure 7.3). The lowercase Greek letter delta (δ) is used to symbolize the resultant *partial* charges on the atoms, either partial positive ($\delta+$) for the atom that has a smaller share of the bonding electrons or partial negative ($\delta-$) for the atom that has a larger share.

Figure 7.3
The bonding continuum from nonpolar covalent **to** ionic. [The symbol δ (Greek delta) means partial charge, either partial positive ($\delta+$) or partial negative ($\delta-$)].

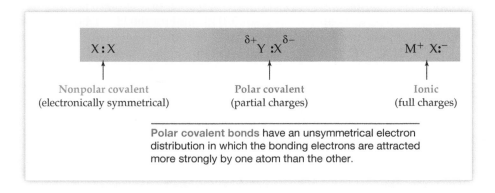

X:X	$\overset{\delta+}{Y} :\overset{\delta-}{X}$	M$^+$ X:$^-$
Nonpolar covalent (electronically symmetrical)	Polar covalent (partial charges)	Ionic (full charges)

Polar covalent bonds have an unsymmetrical electron distribution in which the bonding electrons are attracted more strongly by one atom than the other.

The extent of electron transfer in a compound is most easily visualized with what are called *electrostatic potential maps*, which use color to portray the calculated electron distribution in an isolated, gas-phase molecule. Yellow–green represents a neutral, nonpolar atom; blue represents a deficiency of electrons on an atom (partial positive charge), and red represents a surplus of electrons on an atom (partial negative charge). As examples of different points along the bonding spectrum, look at the three substances Cl_2, HCl, and NaCl.

- Cl_2 The bond in a chlorine molecule is nonpolar covalent, with the bonding electrons attracted equally to the two identical chlorine atoms. A similar situation exists in all such molecules that contain a covalent bond between two identical atoms. Thus, both chlorine atoms in Cl_2 are nonpolar, as shown by their identical yellow–green coloration in an electrostatic potential map.

Cl:Cl   **A nonpolar covalent bond.** Yellow-green represents a neutral, nonpolar atom.

- HCl The bond in a hydrogen chloride molecule is polar covalent. The chlorine atom attracts the bonding electron pair more strongly than hydrogen does, resulting in an unsymmetrical distribution of electrons. Chlorine thus has a partial negative charge (orange in the electrostatic potential map), and hydrogen has a partial positive charge (blue in the electrostatic potential map). Experimentally, the H—Cl, bond has been found to be about 83% covalent and 17% ionic.

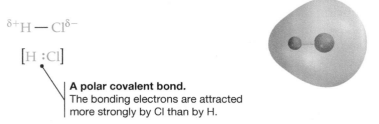

A polar covalent bond.
The bonding electrons are attracted
more strongly by Cl than by H.

- **NaCl** The bond in solid sodium chloride is a largely ionic one between Na^+ and Cl^-. In spite of what we've said previously, though, experiments show that the NaCl bond is only about 80% ionic and that the electron transferred from Na to Cl still spends some of its time near sodium. Thus, the electron-poor sodium atom is blue in an electrostatic potential map, while the electron-rich chlorine is red.

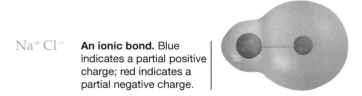

$Na^+ Cl^-$ **An ionic bond.** Blue
indicates a partial positive
charge; red indicates a
partial negative charge.

Bond polarity is due to differences in **electronegativity (EN)**, defined as the ability of an atom in a molecule to attract the shared electrons in a covalent bond. As shown in Figure 7.4, electronegativities are expressed on a unitless scale, with fluorine, the most highly electronegative element, assigned a value of 4.0. Metallic elements on the left of the periodic table attract electrons only weakly and are the least electronegative elements. Halogens and other reactive nonmetals in the upper right of the table attract electrons strongly and are the most electronegative. Figure 7.4 also shows that electronegativity generally decreases down the periodic table within a group.

Figure 7.4
Electronegativity values and trends in the periodic table.

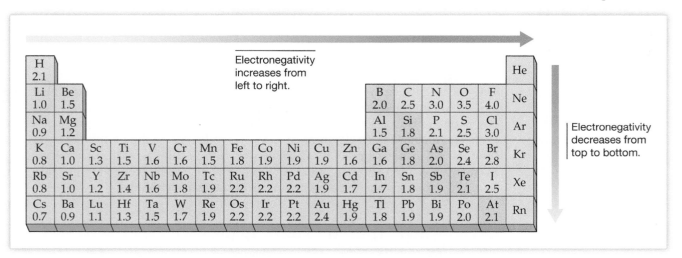

Because electronegativity measures the ability of an atom in a molecule to attract shared electrons, it seems reasonable that it should be related to electron affinity (E_{ea}, Section 6.5) and ionization energy (E_i, Section 6.3). Electron affinity, after all, is a measure of the tendency of an isolated atom to gain an electron, and ionization energy is a measure of the tendency of an isolated atom to lose an electron. In fact, one of the ways in which electronegativities were first calculated was by taking the average of the absolute values of E_{ea} and E_i and setting up a scale with fluorine assigned a value of 4.0.

Remember...
Electron affinity (E_{ea}) is defined as the energy change that occurs when an electron is added to an isolated gaseous atom. (Section 6.5)
Ionization energy (E_i), in contrast, is the amount of energy needed to remove the highest-energy electron from an isolated neutral atom in the gaseous state.   (Section 6.3)

How can we use electronegativity to predict bond polarity? A general but some-what arbitrary guideline is that bonds between atoms with the same or similar electronegativities are nonpolar covalent, bonds between atoms whose electronega-tivities differ by more than about 2 units are substantially ionic, and bonds between atoms whose electronegativities differ by less than 2 units are polar covalent. Thus, we can be reasonably sure that a C—Cl, bond in chloroform, $CHCl_3$, is polar cova-lent, while an Na^+Cl^- bond in sodium chloride is largely ionic.

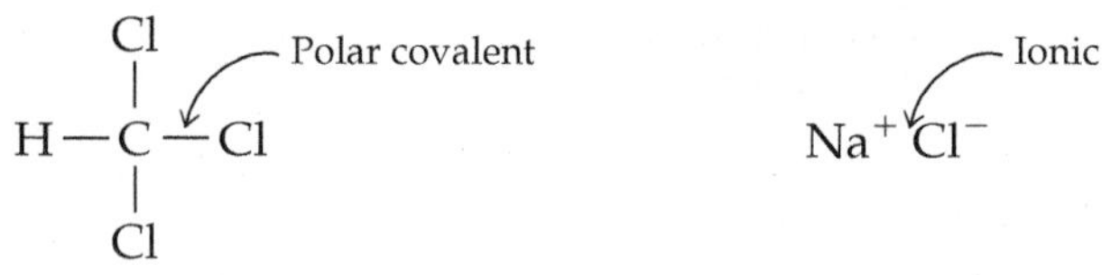

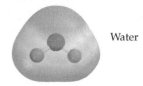

Chlorine:	EN = 3.0		Chlorine:	EN = 3.0
Carbon:	EN = 2.5		Sodium:	EN = 0.9
	Difference = 0.5			Difference = 2.1

▶ **PROBLEM 7.1** Use the electronegativity values in Figure 7.4 to predict whether the bonds in the following compounds are polar covalent or ionic:

(a) $SiCl_4$ (b) $CsBr$ (c) $FeBr_3$ (d) CH_4

▶ **PROBLEM 7.2** Order the following compounds according to the increasing ionic character of their bonds: CCl_4, $BaCl_2$, $TiCl_3$, Cl_2O.

CONCEPTUAL PROBLEM 7.3 An electrostatic potential map of water is shown below. Which atom, H or O, is positively polarized (electron-poor) and which is negatively polarized (electron-rich)? Is this polarity pattern consistent with the electronegativity val-ues of O and H given in Figure 7.4?

Water

7.5 ELECTRON-DOT STRUCTURES

One way to picture the sharing of electrons between atoms in covalent or polar cova-lent bonds is to use **electron-dot structures**, or *Lewis structures*, named after G. N. Lewis of the University of California at Berkeley. An electron-dot structure repre-sents an atom's valence electrons by dots and indicates by the placement of the dots how the valence electrons are distributed in a molecule. A hydrogen molecule, for instance, is written showing a pair of dots between the hydrogen atoms, indicating that the hydrogens share the pair of electrons in a covalent bond:

An electron-pair bond

H·   ·H   ⟶   H:H

Two hydrogen   A hydrogen
atoms   molecule

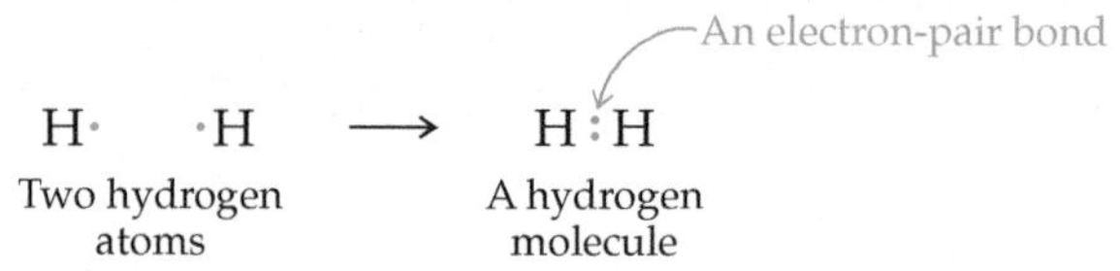

By sharing two electrons in a covalent bond, each hydrogen effectively has one electron pair and the stable, $1s^2$ electron configuration of helium.

This hydrogen shares   ... and this hydrogen
an electron pair ...   shares an electron pair.

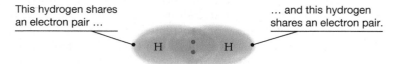

Atoms other than hydrogen also form covalent bonds by sharing electron pairs, and the electron-dot structures of the resultant molecules are drawn by assigning the correct number of valence electrons to each atom. Group 3A atoms, such as boron, have three valence electrons; group 4A atoms, such as carbon, have four valence electrons; and so on across the periodic table. The group 7A element fluorine has seven valence electrons, and an electron-dot structure for the F_2 molecule shows how a covalent bond can form:

$$:\ddot{F}\cdot \qquad \cdot\ddot{F}: \qquad \longrightarrow \qquad :\ddot{F}:\ddot{F}:$$

A bonding pair
A lone pair

Two F atoms
(seven valence electrons
per atom)

An F_2 molecule
(each F is surrounded
by eight valence electrons)

Six of the seven valence electrons in a fluorine atom are already paired in three filled atomic orbitals and thus are not shared in bonding. The seventh fluorine valence electron, however, is unpaired and can be shared in a covalent bond with another fluorine. Each atom in the resultant F_2 molecule thereby gains a noble-gas configuration with eight valence-shell electrons and thus obeys the octet rule, discussed in Section 6.6. The three pairs of nonbonding electrons on each fluorine atom are called **lone pairs**, or *nonbonding pairs*, and the shared electrons are called a **bonding pair**.

The tendency of main-group atoms to fill their s and p subshells and thereby achieve a noble-gas configuration when they form bonds is an important guiding principle that makes it possible to predict the formulas and electron-dot structures of a great many molecules. As a general rule, a main-group atom shares as many of its valence-shell electrons as possible, either until it has no more to share or until it reaches an octet configuration. The following guidelines apply:

- **Group 3A elements**, such as boron, have three valence electrons and can therefore form three electron-pair bonds in neutral molecules such as borane, BH_3. The boron atom in the resultant molecule has only three bonding pairs of electrons, however, and can't reach an electron octet. (The bonding situation in BH_3 is actually more complicated than suggested here; we'll deal with it in Section 19.4.)

$$\cdot\dot{B}\cdot \;+\; 3\,H\cdot \;\longrightarrow\; H\!:\!\ddot{B}\!:\!H$$

Only six electrons around boron

Borane

- **Group 4A elements**, such as carbon, have four valence electrons and form four bonds, as in methane, CH_4. The carbon atom in the resultant molecule has four bonding pairs of electrons.

$$\cdot\dot{C}\cdot \;+\; 4\,H\cdot \;\longrightarrow\; H\!:\!\ddot{C}\!:\!H$$

H

H

Methane

- **Group 5A elements**, such as nitrogen, have five valence electrons and form three bonds, as in ammonia, NH_3. The nitrogen atom in the resultant molecule has three bonding pairs of electrons and one lone pair.

$$\cdot\dot{N}\cdot \;+\; 3\,H\cdot \;\longrightarrow\; H\!:\!\ddot{N}\!:\!H$$

H

Ammonia

Remember...

According to the **octet rule**, main-group elements tend to undergo reactions that give them a noble-gas electron configuration with filled s and p sublevels in their valence electron shell.   (Section 6.6).

- **Group 6A elements**, such as oxygen, have six valence electrons and form two bonds, as in water, H_2O. The oxygen atom in the resultant molecule has two bonding pairs of electrons and two lone pairs.

$$\cdot\ddot{O}\cdot \ + \ 2\,H\cdot \ \longrightarrow \ H\!:\!\ddot{O}\!:\!H$$

Water

- **Group 7A elements** (halogens), such as fluorine, have seven valence electrons and form one bond, as in hydrogen fluoride, HF. The fluorine atom in the resultant molecule has one bonding pair of electrons and three lone pairs.

$$:\!\ddot{F}\cdot \ + \ H\cdot \ \longrightarrow \ H\!:\!\ddot{F}\!:$$

Hydrogen
fluoride

- **Group 8A elements** (noble gases), such as neon, rarely form covalent bonds because they already have valence-shell octets.

$$:\!\ddot{N}\!e\!: \qquad | \text{ Does not form covalent bonds}$$

These conclusions are summarized in Table 7.3.

TABLE 7.3 Covalent Bonding for Second-Row Elements

Group	Number of Valence Electrons	Number of Bonds	Example
3A	3	3	BH_3
4A	4	4	CH_4
5A	5	3	NH_3
6A	6	2	H_2O
7A	7	1	HF
8A	8	0	Ne

Not all covalent bonds contain just one shared electron pair, or **single bond**, like those just discussed. In molecules such as O_2, N_2, and many others, the atoms share more than one pair of electrons, leading to the formation of *multiple* covalent bonds. The oxygen atoms in the O_2 molecule, for example, reach valence-shell octets by sharing two pairs, or four electrons, in a **double bond**. Similarly, the nitrogen atoms in the N_2 molecule share three pairs, or six electrons, in a **triple bond**. (Although the O_2 molecule does have a double bond, the following electron-dot structure is incorrect in some respects, as we'll see in Section 7.14.)

$$\cdot\ddot{O}\cdot \ + \ \cdot\ddot{O}\cdot \ \longrightarrow \ \ddot{O}\!::\!\ddot{O}$$

Two electron pairs
— a double bond

$$:\!\ddot{N}\cdot \ + \ \cdot\ddot{N}\!: \ \longrightarrow \ :\!N\!:::\!N\!:$$

Three electron pairs
— a triple bond

In speaking of molecules with multiple bonds, we often use the term **bond order** to refer to the number of electron pairs shared between atoms. Thus, the F—F, bond in the F_2 molecule has a bond order of 1, the O=O, bond in the O_2 molecule has a bond order of 2, and the N≡N, bond in the N_2 molecule has a bond order of 3.

Multiple bonds are both shorter and stronger than their corresponding single-bond counterparts because there are more shared electrons holding the atoms together. Compare, for example, the O=O double bond in O_2 with the O—O single bond in H_2O_2 (hydrogen peroxide), and compare the N≡N triple bond in N_2 with the N—N single bond in N_2H_4 (hydrazine):

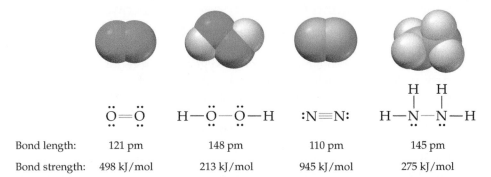

Bond length:	121 pm	148 pm	110 pm	145 pm
Bond strength:	498 kJ/mol	213 kJ/mol	945 kJ/mol	275 kJ/mol

One final point about covalent bonds involves the origin of the bonding electrons. Although most covalent bonds form when two atoms each contribute one electron, bonds can also form when one atom donates both electrons (a lone pair) to another atom that has a vacant valence orbital. The ammonium ion (NH_4^+), for instance, forms when the two lone-pair electrons from the nitrogen atom of ammonia, $:NH_3$, bond to H^+. Such bonds are sometimes called **coordinate covalent bonds**.

An ordinary covalent bond—each atom donates one electron.

$$H\cdot + \cdot H \longrightarrow H:H$$

A coordinate covalent bond—the nitrogen atom donates both electrons.

$$H^+ + \overset{H}{\underset{H}{:\!N\!:}}H \longrightarrow \left[\overset{H}{\underset{H}{H:\!N\!:}}H \right]^+$$

Note that the nitrogen atom in the ammonium ion (NH_4^+) has more than the usual number of bonds—four instead of three—but that it still has an octet of valence electrons. Nitrogen, oxygen, phosphorus, and sulfur form coordinate covalent bonds frequently.

WORKED EXAMPLE 7.1

DRAWING AN ELECTRON-DOT STRUCTURE

Draw an electron-dot structure for phosphine, PH_3.

STRATEGY

The number of covalent bonds formed by a main-group element depends on the element's group number. Phosphorus, a group 5A element, has five valence electrons and can achieve a valence-shell octet by forming three bonds and leaving one lone pair. Each hydrogen supplies one electron.

SOLUTION

$$\overset{H}{\underset{}{H:\!\overset{\cdot\cdot}{P}\!:}H} \qquad \text{Phosphine}$$

▶ **PROBLEM 7.4** Draw electron-dot structures for the following molecules:
(a) H_2S, a poisonous gas produced by rotten eggs
(b) $CHCl_3$, chloroform

▶ **PROBLEM 7.5** Draw an electron-dot structure for the hydronium ion, H_3O^+, and show how a coordinate covalent bond is formed by the reaction of H_2O with H^+.

7.6 ELECTRON-DOT STRUCTURES OF POLYATOMIC MOLECULES

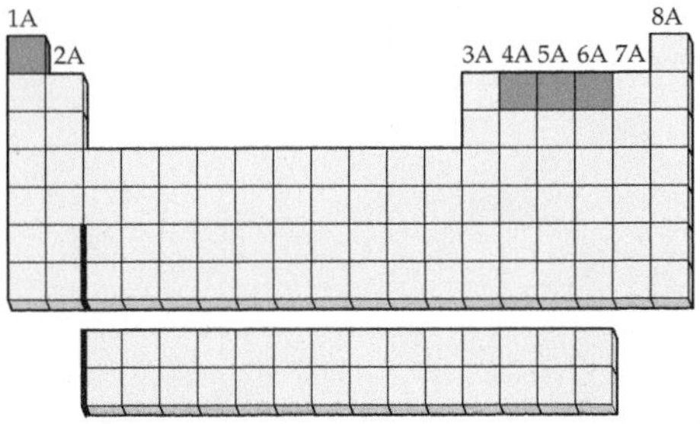

Compounds Containing Only Hydrogen and Second-Row Elements

Many of the naturally occurring compounds on which life is based—proteins, fats, carbohydrates, and numerous others—contain only hydrogen and one or more of the second-row elements carbon, nitrogen, and oxygen. Electron-dot structures are relatively easy to draw for such compounds because the octet rule is almost always followed and the number of bonds formed by each element is predictable (Table 7.3).

For relatively small molecules that contain only a few second-row atoms in addition to hydrogen, the second-row atoms are bonded to one another in a central core, with hydrogens on the periphery. In ethane (C_2H_6), for instance, two carbon atoms, each of which forms four bonds, combine with six hydrogens, each of which forms one bond. Joining the two carbon atoms and adding the appropriate number of hydrogens to each yields only one possible structure:

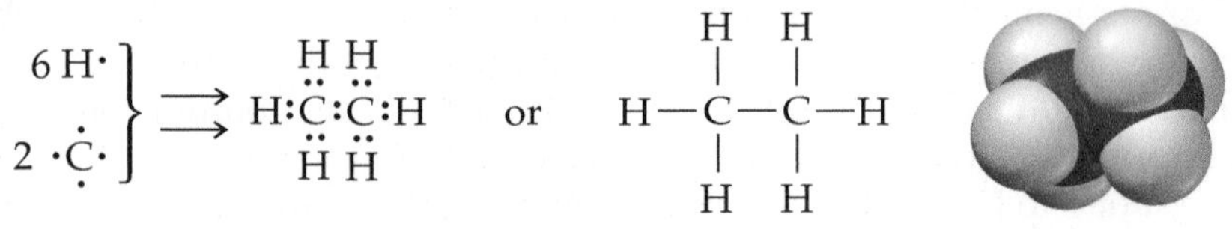

Ethane, C_2H_6

For larger molecules that contain numerous second-row atoms, there is usually more than one possible electron-dot structure. In such cases, some additional knowledge about the order of connections among atoms is necessary before a structure can be drawn. In drawing structures, we'll follow the usual convention of indicating a two-electron covalent bond by a line. Similarly, we'll use two lines between atoms to represent four shared electrons (two pairs) in a double bond, and three lines to represent six shared electrons (three pairs) in a triple bond. Worked Examples 7.2–7.5 and Problems 7.6–7.8 will give you more practice with electron-dot structures.

WORKED EXAMPLE 7.2

DRAWING AN ELECTRON-DOT STRUCTURE

Draw an electron-dot structure for hydrazine, N_2H_4.

STRATEGY

Nitrogen, a group 5A element, has five valence electrons and forms three bonds. Join the two nitrogen atoms, and add two hydrogen atoms to each.

SOLUTION

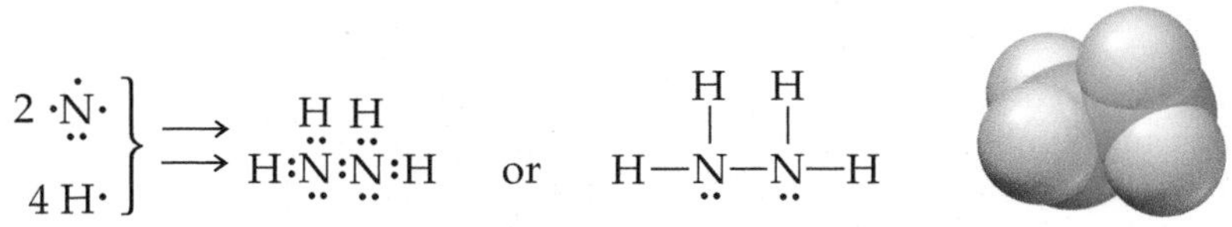

Hydrazine, N_2H_4

WORKED EXAMPLE 7.3

DRAWING AN ELECTRON-DOT STRUCTURE

Draw an electron-dot structure for carbon dioxide, CO_2.

STRATEGY

Connect the atoms so that carbon forms four bonds and each oxygen forms two bonds. The only possible structure contains two carbon–oxygen double bonds.

SOLUTION

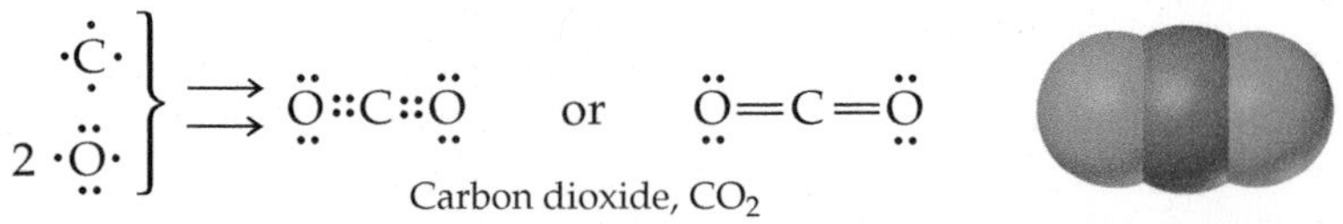

Carbon dioxide, CO_2

WORKED EXAMPLE 7.4

DRAWING AN ELECTRON-DOT STRUCTURE

Draw an electron-dot structure for the deadly gas hydrogen cyanide, HCN.

STRATEGY

First, connect the carbon and nitrogen atoms. The only way the carbon can form four bonds and the nitrogen can form three bonds is if there is a carbon–nitrogen triple bond.

SOLUTION

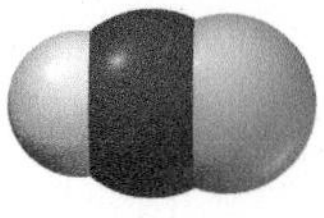

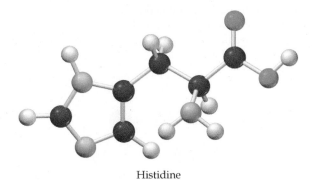

Hydrogen cyanide, HCN

WORKED CONCEPTUAL EXAMPLE 7.5

IDENTIFYING MULTIPLE BONDS IN MOLECULES

The following structure is a representation of histidine, an amino acid constituent of proteins. Only the connections between atoms are shown; multiple bonds are not indicated. Give the chemical formula of histidine, and complete the structure by showing where the multiple bonds and lone pairs are located (red = O, gray = C, blue = N, ivory = H).

Histidine

STRATEGY

Count the atoms of each element to find the formula. Then look at each atom in the structure to find what is needed for completion. Each carbon (gray) should have four bonds, each oxygen (red) should have two bonds and two lone pairs, and each nitrogen (blue) should have three bonds and one lone pair.

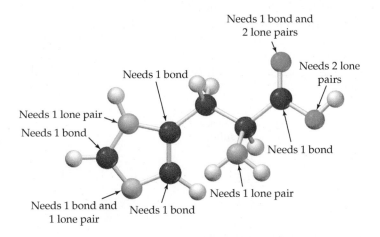

continued on next page

SOLUTION

Histidine has the formula $C_6H_9N_3O_2$.

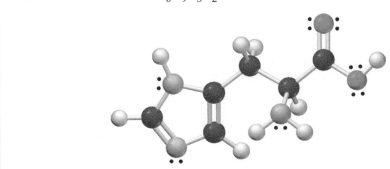

▶ **PROBLEM 7.6** Draw electron-dot structures for the following molecules:

(a) Propane, C_3H_8

(b) Hydrogen peroxide, H_2O_2

(c) Methylamine, CH_5N

(d) Ethylene, C_2H_4

(e) Acetylene, C_2H_2

(f) Phosgene, Cl_2CO

▶ **PROBLEM 7.7** There are two molecules with the formula C_2H_6O. Draw electron-dot structures for both.

CONCEPTUAL PROBLEM 7.8 The following structure is a representation of cytosine, a constituent of the DNA found in all living cells. Only the connections between atoms are shown; multiple bonds are not indicated. Give the formula of cytosine, and complete the structure by showing where the multiple bonds and lone pairs are located (red = O, gray = C, blue = N, ivory = H).

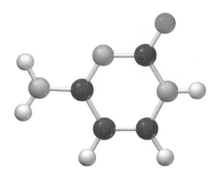

Compounds Containing Elements below the Second Row

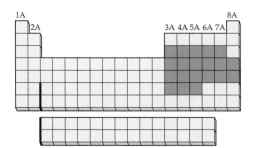

The simple method for drawing electron-dot structures that works so well for compounds of second-row elements occasionally breaks down for compounds that contain elements below the second row of the periodic table where, as noted in Section 6.6, the octet rule sometimes fails. In sulfur tetrafluoride, for instance, the sulfur atom forms four bonds rather than two and has ten electrons in its valence shell rather than eight:

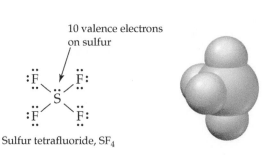

Sulfur tetrafluoride, SF_4

When the octet rule fails, it often does so for elements toward the right side of the periodic table (groups 3A–8A) that are in the third row and lower (**Figure 7.5**). Atoms of these elements are larger than their second-row counterparts, can accommodate more than four atoms close around them, and therefore form more than four bonds. The second-row element nitrogen, for instance, bonds to only three chlorine atoms in forming NCl_3 and thus obeys the octet rule, while the third-row element phosphorus bonds to five chlorine atoms in forming PCl_5 and thus does not follow the octet rule.

Figure 7.5
The octet rule occasionally fails for the main-group elements shown in blue.

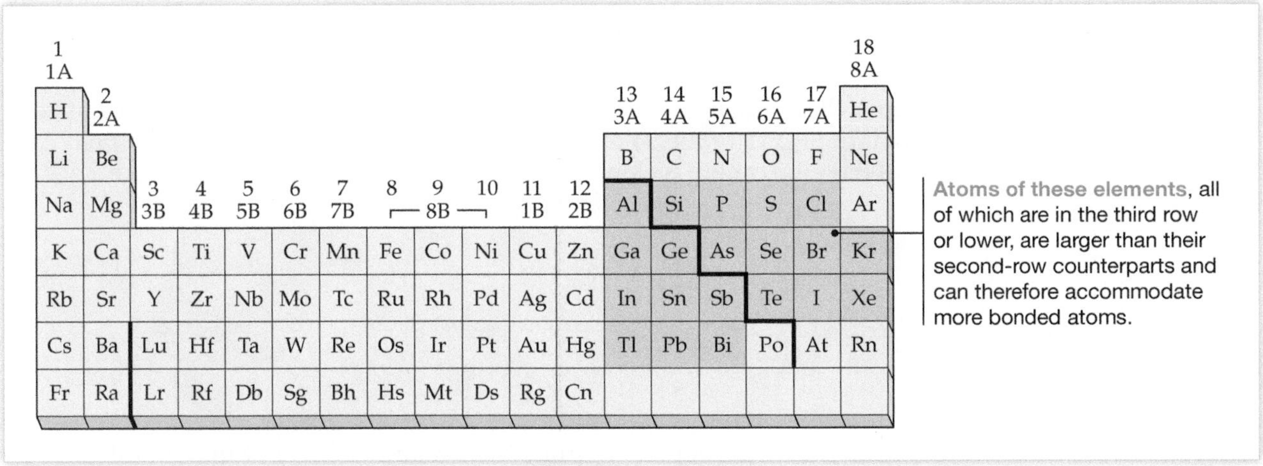

Atoms of these elements, all of which are in the third row or lower, are larger than their second-row counterparts and can therefore accommodate more bonded atoms.

A general method of drawing electron-dot structures that works for any compound is to use the following steps:

Drawing Electron-Dot Structures

Step 1. Find the total number of valence electrons for all atoms in the molecule. Add one additional electron for each negative charge in an anion, and subtract one electron for each positive charge in a cation. In SF_4, for example, the total is 34 — 6 from sulfur and 7 from each of 4 fluorines. In OH^-, the total is 8 — 6 from oxygen, 1 from hydrogen, and 1 for the negative charge. In NH_4^+, the total is 8 — 5 from nitrogen, 1 from each of 4 hydrogens, minus 1 for the positive charge.

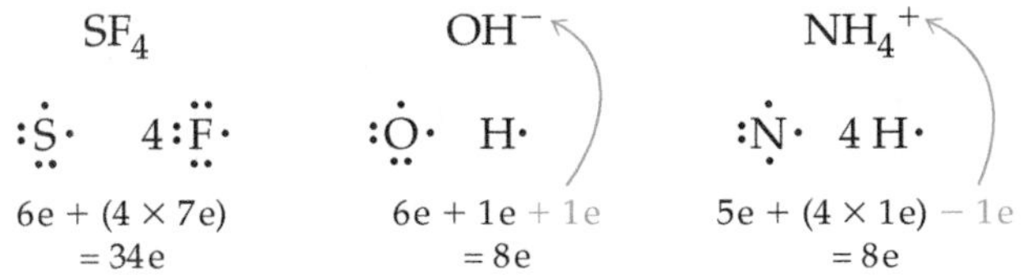

$$SF_4 \qquad\qquad OH^- \qquad\qquad NH_4^+$$

$$:\!\overset{\cdot}{\underset{\cdot\cdot}{S}}\!\cdot \quad 4:\!\overset{\cdot\cdot}{\underset{\cdot\cdot}{F}}\!\cdot \qquad :\!\overset{\cdot}{\underset{\cdot\cdot}{O}}\!\cdot \quad H\cdot \qquad :\!\overset{\cdot}{\underset{\cdot}{N}}\!\cdot \quad 4\,H\cdot$$

$$6e + (4 \times 7e) \qquad 6e + 1e + 1e \qquad 5e + (4 \times 1e) - 1e$$
$$= 34e \qquad\qquad = 8e \qquad\qquad = 8e$$

Step 2. Decide what the connections are between atoms, and draw lines to represent the bonds. Often, you'll be told the connections; other times you'll have to guess. Remember that

• Hydrogen and the halogens usually form only one bond.
• Elements in the second row usually form the number of bonds given in Table 7.3.
• Elements in the third row and lower are often a central atom around which other atoms are grouped and form more bonds than predicted by the octet rule.

Also, it's usually the case that the central atom is the least electronegative one (except H). If, for example, you were asked to predict the connections in SF_4, a good guess would be that each fluorine forms one bond to sulfur, which occurs as the central atom and forms more bonds than are predicted by its group number.

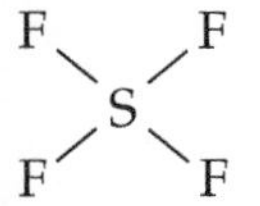

Sulfur tetrafluoride, SF_4

Step 3. Subtract the number of valence electrons used for bonding from the total number calculated in step 1 to find the number that remain. Assign as many of these remaining electrons as necessary to the terminal atoms (other than hydrogen) so that each has an octet. In SF_4, 8 of the 34 total valence electrons are used in covalent bonding, leaving $34 - 8 = 26$. Twenty-four of the 26 are assigned to the four terminal fluorine atoms to reach an octet configuration for each:

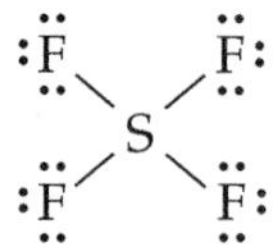

$$:\ddot{F}\diagdown\diagup\ddot{F}:\ \ S\ \ :\ddot{F}\diagdown\diagup\ddot{F}:$$

$8 + 24 = 32$ electrons distributed

Step 4. If unassigned electrons remain after step 3, place them on the central atom. In SF_4, 32 of the 34 electrons have been assigned, leaving the final 2 to be placed on the central S atom:

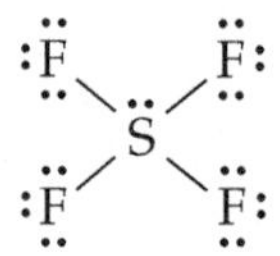

34 electrons distributed

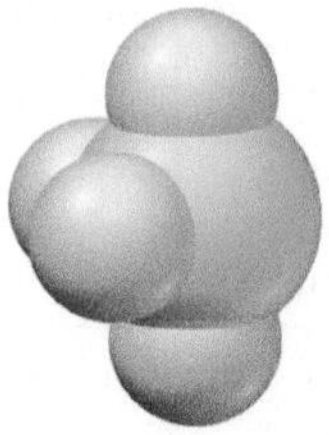

Step 5. If no unassigned electrons remain after step 3 but the central atom does not yet have an octet, use one or more lone pairs of electrons from a neighboring atom to form a multiple bond (either double or triple). Oxygen, carbon, nitrogen, and sulfur often form multiple bonds. Worked Example 7.7 shows how to deal with such a case.

WORKED EXAMPLE 7.6

DRAWING AN ELECTRON-DOT STRUCTURE

Draw an electron-dot structure for phosphorus pentachloride, PCl_5.

STRATEGY

Follow the steps outlined in the text. First, count the total number of valence electrons. Phosphorus has 5, and each chlorine has 7, for a total of 40. Next, decide on the connections between atoms, and draw lines to indicate the bonds. Because chlorine normally forms only one bond, it's likely in the case of PCl_5 that all five chlorines are bonded to a central phosphorus atom:

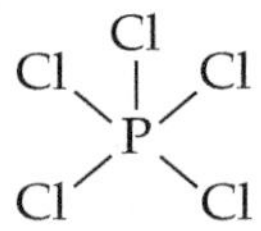

Ten of the 40 valence electrons are necessary for the five P—Cl bonds, leaving 30 to be distributed so that each chlorine has an octet. All 30 remaining valence electrons are used in this step.

SOLUTION

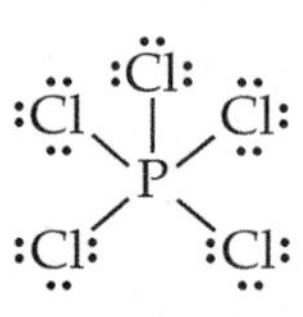

Phosphorus pentachloride, PCl_5
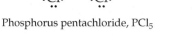

WORKED EXAMPLE 7.7

DRAWING AN ELECTRON-DOT STRUCTURE

Draw an electron-dot structure for formaldehyde, CH_2O, a compound used in manufacturing the adhesives for making plywood and particle board.

STRATEGY

First, count the total number of valence electrons. Carbon has 4, each hydrogen has 1, and the oxygen has 6, for a total of 12. Next, decide on the probable connections between atoms, and draw a line to indicate each bond. In the case of formaldehyde, the less electronegative atom (carbon) is the central atom, and both hydrogens and the oxygen are bonded to carbon:

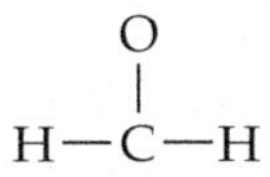

$$
\begin{array}{c}
O \\
| \\
H-C-H
\end{array}
$$

Six of the 12 valence electrons are used for bonds, leaving 6 for assignment to the terminal oxygen atom.

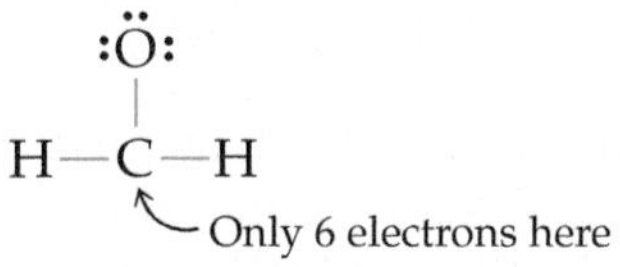

$$
\begin{array}{c}
:\ddot{O}: \\
| \\
H-C-H
\end{array}
$$

↖ Only 6 electrons here

At this point, all the valence electrons are assigned, but the central carbon atom still does not have an octet. We therefore move two of the oxygen electrons from a lone pair into a bonding pair, generating a carbon–oxygen double bond and satisfying the octet rule for both oxygen and carbon.

SOLUTION

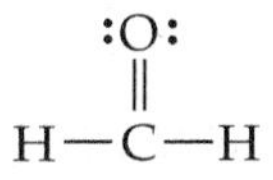

$$
\begin{array}{c}
:\ddot{O}: \\
\| \\
H-C-H
\end{array}
$$

Formaldehyde, CH_2O

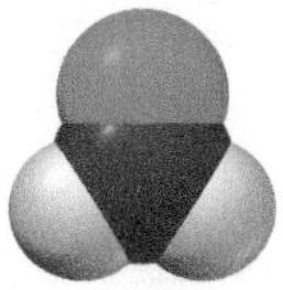

WORKED EXAMPLE 7.8

DRAWING AN ELECTRON-DOT STRUCTURE

Draw an electron-dot structure for XeF_5^+, one of the very few noble-gas ions.

STRATEGY

Count the total number of valence electrons. Xenon has 8, each fluorine has 7, and 1 is subtracted to account for the positive charge, giving a total of 42. Then, decide on the probable connections between atoms, and draw a line for each bond. In the case of XeF_5^+, it's likely that the five fluorines are bonded to xenon, a fifth-row atom.

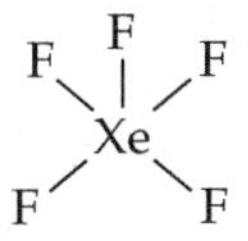

$$
\begin{array}{ccc}
 & F & \\
F & | & F \\
 & \diagdown | \diagup & \\
 & Xe & \\
 & \diagup \quad \diagdown & \\
F & & F
\end{array}
$$

With 10 of the 42 valence electrons used in bonds, distribute as many of the remaining 32 electrons as necessary so that each of the terminal fluorine atoms has an octet. Two electrons still remain, so we assign them to xenon to give the final structure, which has a positive charge.

SOLUTION

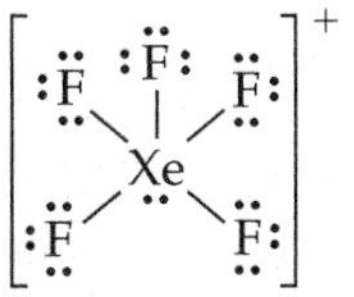

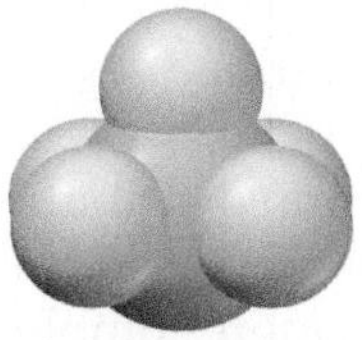

$$
\left[
\begin{array}{ccc}
 & :\ddot{F}: & \\
:\ddot{F} & | & \ddot{F}: \\
 & \diagdown | \diagup & \\
 & Xe & \\
 & \diagup \quad \diagdown & \\
:\ddot{F} & & \ddot{F}:
\end{array}
\right]^+
$$

▶ **PROBLEM 7.9**   Carbon monoxide, CO, is a deadly gas produced by incomplete combustion of fuels. Draw an electron-dot structure for CO.

▶ **PROBLEM 7.10**   Draw an electron-dot structure for each of the following molecules:
(a) $AlCl_3$ (b) ICl_3 (c) $XeOF_4$ (d) HOBr

▶ **PROBLEM 7.11**   Draw an electron-dot structure for each of the following ions:
(a) OH^- (b) H_3S^+ (c) HCO_3^- (d) ClO_4^-

7.7   ELECTRON-DOT STRUCTURES AND RESONANCE

The stepwise procedure given in the previous section for drawing electron-dot structures sometimes leads to an interesting problem. Look at ozone, O_3, for instance. Step 1 says that there are 18 valence electrons in the molecule, and steps 2–4 let us draw the following structure:

$$:\ddot{O}-\ddot{O}-\ddot{O}:$$

We find at this point that the central atom does not yet have an octet, and we therefore have to move one of the lone pairs of electrons on a terminal oxygen to become a bonding pair and give the central oxygen an octet. But do we take a lone pair from the "right-hand" oxygen or the "left-hand" one? Both possibilities lead to acceptable structures:

Move a lone pair from this oxygen?   Or from this oxygen?

$:\ddot{O}-\ddot{O}-\ddot{O}:$

$\longrightarrow$ $\begin{cases} \ddot{O}=\ddot{O}-\ddot{O}: \\ \text{or} \\ :\ddot{O}-\ddot{O}=\ddot{O} \end{cases}$

Which of the two structures for O_3 is correct? In fact, neither is correct by itself. Whenever it's possible to write more than one valid electron-dot structure for a molecule, the actual electronic structure is an *average* of the different possibilities, called a **resonance hybrid**. Note that the two resonance forms differ only in the placement of the valence-shell electrons (both bonding and nonbonding). The total number of valence electrons remains the same in both structures, the connections between atoms remain the same, and the relative positions of the atoms remain the same.

Ozone doesn't have one O=O double bond and one O—O single bond as the individual structures imply. Rather, ozone has two equivalent O—O bonds that we can think of as having a bond order of 1.5, midway between pure single bonds and pure double bonds. Both bonds have an identical length of 128 pm.

We can't draw a single electron-dot structure that indicates the equivalence of the two O—O bonds in O_3 because the conventions we use in drawings to indicate electron placement aren't good enough. Instead, the idea of resonance is indicated by drawing the two (or more) individual electron-dot structures and using a double-headed *resonance arrow* (↔) to show that both contribute to the resonance hybrid. A straight, double-headed arrow always indicates resonance; it is never used for any other purpose.

This double-headed arrow means that the structures on either side are contributors to a resonance hybrid.

$:\ddot{O}-\ddot{O}=\ddot{O} \longleftrightarrow \ddot{O}=\ddot{O}-\ddot{O}:$

The fact that single electron-dot structures can't be written for all molecules indicates that such structures are oversimplified and don't always give an accurate representation of the electron distribution in a molecule. There's a more accurate way of describing electron distributions called *molecular orbital theory*, which we'll look into shortly. This theory is more complex, however, so chemists still make routine use of simple resonance electron-dot structures.

WORKED EXAMPLE 7.9

DRAWING RESONANCE STRUCTURES

The nitrate ion, NO_3^-, has three equivalent oxygen atoms, and its electronic structure is a resonance hybrid of three electron-dot structures. Draw them.

STRATEGY

Begin as you would for drawing any electron-dot structure. There are 24 valence electrons in the nitrate ion: 5 from nitrogen, 6 from each of 3 oxygens, and 1 for the negative charge. The three equivalent oxygens are all bonded to nitrogen, the less electronegative central atom:

$$
\begin{array}{c}
O \\
| \\
N \\
O^{\nearrow} \quad {}^{\nwarrow}O
\end{array}
\qquad \text{6 of 24 valence electrons assigned}
$$

Distributing the remaining 18 valence electrons among the three terminal oxygen atoms completes the octet of each oxygen but leaves nitrogen with only 6 electrons.

$$
\left[\begin{array}{c}
\ddot{\text{:O:}} \\
| \\
N \\
\ddot{\text{:O}}^{\nearrow} \quad {}^{\nwarrow}\ddot{\text{O:}}
\end{array} \right]^{-}
$$

To give nitrogen an octet, one of the oxygen atoms must use a lone pair to form an N—O double bond. But which one? There are three possibilities, and thus three electron-dot structures for the nitrate ion, which differ only in the placement of bonding and lone-pair electrons. The connections between atoms are the same in all three structures, and the atoms have the same positions in all structures.

SOLUTION

$$
\left[\begin{array}{c}
\text{:O:} \\
\| \\
N \\
\ddot{\text{:O}} \quad \ddot{\text{O:}}
\end{array} \right]^{-}
\longleftrightarrow
\left[\begin{array}{c}
\ddot{\text{:O:}} \\
| \\
N \\
\text{:O}^{\nearrow} \quad \ddot{\text{O:}}
\end{array} \right]^{-}
\longleftrightarrow
\left[\begin{array}{c}
\ddot{\text{:O:}} \\
| \\
N \\
\ddot{\text{:O}} \quad \text{O:}
\end{array} \right]^{-}
$$

▶ **PROBLEM 7.12** Called "laughing gas," nitrous oxide (N_2O) is sometimes used by dentists as an anesthetic. Given the connections N—N—O draw two resonance structures for N_2O.

▶ **PROBLEM 7.13** Draw as many resonance structures as possible for each of the following molecules or ions, giving all atoms (except H) octets:
  (a) SO_2 **(b)** CO_3^{2-} **(c)** HCO_2^- **(d)** BF_3

CONCEPTUAL PROBLEM 7.14 The following structure shows the connections between atoms for anisole, a compound used in perfumery. Draw two resonance structures for anisole, showing the positions of the multiple bonds in each (red = O, gray = C, ivory = H).

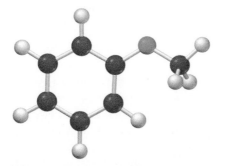

7.8 FORMAL CHARGES

Closely related to the ideas of electronegativity and polar covalent bonds discussed in Section 7.4 is the concept of **formal charges** on specific atoms in electron-dot structures. Formal charges result from a kind of electron "bookkeeping" and can be calculated in the following way: Find the number of valence electrons around an atom in a given electron-dot structure, and compare that value with the number of valence electrons in the isolated atom. If the numbers aren't the same, then the atom in the molecule has either gained or lost electrons and thus has a formal charge. If the atom in a molecule has more electrons than the isolated atom, it has a negative formal charge; if it has fewer electrons, it has a positive formal charge.

$$\text{Formal charge} = \left(\begin{array}{c} \text{Number of} \\ \text{valence electrons} \\ \text{in free atom} \end{array} \right) - \left(\begin{array}{c} \text{Number of} \\ \text{valence electrons} \\ \text{in bonded atom} \end{array} \right)$$

In counting the number of valence electrons in a bonded atom, it's necessary to make a distinction between unshared, nonbonding electrons and shared, bonding electrons. For bookkeeping purposes, an atom can be thought of as "owning" all its nonbonding electrons but only half of its bonding electrons, because the bonding electrons are shared with another atom. Thus, we can rewrite the definition of formal charge as

$$\text{Formal charge} = \left(\begin{array}{c} \text{Number of} \\ \text{valence electrons} \\ \text{in free atom} \end{array} \right) - \frac{1}{2} \left(\begin{array}{c} \text{Number of} \\ \text{bonding} \\ \text{electrons} \end{array} \right) - \left(\begin{array}{c} \text{Number of} \\ \text{nonbonding} \\ \text{electrons} \end{array} \right)$$

In the ammonium ion (NH_4^+), for instance, each of the four equivalent hydrogen atoms has 2 valence electrons in its covalent bond to nitrogen and the nitrogen atom has 8 valence electrons, 2 from each of its four N—H bonds:

$$\left[\begin{array}{c} H \\ H:\overset{\cdot\cdot}{\underset{\cdot\cdot}{N}}:H \\ H \end{array} \right]^+$$

Ammonium ion
8 valence electrons around nitrogen
2 valence electrons around each hydrogen

For bookkeeping purposes, each hydrogen owns half of its 2 shared bonding electrons, or 1, while the nitrogen atom owns half of its 8 shared bonding electrons, or 4. Because an isolated hydrogen atom has 1 electron and the hydrogens in the ammonium ion each still own 1 electron, they have neither gained nor lost electrons and thus have no formal charge. An isolated nitrogen atom, however, has 5 valence electrons, while the nitrogen atom in NH_4^+ owns only 4 and thus has a formal charge of +1. The sum of the formal charges on all the atoms (+1 in this example) must equal the overall charge on the ion.

$$\left[\begin{array}{c} H \\ H:\overset{\cdot\cdot}{\underset{\cdot\cdot}{N}}:H \\ H \end{array} \right]^+$$

For hydrogen: Isolated hydrogen valence electrons   1
Bound hydrogen bonding electrons   2
Bound hydrogen nonbonding electrons   0

Formal charge $= 1 - \frac{1}{2}(2) - 0 = 0$

For nitrogen: Isolated nitrogen valence electrons   5
Bound nitrogen bonding electrons   8
Bound nitrogen nonbonding electrons   0

Formal charge $= 5 - \frac{1}{2}(8) - 0 = +1$

The value of formal charge calculations comes from their application to the resonance structures described in the previous section. It often happens that the resonance structures of a given substance are not equivalent. One of the structures may be "better" than the others, meaning that it approximates the actual electronic structure of the substance more closely. The resonance hybrid in such cases is thus weighted more strongly toward the more favorable structure.

Take the organic substance called acetamide, for instance, a compound related to proteins. We can write two valid resonance structures for acetamide, both of which fulfill the octet rule for the C, N, and O atoms. One of the two structures has no formal charges, while the other has formal charges on the O and N atoms. (Check for yourself that the formal charges are correct.)

This structure is lower in energy.

This structure is higher in energy.

Acetamide

Which of the two structures gives a more accurate representation of the molecule? Because energy is required to separate + and − charges, the structure without formal charges is probably lower in energy than the structure with formal charges. Thus, the actual electronic structure of acetamide is closer to that of the more favorable, lower-energy structure.

As another example, the resonance structure for N_2O that places the formal negative charge on the more electronegative oxygen atom rather than on the less electronegative nitrogen atom is probably a more accurate representation of the molecule.

$$:N{\equiv}\overset{+}{N}-\overset{..}{\underset{..}{O}}:^{-} \longleftrightarrow {}^{-}\overset{..}{\underset{..}{N}}{=}\overset{+}{N}{=}\overset{..}{\underset{..}{O}}$$

This electron-dot structure . . . is more favorable than . . . this one.

WORKED EXAMPLE 7.10

CALCULATING FORMAL CHARGES

Calculate the formal charge on each atom in the following electron-dot structure for SO_2:

$$:\overset{..}{\underset{..}{O}}-\overset{..}{S}{=}\overset{..}{\underset{..}{O}}$$

STRATEGY

Find the number of valence electrons on each atom (its periodic group number). Then subtract half the number of the atom's bonding electrons and all of its nonbonding electrons.

SOLUTION

For sulfur:

Isolated sulfur valence electrons	6
Bound sulfur bonding electrons	6
Bound sulfur nonbonding electrons	2

Formal charge $= 6 - \frac{1}{2}(6) - 2 = +1$

For singly bonded oxygen:

Isolated oxygen valence electrons	6
Bound oxygen bonding electrons	2
Bound oxygen nonbonding electrons	6

Formal charge $= 6 - \frac{1}{2}(2) - 6 = -1$

For doubly bonded oxygen:

Isolated oxygen valence electrons	6
Bound oxygen bonding electrons	4
Bound oxygen nonbonding electrons	4

Formal charge $= 6 - \frac{1}{2}(4) - 4 = 0$

The sulfur atom of SO_2 has a formal charge of +1, and the singly bonded oxygen atom has a formal charge of −1. We might therefore write the structure for SO_2 as

$$^{-}:\overset{..}{\underset{..}{O}}-\overset{+}{\overset{..}{S}}{=}\overset{..}{\underset{..}{O}}$$

▶ **PROBLEM 7.15**   Calculate the formal charge on each atom in the three resonance structures for the nitrate ion in Worked Example 7.9.

▶ **PROBLEM 7.16**   Calculate the formal charge on each atom in the following electron-dot structures:

(a) Cyanate ion: $\left[\ddot{N}=C=\ddot{O} \right]^{-}$ **(b)** Ozone: $:\ddot{O}-\ddot{O}=\ddot{O}$

7.9   MOLECULAR SHAPES: THE VSEPR MODEL

Look at the following ball-and-stick models of water, ammonia, and methane. Each of these molecules—and every other molecule as well—has a specific three-dimensional shape. Often, particularly for biologically important molecules, three-dimensional shape plays a crucial part in determining the molecule's chemistry.

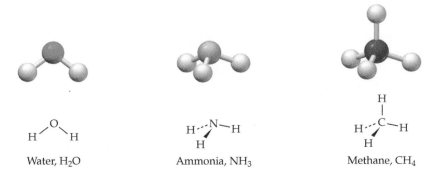

Water, H_2O Ammonia, NH_3 Methane, CH_4

Like so many other properties, the shape of a molecule is determined by the electronic structure of its atoms. That shape can often be predicted using what is called the **valence-shell electron-pair repulsion (VSEPR) model.** Electrons in bonds and in lone pairs can be thought of as "charge clouds" that repel one another and stay as far apart as possible, thus causing molecules to assume specific shapes. There are only two steps to remember in applying the VSEPR model:

⇐ **Applying the VSEPR Model**

Step 1.   Write an electron-dot structure for the molecule, as described in Section 7.6, and count the number of electron charge clouds surrounding the atom of interest. A charge cloud is simply a group of electrons, either in a bond or in a lone pair. Thus, the number of charge clouds is the total number of bonds and lone pairs. Multiple bonds count the same as single bonds because it doesn't matter how many electrons occupy each cloud.

Step 2.   Predict the geometric arrangement of charge clouds around each atom by assuming that the clouds are oriented in space as far away from one another as possible. How they achieve this orientation depends on their number. Let's look at the possibilities.

Two Charge Clouds

When there are only two charge clouds on an atom, as occurs on the carbon atoms of CO_2 (two double bonds) and HCN (one single bond and one triple bond), the clouds are farthest apart when they point in opposite directions. Thus, CO_2 and HCN are linear molecules with **bond angles** of 180°.

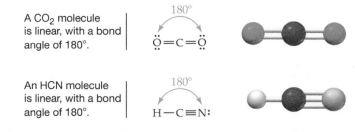

A CO_2 molecule is linear, with a bond angle of 180°.

An HCN molecule is linear, with a bond angle of 180°.

Three Charge Clouds

When there are three charge clouds on an atom, as occurs on the carbon atom of formaldehyde (two single bonds and one double bond) and the sulfur atom of SO_2 (one single bond, one double bond, and one lone pair), the clouds are farthest apart when they lie in the same plane and point to the corners of an equilateral triangle. Thus, a formaldehyde molecule has a *trigonal planar* shape, with H—C—H and H—C=O bond angles near 120°. Similarly, an SO_2 molecule has a trigonal planar arrangement of its three charge clouds on sulfur, but one corner of the triangle is occupied by a lone pair and two corners by oxygen atoms. The molecule therefore has a *bent* shape, with an O—S=O bond angle of approximately 120° rather than 180°. (For consistency, we'll use the word *shape* to refer to the overall arrangement of atoms in a molecule, not to the geometric arrangement of charge clouds around a specific atom.)

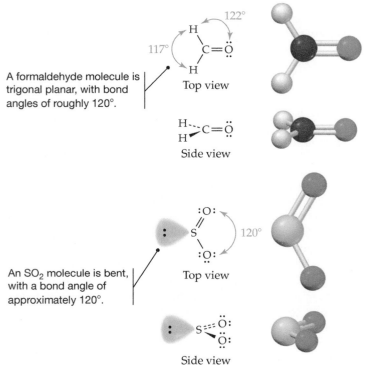

A formaldehyde molecule is trigonal planar, with bond angles of roughly 120°.

Top view

Side view

An SO_2 molecule is bent, with a bond angle of approximately 120°.

Top view

Side view

Four Charge Clouds

When there are four charge clouds on an atom, as occurs on the central atoms in CH_4 (four single bonds), NH_3 (three single bonds and one lone pair), and H_2O (two single bonds and two lone pairs), the clouds are farthest apart if they extend toward the corners of a regular tetrahedron. As illustrated in **Figure 7.6**, a regular tetrahedron is a geometric solid whose four identical faces are equilateral triangles. The central atom lies in the center of the tetrahedron, the charge clouds point toward the four corners, and the angle between two lines drawn from the center to any two corners is 109.5°.

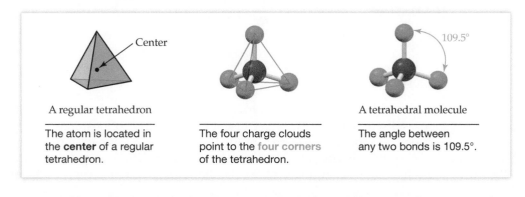

A regular tetrahedron

A tetrahedral molecule

| The atom is located in the **center** of a regular tetrahedron. | The four charge clouds point to the **four corners** of the tetrahedron. | The angle between any two bonds is 109.5°. |

Figure 7.6
The tetrahedral geometry of an atom with four charge clouds.

Because valence electron octets are so common, particularly for second-row elements, the atoms in a great many molecules have geometries based on the tetrahedron. Methane, for example, has a tetrahedral shape, with $H-C-H$ bond angles of 109.5°. In NH_3, the nitrogen atom has a tetrahedral arrangement of its four charge clouds, but one corner of the tetrahedron is occupied by a lone pair, resulting in a *trigonal pyramidal* shape for the molecule. Similarly, H_2O has two corners of the tetrahedron occupied by lone pairs and thus has a *bent* shape.

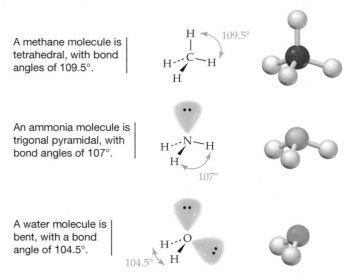

A methane molecule is tetrahedral, with bond angles of 109.5°.

An ammonia molecule is trigonal pyramidal, with bond angles of 107°.

A water molecule is bent, with a bond angle of 104.5°.

Note how the three-dimensional shapes of the molecules in the preceding three structures are drawn. Solid lines are assumed to be in the plane of the paper, dashed lines recede behind the plane of the paper away from the viewer, and heavy, wedged lines protrude out of the paper toward the viewer. Note also that the $H-N-H$ bond angles in ammonia (107°) and the $H-O-H$ bond angle in water (104.5°) are less than the ideal 109.5° tetrahedral value. The angles are diminished somewhat from the tetrahedral value because of the presence of lone pairs. Charge clouds of lone-pair electrons spread out more than charge clouds of bonding electrons because they aren't confined to the space between two nuclei. As a result, the somewhat enlarged lone-pair charge clouds tend to compress the bond angles in the rest of the molecule.

Five Charge Clouds

Five charge clouds, such as are found on the central atoms in PCl_5, SF_4, ClF_3, and I_3^-, are oriented toward the corners of a geometric figure called a *trigonal bipyramid*. Three clouds lie in a plane and point toward the corners of an equilateral triangle, the fourth cloud points directly up, and the fifth cloud points down:

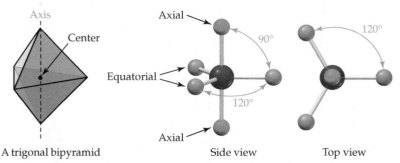

A trigonal bipyramid   Side view   Top view

Trigonal bipyramidal geometry differs from the linear, trigonal planar, and tetrahedral geometries discussed previously because it has two kinds of positions—three *equatorial* positions (around the "equator" of the bipyramid) and two *axial* positions (along the "axis" of the bipyramid). The three equatorial positions are at angles of 120° to one another and at an angle of 90° to the axial positions. The two axial positions are at angles of 180° to each other and at an angle of 90° to the equatorial positions.

Different substances containing a trigonal bipyramidal arrangement of charge clouds on an atom adopt different shapes, depending on whether the five charge clouds contain bonding or nonbonding electrons. Phosphorus pentachloride, for instance, has all five positions around phosphorus occupied by chlorine atoms and thus has a trigonal bipyramidal shape:

A PCl$_5$ molecule is trigonal bipyramidal.

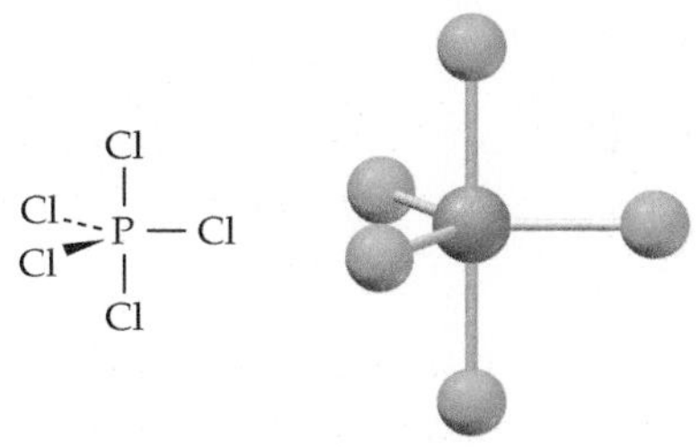

The sulfur atom in SF$_4$ is bonded to four other atoms and has one nonbonding electron lone pair. Because an electron lone pair spreads out and occupies more space than a bonding pair, the nonbonding electrons in SF$_4$ occupy an equatorial position where they are close to (90° away from) only two charge clouds. Were they instead to occupy an axial position, they would be close to three charge clouds. As a result, SF$_4$ has a shape often described as that of a seesaw. The two axial bonds form the board, and the two equatorial bonds form the legs of the seesaw. (You have to tilt your head 90° to see it in the following image.)

An SF$_4$ molecule is shaped like a seesaw (turn 90° to see it).

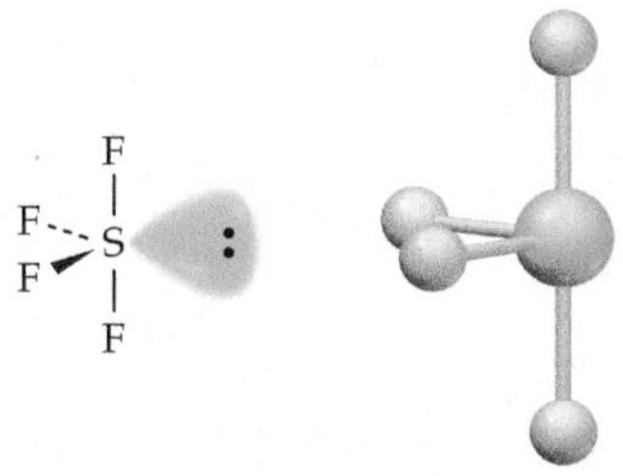

The chlorine atom in ClF$_3$ is bonded to three other atoms and has two nonbonding electron lone pairs. Both lone pairs occupy equatorial positions, resulting in a T shape for the ClF$_3$ molecule. (As with the seesaw, you have to tilt your head 90° to see the T in the image below.)

A ClF$_3$ molecule is T-shaped.

The central iodine atom in the I$_3^-$ ion is bonded to two other atoms and has three lone pairs. All three lone pairs occupy equatorial positions, resulting in a linear shape for I$_3^-$.

An I$_3^-$ ion is linear.

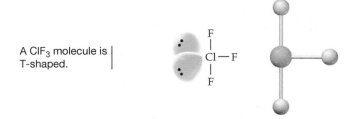

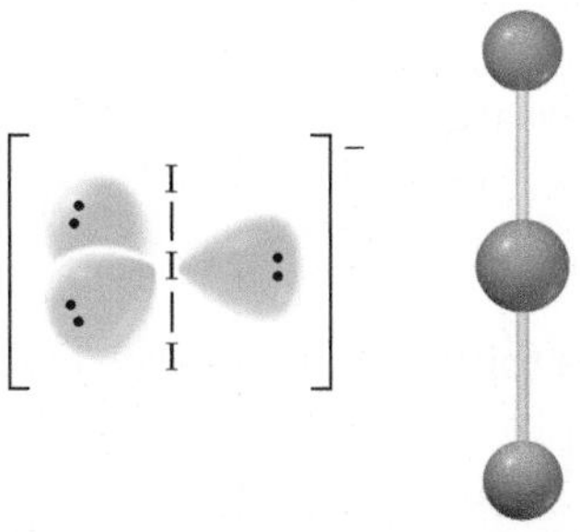

Six Charge Clouds

Six charge clouds around an atom orient toward the six corners of a regular octahedron, a geometric solid whose eight faces are equilateral triangles. All six positions are equivalent, and the angle between any two adjacent positions is 90°.

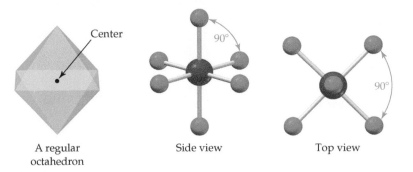

A regular octahedron   Side view   Top view

As was true in the case of five charge clouds, different shapes are possible for molecules having atoms with six charge clouds, depending on whether the clouds are of bonding or nonbonding electrons. In sulfur hexafluoride, for instance, all six positions around sulfur are occupied by fluorine atoms:

An SF_6 molecule is octahedral.

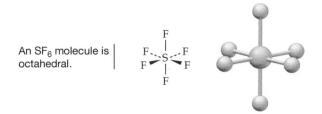

The antimony atom in the $SbCl_5{}^{2-}$ ion also has six charge clouds but is bonded to only five atoms and has one nonbonding electron lone pair. As a result, the ion has a *square pyramidal* shape—a pyramid with a square base:

An $SbCl_5{}^{2-}$ ion has a square pyramidal shape.

The xenon atom in XeF_4 is bonded to four atoms and has two lone pairs. The lone pairs orient as far away from each other as possible to minimize electronic repulsions, giving the molecule a *square planar* shape:

An XeF_4 molecule has a square planar shape.

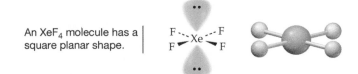

All the geometries for two to six charge clouds are summarized in Table 7.4.

TABLE 7.4 Geometry around Atoms with 2, 3, 4, 5, and 6 Charge Clouds

Number of Bonds	Number of Lone Pairs	Number of Charge Clouds	Geometry		Example
2	0	2		Linear	$O{=}C{=}O$
3	0	3		Trigonal planar	
2	1			Bent	
4	0	4		Tetrahedral	
3	1			Trigonal pyramidal	
2	2			Bent	
5	0	5		Trigonal bipyramidal	
4	1			Seesaw	
3	2			T-shaped	
2	3			Linear	
6	0	6		Octahedral	
5	1			Square pyramidal	
4	2			Square planar	

Shapes of Larger Molecules

The geometries around individual atoms in larger molecules can also be predicted from the rules summarized in Table 7.4. For example, each of the two carbon atoms in ethylene ($H_2C=CH_2$) has three charge clouds, giving rise to trigonal planar geometry for each carbon. The molecule as a whole has a planar shape, with $H-C-C$ and $H-C-H$ bond angles of approximately $120°$.

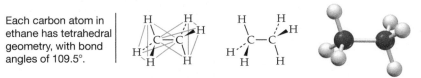

Each carbon atom in ethylene has trigonal planar geometry. As a result, the entire molecule is planar, with bond angles of 120°.

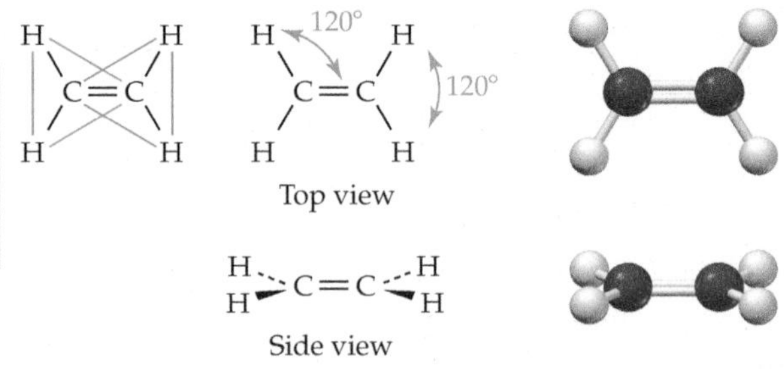

Top view

Side view

Carbon atoms bonded to four other atoms are each at the center of a tetrahedron. As shown below for ethane, H_3C-CH_3, the two tetrahedrons are joined so that the central carbon atom of one is a corner atom of the other.

Each carbon atom in ethane has tetrahedral geometry, with bond angles of 109.5°.

WORKED EXAMPLE 7.11

USING THE VSEPR MODEL TO PREDICT A SHAPE

Predict the shape of BrF_5.

STRATEGY

First, draw an electron-dot structure for BrF_5 to determine that the central bromine atom has six charge clouds (five bonds and one lone pair). Then predict how the six charge clouds are arranged.

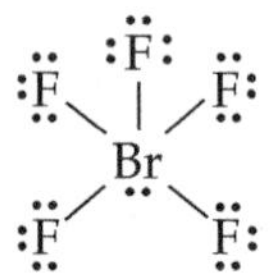

Bromine pentafluoride

SOLUTION

Six charge clouds imply an octahedral arrangement. The five attached atoms and one lone pair give BrF_5 a square pyramidal shape:

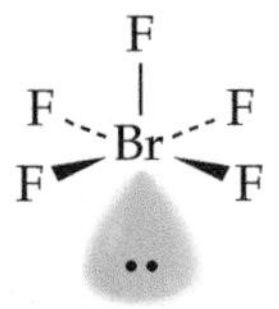

▶ **PROBLEM 7.17**   Predict the shapes of the following molecules or ions:
(a) O_3 (b) H_3O^+ (c) XeF_2 (d) PF_6^-
(e) $XeOF_4$ (f) AlH_4^- (g) BF_4^- (h) $SiCl_4$
(i) ICl_4^- (j) $AlCl_3$

▶ **PROBLEM 7.18**   Acetic acid, CH_3CO_2H, is the main organic constituent of vinegar. Draw an electron-dot structure for acetic acid, and show its overall shape. (The two carbons are connected by a single bond, and both oxygens are connected to the same carbon.)

CONCEPTUAL PROBLEM 7.19 What is the geometry around the central atom in each of the following molecular models?

(a)   **(b)**

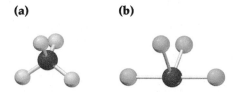

7.10 VALENCE BOND THEORY

The electron-dot structures described in Sections 7.5 and 7.6 provide a simple way to predict the distribution of valence electrons in a molecule, and the VSEPR model discussed in Section 7.9 provides a simple way to predict molecular shapes. Neither model, however, says anything about the electronic nature of covalent bonds. To describe bonding, a quantum mechanical model called **valence bond theory** has been developed.

Valence bond theory provides an easily visualized orbital picture of how electron pairs are shared in a covalent bond. In essence, a covalent bond results when two atoms approach each other closely enough so that a singly occupied valence orbital on one atom spatially *overlaps* a singly occupied valence orbital on the other atom. The now-paired electrons in the overlapping orbitals are attracted to the nuclei of both atoms and thus bond the two atoms together. In the H_2 molecule, for instance, the H—H bond results from the overlap of two singly occupied hydrogen $1s$ orbitals.

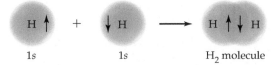

1s   1s H_2 molecule

Recall that atomic orbitals arise from the Schrödinger wave equation and that the two lobes of a p atomic orbital have different phases, as represented by different colors. In the valence bond model, the two overlapping lobes must be of the same phase, and the strength of the covalent bond that forms depends on the amount of orbital overlap: the greater the overlap, the stronger the bond. This, in turn, means that bonds formed by overlap of other than s orbitals have a directionality to them. In the F_2 molecule, for instance, each fluorine atom has the electron configuration [He] $2s^2\,2p_x^2\,2p_y^2\,2p_z^1$ and the F—F bond results from the overlap of two singly occupied $2p$ orbitals. The two $2p$ orbitals must point directly at each other for optimum overlap to occur, and the F—F bond forms along the orbital axis. Such bonds that result from head-on orbital overlap are called **sigma (σ) bonds.**

Remember...
The **Schrödinger wave equation** focuses on the wavelike properties of atoms to describe the quantum mechanical model of atomic structure. The solutions to the wave equation are called wave functions, or orbitals. (Section 5.6)

The two lobes of a p orbital have different mathematical signs in the wave function, corresponding to the different **phases** of a wave. (Section 5.7)

Bonds form between two lobes of the same phase.	A sigma (σ) bond forms from head-on orbital overlap.

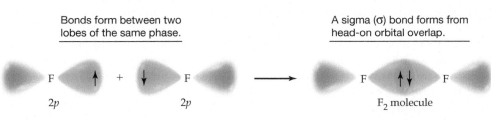

2p   2p F_2 molecule

In HCl, the covalent bond involves overlap of a hydrogen $1s$ orbital with a chlorine $3p$ orbital and forms along the p-orbital axis:

1s   3p   HCl molecule

The key ideas of valence bond theory can be summarized as follows:

 **Principles of Valence Bond Theory**

- Covalent bonds are formed by overlap of atomic orbitals, each of which contains one electron of opposite spin. The two overlapping lobes must be of the same phase.
- Each of the bonded atoms maintains its own atomic orbitals, but the electron pair in the overlapping orbitals is shared by both atoms.
- The greater the amount of orbital overlap, the stronger the bond. This leads to a directional character for the bond when other than s orbitals are involved.

7.11 HYBRIDIZATION AND sp^3 HYBRID ORBITALS

How does valence bond theory describe the electronic structure of complex polyatomic molecules, and how does it account for the observed geometries around atoms in molecules? Let's look first at a simple tetrahedral molecule such as methane, CH_4. There are several problems to be dealt with.

Carbon has the ground-state electron configuration [He] $2s^2 2p_x{}^1 2p_y{}^1$. It thus has four valence electrons, two of which are paired in a 2s orbital and two of which are unpaired in different 2p orbitals that we'll arbitrarily designate as $2p_x$ and $2p_y$. But how can carbon form four bonds if two of its valence electrons are already paired and only two unpaired electrons remain for sharing? The answer is that an electron must be promoted from the lower-energy 2s orbital to the vacant, higher-energy $2p_z$ orbital, giving an *excited-state configuration* [He] $2s^1 2p_x{}^1 2p_y{}^1 2p_z{}^1$ that has *four* unpaired electrons and can thus form four bonds.

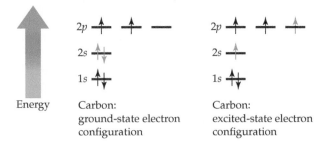

A second problem is more difficult to resolve: If excited-state carbon uses two kinds of orbitals for bonding, 2s and 2p, how can it form four *equivalent* bonds? Furthermore, if the three 2p orbitals in carbon are at angles of 90° to one another, and if the 2s orbital has no directionality, how can carbon form bonds with angles of 109.5° directed to the corners of a regular tetrahedron? The answers to these questions were provided in 1931 by Linus Pauling, who introduced the idea of *hybrid orbitals*.

Pauling showed how the quantum mechanical wave functions for s and p atomic orbitals derived from the Schrödinger wave equation can be mathematically combined to form a new set of equivalent wave functions called **hybrid atomic orbitals.** When one s orbital combines with three p orbitals, as occurs in an excited-state carbon atom, four equivalent hybrid orbitals, called sp^3 **hybrids**, result. (The superscript 3 in the name sp^3 tells how many p atomic orbitals are combined to construct the hybrid orbitals, not how many electrons occupy the orbital.)

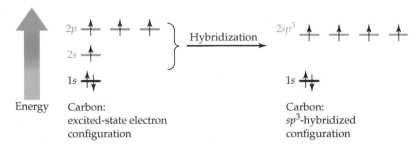

Each of the four equivalent *sp*³ hybrid orbitals has two lobes of different phase like an atomic *p* orbital (Section 5.7) but one of the lobes is larger than the other, giving the orbital a directionality. The four large lobes are oriented toward the four corners of a tetrahedron at angles of 109.5°, as shown in Figure 7.7. For consistency in the use of colors, we'll routinely show the different phases of orbitals in red and blue and will show the large lobes of the resultant hybrid orbitals in green.

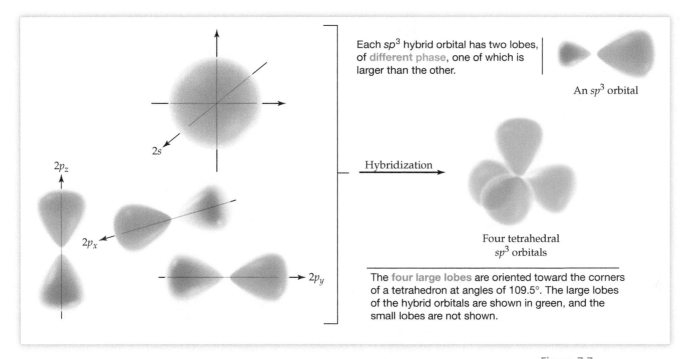

Each *sp*³ hybrid orbital has two lobes, of **different phase**, one of which is larger than the other.

An *sp*³ orbital

Hybridization

Four tetrahedral *sp*³ orbitals

The **four large lobes** are oriented toward the corners of a tetrahedron at angles of 109.5°. The large lobes of the hybrid orbitals are shown in green, and the small lobes are not shown.

Figure 7.7
The formation of four *sp*³ hybrid orbitals by combination of an atomic *s* orbital with three atomic *p* orbitals.

The shared electrons in a covalent bond made with a spatially directed hybrid orbital spend most of their time in the region between the two bonded nuclei. As a result, covalent bonds made with *sp*³ hybrid orbitals are often strong ones. In fact, the energy released on forming the four strong C—H bonds in CH_4 more than compensates for the energy required to form the excited state of carbon. Figure 7.8 shows how the four C—H sigma bonds in methane can form by head-on overlap of carbon *sp*³ hybrid orbitals with hydrogen 1*s* orbitals.

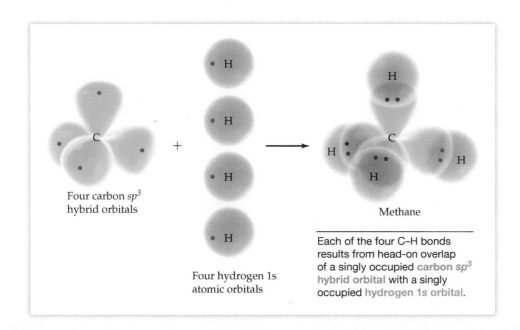

Four carbon *sp*³ hybrid orbitals

+

Four hydrogen 1s atomic orbitals

Methane

Each of the four C–H bonds results from head-on overlap of a singly occupied **carbon *sp*³ hybrid orbital** with a singly occupied **hydrogen 1s orbital**.

Figure 7.8
The bonding in methane (CH_4).

The same kind of sp^3 hybridization that describes the bonds to carbon in the tetrahedral methane molecule can also be used to describe bonds to nitrogen in the trigonal pyramidal ammonia molecule, to oxygen in the bent water molecule, and to all other atoms that the VSEPR model predicts to have a tetrahedral arrangement of four charge clouds.

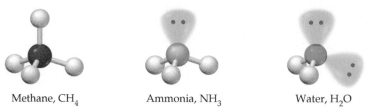

Methane, CH_4 Ammonia, NH_3 Water, H_2O

▶ **PROBLEM 7.20**   Describe the bonding in ethane, C_2H_6, and tell what kinds of orbitals on each atom overlap to form the C—C and C—H bonds.

7.12   OTHER KINDS OF HYBRID ORBITALS

Other geometries shown in Table 7.4 can also be accounted for by specific kinds of orbital hybridization, although the situation becomes more complex for atoms with five and six charge clouds. Let's look at each.

sp^2 Hybridization

Atoms with three charge clouds undergo hybridization by combination of one atomic s orbital with two p orbitals, resulting in three sp^2 **hybrid orbitals.** These three sp^2 hybrids lie in a plane and are oriented toward the corners of an equilateral triangle at angles of $120°$ to one another. One p orbital remains unchanged and is oriented at a $90°$ angle to the plane of the sp^2 hybrids, as shown in **Figure 7.9.**

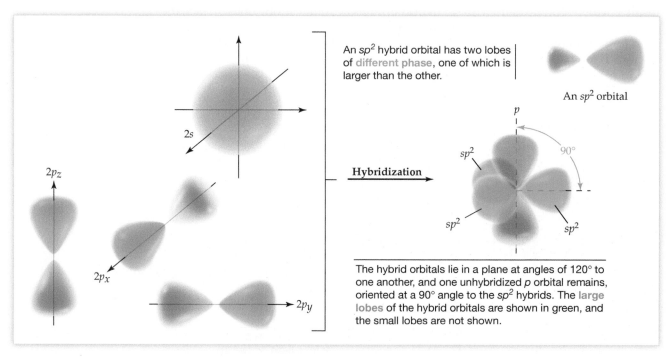

An sp^2 hybrid orbital has two lobes of different phase, one of which is larger than the other.

An sp^2 orbital

Hybridization

The hybrid orbitals lie in a plane at angles of $120°$ to one another, and one unhybridized p orbital remains, oriented at a $90°$ angle to the sp^2 hybrids. The large lobes of the hybrid orbitals are shown in green, and the small lobes are not shown.

Figure 7.9
The formation of sp^2 hybrid orbitals by combination of one s orbital and two p orbitals.

The presence of the unhybridized p orbital on an sp^2-hybridized atom has some interesting consequences. Look, for example, at ethylene, $H_2C{=}CH_2$, a colorless gas used as starting material for the industrial preparation of polyethylene. Each carbon atom in ethylene has three charge clouds and is sp^2-hybridized. When two sp^2-hybridized carbon atoms approach each other with sp^2 orbitals aligned head-on for σ bonding, the unhybridized p orbitals on the carbons also approach each other and form a bond, but in a parallel, sideways manner rather than head-on. Such a sideways bond, in which the shared electrons occupy regions above and below a line connecting the nuclei rather than directly between the nuclei, is called a **pi (π) bond** (Figure 7.10). In addition, four C—H bonds form in ethylene by overlap of the remaining four sp^2 orbitals with hydrogen $1s$ orbitals.

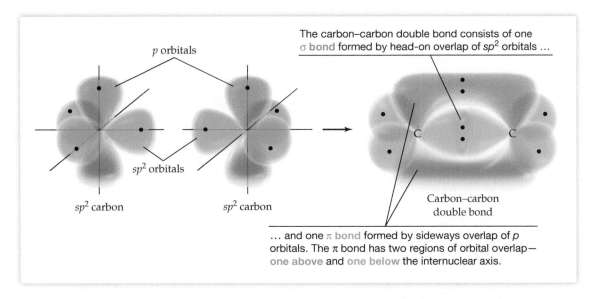

The carbon–carbon double bond consists of one σ bond formed by head-on overlap of sp^2 orbitals ...

p orbitals

sp^2 orbitals

sp^2 carbon

sp^2 carbon

Carbon–carbon double bond

... and one π bond formed by sideways overlap of p orbitals. The π bond has two regions of orbital overlap— one above and one below the internuclear axis.

Figure 7.10
The structure of a carbon–carbon double bond.

The π bond has two regions of orbital overlap, one above and one below a line drawn between the nuclei, the *internuclear axis*. Both regions are part of the same bond, and the two shared electrons are spread over both regions. As always, the p lobes must be of the same phase for overlap leading to bond formation. The net result of both σ and π overlap is the sharing of four electrons and the formation of a carbon–carbon double bond.

▶ PROBLEM 7.21 Describe the hybridization of the carbon atom in formaldehyde, $H_2C{=}O$, and make a rough sketch of the molecule showing the orbitals involved in bonding.

sp Hybridization

Atoms with two charge clouds undergo hybridization by combination of one atomic s orbital with one p orbital, resulting in two *sp* **hybrid orbitals** that are oriented 180° from each other. Since only one p orbital is involved when an atom undergoes sp hybridization, the other two p orbitals are unchanged and are oriented at 90° angles to the sp hybrids, as shown in Figure 7.11.

One of the simplest examples of sp hybridization occurs in acetylene, $H{-}C{\equiv}C{-}H$, a colorless gas used in welding. Both carbon atoms in the acetylene molecule have linear geometry and are sp-hybridized. When the two sp-hybridized carbon atoms approach each other with their sp orbitals aligned head-on for σ bonding, the unhybridized p orbitals on each carbon are aligned for π bonding. Two p orbitals are aligned in an up/down position, and two are aligned in an in/out position. Thus, there are two mutually perpendicular π bonds that form by sideways

Figure 7.11
sp **Hybridization.**

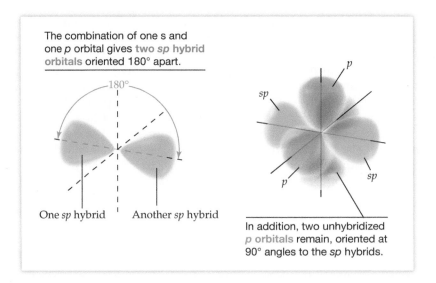

The combination of one s and one *p* orbital gives **two *sp* hybrid orbitals** oriented 180° apart.

One *sp* hybrid   Another *sp* hybrid

In addition, two unhybridized *p* orbitals remain, oriented at 90° angles to the *sp* hybrids.

overlap of *p* orbitals, along with one σ bond that forms by head-on overlap of the *sp* orbitals. The net result is the sharing of six electrons and formation of a triple bond (Figure 7.12). In addition, two C—H bonds form in acetylene by overlap of the remaining two *sp* orbitals with hydrogen 1*s* orbitals.

Figure 7.12
Formation of a triple bond by two *sp*-hybridized atoms.

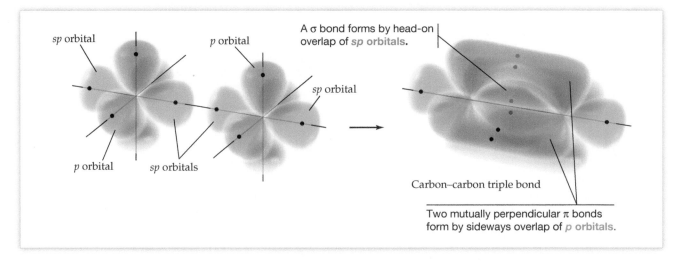

sp orbital   *p* orbital   A σ bond forms by head-on overlap of *sp* orbitals.

sp orbital

p orbital   *sp* orbitals

Carbon–carbon triple bond

Two mutually perpendicular π bonds form by sideways overlap of *p* orbitals.

▶ **PROBLEM 7.22** Describe the hybridization of the carbon atom in the hydrogen cyanide molecule, H—C≡N, and make a rough sketch to show the hybrid orbitals it uses for bonding.

Atoms with Five and Six Charge Clouds

Main-group atoms with five or six charge clouds, such as the phosphorus in PCl_5 and the sulfur in SF_6, were at one time thought to undergo hybridization by combination of five and six atomic orbitals, respectively. Because a given shell has a total of only four *s* and *p* orbitals, however, the need to use five or six orbitals implies that *d* orbitals are involved. As we'll see in Section 20.11, hybridization involving *d* orbitals is indeed involved for many compounds of transition metals. Recent quantum mechanical calculations indicate, however, that main-group compounds do not use *d* orbitals in hybridization but instead use a more complex bonding pattern that is not easily explained by valence bond theory.

A summary of the three common kinds of hybridization for main-group elements and the geometry that each corresponds to is given in Table 7.5.

TABLE 7.5   Hybrid Orbitals and Their Geometry

Number of Charge Clouds	Arrangement of Charge Clouds	Hybridization
2	Linear	sp
3	Trigonal planar	sp^2
4	Tetrahedral	sp^3

WORKED EXAMPLE 7.12

PREDICTING THE HYBRIDIZATION OF AN ATOM

Describe the hybridization of the carbon atoms in allene, $H_2C{=}C{=}CH_2$, and make a rough sketch of the molecule showing its hybrid orbitals.

STRATEGY

Draw an electron-dot structure to find the number of charge clouds on each atom.

Two charge clouds

Three charge clouds — H \ C=C=C / H — Three charge clouds

H   H

Then predict the geometry around each atom using the VSEPR model (Table 7.5).

SOLUTION

Because the central carbon atom in allene has two charge clouds (two double bonds), it has a linear geometry and is sp-hybridized. Because the two terminal carbon atoms have three charge clouds each (one double bond and two C—H bonds), they have trigonal planar geometry and are sp^2-hybridized. The central carbon uses its sp orbitals to form two σ bonds at 180° angles and uses its two unhybridized p orbitals to form π bonds, one to each of the terminal carbons. Each terminal carbon atom uses an sp^2 orbital for σ bonding to carbon, a p orbital for π bonding, and its two remaining sp^2 orbitals for C—H bonds. Note that the mutually perpendicular arrangement of the two π bonds results in a similar perpendicular arrangement of the two CH_2 groups.

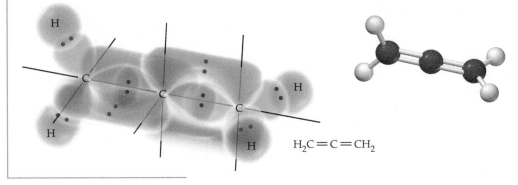

$H_2C{=}C{=}CH_2$

▶ **PROBLEM 7.23**   Describe the hybridization of the carbon atom in carbon dioxide, and make a rough sketch of the molecule showing its hybrid orbitals and π bonds.

▶ **PROBLEM 7.24**   Describe the hybridization of the carbon atom in the poisonous gas phosgene, Cl_2CO, and make a rough sketch of the molecule showing its hybrid orbitals and π bonds.

CONCEPTUAL PROBLEM 7.25   Identify each of the following sets of hybrid orbitals:

(a)   **(b)**   **(c)**

7.13 MOLECULAR ORBITAL THEORY: THE HYDROGEN MOLECULE

The valence bond model that describes covalent bonding through orbital overlap is easy to visualize and leads to a satisfactory description for most molecules. It does, however, have some problems. Perhaps the most serious flaw in the valence bond model is that it sometimes leads to an incorrect electronic description. For this reason, another bonding description called **molecular orbital (MO) theory** is often used. The molecular orbital model is more complex and less easily visualized than the valence bond model, particularly for larger molecules, but it sometimes gives a more satisfactory accounting of chemical and physical properties.

To introduce some of the basic ideas of molecular orbital theory, let's look again at orbitals. The concept of an orbital derives from the quantum mechanical wave equation, in which the square of the wave function gives the probability of finding an electron within a given region of space. The kinds of orbitals that we've been concerned with up to this point are called *atomic orbitals* because they are characteristic of individual atoms. Atomic orbitals on the same atom can combine to form hybrids, and atomic orbitals on different atoms can overlap to form covalent bonds, but the orbitals and the electrons in them remain localized on specific atoms.

> **Atomic orbital** A wave function whose square gives the probability of finding an electron within a given region of space *in an atom*.

Molecular orbital theory takes a different approach to bonding by considering the molecule as a whole rather than concentrating on individual atoms. A **molecular orbital** is to a molecule what an atomic orbital is to an atom.

> **Molecular orbital** A wave function whose square gives the probability of finding an electron within a given region of space *in a molecule*.

Like atomic orbitals, molecular orbitals have specific energy levels and specific shapes, and they can be occupied by a maximum of two electrons with opposite spins. The energy and shape of a molecular orbital depend on the size and complexity of the molecule and can thus be fairly complicated, but the fundamental analogy between atomic and molecular orbitals remains. Let's look at the molecular orbital description of the simple diatomic molecule H_2 to see some general features of MO theory.

Imagine what might happen when two isolated hydrogen atoms approach each other and begin to interact. The $1s$ orbitals begin to blend together, and the electrons spread out over both atoms. Molecular orbital theory says that there are two ways for the orbital interaction to occur—an additive way and a subtractive way. The additive interaction leads to formation of a molecular orbital that is roughly egg-shaped, whereas the subtractive interaction leads to formation of a molecular orbital that contains a **node** between atoms (Figure 7.13).

Remember...

A **node** is a surface of zero electron probability separating regions of nonzero probability within an orbital. (Section 5.7)

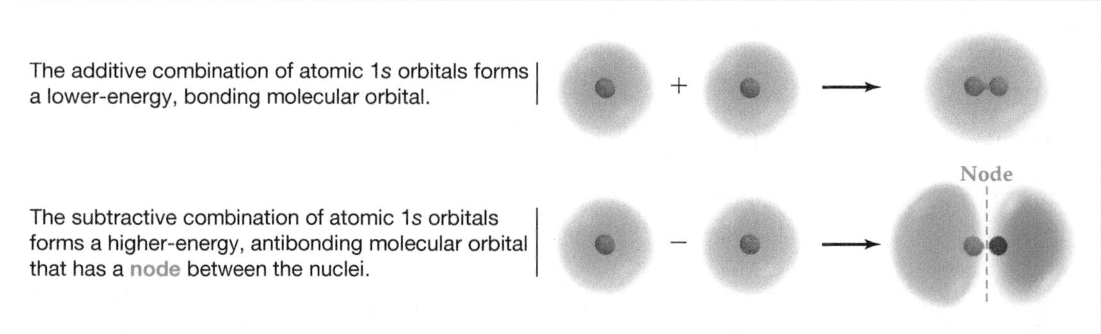

The additive combination of atomic $1s$ orbitals forms a lower-energy, bonding molecular orbital.

The subtractive combination of atomic $1s$ orbitals forms a higher-energy, antibonding molecular orbital that has a **node** between the nuclei.

Node

Figure 7.13
Formation of molecular orbitals in the H_2 molecule.

The additive combination, denoted σ, is lower in energy than the two isolated 1s orbitals and is called a **bonding molecular orbital** because any electrons it contains spend most of their time in the region between the two nuclei, bonding the atoms together. The subtractive combination, denoted σ* and spoken as "sigma star," is higher in energy than the two isolated 1s orbitals and is called an **antibonding molecular orbital.** Any electrons it contains can't occupy the central region between the nuclei and can't contribute to bonding.

Diagrams of the sort shown in Figure 7.14 are used to show the energy relationships of the various orbitals. The two isolated H atomic orbitals are shown on either side, and the two H_2 molecular orbitals are shown in the middle. Each of the starting hydrogen atomic orbitals has one electron, which pair up and occupy the lower-energy bonding MO after covalent bond formation.

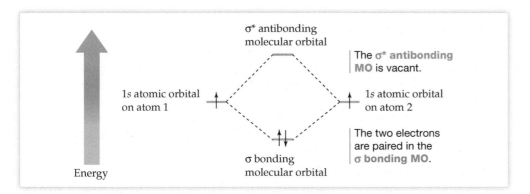

Figure 7.14
Energy levels of molecular orbitals for the H_2 molecule.

Similar MO diagrams can be drawn, and predictions about stability can be made, for related diatomic species such as H_2^- and He_2. For example, we might imagine constructing the H_2^- ion by bringing together a neutral H· atom with one electron and an H:⁻ anion with two electrons. Since the resultant H_2^- ion has three electrons, two of them will occupy the lower-energy bonding σ MO and one will occupy the higher-energy antibonding σ* MO as shown in Figure 7.15a. Two electrons are lowered in energy while only one electron is raised in energy, so a net gain in stability results. We therefore predict (and find experimentally) that the H_2^- ion is stable.

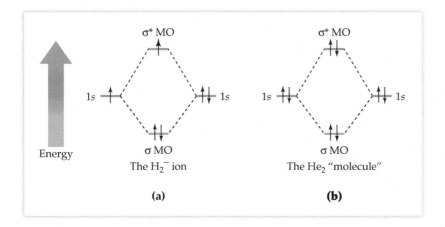

Figure 7.15
Energy levels of molecular orbitals for (a) the stable H_2^- ion and (b) the unstable He_2 molecule.

What about He_2? A hypothetical He_2 molecule has four electrons, two of which occupy the lower-energy bonding orbital and two of which occupy the higher-energy antibonding orbital, as shown in Figure 7.15b. Since the decrease in energy for the two bonding electrons is counteracted by the increase in energy for the two antibonding electrons, the He_2 molecule has no net bonding energy and is not stable.

Bond orders—the number of electron pairs shared between atoms (Section 7.5)—can be calculated from MO diagrams by subtracting the number of antibonding electrons from the number of bonding electrons and dividing the difference by 2:

$$\text{Bond order} = \frac{\left(\begin{array}{c}\text{Number of}\\\text{bonding electrons}\end{array}\right) - \left(\begin{array}{c}\text{Number of}\\\text{antibonding electrons}\end{array}\right)}{2}$$

The H_2 molecule, for instance, has a bond order of 1 because it has two bonding electrons and no antibonding electrons. In the same way, the H_2^- ion has a bond order of 1/2, and the hypothetical He_2 molecule has a bond order of 0, which accounts for the instability of He_2.

The key ideas of the molecular orbital theory of bonding can be summarized as follows:

Key Ideas of Molecular Orbital Theory

- Molecular orbitals are to molecules what atomic orbitals are to atoms. A molecular orbital describes a region of space in a molecule where electrons are most likely to be found, and it has a specific size, shape, and energy level.
- Molecular orbitals are formed by combining atomic orbitals on different atoms. The number of molecular orbitals formed is the same as the number of atomic orbitals combined.
- Molecular orbitals that are lower in energy than the starting atomic orbitals are bonding, and MOs that are higher in energy than the starting atomic orbitals are antibonding.
- Electrons occupy molecular orbitals beginning with the MO of lowest energy. A maximum of two electrons can occupy each orbital, and their spins are paired.
- Bond order can be calculated by subtracting the number of electrons in antibonding MOs from the number in bonding MOs and dividing the difference by 2.

▶ **PROBLEM 7.26**   Construct an MO diagram for the He_2^+ ion. Is this ion likely to be stable? What is its bond order?

7.14   MOLECULAR ORBITAL THEORY: OTHER DIATOMIC MOLECULES

Having looked at bonding in the H_2 molecule, let's move up a level in complexity by looking at the bonding in several second-row diatomic molecules—N_2, O_2, and F_2. The valence bond model developed in Section 7.10 predicts that the nitrogen atoms in N_2 are triply bonded and have one lone pair each, that the oxygen atoms in O_2 are doubly bonded and have two lone pairs each, and that the fluorine atoms in F_2 are singly bonded and have three lone pairs each:

Valence bond
theory predicts: $:N\equiv N:$ $\ddot{O}=\ddot{O}$ $:\ddot{F}-\ddot{F}:$

1 σ bond   1 σ bond   1 σ bond
and 2 π bonds   and 1 π bond

Unfortunately, this simple valence bond picture can't be right because it predicts that the electrons in all three molecules are *spin-paired*. In other words, the electron-dot structures indicate that the occupied atomic orbitals in all three molecules contain two electrons each. It can be demonstrated experimentally, however, that the O_2 molecule has two electrons that are not spin-paired and that these electrons therefore must be in different, singly occupied orbitals.

Experimental evidence for the electronic structure of O_2 rests on the observation that substances with unpaired electrons are attracted by magnetic fields and are thus said to be **paramagnetic.** The more unpaired electrons a substance has, the stronger the paramagnetic attraction. Substances whose electrons are all spin-paired, by contrast, are weakly repelled by magnetic fields and are said to be **diamagnetic.** Both N_2 and F_2 are diamagnetic, just as predicted by their electron-dot structures, but O_2 is paramagnetic. When liquid O_2 is poured over the poles of a strong magnet, the O_2 sticks to the poles, as shown in Figure 7.16.

Why is O_2 paramagnetic? Although electron-dot structures and valence bond theory fail in their descriptions, MO theory explains the experimental results nicely. In a molecular orbital description of N_2, O_2, and F_2, two atoms come together and their valence-shell atomic orbitals interact to form molecular orbitals. Four orbital interactions occur, leading to the formation of four bonding MOs and four antibonding MOs, whose relative energies are shown in Figure 7.17. (Note that the relative energies of the σ_{2p} and π_{2p} orbitals in N_2 are different from those in O_2 and F_2.)

Figure 7.16
Paramagnetism. Why does liquid O_2 stick to the poles of a magnet?

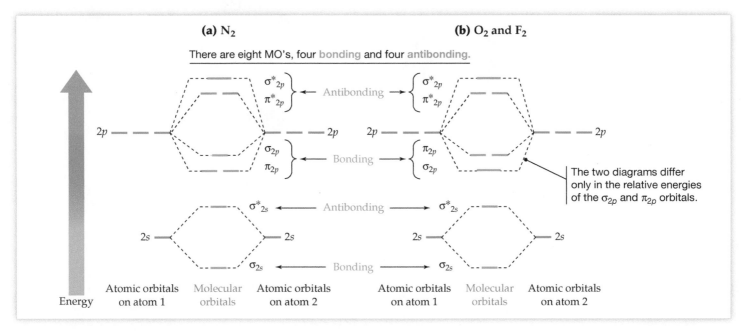

Figure 7.17
Energy levels of molecular orbitals for (a) N_2 and (b) O_2 and F_2.

The diagrams in Figure 7.17 show the following orbital interactions:

- The 2s orbitals interact to give σ_{2s} and σ^*_{2s} MOs.

- The two 2p orbitals that lie on the internuclear axis interact head-on to give σ_{2p} and σ^*_{2p} MOs.

- The two remaining pairs of 2p orbitals that are perpendicular to the internuclear axis interact in a sideways manner to give two degenerate π_{2p} and two degenerate π^*_{2p} MOs oriented 90° apart.

Remember...

Degenerate orbitals are those that have the same energy. (Section 5.11)

The shapes of the σ_{2p}, σ^*_{2p}, π_{2p}, and π^*_{2p} MOs are shown in Figure 7.18.

When appropriate numbers of valence electrons are added to occupy the molecular orbitals, the results shown in Figure 7.19 are obtained. Both N_2 and F_2 have all their electrons spin-paired, but O_2 has two unpaired electrons in the degenerate π^*_{2p} orbitals. Both N_2 and F_2 are therefore diamagnetic, whereas O_2 is paramagnetic.

We should also point out that MO diagrams like those in Figure 7.19 are usually obtained from mathematical calculations and can't necessarily be predicted. MO theory is therefore less easy to visualize and understand on an intuitive level than valence bond theory.

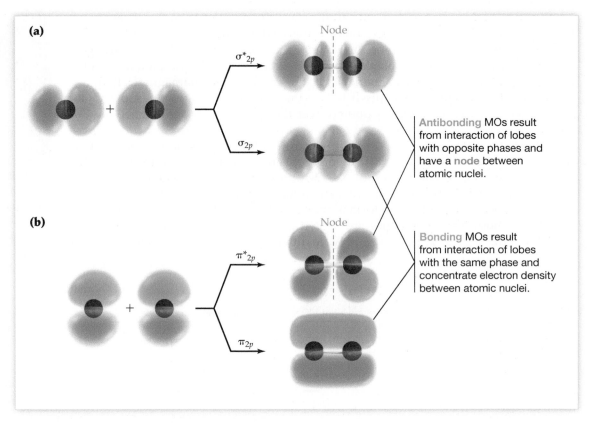

Figure 7.18
Formation of (a) σ_{2p} and σ^*_{2p} MOs by head-on interaction of two p atomic orbitals, and (b) π_{2p} and π^*_{2p} MOs by sideways interaction.

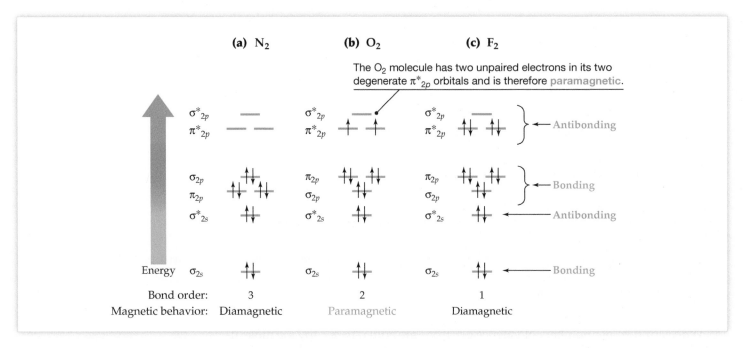

Figure 7.19
Energy levels of molecular orbitals for the second-row diatomic molecules (a) N_2, (b) O_2, and (c) F_2.

▶ **PROBLEM 7.27** The B_2 and C_2 molecules have MO diagrams similar to that of N_2 in Figure 7.17a. What MOs are occupied in B_2 and C_2, and what is the bond order in each? Would you expect either of these substances to be paramagnetic?

7.15 COMBINING VALENCE BOND THEORY AND MOLECULAR ORBITAL THEORY

Whenever two different theories explain the same concept, the question comes up: Which theory is better? The question isn't easy to answer, though, because it depends on what is meant by "better." Valence bond theory is better because of its simplicity and ease of visualization, but MO theory is better because of its accuracy. Best of all, though, is a joint use of the two theories that combines the strengths of both.

Valence bond theory has two main problems: (1) For molecules such as O_2, valence bond theory makes an incorrect prediction about electronic structure. (2) For molecules such as O_3, no single structure is adequate and the concept of resonance involving two or more structures must be added (Section 7.7). The first problem occurs infrequently, but the second is much more common. To better deal with resonance, chemists often use a combination of bonding theories in which the σ bonds in a given molecule are described by valence bond theory and π bonds in the same molecule are described by MO theory.

Take O_3, for instance. Valence bond theory says that ozone is a resonance hybrid of two equivalent structures, both of which have two O—O σ bonds and one O=O π bond (Section 7.7). One structure has a lone pair of electrons in the p orbital on the left-hand oxygen atom and a π bond to the right-hand oxygen. The other structure has a lone pair of electrons in the p orbital on the right-hand oxygen and a π bond to the left-hand oxygen. The actual structure of O_3 is an average of the two resonance forms in which four electrons occupy the entire region encompassed by the overlapping set of three p orbitals. The only difference between the resonance structures is in the placement of p electrons. The atoms themselves are in the same positions in both, and the geometries are the same in both (Figure 7.20).

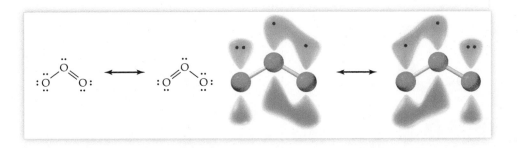

Figure 7.20
The structure of ozone.

Valence bond theory thus gives a good description of the ozone O—O σ bonds, whose electrons are localized between specific pairs of atoms, but a poor description of the π bonds among p atomic orbitals, whose four electrons are spread out, or *delocalized*, over the molecule. Yet this is exactly what MO theory does best—describe bonds in which electrons are delocalized throughout a molecule. Thus, a combination of valence bond theory and MO theory is used. The σ bonds are best described in valence bond terminology as being localized between pairs of atoms, and the π electrons are best described by MO theory as being delocalized over the entire molecule.

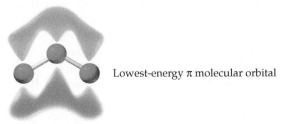

Lowest-energy π molecular orbital

▶ **PROBLEM 7.28** Draw two resonance structures for the formate ion, HCO_2^-, and sketch a π molecular orbital showing how the π electrons are delocalized over both oxygen atoms.

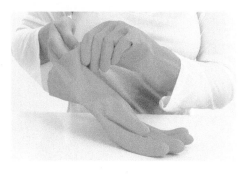

▲ A right hand fits only into a right-handed glove with a complementary shape, not into a left-handed glove.

INQUIRY HOW DOES MOLECULAR SHAPE LEAD TO HANDEDNESS IN MOLECULES?

Why does a right-handed glove fit only on your right hand and not on your left hand? Why do the threads on a lightbulb twist only in one direction so that you have to turn the bulb clockwise to screw it in? The reason has to do with the shapes of the glove and the lightbulb threads and the fact that both have a *handedness* to them. When the right-handed glove is held up to a mirror, the reflected image looks like a left-handed glove. (Try it.) When the lightbulb with clockwise threads is reflected in a mirror, the threads in the mirror image twist in a counterclockwise direction.

Molecules too can have shapes that give them a handedness and can thus exist in mirror-image forms, one right-handed and one left-handed. Take, for example, the main classes of biomolecules found in living organisms: carbohydrates (sugars), proteins, fats, and nucleic acids. These and most other biomolecules are handed, and usually only one of the two possible mirror-image forms occurs naturally in a given organism. The other form can often be made in the laboratory but does not occur naturally.

The biological consequences of molecular shape can be dramatic. Look at the structures of dextromethorphan and levomethorphan, for instance. (The Latin prefixes *dextro-* and *levo-* mean "right" and "left," respectively.) Dextromethorphan is a common cough suppressant found in many over-the-counter cold medicines, but its mirror-image, levomethorphan, is a powerful narcotic pain-reliever similar in its effects to morphine. The two substances are chemically identical except for their handedness, yet their biological properties are very different.

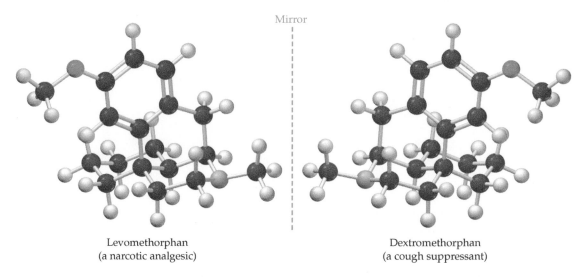

Mirror

Levomethorphan
(a narcotic analgesic)

Dextromethorphan
(a cough suppressant)

▲ The gray spheres in these structures represent carbon atoms, the ivory spheres represent hydrogen, the red spheres represent oxygen, and the blue spheres represent nitrogen.

As another example of the effects of shape and molecular handedness, look at the substance called *carvone*. Left-handed carvone occurs in mint plants and has the characteristic odor of spearmint, while right-handed carvone occurs in several herbs and has the odor of caraway seeds. Again, the two structures are the same except for their handedness, yet they have entirely different odors.

Why do different mirror-image forms of molecules have different biological properties? The answer goes back to the question about why a right-handed glove fits only the right hand. A right hand in a right-handed glove is a perfect match because the two shapes are complementary. Putting the right hand into a left-handed glove produces a mismatch because the two shapes are *not* complementary. In the same way, handed molecules such as dextromethorphan and carvone have specific shapes that match only complementary-shaped receptor sites in the body. The

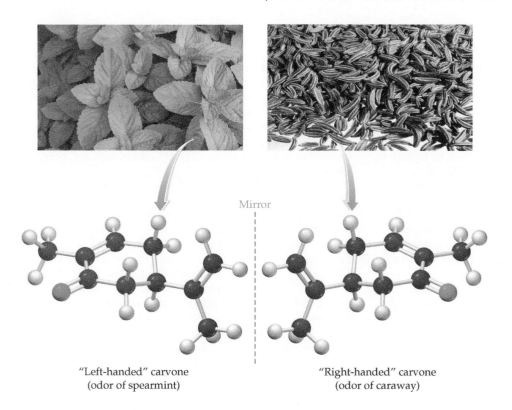

◄ Two plants both produce carvone, but the mint leaves yield the "left-handed" form, while the caraway seeds yield the "right-handed" form.

Mirror

"Left-handed" carvone
(odor of spearmint)

"Right-handed" carvone
(odor of caraway)

mirror-image forms of the molecules can't fit into the receptor sites and thus don't elicit the same biological response.

Precise molecular shape is critically important to every living organism. Almost every chemical interaction in living systems is governed by complementarity between handed molecules and their glovelike receptors.

▶ **PROBLEM 7.29** Why is molecular shape so important in biological chemistry?

CONCEPTUAL PROBLEM 7.30 One of the following two molecules has a handedness to it and can exist in two mirror-image forms; the other does not. Which is which? Why?

(a)   **(b)**

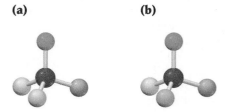

SUMMARY

A **covalent bond** results from the sharing of electrons between atoms. Every covalent bond has a specific **bond length** that leads to optimum stability and a specific **bond dissociation energy** that describes the strength of the bond. Energy is released when a bond is formed, and energy is absorbed when a bond is broken. As a general rule, a main-group atom shares as many of its valence-shell electrons as possible, either until it has no more to share or until it reaches an octet. Atoms in the third and lower rows of the periodic table can accommodate more than the number of bonds predicted by the octet rule.

An **electron-dot structure** represents an atom's valence electrons by dots and shows the two electrons in a **single bond** as a pair of dots shared between atoms. In the same way, a **double bond** is represented as four dots or two lines between atoms, and a **triple bond** is represented as six dots or three lines between atoms. Occasionally, a molecule can be represented by more than one electron-dot structure. In such cases, no single structure is adequate by itself. The actual electronic structure of the molecule is a **resonance hybrid** of the different individual structures.

In a bond between dissimilar atoms, such as that in HCl, one atom often attracts the bonding electrons more strongly than the other, giving rise to a **polar covalent bond.** Bond polarity is due to differences in **electronegativity,** the ability of an atom in a molecule to attract shared electrons. Electronegativity increases from left to right across a row and generally decreases from top to bottom in a group of the periodic table.

Molecular shape can often be predicted using the **valence-shell electron-pair repulsion (VSEPR) model,** which treats the electrons around atoms as charge clouds that repel one another and therefore orient themselves as far away from one another as possible. Atoms with two charge clouds adopt a linear arrangement of the clouds, atoms with three charge clouds adopt a trigonal planar arrangement, and atoms with four charge clouds adopt a tetrahedral arrangement. Similarly, atoms with five charge clouds are trigonal bipyramidal and atoms with six charge clouds are octahedral.

According to **valence bond theory,** covalent bond formation occurs by the overlap of two singly occupied atomic orbital lobes of the same phase, either head-on along the internuclear axis to form a **σ bond** or sideways above and below the internuclear axis to form a **π bond.** The observed geometry of covalent bonding in main-group compounds is described by assuming that s and p atomic orbitals combine to generate **hybrid orbitals,** which are strongly oriented in specific directions: sp **hybrid orbitals** have linear geometry, sp^2 **hybrid orbitals** have trigonal planar geometry, and sp^3 **hybrid orbitals** have tetrahedral geometry. The bonding of main-group atoms with five and six charge clouds is more complex.

Molecular orbital theory sometimes gives a more accurate picture of electronic structure than the valence bond model. A **molecular orbital** is a wave function whose square gives the probability of finding an electron in a given region of space in a molecule. Combination of two atomic orbitals gives two molecular orbitals, a **bonding MO** that is lower in energy than the starting atomic orbitals and an **antibonding MO** that is higher in energy than the starting atomic orbitals. Molecular orbital theory is particularly useful for describing delocalized π bonding in molecules.

KEY WORDS

CONCEPTUAL PROBLEMS

Problems 7.1–7.30 appear within the chapter.

7.31 Two electrostatic potential maps are shown, one of methyllithium (CH₃Li) and the other of chloromethane (CH₃Cl). Based on their polarity patterns, which do you think is which?

(a)

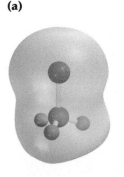

(b)

7.32 What is the geometry around the central atom in each of the following molecular models?

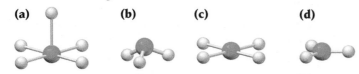

(a)   **(b)**   **(c)**   **(d)**

7.33 What is the geometry around the central atom in each of the following molecular models? (There may be a "hidden" atom directly behind a visible atom in some cases.)

(a)   **(b)**   **(c)**

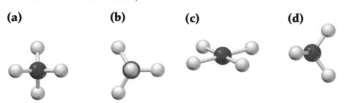

7.34 Three of the following molecular models have a tetrahedral central atom, and one does not. Which is the odd one? (There may be a "hidden" atom directly behind a visible atom in some cases.)

(a)   **(b)**   **(c)**   **(d)**

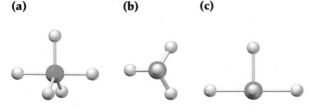

7.35 The VSEPR model is a simple predictive tool that is usually, but not always, correct. Take urea, for instance, a waste product excreted in animal urine:

Urea

What hybridization would you expect for the C and N atoms in urea according to the VSEPR model, and what approximate values would you expect for the various bond angles? What are the actual hybridizations and bond angles based on the molecular model shown? (Red = O, gray = C, blue = N, ivory = H):

7.36 The following ball-and-stick molecular model is a representation of acetaminophen, the active ingredient in such over-the-counter headache remedies as Tylenol (red = O, gray = C, blue = N, ivory = H):

(a) What is the formula of acetaminophen?

(b) Indicate the positions of the multiple bonds in acetaminophen.

(c) What is the geometry around each carbon?

(d) What is the hybridization of each carbon?

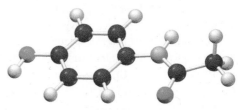

Acetaminophen

7.37 The following ball-and-stick molecular model is a representation of thalidomide, a drug that causes birth defects when taken by expectant mothers but is valuable for its use against leprosy. The lines indicate only the connections between atoms, not whether the bonds are single, double, or triple (red = O, gray = C, blue = N, ivory = H).

(a) What is the formula of thalidomide?

(b) Indicate the positions of the multiple bonds in thalidomide.

(c) What is the geometry around each carbon?

(d) What is the hybridization of each carbon?

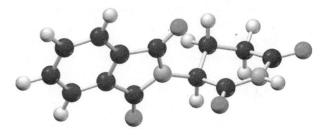

Thalidomide

SECTION PROBLEMS

Electronegativity and Polar Covalent Bonds (Section 7.4)

7.38 What general trends in electronegativity occur in the periodic table?

7.39 Predict the electronegativity of the undiscovered element with $Z = 119$.

7.40 Order the following elements according to increasing electronegativity: Li, Br, Pb, K, Mg, C.

7.41 Order the following elements according to decreasing electronegativity: C, Ca, Cs, Cl, Cu.

7.42 Which of the following substances are largely ionic, and which are covalent?

(a) HF   (b) HI   (c) $PdCl_2$

(d) BBr_3 (e) NaOH   (f) CH_3Li

7.43 Use the electronegativity data in Figure 7.4 to predict which bond in each of the following pairs is more polar:

(a) C—H or C—Cl   (b) Si—Li or Si—Cl

(c) N—Cl or N—Mg

7.44 Show the direction of polarity for each of the bonds in Problem 7.43, using the δ+/δ− notation.

7.45 Show the direction of polarity for each of the covalent bonds in Problem 7.42, using the δ+/δ− notation.

7.46 Which of the substances $CdBr_2$, P_4, BrF_3, MgO, NF_3, $BaCl_2$, $POCl_3$, and LiBr are:

(a) largely ionic?   (b) nonpolar covalent?

(c) polar covalent?

7.47 Which of the substances S_8, $CaCl_2$, $SOCl_2$, NaF, CBr_4, BrCl, LiF, and AsH_3 are:

(a) largely ionic?   (b) nonpolar covalent?

(c) polar covalent?

7.48 Using only the elements P, Br, and Mg, give formulas for the following:

(a) an ionic compound

(b) a molecular compound with polar covalent bonds that obeys the octet rule and has no formal charges

7.49 Using only the elements Ca, Cl, Si, give formulas for the following:

(a) an ionic compound

(b) a molecular compound with polar covalent bonds that obeys the octet rule and has no formal charges

7.50 Which compound do you expect to have the stronger N—N bond, N_2H_2 or N_2H_4? Explain.

7.51 Which compound do you expect to have the stronger N—O bond, NO or NO_2? Explain.

7.52 Name the following molecular compounds:

(a) PCl_3 (b) N_2O_3 (c) P_4O_7

(d) BrF_3 (e) NCl_3 (f) P_4O_6

(g) S_2F_2 (h) SeO_2

7.53 Write formulas for the following molecular compounds:

(a) Disulfur dichloride

(b) Iodine monochloride

(c) Nitrogen triiodide

(d) Dichlorine monoxide

(e) Chlorine trioxide

(f) Tetrasulfur tetranitride

Electron-Dot Structures and Resonance (Sections 7.5–7.7)

7.54 Why does the octet rule apply primarily to main-group elements, not to transition metals?

7.55 Which of the following substances contains an atom that does not follow the octet rule?

(a) $AlCl_3$ (b) PCl_3 (c) PCl_5 (d) $SiCl_4$

7.56 Draw electron-dot structures for the following molecules or ions:

(a) CBr_4 (b) NCl_3 (c) C_2H_5Cl

(d) BF_4^- (e) O_2^{2-} (f) NO^+

7.57 Draw electron-dot structures for the following molecules, which contain atoms from the third row or lower:

(a) $SbCl_3$ (b) KrF_2 (c) ClO_2

(d) PF_5 (e) H_3PO_4 (f) $SeOCl_2$

7.58 Draw as many resonance structures as you can that obey the octet rule for each of the following molecules or ions:

(a) HN_3 (b) SO_3 (c) SCN^-

7.59 Draw as many resonance structures as you can for the following nitrogen-containing compounds. Not all will obey the octet rule.

(a) N_2O (b) NO   (c) NO_2 (d) N_2O_3 ($ONNO_2$)

7.60 Oxalic acid, $H_2C_2O_4$, is a mildly poisonous substance found in the leaves of rhubarb, spinach, and many other plants. (You'd have to eat about 15 lb or so of spinach leaves to ingest a lethal amount.) If oxalic acid has a C—C single bond and no C—H bond, draw its electron-dot structure showing lone pairs and identifying any multiple bonds.

7.61 Draw an electron-dot structure for carbon disulfide, CS_2, showing lone pairs and identifying any multiple bonds.

7.62 Which of the following pairs of structures represent resonance forms, and which do not?

(a)   H—C≡N—O̤:   and   H—C=N̈—O̤:

(b)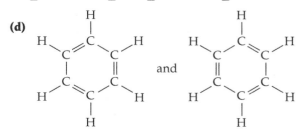

(c)
$$\left[\begin{array}{c} :Ö: \quad\quad H \\ \diagdown \quad / \\ C=C \\ / \quad\quad \diagdown \\ H \quad\quad H \end{array} \right]^- \text{ and } \left[\begin{array}{c} :O: \quad\quad H \\ \parallel \quad / \\ C—C: \\ / \quad\quad \diagdown \\ H \quad\quad H \end{array} \right]^-$$

(d)
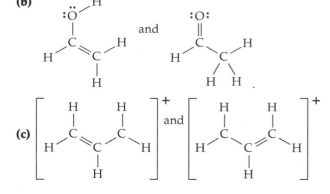

7.63 Which of the following pairs of structures represent resonance forms, and which do not?

(a)
$$\begin{array}{ccc} :\ddot{F}: & & :\ddot{F}: \\ \diagdown & & \diagdown \\ B—\ddot{F}: \text{ and } & B=\ddot{F} \\ / & & / \\ :\ddot{F}: & & :\ddot{F}: \end{array}$$

(b)
(structure with :Ö—H and :O: forms)

(c)
$$\left[\begin{array}{c} H \quad\quad H \\ | \quad\quad | \\ C=C \\ / \quad\quad \diagdown \\ H \quad\quad H \\ | \\ H \end{array} \right]^+ \text{ and } \left[\begin{array}{c} H \quad\quad H \\ | \quad\quad | \\ C—C \\ / \quad\quad \diagdown \\ H \quad\quad H \\ | \\ H \end{array} \right]^+$$

7.64 Identify the third-row elements, X, that form the following ions:

(a)
$$\left[\begin{array}{c} :\ddot{Cl}: \\ | \\ :\ddot{Cl}—X—\ddot{Cl}: \\ | \\ :\ddot{Cl}: \end{array} \right]^-$$

(b)
$$\left[\begin{array}{c} H \\ | \\ H—X—H \\ | \\ H \end{array} \right]^+$$

7.65 Identify the fourth-row elements, X, that form the following compounds:

(a)

Ö=Ẍ—Ö:

(b)

:F̈   F̈:
  \ .. /
   .Ẍ.

7.66 Write electron-dot structures for molecules with the following connections, showing lone pairs and identifying any multiple bonds:

(a)

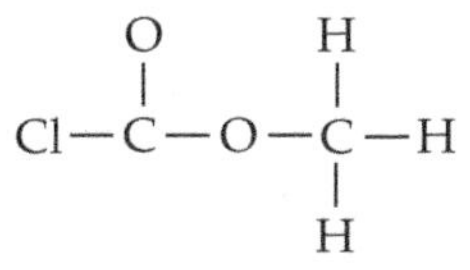

O   H
| |
Cl—C—O—C—H
     |
     H

(b)

H
|
H—C—C—C—H
   |
   H

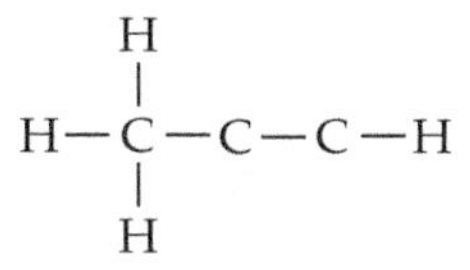

7.67 Write electron-dot structures for molecules with the following connections, showing lone pairs and identifying any multiple bonds:

(a)

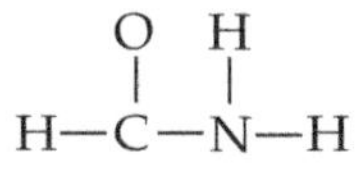

O   H
| |
H—C—N—H

(b)

H
|
H—C—C—N—O
   |
   H

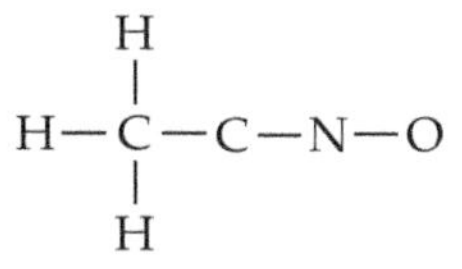

Formal Charges (Section 7.8)

7.68 Draw an electron-dot structure for carbon monoxide, CO, and assign formal charges to both atoms.

7.69 Assign formal charges to the atoms in the following structures:

(a)

H
|
H—N—Ö—H
   ..

(b)

$$\left[H-\ddot{N}-\underset{\underset{H}{|}}{\overset{\overset{H}{|}}{C}}-H \right]^-$$

(c)

:Ö:
|
:Cl—P—Cl:
   |
   :Cl:
   ..

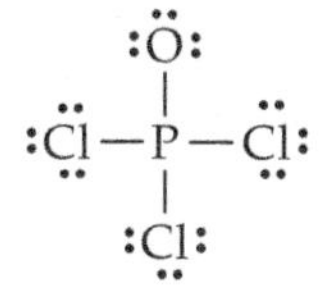

7.70 Assign formal charges to the atoms in the following resonance forms of ClO_2^-:

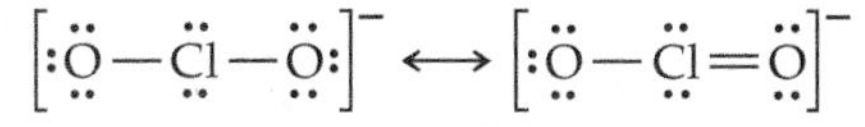

$$\left[:\ddot{O}-\ddot{C}l-\ddot{O}: \right]^- \longleftrightarrow \left[:\ddot{O}-\ddot{C}l=\ddot{O}: \right]^-$$

7.71 Assign formal charges to the atoms in the following resonance forms of H_2SO_3:

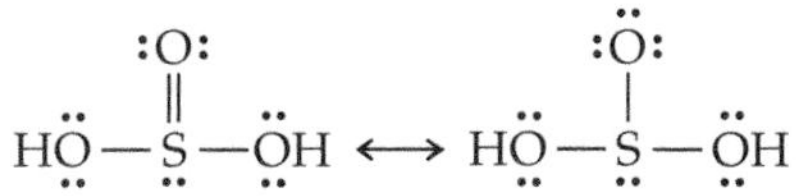

:O:
‖
HÖ—S—ÖH   ⟷   HÖ—S—ÖH
                    |
                   :O:

7.72 Assign formal charges to the atoms in the following structures. Which of the two do you think is the more important contributor to the resonance hybrid?

(a)

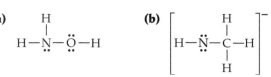

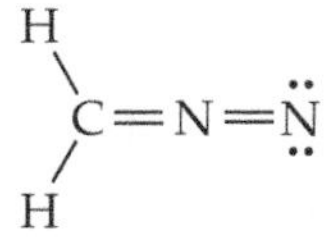

(b)

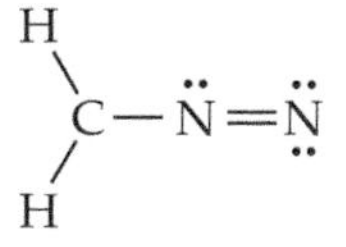

H
\
 C—N̈=N̈
/   ..
H

7.73 Calculate formal charges for the C and O atoms in the following two resonance structures. Which structure do you think is the more important contributor to the resonance hybrid? Explain.

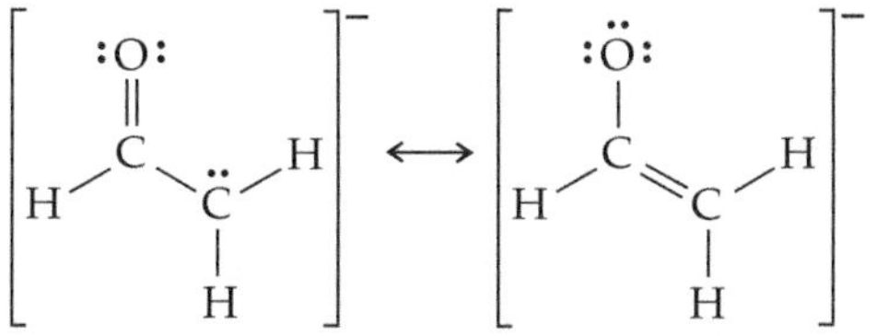

$$\left[\begin{array}{c} :\overset{..}{O}: \\ \| \\ C \\ H \diagup \quad \diagdown H \\ \ddot{C} \\ | \\ H \end{array} \right]^- \longleftrightarrow \left[\begin{array}{c} :\ddot{O}: \\ | \\ C \\ H \diagup \quad \diagdown H \\ \| \\ C \\ | \\ H \end{array} \right]^-$$

7.74 Draw two electron-dot resonance structures that obey the octet rule for trichloronitromethane, CCl_3NO_2, and show the formal charges on N and O in both structures. (Carbon is connected to the chlorines and to nitrogen; nitrogen is also connected to both oxygens.)

7.75 Draw two electron-dot resonance structures that obey the octet rule for nitrosyl chloride, NOCl (nitrogen is the central atom). Show formal charges, if present, and predict which of the two structures is a more accurate representation of the molecule.

The VSEPR Model (Section 7.9)

7.76 What geometric arrangement of charge clouds do you expect for atoms that have the following number of charge clouds?
(a) 3   (b) 5   (c) 2   (d) 6

7.77 What shape do you expect for molecules that meet the following descriptions?
(a) A central atom with two lone pairs and three bonds to other atoms
(b) A central atom with two lone pairs and two bonds to other atoms
(c) A central atom with two lone pairs and four bonds to other atoms

7.78 How many charge clouds are there around the central atom in molecules that have the following geometry?
(a) Tetrahedral   (b) Octahedral
(c) Bent   (d) Linear
(e) Square pyramidal   (f) Trigonal pyramidal

7.79 How many charge clouds are there around the central atom in molecules that have the following geometry?
(a) Seesaw   (b) Square planar
(c) Trigonal bipyramidal   (d) T-shaped
(e) Trigonal planar   (f) Linear

7.80 What shape do you expect for each of the following molecules?
(a) H_2Se (b) $TiCl_4$ (c) O_3 (d) GaH_3

7.81 What shape do you expect for each of the following molecules?
(a) XeO_4 (b) SO_2Cl_2 (c) OsO_4 (d) SeO_2

7.82 What shape do you expect for each of the following molecules or ions?
(a) SbF_5 (b) IF_4^+ (c) SeO_3^{2-} (d) CrO_4^{2-}

7.83 Predict the shape of each of the following ions:
(a) NO_3^- (b) NO_2^+ (c) NO_2^-

7.84 What shape do you expect for each of the following anions?
(a) PO_4^{3-} (b) MnO_4^- (c) SO_4^{2-}
(d) SO_3^{2-} (e) ClO_4^- (f) SCN^-

7.85 What shape do you expect for each of the following cations?
(a) XeF_3^+ (b) SF_3^+ (c) ClF_2^+ (d) CH_3^+

7.86 What bond angles do you expect for each of the following?
(a) The F—S—F angle in SF_2
(b) The H—N—N angle in N_2H_2
(c) The F—Kr—F angle in KrF_4
(d) The Cl—N—O angle in NOCl

7.87 What bond angles do you expect for each of the following?
(a) The Cl—P—Cl angle in PCl_6^-
(b) The Cl—I—Cl angle in ICl_2^-
(c) The O—S—O angle in SO_4^{2-}
(d) The O—B—O angle in BO_3^{3-}

7.88 Acrylonitrile is used as the starting material for manufacturing acrylic fibers. Predict values for all bond angles in acrylonitrile.

$$H_2C=C-C\equiv N:$$

with an H on the central C. Acrylonitrile

7.89 Predict values for all bond angles in dimethyl sulfoxide, a powerful solvent used in veterinary medicine to treat inflammation.

$$H_3C-S-CH_3$$

with :O: above the S. Dimethyl sulfoxide

7.90 Oceanographers study the mixing of water masses by releasing tracer molecules at a site and then detecting their presence at other places. The molecule trifluoromethyl-sulfur pentafluoride is one such tracer. Draw an electron-dot structure for CF_3SF_5, and predict the bond angles around both carbon and sulfur.

7.91 A potential replacement for the chlorofluorocarbon refrigerants that harm the Earth's protective ozone layer is a compound called E143a, or trifluoromethyl methyl ether, F_3COCH_3. Draw an electron-dot structure for F_3COCH_3, and predict the geometry around both the carbons and the oxygen.

7.92 Explain why cyclohexane, a substance that contains a six-membered ring of carbon atoms, is not flat but instead has a puckered, nonplanar shape. Predict the values of the C—C—C bond angles.

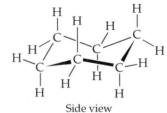

Cyclohexane   Side view

7.93 Like cyclohexane (Problem 7.92), benzene also contains a six-membered ring of carbon atoms, but it is flat rather than puckered. Explain, and predict the values of the C—C—C bond angles.

Benzene

Valence Bond Theory and Molecular Orbital Theory (Sections 7.10–7.15)

7.94 What is the difference in spatial distribution between electrons in a π bond and electrons in a σ bond?

7.95 What is the difference in spatial distribution between electrons in a bonding MO and electrons in an antibonding MO?

7.96 What hybridization do you expect for atoms that have the following numbers of charge clouds?
(a) 2   (b) 3   (c) 4

7.97 What spatial arrangement of charge clouds corresponds to each of the following kinds of hybridization?
(a) sp^3 (b) sp^2 (c) sp

7.98 What hybridization would you expect for the indicated atom in each of the following molecules?
(a) $H_2C=O$ (b) BH_3 (c) CH_3SH (d) $H_2C=NH$

7.99 What hybridization would you expect for the indicated atom in each of the following ions?
(a) BH_4^- (b) HCO_2^- (c) CH_3^+ (d) CH_3^-

7.100 Oxaloacetic acid is an intermediate involved in the citric acid cycle of food metabolism. What are the hybridizations of the various carbon atoms in oxaloacetic acid, and what are the approximate values of the various bond angles?

$$H-O-C-C-C-C-O-H$$

Oxaloacetic acid

7.101 The atoms in the amino acid glycine are connected as shown:

$$H-N-C-C-O-H$$

(a) Draw an electron-dot structure for glycine, showing lone pairs and identifying any multiple bonds.
(b) Predict approximate values for the H—C—H, O—C—O, and H—N—H bond angles.
(c) Which hybrid orbitals are used by the C and N atoms?

7.102 Use the MO energy diagram in Figure 7.17b to describe the bonding in O_2^+, O_2, and O_2^-. Which of the three is likely to be stable? What is the bond order of each? Which contain unpaired electrons?

7.103 Use the MO energy diagram in Figure 7.17a to describe the bonding in N_2^+, N_2, and N_2^-. Which of the three is likely to be stable? What is the bond order of each? Which contain unpaired electrons?

7.104 The C_2 molecule can be represented by an MO diagram similar to that in Figure 7.17a.
(a) What is the bond order of C_2?
(b) To increase the bond order of C_2, should you add or remove an electron?
(c) Give the charge and the bond order of the new species made in part (b).

7.105 Look at the molecular orbital diagram for O_2 in Figure 7.19 and answer the following questions:
(a) What is the bond order of O_2?
(b) To increase the bond order of O_2, should you add or remove an electron?
(c) Give the charge and the bond order of the new species made in part (b).

7.106 Look at the MO diagrams of corresponding neutral diatomic species in Figure 7.19, and predict whether each of the following ions is diamagnetic or paramagnetic. Diagrams for Li_2 and C_2 are similar to N_2; Cl_2 is similar to F_2.

(a) C_2^{2-} (b) C_2^{2+} (c) F_2^- (d) Cl_2 (e) Li_2^+

7.107 Look at the MO diagrams of corresponding neutral diatomic species in Figure 7.19, and predict whether each of the following ions is diamagnetic or paramagnetic. MO diagrams for Li_2 and C_2 are similar to N_2; Cl_2 is similar to F_2.

(a) O_2^{2+} (b) N_2^{2+} (c) C_2^+ (d) F_2^{2+} (e) Cl_2^+

7.108 Make a sketch showing the location and geometry of the p orbitals in the allyl cation. Describe the bonding in this cation using a localized valence bond model for σ bonding and a delocalized MO model for π bonding.

$$H_2C{=}\overset{\overset{\displaystyle H}{|}}{C}{-}CH_2{}^+ \quad \text{Allyl cation}$$

7.109 Make a sketch showing the location and geometry of the p orbitals in the nitrite ion, NO_2^-. Describe the bonding in this ion using a localized valence bond model for σ bonding and a delocalized MO model for π bonding.

CHAPTER PROBLEMS

7.110 Vitamin C (ascorbic acid) has the following connections among atoms. Complete the following electron-dot structure for vitamin C, showing lone pairs and identifying any multiple bonds:

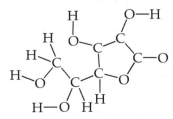

Vitamin C

7.111 Tell the hybridization of each carbon atom in ascorbic acid (Problem 7.110).

7.112 Sinapaldehyde, a compound present in the toasted wood used for aging wine, has the following connections among atoms. Complete the electron-dot structure for sinapaldehyde, identify any multiple bonds in the molecule, and tell the hybridization of each carbon atom.

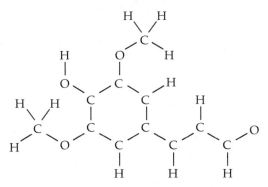

Sinapaldehyde

7.113 Thiofulminic acid, $H{-}C{\equiv}N{-}S$ has recently been detected at very low temperatures.

(a) Draw an electron-dot structure for thiofulminic acid, and assign formal charges.

(b) A related compound with the same formula and the connection $H{-}N{-}C{-}S$ is also known. Draw an electron-dot structure for this related compound and assign formal charges.

(c) Which of the two molecules is likely to be more stable? Explain.

7.114 The odor of cinnamon oil is due to cinnamaldehyde, C_9H_8O. What is the hybridization of each carbon atom in cinnamaldehyde? How many σ bonds and how many π bonds does cinnamaldehyde have?

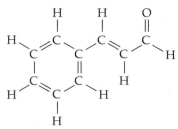

Cinnamaldehyde

7.115 Draw three resonance structures for sulfur tetroxide, SO_4, whose connections are shown below. (This is a neutral molecule; it is not sulfate ion.) Assign formal charges to the atoms in each structure.

$$\overset{\displaystyle O}{\underset{\displaystyle O{-}S{-}O}{\overset{|}{\underset{|}{O}}}}$$

Sulfur tetroxide

7.116 Draw two resonance structures for methyl isocyanate, CH_3NCO, a toxic gas that was responsible for the deaths of at least 3000 people when it was accidentally released into the atmosphere in December 1984 in Bhopal, India. Assign formal charges to the atoms in each resonance structure.

7.117 There are two possible shapes for diimide, $H{-}N{=}N{-}H$ Draw both, and tell whether they are resonance forms.

7.118 Boron trifluoride reacts with dimethyl ether to form a compound with a coordinate covalent bond:

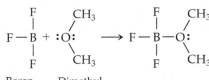

Boron trifluoride   Dimethyl ether

(a) Assign formal charges to the B and O atoms in both the reactants and product.

(b) Describe the geometry and hybridization of the B and O atoms in both reactants and product.

7.119 What is the hybridization of the B and N atoms in borazine, what are the values of the B—N—B and N—B—N bond angles, and what is the overall shape of the molecule?

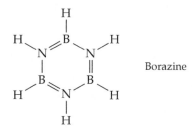

Borazine

7.120 Benzyne, C_6H_4, is a highly energetic and reactive molecule. What hybridization do you expect for the two triply bonded carbon atoms? What are the "theoretical" values for the C—C≡C bond angles? Why do you suppose benzyne is so reactive?

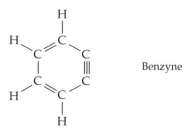

Benzyne

7.121 Propose structures for molecules that meet the following descriptions:
(a) Contains a C atom that has two π bonds and two σ bonds
(b) Contains an N atom that has one π bond and two σ bonds
(c) Contains an S atom that has a coordinate covalent bond

7.122 Write an electron-dot structure for chloral hydrate, also known in old detective novels as "knockout drops."

$$Cl-\overset{\overset{\displaystyle Cl}{|}}{\underset{\underset{\displaystyle Cl}{|}}{C}}-\overset{\overset{\displaystyle O-H}{|}}{\underset{\underset{\displaystyle H}{|}}{C}}-O-H \qquad \text{Chloral hydrate}$$

7.123 Draw a molecular orbital energy diagram for Li_2. What is the bond order? Is the molecule likely to be stable? Explain.

7.124 Calcium carbide, CaC_2, reacts with water to produce acetylene, C_2H_2, and is sometimes used as a convenient source of that substance. Use the MO energy diagram in Figure 7.17a to describe the bonding in the carbide anion, C_2^{2-}. What is its bond order?

7.125 Use VSEPR theory to answer the following questions:
(a) Which molecule, BF_3 or PF_3, has the smaller F—X—F angles?
(b) Which ion, PCl_4^+ or ICl_2^-, has the smaller Cl—X—Cl angles?
(c) Which ion, CCl_3^- or PCl_6^-, has the smaller Cl—X—Cl angles?

7.126 The overall energy change during a chemical reaction can be calculated from a knowledge of bond dissociation energies using the following relationship:

Energy change = D (Bonds broken) − D (Bonds formed)

Use the data in Table 7.1 to calculate an energy change for the reaction of methane with chlorine.

$$CH_4(g) + Cl_2(g) \longrightarrow CH_3Cl(g) + HCl(g)$$

7.127 The following molecular model is that of aspartame, $C_{14}H_{18}N_2O_5$, known commercially as NutraSweet. Only the connections between atoms are shown; multiple bonds are not indicated. Complete the structure by indicating the positions of the multiple bonds and lone pairs.

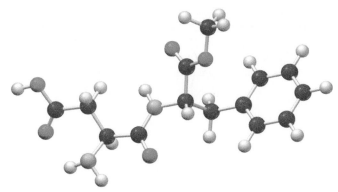

Aspartame

7.128 The N_2O_5 molecule has six N—O σ bonds and two N—O π bonds, but has no N—N bonds and no O—O bonds. Draw eight resonance structures for N_2O_5, and assign formal charges to the atoms in each. Which resonance structures make the more important contributions to the resonance hybrid?

7.129 In the cyanate ion, OCN^-, carbon is the central atom.
(a) Draw as many resonance structures as you can for OCN^-, and assign formal charges to the atoms in each.
(b) Which resonance structure makes the greatest contribution to the resonance hybrid? Which makes the least contribution? Explain.
(c) Is OCN^- linear or bent? Explain.
(d) Which hybrid orbitals are used by the C atom, and how many π bonds does the C atom form?

7.130 Aspirin has the following connections among atoms. Complete the electron-dot structure for aspirin, tell how many σ bonds and how many π bonds the molecule contains, and tell the hybridization of each carbon atom.

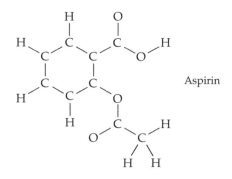

Aspirin

7.131 The cation $[H-C-N-Xe-F]^+$ is entirely linear. Draw an electron-dot structure consistent with that geometry, and tell the hybridization of the C and N atoms.

7.132 At high temperatures, sulfur vapor is predominantly in the form of $S_2(g)$ molecules.
(a) Assuming that the molecular orbitals for third-row diatomic molecules are analogous to those for second-row molecules, construct an MO diagram for the valence orbitals of $S_2(g)$.
(b) Is S_2 likely to be paramagnetic or diamagnetic?
(c) What is the bond order of $S_2(g)$?

(d) When two electrons are added to S_2, the disulfide ion S_2^{2-} is formed. Is the bond length in S_2^{2-} likely to be shorter or longer than the bond length in S_2? Explain.

7.133 Carbon monoxide is produced by incomplete combustion of fossil fuels.

(a) Give the electron configuration for the valence molecular orbitals of CO. The orbitals have the same energy order as those of the N_2 molecule.

(b) Do you expect CO to be paramagnetic or diamagnetic?

(c) What is the bond order of CO? Does this match the bond order predicted by the electron-dot structure?

(d) CO can react with OH^- to form the formate ion, HCO_2^-. Draw an electron-dot structure for the formate ion, and give any resonance structures if appropriate.

7.134 Draw an electron-dot structure for each of the following substances, and predict the molecular geometry of every nonterminal atom.

(a) $F_3S—S—F$ **(b)** $CH_3—C≡C—CO_2^-$

7.135 The ion I_5^- is shaped like a big "V." Draw an electron-dot structure consistent with this overall geometry.

MULTICONCEPT PROBLEMS

7.136 The neutral OH molecule has been implicated in certain ozone-destroying processes that take place in the upper atmosphere.

(a) Draw electron-dot structures for the OH molecule and the OH^- ion.

(b) Electron affinity can be defined for molecules just as it is defined for single atoms. Assuming that the electron added to OH is localized in a single atomic orbital on one atom, identify which atom is accepting the electron, and give the n and l quantum numbers of the atomic orbital.

(c) The electron affinity of OH is similar to but slightly more negative than that of O atoms. Explain.

7.137 Suppose that the Pauli exclusion principle were somehow changed to allow three electrons per orbital rather than two.

(a) Instead of an octet, how many outer-shell electrons would be needed for a noble-gas electron configuration?

(b) How many electrons would be shared in a covalent bond?

(c) Give the electron configuration, and draw an electron-dot structure for element X with $Z = 12$.

(d) Draw an electron-dot structure for the molecule X_2.

(e) Assuming that the molecular orbital energy diagram in Figure 7.17b is valid, tell the bond order for the X_2 molecule.

7.138 The dichromate ion, $Cr_2O_7^{2-}$, has neither Cr—Cr nor O—O bonds.

(a) Taking both $4s$ and $3d$ electrons into account, draw an electron-dot structure that minimizes the formal charges on the atoms.

(b) How many outer-shell electrons does each Cr atom have in your electron-dot structure? What is the likely geometry around the Cr atoms?

7.139 Just as individual bonds in a molecule are often polar, molecules as a whole are also often polar because of the net sum of individual bond polarities. There are three possible structures for substances with the formula $C_2H_2Cl_2$, two of which are polar overall and one of which is not.

(a) Draw the three possible structures for $C_2H_2Cl_2$, predict an overall shape for each, and explain how they differ.

(b) Which of the three structures is nonpolar, and which two are polar? Explain.

(c) Two of the three structures can be interconverted by a process called cis–trans isomerization, in which

rotation around the central carbon–carbon bond takes place when the molecules are irradiated with ultraviolet light. If light with a wavelength of approximately 200 nm is required for isomerization, how much energy in kJ/mol is involved?

(d) Sketch the orbitals involved in the central carbon–carbon bond, and explain why so much energy is necessary for bond rotation to occur.

7.140 Cyclooctatetraene dianion, $C_8H_8^{2-}$, is an organic ion with the structure shown. Considering only the π bonds and not the σ bonds, cyclooctatetraene dianion can be described by the following energy diagram of its π molecular orbitals:

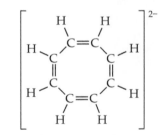

Cyclooctatetraene dianion

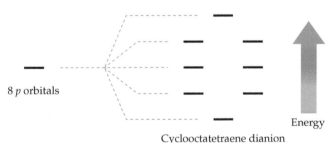

Cyclooctatetraene dianion
pi (π) molecular orbitals

(a) What is the hybridization of the 8 carbon atoms?

(b) Three of the π molecular orbitals are bonding, three are antibonding, and two are *nonbonding*, meaning that they have the same energy level as isolated p orbitals. Which is which?

(c) Complete the MO energy diagram by assigning the appropriate numbers of p electrons to the various molecular orbitals, indicating the electrons using up/down arrows ($\uparrow\downarrow$).

(d) Based on your MO energy diagram, is the dianion paramagnetic or diamagnetic?

CHAPTER 8

Thermochemistry: Chemical Energy

Many chemical reactions occur for the same reason that water goes down this falls rather than up. Potential energy is lowered in both cases.

CONTENTS

Why do chemical reactions occur? Stated simply, the answer involves *stability*. For a reaction to take place spontaneously, the final products of the reaction must be more stable than the starting reactants.

But what is "stability," and what does it mean to say that one substance is more stable than another? The key factor in determining the stability of a substance is energy. Less stable substances have higher energy and are generally converted into more stable substances with lower energy. But what, in turn, does it mean for a substance to have higher or lower energy? We'll explore some different forms of energy in this chapter and look at the subject of **thermochemistry**, the absorption or release of heat energy that accompanies chemical reactions.

8.1 ENERGY AND ITS CONSERVATION

You might recall from Section 1.11 that energy is defined as the capacity to supply heat or do work. The fuel in your car, for instance, contains energy that is released on combustion and propels the car forward. You might also recall that energy is described as either *kinetic* or *potential*. Kinetic energy (E_K) is the energy of motion and is given by the equation

$$E_K = \frac{1}{2}mv^2 \qquad \text{where } m = \text{mass and } v = \text{velocity}$$

Potential energy (E_P), by contrast, is stored energy—perhaps stored in a molecule because of reactions it can undergo.

Let's pursue the relationship between potential energy and kinetic energy a bit further. According to the **conservation of energy law**, energy can be neither created nor destroyed; it can only be converted from one form into another.

Conservation of Energy Law   Energy cannot be created or destroyed; it can only be converted from one form into another.

To take an example, think about a hydroelectric dam. The water sitting motionless in the reservoir behind the dam has potential energy because of its height above the outlet stream, but it has no kinetic energy because it isn't moving ($v = 0$). When the water falls through the penstocks of the dam, however, its height and potential energy decrease while its velocity and kinetic energy increase. The moving water then spins the turbine of a generator, converting its kinetic energy into electrical energy (**Figure 8.1**).

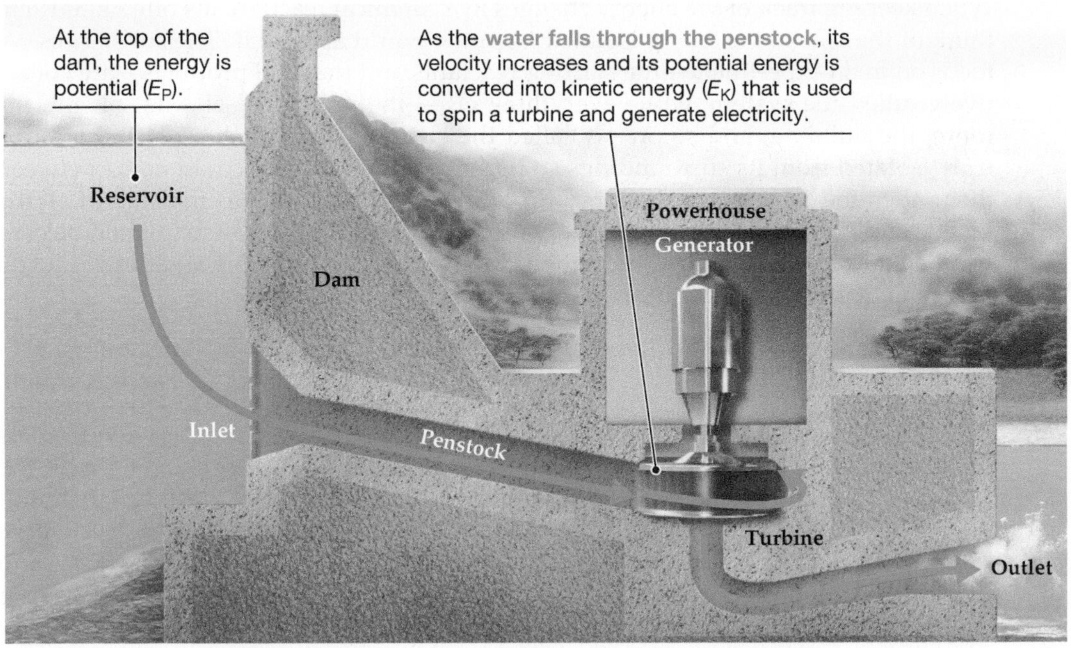

Remember...

Energy is the capacity to supply heat or do work and is classified as either **kinetic energy**—the energy of motion—or **potential energy**—stored energy not yet released. (Section 1.11)

At the top of the dam, the energy is potential (E_P).

As the water falls through the penstock, its velocity increases and its potential energy is converted into kinetic energy (E_K) that is used to spin a turbine and generate electricity.

Reservoir

Powerhouse

Generator

Dam

Inlet

Penstock

Turbine

Outlet

Figure 8.1
Conservation of energy. The total amount of energy contained by the water in the reservoir is constant.

The conversion of the kinetic energy in falling water into electricity illustrates several other important points about energy. One is that energy has many forms. Thermal energy, for example, seems different from the kinetic energy of falling water, yet is really quite similar. *Thermal energy* is just the kinetic energy of molecular motion, which we measure by finding the **temperature** of an object. An object has a low temperature and we perceive it as cold if its atoms or molecules are moving slowly. Conversely, an object has a high temperature and we perceive it as hot if its atoms or molecules are moving rapidly and are colliding forcefully with a thermometer or other measuring device.

Heat, in turn, is the amount of thermal energy transferred from one object to another as the result of a temperature difference between the two. Rapidly moving molecules in a hotter object collide with more slowly moving molecules in a colder object, transferring kinetic energy and causing the slower moving molecules to speed up.

Chemical energy is another kind of energy that seems different from that of the water in a reservoir, yet again is really quite similar. Chemical energy is a kind of potential energy in which chemical bonds act as the storage medium. Just as water releases its potential energy when it falls to a more stable position, chemicals can release their potential energy in the form of heat or light when they undergo reactions and form more stable products. We'll explore this topic shortly.

A second point illustrated by falling water involves the conservation of energy law. To keep track of all the energy involved, it's necessary to take into account the entire chain of events that ensue from the falling water: the sound of the crashing water, the heating of the rocks at the bottom of the dam, the driving of turbines and electrical generators, the transmission of electrical power, the appliances powered by the electricity, and so on. Carrying the process to its logical extreme, it's necessary to take the entire universe into account when keeping track of all the energy in the water because the energy lost in one form *always* shows up elsewhere in another form. So important is the conservation of energy law that it's also known as the **first law of thermodynamics**.

First Law of Thermodynamics   Energy cannot be created or destroyed; it can only be converted from one form into another.

8.2 INTERNAL ENERGY AND STATE FUNCTIONS

When keeping track of the energy changes in a chemical reaction, it's often helpful to think of the reaction as being isolated from the world around it. The substances we focus on in an experiment—the starting reactants and the final products—are collectively called the **system**, while everything else—the reaction flask, the solvent, the room, the building, and so on—is called the **surroundings**. If the system could be truly isolated from its surroundings so that no energy transfer could occur between them, then the total **internal energy (E)** of the system, defined as the sum of all the kinetic and potential energies for every molecule or ion in the system, would be conserved and remain constant throughout the reaction. In fact, this assertion is just a restatement of the first law of thermodynamics:

First Law of Thermodynamics (Restated)   The total internal energy E of an isolated system is constant.

In practice, of course, it's not possible to truly isolate a chemical reaction from its surroundings. In any real situation, the chemicals are in physical contact with the walls of a flask or container, and the container itself is in contact with the surrounding air or laboratory bench. What's important, however, is not that the system be isolated but that we be able to measure accurately any energy that enters the system from the surroundings or leaves the system and flows to the surroundings (**Figure 8.2**). That is, we must be able to measure any *change* in the internal energy of the

Figure 8.2
Energy changes in a chemical reaction.

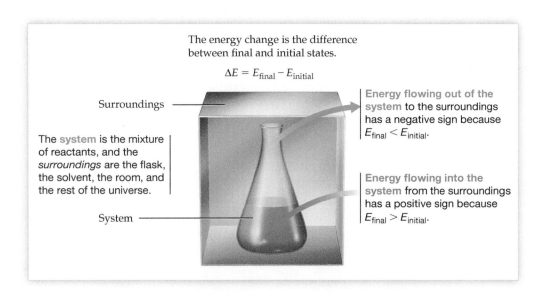

The energy change is the difference between final and initial states.

$$\Delta E = E_{final} - E_{initial}$$

Surroundings

The system is the mixture of reactants, and the *surroundings* are the flask, the solvent, the room, and the rest of the universe.

System

Energy flowing out of the system to the surroundings has a negative sign because $E_{final} < E_{initial}$.

Energy flowing into the system from the surroundings has a positive sign because $E_{final} > E_{initial}$.

system, ΔE. The energy change ΔE represents the difference in internal energy between the final state of the system after reaction and the initial state of the system before reaction:

$$\Delta E = E_{final} - E_{initial}$$

By convention, energy changes are measured from the point of view of the system. Any energy that flows *from* the system *to* the surroundings has a negative sign because the system has lost it (that is, E_{final} is smaller than $E_{initial}$). Any energy that flows *to* the system *from* the surroundings has a positive sign because the system has gained it (E_{final} is larger than $E_{initial}$). If, for instance, we were to burn 1.00 mol of methane in the presence of 2.00 mol of oxygen, 802 kJ would be released as heat and transferred from the system to the surroundings. The system has 802 kJ less energy, so $\Delta E = -802$ kJ. This energy flow can be detected and measured by placing the reaction vessel in a water bath and noting the temperature rise of the bath during the reaction.

$$CH_4(g) + 2\,O_2(g) \longrightarrow CO_2(g) + 2\,H_2O(g) + 802\text{ kJ energy} \qquad \Delta E = -802\text{ kJ}$$

The methane combustion experiment tells us that the products of the reaction, $CO_2(g)$ and $2\,H_2O(g)$, have 802 kJ less internal energy than the reactants, $CH_4(g)$ and $2\,O_2(g)$, even though we don't know the exact values at the beginning ($E_{initial}$) and end (E_{final}) of the reaction. Note that the value $\Delta E = -802$ kJ for the reaction refers to the energy released when reactants are converted to products *in the molar amounts represented by coefficients in the balanced equation*. That is, 802 kJ is released when 1 mol of gaseous methane reacts with 2 mol of gaseous oxygen to give 1 mol of gaseous carbon dioxide and 2 mol of gaseous water vapor.

The internal energy of a system depends on many things: chemical identity, sample size, temperature, pressure, physical state (gas, liquid, or solid), and so forth. What the internal energy does not depend on is the system's past history. It doesn't matter what the system's temperature or physical state was an hour ago, and it doesn't matter how the chemicals were obtained. All that matters is the present condition of the system. Thus, internal energy is said to be a **state function**, one whose value depends only on the present state of the system. Pressure, volume, and temperature are other examples of state functions, but work and heat are not.

State Function A function or property whose value depends only on the present state, or condition, of the system, not on the path used to arrive at that state.

We can illustrate the idea of a state function by imagining a cross-country trip, say from the Artichoke Capitol of the World (Castroville, California), to the Hub of the Universe (Boston, Massachusetts). You are the system, and your position is a state function because how you got to wherever you are is irrelevant. Because your position is a state function, the *change* in your position after you complete your travel (Castroville and Boston are about 2720 miles apart) is independent of the path you take, whether through North Dakota or Louisiana (Figure 8.3).

Figure 8.3

State functions. Because your position is a state function, the change in your position on going from Castroville, California, to Boston, Massachusetts, is independent of the path you take.

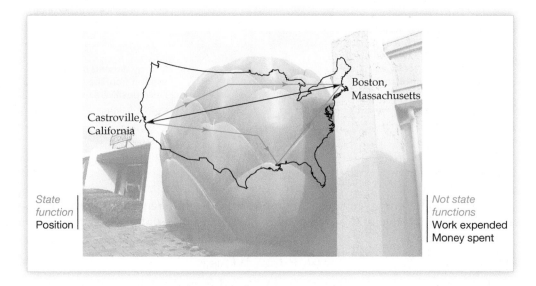

The cross-country trip shown in Figure 8.3 illustrates an important point about state functions: their reversibility. Imagine that, after traveling from Castroville to Boston, you turn around and go back. Because your final position is now identical to your initial position, the change in your position is zero. The overall change in any state function is zero when the system returns to its original condition. For a nonstate function, however, the overall change is not zero when the system returns to its original condition. Any work you do in making the trip, for instance, is not recovered when you return to your initial position, and any money or time you spend does not reappear.

▶ **PROBLEM 8.1** Which of the following are state functions, and which are not?

(a) The temperature of an ice cube

(b) The volume of an aerosol can

(c) The amount of time required for Paula Radcliffe to run her world-record marathon: 2:15:25

8.3 EXPANSION WORK

Just as energy comes in many forms, so too does *work*. In physics, **work (*w*)** is defined as the force (*F*) that produces the movement of an object times the distance moved (*d*):

$$\text{Work} = \text{Force} \times \text{Distance}$$
$$w = F \times d$$

When you run up stairs, for instance, your leg muscles provide a force sufficient to overcome gravity and lift you higher. When you swim, you provide a force sufficient to push water out of the way and pull yourself forward.

The most common type of work encountered in chemical systems is the *expansion work* (also called *pressure–volume*, or *PV, work*) done as the result of a volume change in the system. In the combustion reaction of propane (C_3H_8) with oxygen, for instance, the balanced equation says that 7 moles of products come from 6 moles of reactants:

▲ This runner going uphill is doing a lot of work to overcome gravity.

$$C_3H_8(g) + 5\,O_2(g) \longrightarrow 3\,CO_2(g) + 4\,H_2O(g)$$

6 mol of gas   7 mol of gas

If the reaction takes place inside a container outfitted with a movable piston, the greater volume of gas in the product will force the piston outward against the pressure of the atmosphere (P), moving air molecules aside and thereby doing work (**Figure 8.4**).

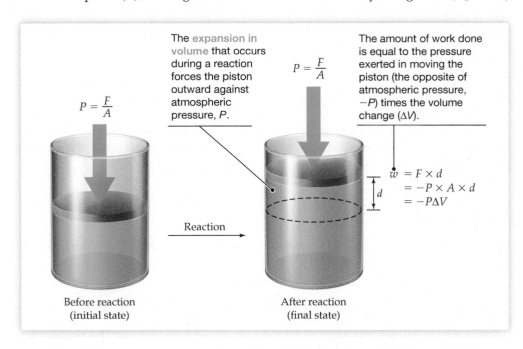

The expansion in volume that occurs during a reaction forces the piston outward against atmospheric pressure, P.

$$P = \frac{F}{A}$$

The amount of work done is equal to the pressure exerted in moving the piston (the opposite of atmospheric pressure, $-P$) times the volume change (ΔV).

$P = \frac{F}{A}$

$$\begin{aligned} w &= F \times d \\ &= -P \times A \times d \\ &= -P\Delta V \end{aligned}$$

Reaction

Before reaction (initial state)   After reaction (final state)

Figure 8.4
Expansion work in a chemical reaction.

A short calculation gives the exact amount of work done during the expansion. We know from physics that force (F) is area (A) times pressure (P). In Figure 8.4, the force that the expanding gas exerts is the area of the piston times the pressure that the gas exerts against the piston. This pressure is equal in magnitude but opposite in sign to the external atmospheric pressure that opposes the movement, so it has the value $-P$.

$$F = -P \times A \qquad \text{where } P \text{ is the external atmospheric pressure}$$

If the piston is pushed out a distance d, then the amount of work done is equal to force times distance, or pressure times area times distance:

$$w = F \times d = -P \times A \times d$$

This equation can be simplified by noticing that the area of the piston times the distance the piston moves is just the volume change in the system: $\Delta V = A \times d$. Thus, the amount of work done is equal to the pressure the gas exerts against the piston times the volume change, hence the name PV work:

A negative value   A positive value

$$w = -P\Delta V \qquad\qquad \text{Work done during expansion}$$

What about the sign of the work done during the expansion? Because the work is done by the system to move air molecules aside as the piston rises, work energy must be leaving the system. Thus, the negative sign of the work in the preceding equation is consistent with the convention previously established for ΔE (Section 8.2), whereby we always adopt the point of view of the system. Any energy that flows out of the system has a negative sign because the system has lost it ($E_{\text{final}} < E_{\text{initial}}$).

If the pressure is given in the unit atmospheres (atm) and the volume change is given in liters, then the amount of work done has the unit liter atmosphere (L · atm), where 1 atm = 101×10^3 kg/(m · s²). Thus, 1 L · atm = 101 J:

$$1\,\text{L}\cdot\text{atm} = (1\,\text{L})\left(\frac{10^{-3}\,\text{m}^3}{1\,\text{L}}\right)\left(101 \times 10^3 \,\frac{\text{kg}}{\text{m}\cdot\text{s}^2}\right) = 101\,\frac{\text{kg}\cdot\text{m}^2}{\text{s}^2} = 101\,\text{J}$$

When a reaction takes place with a contraction in volume rather than an expansion, the ΔV term has a negative sign and the work has a positive sign. This is again consistent with adopting the point of view of the system because the system has now gained work energy ($E_{final} > E_{initial}$). An example is the industrial synthesis of ammonia by reaction of hydrogen with nitrogen. Four moles of gaseous reactants yield only 2 mol of gaseous products, so the volume of the system contracts and work is gained by the system.

$$3\,H_2(g) \; + \; N_2(g) \longrightarrow 2\,NH_3(g)$$

4 mol of gas   2 mol of gas

A positive value   A negative value

$$w = -P\Delta V$$ Work gained during contraction

If there is no volume change, then $\Delta V = 0$ and there is no work. Such is the case for the combustion of methane, where 3 mol of gaseous reactants give 3 mol of gaseous products: $CH_4(g) + 2\,O_2(g) \longrightarrow CO_2(g) + 2\,H_2O(g)$

WORKED EXAMPLE 8.1

CALCULATING THE AMOUNT OF *PV* WORK

Calculate the work in kilojoules done during a reaction in which the volume expands from 12.0 L to 14.5 L against an external pressure of 5.0 atm.

STRATEGY

Expansion work done during a chemical reaction is calculated with the formula $w = -P\Delta V$, where P is the external pressure opposing the change in volume. In this instance, $P = 5.0$ atm and $\Delta V = (14.5 - 12.0)$ L $= 2.5$ L. Remember that an expanding system loses work energy, which thus has a negative sign.

SOLUTION

$$w = -(5.0\text{ atm})(2.5\text{ L}) = -12.5\text{ L} \cdot \text{atm}$$

$$(-12.5\text{ L} \cdot \text{atm})\left(101\,\frac{J}{L \cdot \text{atm}}\right) = -1.3 \times 10^3\,J = -1.3\text{ kJ}$$

▶ **PROBLEM 8.2** Calculate the work in kilojoules done during a synthesis of ammonia in which the volume contracts from 8.6 L to 4.3 L at a constant external pressure of 44 atm. In which direction does the work energy flow? What is the sign of the energy change?

CONCEPTUAL PROBLEM 8.3 How much work is done in kilojoules, and in which direction, as a result of the following reaction?

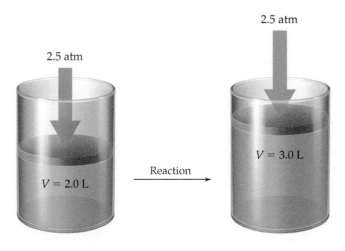

2.5 atm

2.5 atm

$V = 3.0$ L

Reaction

$V = 2.0$ L

8.4 ENERGY AND ENTHALPY

We've seen up to this point that a system can exchange energy with its surroundings either by transferring heat or by doing work. Using the symbol q to represent transferred heat and the formula $w = -P\Delta V$, we can represent the total change in internal energy of a system, ΔE, as

$$\Delta E = q + w = q - P\Delta V$$

where q has a positive sign if the system gains heat and a negative sign if the system loses heat. Rearranging the equation to solve for q gives the amount of heat transferred:

$$q = \Delta E + P\Delta V$$

Let's look at two ways in which a chemical reaction might be carried out. On the one hand, a reaction might be carried out in a closed container with a constant volume, so that $\Delta V = 0$. In such a case, no PV work can be done so the energy change in the system is due entirely to heat transfer. We indicate this heat transfer at constant volume by the symbol q_v.

$$q_v = \Delta E \qquad \text{At constant volume; } \Delta V = 0$$

Alternatively, a reaction might be carried out in an open flask or other apparatus that keeps the pressure constant and allows the volume of the system to change freely. In such a case, $\Delta V \neq 0$ and the energy change in the system is due to both heat transfer and PV work. We indicate the heat transfer at constant pressure by the symbol q_p:

$$q_p = \Delta E + P\Delta V \qquad \text{At constant pressure}$$

Because reactions carried out at constant pressure in open containers are so common in chemistry, the heat change q_P for such a process is given a special symbol and is called the **heat of reaction**, or **enthalpy change (ΔH)**. The **enthalpy (H)** of a system is the name given to the quantity $E + PV$.

$$q_p = \Delta E + P\Delta V = \overset{\displaystyle\frown\text{Enthalpy change}}{\Delta H}$$

Note that only the enthalpy *change* during a reaction is important. As with internal energy, enthalpy is a state function whose value depends only on the current state of the system, not on the path taken to arrive at that state. Thus, we don't need to know the exact value of the system's enthalpy before and after a reaction. We need to know only the difference between final and initial states:

$$\Delta H = H_{final} - H_{initial}$$
$$= H_{products} - H_{reactants}$$

How big a difference is there between $q_v = \Delta E$, the heat flow at constant volume, and $q_p = \Delta H$, the heat flow at constant pressure? Let's look again at the combustion reaction of propane, C_3H_8, with oxygen as an example. When the reaction is carried out in a closed container at constant volume, no PV work is possible so all the energy released is released as heat: $\Delta E = -2046$ kJ. When the same reaction is carried out in an open container at constant pressure, however, only 2044 kJ of heat is released ($\Delta H = -2044$ kJ). The difference, 2 kJ, is due to the small amount of expansion work done against the atmosphere as 6 mol of gaseous reactants are converted into 7 mol of gaseous products.

$$C_3H_8(g) + 5\,O_2(g) \longrightarrow 3\,CO_2(g) + 4\,H_2O(g) \quad \begin{aligned} \Delta E &= -2046 \text{ kJ} \\ \Delta H &= -2044 \text{ kJ} \\ P\Delta V &= +2 \text{ kJ} \end{aligned}$$

Propane

▲ Chemical reactions are often carried out in open vessels at constant atmospheric pressure.

That is:

$$\left[\begin{array}{c} q_v = \quad q_p \quad + \quad w \\ \Delta E = \quad \Delta H \quad - \quad P\Delta V \\ -2046 \text{ kJ} = -2044 \text{ kJ} - (+2 \text{ kJ}) \end{array}\right]$$

What is true of the propane + oxygen reaction is also true of most other reactions: The difference between ΔH and ΔE is usually small, so the two quantities are nearly equal. Of course, if no volume change occurs and no work is done, such as in the combustion of methane in which 3 mol of gaseous reactants give 3 mol of gaseous products, then ΔH and ΔE are the same:

$$CH_4(g) + 2 O_2(g) \longrightarrow CO_2(g) + 2 H_2O(g) \qquad \Delta E = \Delta H = -802 \text{ kJ}$$

CONCEPTUAL PROBLEM 8.4   The following reaction has $\Delta E = -186$ kJ/mol.

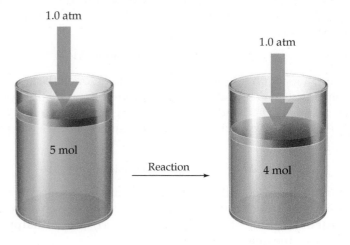

(a) Is the sign of $P\Delta V$ positive or negative? Explain.
(b) What is the sign and approximate magnitude of ΔH? Explain.

8.5   THE THERMODYNAMIC STANDARD STATE

The value of the enthalpy change ΔH reported for a reaction is the amount of heat released or absorbed when reactants are converted to products at the same temperature and pressure and in the molar amounts represented by coefficients in the balanced chemical equation. In the combustion reaction of propane discussed in the previous section, for instance, the reaction of 1 mol of propane gas with 5 mol of oxygen gas to give 3 mol of CO_2 gas and 4 mol of water vapor releases 2044 kJ. The actual amount of heat released in a specific reaction, however, depends on the actual amounts of reactants. Thus, reaction of 0.5000 mol of propane with 2.500 mol of O_2 releases 0.5000×2044 kJ = 1022 kJ.

Note that the physical states of reactants and products must be specified as solid (s), liquid (l), gaseous (g), or aqueous (aq) when enthalpy changes are reported. The enthalpy change for the reaction of propane with oxygen is $\Delta H = -2044$ kJ if water is produced as a gas but $\Delta H = -2220$ kJ if water is produced as a liquid.

$$C_3H_8(g) + 5 O_2(g) \longrightarrow 3 CO_2(g) + 4 H_2O(g) \qquad \Delta H = -2044 \text{ kJ}$$
$$C_3H_8(g) + 5 O_2(g) \longrightarrow 3 CO_2(g) + 4 H_2O(l) \qquad \Delta H = -2220 \text{ kJ}$$

The difference of 176 kJ between the values of ΔH for the two reactions arises because the conversion of liquid water to gaseous water requires energy. If liquid water is produced, ΔH is larger (more negative), but if gaseous water is produced, ΔH is smaller (less negative) because 44.0 kJ/mol is needed for the vaporization.

$$H_2O(l) \longrightarrow H_2O(g) \qquad\qquad \Delta H = 44.0 \text{ kJ}$$
$$\text{or}\qquad 4\,H_2O(l) \longrightarrow 4\,H_2O(g) \qquad\qquad \Delta H = 176 \text{ kJ}$$

In addition to specifying the physical state of reactants and products when reporting an enthalpy change, it's also necessary to specify the pressure and temperature. To ensure that all measurements are reported in the same way so that different reactions can be compared, a set of conditions called the **thermodynamic standard state** has been defined.

 **Thermodynamic Standard State**   Most stable form of a substance at 1 atm pressure* and at a specified temperature, usually 25 °C; 1 M concentration for all substances in solution.

Measurements made under these standard conditions are indicated by addition of the superscript ° to the symbol of the quantity reported. Thus, an enthalpy change measured under standard conditions is called a **standard enthalpy of reaction** and is indicated by the symbol $\Delta H°$. The reaction of propane with oxygen, for example, might be written

$$C_3H_8(g) + 5\,O_2(g) \longrightarrow 3\,CO_2(g) + 4\,H_2O(g) \qquad\qquad \Delta H° = -2044 \text{ kJ}$$

WORKED EXAMPLE 8.2

CALCULATING ΔE FOR A REACTION

The reaction of nitrogen with hydrogen to make ammonia has $\Delta H° = -92.2$ kJ. What is the value of ΔE in kilojoules if the reaction is carried out at a constant pressure of 40.0 atm and the volume change is -1.12 L?

$$N_2(g) + 3\,H_2(g) \longrightarrow 2\,NH_3(g) \qquad\qquad \Delta H° = -92.2 \text{ kJ}$$

STRATEGY

We are given an enthalpy change ΔH, a volume change ΔV, and a pressure P and asked to find an energy change ΔE. Rearrange the equation $\Delta H = \Delta E + P\Delta V$ to the form $\Delta E = \Delta H - P\Delta V$ and substitute the appropriate values for ΔH, P, and ΔV:

SOLUTION

$$\Delta E = \Delta H - P\Delta V$$
$$\text{where}\quad \Delta H = -92.2 \text{ kJ}$$
$$P\Delta V = (40.0 \text{ atm})(-1.12 \text{ L}) = -44.8 \text{ L}\cdot\text{atm}$$
$$= (-44.8 \text{ L}\cdot\text{atm})\left(101\,\frac{J}{L\cdot atm}\right) = -4520 \text{ J} = -4.52 \text{ kJ}$$
$$\Delta E = (-92.2 \text{ kJ}) - (-4.52 \text{ kJ}) = -87.7 \text{ kJ}$$

Note that ΔE is smaller (less negative) than ΔH for this reaction because the volume change is negative. The products have less volume than the reactants so a contraction occurs and a small amount of PV work is gained by the system.

▶ **PROBLEM 8.5**   The reaction between hydrogen and oxygen to yield water vapor has $\Delta H° = -484$ kJ. How much PV work is done, and what is the value of ΔE in kilojoules for the reaction of 0.50 mol of H_2 with 0.25 mol of O_2 at atmospheric pressure if the volume change is -5.6 L?

$$2\,H_2(g) + O_2(g) \longrightarrow 2\,H_2O(g) \qquad\qquad \Delta H° = -484 \text{ kJ}$$

---

*The standard pressure, listed here and in most other books as 1 atmosphere (atm), has been redefined to be 1 *bar*, which is equal to 0.986 923 atm. The difference is small, however.

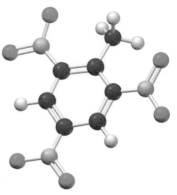

Trinitrotoluene

▶ **PROBLEM 8.6** The explosion of 2.00 mol of solid trinitrotoluene (TNT; $C_7H_5N_3O_6$) with a volume of approximately 274 mL produces gases with a volume of 448 L at room temperature and 1.0 atm pressure. How much PV work in kilojoules is done during the explosion?

$$2\,C_7H_5N_3O_6(s) \longrightarrow 12\,CO(g) + 5\,H_2(g) + 3\,N_2(g) + 2\,C(s)$$

8.6 ENTHALPIES OF PHYSICAL AND CHEMICAL CHANGE

Almost every change in a system involves either a gain or a loss of enthalpy. The change can be either physical, such as the melting of a solid to a liquid, or chemical, such as the burning of propane. Let's look at examples of both kinds.

Enthalpies of Physical Change

What would happen if you started with a block of ice at a low temperature, say $-10\ °C$, and slowly increased its enthalpy by adding heat? The initial input of heat would cause the temperature of the ice to rise until it reached $0\ °C$. Additional heat would then cause the ice to melt without raising its temperature as the added energy is expended in overcoming the forces that hold H_2O molecules together in the ice crystal. The amount of heat necessary to melt a substance without changing its temperature is called the *enthalpy of fusion*, or *heat of fusion* (ΔH_{fusion}). For H_2O, $\Delta H_{fusion} = 6.01\ kJ/mol$ at $0\ °C$.

Once the ice has melted, further input of heat raises the temperature of the liquid water until it reaches $100\ °C$, and adding still more heat then causes the water to boil. Once again, energy is necessary to overcome the forces holding molecules together in the liquid, so the temperature does not rise again until all the liquid has been converted into vapor. The amount of heat required to vaporize a substance without changing its temperature is called the *enthalpy of vaporization*, or *heat of vaporization* (ΔH_{vap}). For H_2O, $\Delta H_{vap} = 40.7\ kJ/mol$ at $100\ °C$.

Another kind of physical change in addition to melting and boiling is **sublimation**, the direct conversion of a solid to a vapor without going through a liquid state. Solid CO_2 (dry ice), for example, changes directly from solid to vapor at atmospheric pressure without first melting to a liquid. Since enthalpy is a state function, the enthalpy change on going from solid to vapor must be constant regardless of the path taken. Thus, at a given temperature, a substance's *enthalpy of sublimation*, or *heat of sublimation* (ΔH_{subl}), equals the sum of the heat of fusion and heat of vaporization (Figure 8.5).

Figure 8.5
Enthalpy as a state function. Because enthalpy is a state function, the value of the enthalpy change from solid to vapor does not depend on the path taken between the two states.

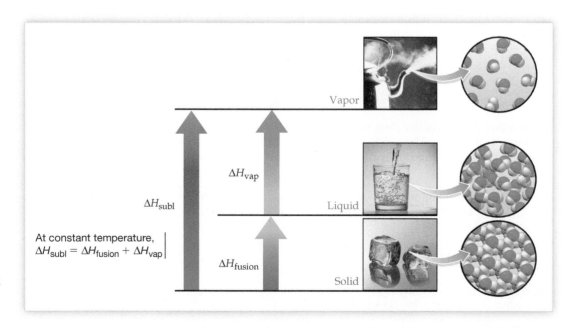

At constant temperature,
$\Delta H_{subl} = \Delta H_{fusion} + \Delta H_{vap}$

ΔH_{vap}

ΔH_{subl}

ΔH_{fusion}

Vapor

Liquid

Solid

Enthalpies of Chemical Change

We saw in Section 8.4 that an enthalpy change is often called a *heat of reaction* because it is a measure of the heat flow into or out of a system at constant pressure. If the products of a reaction have more enthalpy than the reactants, then heat has flowed into the system from the surroundings and ΔH has a positive sign. Such reactions are said to be **endothermic** (*endo* means "within," so heat flows in). The reaction of 1 mol of barium hydroxide octahydrate* with ammonium chloride, for example, absorbs 80.3 kJ from the surroundings ($\Delta H° = +80.3$ kJ). The surroundings, having lost heat, become cold—so cold, in fact, that the temperature drops below freezing (**Figure 8.6**).

$$Ba(OH)_2 \cdot 8\,H_2O(s) + 2\,NH_4Cl(s) \longrightarrow$$
$$BaCl_2(aq) + 2\,NH_3(aq) + 10\,H_2O(l) \qquad \Delta H° = +80.3 \text{ kJ}$$

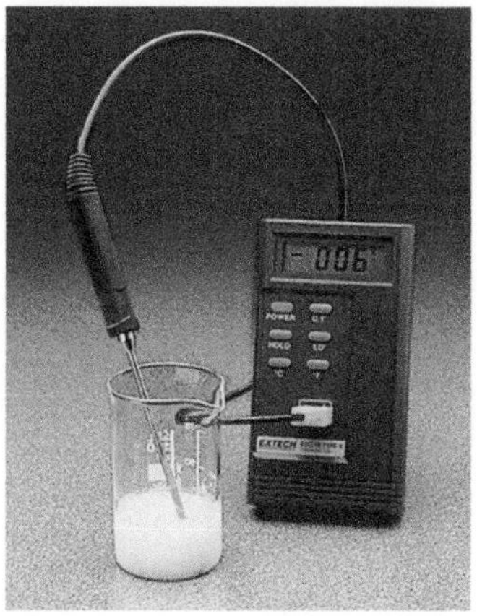

If the products of a reaction have less enthalpy than the reactants, then heat has flowed out of the system to the surroundings and ΔH has a negative sign. Such reactions are said to be **exothermic** (*exo* means "out," so heat flows out). The so-called thermite reaction of aluminum with iron(III) oxide, for instance, releases so much heat ($\Delta H° = -852$ kJ), and the surroundings get so hot, that the reaction is used in construction work to weld iron.

$$2\,Al(s) + Fe_2O_3(s) \longrightarrow 2\,Fe(s) + Al_2O_3(s) \qquad \Delta H° = -852 \text{ kJ}$$

As noted previously, the value of $\Delta H°$ given for an equation assumes that the equation is balanced to represent the numbers of moles of reactants and products, that all substances are in their standard states, and that the physical state of each substance is as specified. The actual amount of heat released in a specific reaction depends on the amounts of reactants, as illustrated in Worked Example 8.3.

It should also be emphasized that $\Delta H°$ values refer to the reaction going in the direction written. For the reverse reaction, the sign of $\Delta H°$ must be changed. Because of the reversibility of state functions (Section 8.2), the enthalpy change for a reverse reaction is equal in magnitude but opposite in sign to that for the corresponding forward reaction. For example, the reaction of iron with aluminum oxide to yield aluminum and iron oxide (the reverse of the thermite reaction) would be endothermic and have $\Delta H° = +852$ kJ:

$$2\,Fe(s) + Al_2O_3(s) \longrightarrow 2\,Al(s) + Fe_2O_3(s) \qquad \Delta H° = +852 \text{ kJ}$$
$$2\,Al(s) + Fe_2O_3(s) \longrightarrow 2\,Fe(s) + Al_2O_3(s) \qquad \Delta H° = -852 \text{ kJ}$$

Figure 8.6
The endothermic reaction of barium hydroxide octahydrate with ammonium chloride. The reaction draws so much heat from the surroundings that the temperature falls below 0 °C.

WORKED EXAMPLE 8.3

CALCULATING THE AMOUNT OF HEAT RELEASED IN A REACTION

How much heat in kilojoules is evolved when 5.00 g of aluminum reacts with a stoichiometric amount of Fe_2O_3?

$$2\,Al(s) + Fe_2O_3(s) \longrightarrow 2\,Fe(s) + Al_2O_3(s) \qquad \Delta H° = -852 \text{ kJ}$$

STRATEGY

According to the balanced equation, 852 kJ of heat is evolved from the reaction of 2 mol of Al. To find out how much heat is evolved from the reaction of 5.00 g of Al, we have to find out how many moles of aluminum are in 5.00 g.

SOLUTION

The molar mass of Al is 26.98 g/mol, so 5.00 g of Al equals 0.185 mol:

$$5.00 \text{ g Al} \times \frac{1 \text{ mol Al}}{26.98 \text{ g Al}} = 0.185 \text{ mol Al}$$

continued on next page

---

*Barium hydroxide octahydrate, $Ba(OH)_2 \cdot 8\,H_2O$, is a crystalline compound that contains eight water molecules clustered around the barium ion. We'll learn more about hydrates in Section 18.14.

Because 2 mol of Al releases 852 kJ of heat, 0.185 mol of Al releases 78.8 kJ of heat:

$$0.185 \text{ mol Al} \times \frac{852 \text{ kJ}}{2 \text{ mol Al}} = 78.8 \text{ kJ}$$

BALLPARK CHECK

Since the molar mass of Al is about 27 g, 5 g of aluminum is roughly 0.2 mol, and the heat evolved is about (852 kJ/2 mol)(0.2 mol), or approximately 85 kJ.

▶ PROBLEM 8.7   How much heat in kilojoules is evolved or absorbed in each of the following reactions?

(a) Burning of 15.5 g of propane:

$$C_3H_8(g) + 5\,O_2(g) \longrightarrow 3\,CO_2(g) + 4\,H_2O(l) \qquad \Delta H° = -2220 \text{ kJ}$$

(b) Reaction of 4.88 g of barium hydroxide octahydrate with ammonium chloride:

$$Ba(OH)_2 \cdot 8\,H_2O(s) + 2\,NH_4Cl(s) \longrightarrow$$
$$BaCl_2(aq) + 2\,NH_3(aq) + 10\,H_2O(l) \qquad \Delta H° = +80.3 \text{ kJ}$$

▶ PROBLEM 8.8   Nitromethane (CH_3NO_2), sometimes used as a fuel in drag racers, burns according to the following equation. How much heat is released by burning 100.0 g of nitromethane?

$$4\,CH_3NO_2(l) + 7\,O_2(g) \longrightarrow 4\,CO_2(g) + 6\,H_2O(g) + 4\,NO_2(g) \qquad \Delta H° = -2441.6 \text{ kJ}$$

8.7 CALORIMETRY AND HEAT CAPACITY

The amount of heat transferred during a reaction can be measured with a device called a *calorimeter*, shown schematically in Figure 8.7. At its simplest, a calorimeter is just an insulated vessel with a stirrer, a thermometer, and a loose-fitting lid to keep the contents at atmospheric pressure. The reaction is carried out inside the vessel, and the heat evolved or absorbed is calculated from the temperature change. Because the pressure inside the calorimeter is constant (atmospheric pressure), the temperature measurement makes it possible to calculate the enthalpy change ΔH during a reaction.

Figure 8.7
A calorimeter for measuring the heat flow in a reaction at constant pressure (ΔH).

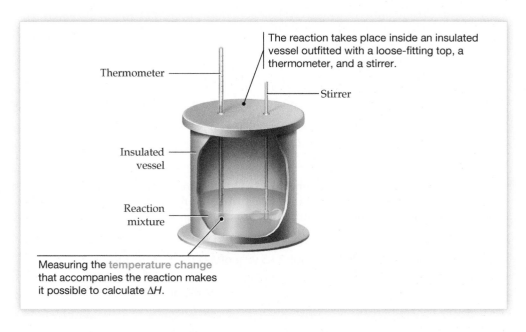

The reaction takes place inside an insulated vessel outfitted with a loose-fitting top, a thermometer, and a stirrer.

Thermometer

Stirrer

Insulated vessel

Reaction mixture

Measuring the temperature change that accompanies the reaction makes it possible to calculate ΔH.

A somewhat more complicated device called a *bomb calorimeter* is used to measure the heat released during a combustion reaction, or burning of a flammable substance. (More generally, a *combustion* reaction is any reaction that produces a flame.) The sample is placed in a small cup and sealed in an oxygen atmosphere inside a steel bomb that is itself placed in an insulated, water-filled container (Figure 8.8). The reactants are ignited electrically, and the evolved heat is calculated from the temperature change of the surrounding water. Since the reaction takes place at constant volume rather than constant pressure, the measurement provides a value for ΔE rather than ΔH.

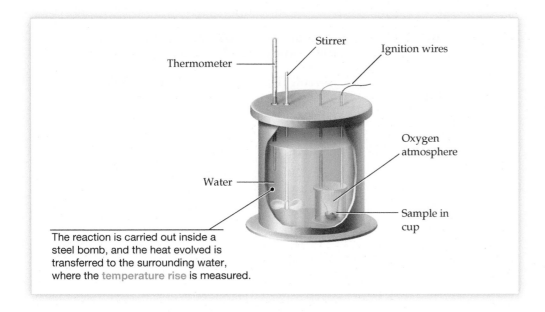

Figure 8.8
A bomb calorimeter for measuring the heat evolved at constant volume (ΔE) in a combustion reaction.

How can the temperature change inside a calorimeter be used to calculate ΔH (or ΔE) for a reaction? When a calorimeter and its contents absorb a given amount of heat, the temperature rise that results depends on the calorimeter's *heat capacity*. **Heat capacity (C)** is the amount of heat required to raise the temperature of an object or substance by a given amount, a relationship that can be expressed by the equation

$$C = \frac{q}{\Delta T}$$

where q is the quantity of heat transferred and ΔT is the temperature change that results ($\Delta T = T_{final} - T_{initial}$).

The greater the heat capacity, the greater the amount of heat needed to produce a given temperature change. A bathtub full of water, for instance, has a greater heat capacity than a coffee cup full, and it therefore takes far more heat to warm the tubful than the cupful. The exact amount of heat absorbed is equal to the heat capacity times the temperature rise:

$$q = C \times \Delta T$$

Heat capacity is an extensive property, so its value depends on both the size of an object and its composition. To compare different substances, it's useful to define a quantity called the *specific heat capacity*, or simply **specific heat**, the amount of heat necessary to raise the temperature of 1 g of a substance by 1 °C. The amount of heat necessary to raise the temperature of a given object, then, is the specific heat times the mass of the object times the rise in temperature:

$$q = \text{Specific heat} \times \text{Mass of substance} \times \Delta T$$

Worked Example 8.5 shows how specific heats are used in calorimetry calculations.

Closely related to specific heat is the **molar heat capacity (C_m)**, defined as the amount of heat necessary to raise the temperature of 1 mol of a substance by 1 °C.

Remember...

Extensive properties, such as length and volume, have values that depend on the sample size. Intensive properties, such as temperature and melting point, have values that do not depend on the amount of the sample. (Section 1.4)

The amount of heat necessary to raise the temperature of a given number of moles of a substance is thus

$$q = C_m \times \text{Moles of substance} \times \Delta T$$

Values of specific heats and molar heat capacities for some common substances are given in Table 8.1. The values are temperature dependent, so the temperatures at which the measurements are taken must be specified.

TABLE 8.1   Specific Heats and Molar Heat Capacities for Some Common Substances at 25 °C

Substance	Specific Heat $J/(g \cdot °C)$	Molar Heat Capacity $J/(mol \cdot °C)$
Air (dry)	1.01	29.1
Aluminum	0.897	24.2
Copper	0.385	24.4
Gold	0.129	25.4
Iron	0.449	25.1
Mercury	0.140	28.0
NaCl	0.859	50.2
Water(s)*	2.03	36.6
Water(l)	4.179	75.3

*At −11 °C

As indicated in Table 8.1, the specific heat of liquid water is considerably higher than that of most other substances, so a large transfer of heat is necessary to either cool or warm a given amount of water. One consequence is that large lakes or other bodies of water tend to moderate the air temperature in surrounding areas. Another consequence is that the human body, which is about 60% water, is able to maintain a relatively steady internal temperature under changing outside conditions.

▲ Lake Chelan in the North Cascades of Washington State is the third deepest freshwater lake in the United States at 1486 ft. Such large masses of water moderate the temperature of the surroundings because of their high heat capacity.

WORKED EXAMPLE 8.4

CALCULATING A SPECIFIC HEAT

What is the specific heat of silicon if it takes 192 J to raise the temperature of 45.0 g of Si by 6.0 °C?

STRATEGY

To find a specific heat of a substance, calculate the amount of energy necessary to raise the temperature of 1 g of the substance by 1 °C.

SOLUTION

$$\text{Specific heat of Si} = \frac{192 \text{ J}}{(45.0 \text{ g})(6.0 \text{ °C})} = 0.71 \text{ J/(g} \cdot \text{°C)}$$

WORKED EXAMPLE 8.5

CALCULATING ΔH IN A CALORIMETRY EXPERIMENT

Aqueous silver ion reacts with aqueous chloride ion to yield a white precipitate of solid silver chloride:

$$\text{Ag}^+(aq) + \text{Cl}^-(aq) \longrightarrow \text{AgCl}(s)$$

When 10.0 mL of 1.00 M AgNO$_3$ solution is added to 10.0 mL of 1.00 M NaCl solution at 25.0 °C in a calorimeter, a white precipitate of AgCl forms and the temperature of the

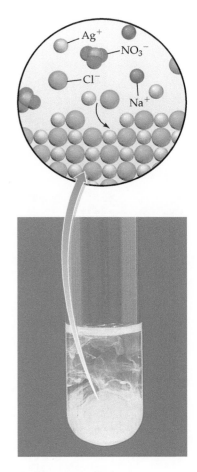

The reaction of aqueous $AgNO_3$ with aqueous NaCl to yield solid AgCl is an exothermic process.

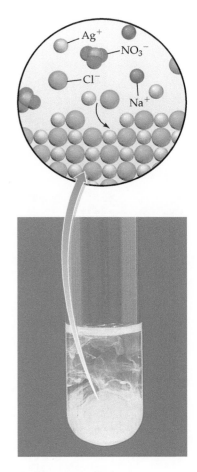

The reaction of aqueous AgNO₃ with aqueous NaCl to yield solid AgCl is an exothermic process.

aqueous mixture increases to 32.6 °C. Assuming that the specific heat of the aqueous mixture is 4.18 J/(g·°C), that the density of the mixture is 1.00 g/mL, and that the calorimeter itself absorbs a negligible amount of heat, calculate ΔH in kilojoules for the reaction.

STRATEGY

Because the temperature rises during the reaction, heat must be released and ΔH must be negative. The amount of heat evolved during the reaction is equal to the amount of heat absorbed by the mixture:

Heat evolved = Specific heat × Mass of mixture × Temperature change

Calculating the heat evolved on a per-mole basis then gives the enthalpy change ΔH.

SOLUTION

Specific heat = 4.18 J/(g·°C)

$$\text{Mass} = (20.0 \text{ mL})\left(1.00 \frac{g}{mL}\right) = 20.0 \text{ g}$$

Temperature change = 32.6 °C − 25.0 °C = 7.6 °C

$$\text{Heat evolved} = \left(4.18 \frac{J}{g \cdot °C}\right)(20.0 \text{ g})(7.6 °C) = 6.4 \times 10^2 \text{ J}$$

According to the balanced equation, the number of moles of AgCl produced equals the number of moles of Ag^+ (or Cl^-) reacted:

$$\text{Moles of } Ag^+ = (10.0 \text{ mL})\left(\frac{1.00 \text{ mol } Ag^+}{1000 \text{ mL}}\right) = 1.00 \times 10^{-2} \text{ mol } Ag^+$$

Moles of AgCl = 1.00×10^{-2} mol AgCl

$$\text{Heat evolved per mole of AgCl} = \frac{6.4 \times 10^2 \text{ J}}{1.00 \times 10^{-2} \text{ mol AgCl}} = 64 \text{ kJ/mol AgCl}$$

Therefore, $\Delta H = -64$ kJ (negative because heat is released)

▶ **PROBLEM 8.9** Assuming that Coca Cola has the same specific heat as water [4.18 J/(g·°C)], calculate the amount of heat in kilojoules transferred when one can (about 350 g) is cooled from 25 °C to 3 °C.

▶ **PROBLEM 8.10** What is the specific heat of lead if it takes 97.2 J to raise the temperature of a 75.0 g block by 10.0 °C?

▶ **PROBLEM 8.11** When 25.0 mL of 1.0 M H_2SO_4 is added to 50.0 mL of 1.0 M NaOH at 25.0 °C in a calorimeter, the temperature of the aqueous solution increases to 33.9 °C. Assuming that the specific heat of the solution is 4.18 J/(g·°C), that its density is 1.00 g/mL, and that the calorimeter itself absorbs a negligible amount of heat, calculate ΔH in kilojoules for the reaction.

$$H_2SO_4(aq) + 2\,NaOH(aq) \longrightarrow 2\,H_2O(l) + Na_2SO_4(aq)$$

8.8 HESS'S LAW

Now that we've discussed in general terms the energy changes that occur during chemical reactions, let's look at a specific example in detail. In particular, let's look at the *Haber process*, the industrial method by which more than 120 million metric tons of ammonia is produced each year worldwide, primarily for use as fertilizer (1 metric ton = 1000 kg). The reaction of hydrogen with nitrogen to make ammonia is exothermic, with $\Delta H° = -92.2$ kJ.

$$3\,H_2(g) + N_2(g) \longrightarrow 2\,NH_3(g) \qquad \Delta H° = -92.2 \text{ kJ}$$

If we dig into the details of the reaction, we find that it's not as simple as it looks. In fact, the overall reaction occurs in a series of steps, with hydrazine (N_2H_4) produced at an intermediate stage:

$$2\,H_2(g) + N_2(g) \longrightarrow N_2H_4(g) \xrightarrow{\;H_2\;} 2\,NH_3(g)$$
$$ \text{Hydrazine} \qquad\quad \text{Ammonia}$$

The enthalpy change for the conversion of hydrazine to ammonia can be measured as $\Delta H° = -187.6$ kJ, but if we wanted to measure $\Delta H°$ for the formation of hydrazine from hydrogen and nitrogen, we would have difficulty because the reaction doesn't go cleanly. Some of the hydrazine is converted into ammonia and some of the starting nitrogen remains.

Fortunately, there's a way around the difficulty—a way that makes it possible to measure an energy change indirectly when a direct measurement can't be made. The trick is to realize that, because enthalpy is a state function, ΔH is the same no matter what path is taken between two states. Thus, the sum of the enthalpy changes for the individual steps in a sequence must equal the enthalpy change for the overall reaction, a statement known as **Hess's law**:

> ◁▥— **Hess's law**   The overall enthalpy change for a reaction is equal to the sum the enthalpy changes for the individual steps in the reaction.

Reactants and products in the individual steps can be added and subtracted like algebraic quantities in determining the overall equation. In the synthesis of ammonia, for example, the sum of steps 1 and 2 is equal to the overall reaction. Thus, the sum of the enthalpy changes for steps 1 and 2 is equal to the enthalpy change for the overall reaction. With this knowledge, we can calculate the enthalpy change for step 1. **Figure 8.9** shows the situation pictorially, and Worked Examples 8.6 and 8.7 give additional examples of Hess's law calculations.

Step 1. $2\,H_2(g) + N_2(g) \longrightarrow N_2H_4(g)$ $\Delta H°_1 = ?$

Step 2. $N_2H_4(g) + H_2(g) \longrightarrow 2\,NH_3(g)$ $\Delta H°_2 = -187.6$ kJ

Overall reaction $3\,H_2(g) + N_2(g) \longrightarrow 2\,NH_3(g)$ $\Delta H°_{reaction} = -92.2$ kJ

Since $\Delta H°_1 + \Delta H°_2 = \Delta H°_{reaction}$

then $\Delta H°_1 = \Delta H°_{reaction} - \Delta H°_2$

$$= (-92.2 \text{ kJ}) - (-187.6 \text{ kJ}) = +95.4 \text{ kJ}$$

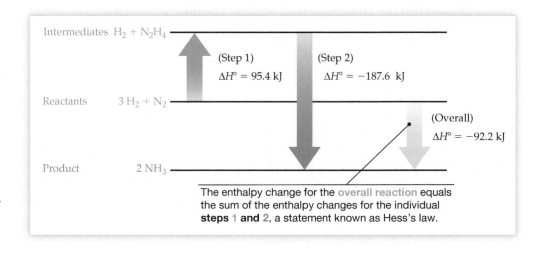

Figure 8.9
Enthalpy changes for steps in the synthesis of ammonia from nitrogen and hydrogen. If $\Delta H°$ values for step 2 and for the overall reaction are known, then $\Delta H°$ for step 1 can be calculated.

WORKED EXAMPLE 8.6

USING HESS'S LAW TO CALCULATE $\Delta H°$

Methane, the main constituent of natural gas, burns in oxygen to yield carbon dioxide and water:

$$CH_4(g) + 2\,O_2(g) \longrightarrow CO_2(g) + 2\,H_2O(l)$$

Use the following information to calculate $\Delta H°$ in kilojoules for the combustion of methane:

$$CH_4(g) + O_2(g) \longrightarrow CH_2O(g) + H_2O(g) \qquad \Delta H° = -275.6 \text{ kJ}$$
$$CH_2O(g) + O_2(g) \longrightarrow CO_2(g) + H_2O(g) \qquad \Delta H° = -526.7 \text{ kJ}$$
$$H_2O(l) \longrightarrow H_2O(g) \qquad\qquad\qquad\quad \Delta H° = 44.0 \text{ kJ}$$

STRATEGY

It often takes some trial and error, but the idea is to combine the individual reactions so that their sum is the desired reaction. The important points are that:

- All the reactants [$CH_4(g)$ and $O_2(g)$] must appear on the left.
- All the products [$CO_2(g)$ and $H_2O(l)$] must appear on the right.
- All intermediate products [$CH_2O(g)$ and $H_2O(g)$] must occur on *both* the left and the right so that they cancel.
- A reaction written in the reverse of the direction given [$H_2O(g) \longrightarrow H_2O(l)$] must have the sign of its $\Delta H°$ reversed (Section 8.6).
- If a reaction is multiplied by a coefficient [$H_2O(g) \longrightarrow H_2O(l)$ is multiplied by 2], then $\Delta H°$ for the reaction must be multiplied by that same coefficient.

SOLUTION

$$CH_4(g) + O_2(g) \longrightarrow \cancel{CH_2O(g)} + \cancel{H_2O(g)} \qquad\qquad \Delta H° = -275.6 \text{ kJ}$$
$$\cancel{CH_2O(g)} + O_2(g) \longrightarrow CO_2(g) + \cancel{H_2O(g)} \qquad\qquad \Delta H° = -526.7 \text{ kJ}$$
$$\underline{2\,[\cancel{H_2O(g)} \longrightarrow H_2O(l)] \qquad\qquad 2\,[\Delta H° = -44.0 \text{ kJ}] = -88.0 \text{ kJ}}$$
$$CH_4(g) \longrightarrow 2\,O_2(g) \longrightarrow CO_2(g) + 2\,H_2O(l) \qquad \Delta H° = -890.3 \text{ kJ}$$

WORKED EXAMPLE 8.7

USING HESS'S LAW TO CALCULATE $\Delta H°$

Water gas is the name for the mixture of CO and H_2 prepared by reaction of steam with carbon at 1000 °C:

$$C(s) + H_2O(g) \longrightarrow CO(g) + H_2(g)$$
$$\text{"Water gas"}$$

The hydrogen is then purified and used as a starting material for preparing ammonia. Use the following information to calculate $\Delta H°$ in kilojoules for the water-gas reaction:

$$C(s) + O_2(g) \longrightarrow CO_2(g) \qquad \Delta H° = -393.5 \text{ kJ}$$
$$2\,CO(g) + O_2(g) \longrightarrow 2\,CO_2(g) \qquad \Delta H° = -566.0 \text{ kJ}$$
$$2\,H_2(g) + O_2(g) \longrightarrow 2\,H_2O(g) \qquad \Delta H° = -483.6 \text{ kJ}$$

STRATEGY

As in Worked Example 8.6, the idea is to find a combination of the individual reactions whose sum is the desired reaction. In this instance, it's necessary to reverse the second and third steps and to multiply both by 1/2 to make the overall equation balance. In so doing, the signs of the enthalpy changes for those steps must be changed and multiplied by 1/2. Note that $CO_2(g)$ and $O_2(g)$ cancel because they appear on both the right and left sides of equations.

continued on next page

SOLUTION

$$C(s) + O_2(g) \longrightarrow CO_2(g) \qquad\qquad\qquad \Delta H° = -393.5 \text{ kJ}$$
$$1/2\,[2\,CO_2(g) \longrightarrow 2\,CO(g) + O_2(g)] \qquad 1/2\,[\Delta H° = 566.0 \text{ kJ}] = \quad 283.0 \text{ kJ}$$
$$1/2\,[2\,H_2O(g) \longrightarrow 2\,H_2(g) + O_2(g) \qquad 1/2\,[\Delta H° = 483.6 \text{ kJ}] = \quad 241.8 \text{ kJ}$$

$$C(s) + H_2O(g) \longrightarrow CO(g) + H_2(g) \qquad\qquad\qquad \Delta H° = \quad 131.3 \text{ kJ}$$

The water-gas reaction is endothermic by 131.3 kJ.

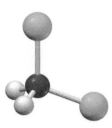

Methylene chloride

▶ **PROBLEM 8.12**   The industrial degreasing solvent methylene chloride, CH_2Cl_2, is prepared from methane by reaction with chlorine:

$$CH_4(g) + 2\,Cl_2(g) \longrightarrow CH_2Cl_2(g) + 2\,HCl(g)$$

Use the following data to calculate $\Delta H°$ in kilojoules for the reaction:

$$CH_4(g) + Cl_2(g) \longrightarrow CH_3Cl(g) + HCl(g) \qquad \Delta H° = \quad -98.3 \text{ kJ}$$
$$CH_3Cl(g) + Cl_2(g) \longrightarrow CH_2Cl_2(g) + HCl(g) \qquad \Delta H° = -104 \text{ kJ}$$

CONCEPTUAL PROBLEM 8.13   The reaction of A with B to give D proceeds in two steps and can be represented by the following Hess's law diagram.

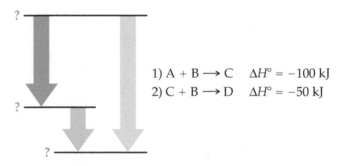

1) $A + B \longrightarrow C \quad \Delta H° = -100 \text{ kJ}$
2) $C + B \longrightarrow D \quad \Delta H° = -50 \text{ kJ}$

(a) What is the equation and $\Delta H°$ for the net reaction?
(b) Which arrow on the diagram corresponds to which step, and which arrow corresponds to the net reaction?
(c) The diagram shows three energy levels. The energies of which substances are represented by each?

CONCEPTUAL PROBLEM 8.14   Draw a Hess's law diagram similar to that in Problem 8.13 depicting the energy changes for the reaction in Problem 8.12.

8.9   STANDARD HEATS OF FORMATION

Where do the $\Delta H°$ values we've been using in previous sections come from? There are so many chemical reactions—hundreds of millions are known—that it's impossible to measure $\Delta H°$ for all of them. A better way is needed.

The most efficient way to manage with the smallest number of experimental measurements is to use what are called **standard heats of formation ($\Delta H°_f$)**.

◀▶ **Standard Heat of Formation**   The enthalpy change $\Delta H°_f$ for the formation of 1 mol of a substance in its standard state from its constituent elements in their standard states.

Note several points about this definition. First, the "reaction" to form a substance from its constituent elements can be (and often is) hypothetical. We can't combine carbon and hydrogen in the laboratory to make methane, for instance, yet the heat of formation for methane is $\Delta H°_f = -74.8$ kJ/mol, which corresponds to the standard enthalpy change for the hypothetical reaction

$$C(s) + 2 H_2(g) \longrightarrow CH_4(g) \qquad \Delta H° = -74.8 \text{ kJ}$$

Second, each substance in the reaction must be in its most stable, standard form at 1 atm pressure and the specified temperature (usually 25 °C). Carbon, for instance, is most stable as solid graphite rather than as diamond under these conditions, and hydrogen is most stable as gaseous H_2 molecules rather than as H atoms. Table 8.2 gives standard heats of formation for some common substances, and Appendix B gives a more detailed list.

TABLE 8.2   Standard Heats of Formation for Some Common Substances at 25 °C

Substance	Formula	$\Delta H°_f$ (kJ/mol)	Substance	Formula	$\Delta H°_f$ (kJ/mol)
Acetylene	$C_2H_2(g)$	227.4	Hydrogen chloride	$HCl(g)$	−92.3
Ammonia	$NH_3(g)$	−46.1	Iron(III) oxide	$Fe_2O_3(s)$	−824.2
Carbon dioxide	$CO_2(g)$	−393.5	Magnesium carbonate	$MgCO_3(s)$	−1095.8
Carbon monoxide	$CO(g)$	−110.5	Methane	$CH_4(g)$	−74.8
Ethanol	$C_2H_5OH(l)$	−277.7	Nitric oxide	$NO(g)$	91.3
Ethylene	$C_2H_4(g)$	52.3	Water (g)	$H_2O(g)$	−241.8
Glucose	$C_6H_{12}O_6(s)$	−1273.3	Water (l)	$H_2O(l)$	−285.8

No elements are listed in Table 8.2 because, by definition, the most stable form of any element in its standard state has $\Delta H°_f = 0$ kJ; that is, the enthalpy change for the formation of an element from itself is zero. Defining $\Delta H°_f$ as zero for all elements thus establishes a thermochemical "sea level," or reference point, from which other enthalpy changes are measured.

How can standard heats of formation be used for thermochemical calculations? The standard enthalpy change for any chemical reaction is found by subtracting the sum of the heats of formation of all reactants from the sum of the heats of formation of all products, with each heat of formation multiplied by the coefficient of that substance in the balanced equation.

$$\Delta H°_{reaction} = \Delta H°_f \text{ (Products)} - \Delta H°_f \text{ (Reactants)}$$

To find $\Delta H°$ for the reaction

$$a\,A + b\,B + \cdots \longrightarrow c\,C + d\,D + \cdots$$

Subtract the sum of the heats of formation for these reactants . . .	. . . from the sum of the heats of formation for these products.

$$\Delta H°_{reaction} = [c\,\Delta H°_f(C) + d\,\Delta H°_f(D) + \cdots] - [a\,\Delta H°_f(A) + b\,\Delta H°_f(B) + \cdots]$$

As an example, let's calculate $\Delta H°$ for the fermentation of glucose to make ethyl alcohol (ethanol), the reaction that occurs during the production of alcoholic beverages:

$$C_6H_{12}O_6(s) \longrightarrow 2\,C_2H_5OH(l) + 2\,CO_2(g) \qquad \Delta H° = ?$$

Using the data in Table 8.2 gives the following answer:

$$\Delta H° = [2\,\Delta H°_f \text{ (Ethanol)} + 2\,\Delta H°_f \text{ (CO}_2)] - [\Delta H°_f \text{ (Glucose)}]$$
$$= (2 \text{ mol})(-277.7 \text{ kJ/mol}) + (2 \text{ mol})(-393.5 \text{ kJ/mol}) - (1 \text{ mol})(-1273.3 \text{ kJ/mol})$$
$$= -69.1 \text{ kJ}$$

▲ Fermentation of the sugar from grapes yields the ethyl alcohol in wine.

The fermentation reaction is exothermic by 69.1 kJ.

Why does this calculation "work"? It works because enthalpy is a state function and the calculation is really just an application of Hess's law. That is, the sum of the individual equations corresponding to the heat of formation for each substance in the reaction equals the enthalpy change for the overall reaction:

(1) $C_6H_{12}O_6(s) \longrightarrow 6\,C(s) + 6\,H_2(g) + 3\,O_2(g)$ $-\Delta H°_f = +1273.3$ kJ

(2) $2\,[2\,C(s) + 3\,H_2(g) + 1/2\,O_2(g) \longrightarrow C_2H_5OH(l)]$ $2\,[\Delta H°_f = -277.7$ kJ$] = -555.4$ kJ

(3) $2\,[C(s) + O_2(g) \longrightarrow CO_2(g)]$ $2\,[\Delta H°_f = -393.5$ kJ$] = -787.0$ kJ

Net $C_6H_{12}O_6(s) \longrightarrow 2\,C_2H_5OH(l) + 2\,CO_2(g)$ $\Delta H° = -69.1$ kJ

Note that reaction (1) represents the formation of glucose from its elements written in reverse, so the sign of $\Delta H°_f$ is reversed. Note also that reactions (2) and (3), which represent the formation of ethyl alcohol and carbon dioxide, respectively, are multiplied by 2 to arrive at the balanced equation for the overall reaction.

When we use heats of formation to calculate standard reaction enthalpies, what we're really doing is referencing the enthalpies of both products and reactants to the same point: their constituent elements. By thus referencing product and reactant enthalpies to the same point, they are referenced to each other and the difference between them is the reaction enthalpy (Figure 8.10). Worked Examples 8.8 and 8.9 further illustrate how to use standard heats of formation.

Figure 8.10
The standard reaction enthalpy, $\Delta H°$, for the generalized reaction A → B. The value of $\Delta H°$ for the reaction is the difference between the standard heats of formation of product B and reactant A.

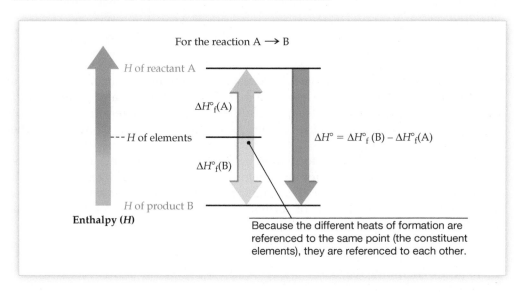

WORKED EXAMPLE 8.8

USING STANDARD HEATS OF FORMATION TO CALCULATE $\Delta H°$

Calculate $\Delta H°$ in kilojoules for the synthesis of lime (CaO) from limestone ($CaCO_3$), the key step in the manufacture of cement.

$CaCO_3(s) \longrightarrow CaO(s) + CO_2(g)$ $\Delta H°_f\,[CaCO_3(s)] = -1207.6$ kJ/mol
$\Delta H°_f\,[CaO(s)] = -634.9$ kJ/mol
$\Delta H°_f\,[CO_2(g)] = -393.5$ kJ/mol

STRATEGY

Subtract the heat of formation of the reactant from the sum of the heats of formation of the products.

SOLUTION

$\Delta H° = [\Delta H°_f\,(CaO) + \Delta H°_f\,(CO_2)] - [\Delta H°_f\,(CaCO_3)]$
$= (1\text{ mol})(-634.9\text{ kJ/mol}) + (1\text{ mol})(-393.5\text{ kJ/mol}) - (1\text{ mol})(-1207.6\text{ kJ/mol})$
$= 179.2$ kJ

The reaction is endothermic by 179.2 kJ.

WORKED EXAMPLE 8.9

USING STANDARD HEATS OF FORMATION TO CALCULATE $\Delta H°$

Oxyacetylene welding torches burn acetylene gas, $C_2H_2(g)$. Use the information in Table 8.2 to calculate $\Delta H°$ in kilojoules for the combustion reaction of acetylene to yield $CO_2(g)$ and $H_2O(g)$.

STRATEGY

Write the balanced equation, look up the appropriate heats of formation for each reactant and product in Table 8.2, and then carry out the calculation, making sure to multiply each $\Delta H°_f$ by the coefficient given in the balanced equation. Remember also that $\Delta H°_f (O_2) = 0$ kJ/mol.

SOLUTION

The balanced equation is

$$2\, C_2H_2(g) + 5\, O_2(g) \longrightarrow 4\, CO_2(g) + 2\, H_2O(g)$$

The necessary heats of formation are

$$\Delta H°_f [C_2H_2(g)] = 227.4 \text{ kJ/mol} \qquad \Delta H°_f [H_2O(g)] = -241.8 \text{ kJ/mol}$$

$$\Delta H°_f [CO_2(g)] = -393.5 \text{ kJ/mol}$$

The standard enthalpy change for the reaction is

$$\Delta H° = [4\, \Delta H°_f (CO_2)] + 2\, \Delta H°_f (H_2O)] - [2\, \Delta H°_f (C_2H_2)]$$

$$= (4 \text{ mol})(-393.5 \text{ kJ/mol}) + (2 \text{ mol})(-241.8 \text{ kJ/mol}) - (2 \text{ mol})(227.4 \text{ kJ/mol})$$

$$= -2512.4 \text{ kJ}$$

▲ Acetylene burns at a high temperature, making the reaction useful for cutting and welding iron.

▶ **PROBLEM 8.15**   Use the information in Table 8.2 to calculate $\Delta H°$ in kilojoules for the reaction of ammonia with O_2 to yield nitric oxide (NO) and $H_2O(g)$, a step in the Ostwald process for the commercial production of nitric acid.

▶ **PROBLEM 8.16**   Use the information in Table 8.2 to calculate $\Delta H°$ in kilojoules for the photosynthesis of glucose ($C_6H_{12}O_6$) and O_2 from CO_2 and liquid H_2O, a reaction carried out by all green plants.

8.10 BOND DISSOCIATION ENERGIES

The procedure described in the previous section for determining heats of reaction from heats of formation is extremely useful, but it still presents a problem. To use the method, it's necessary to know $\Delta H°_f$ for every substance in a reaction. This implies, in turn, that vast numbers of measurements are needed because there are over 40 million known chemical compounds. In practice, though, only a few thousand $\Delta H°_f$ values have been determined.

For those reactions where insufficient $\Delta H°_f$ data are available to allow an exact calculation of $\Delta H°$, it's often possible to estimate $\Delta H°$ by using the average **bond dissociation energies (D)** discussed previously in Section 7.2. Although we didn't identify it as such at the time, a bond dissociation energy is really just a standard enthalpy change for the corresponding bond-breaking reaction.

$$\text{For the reaction } X\!-\!Y \longrightarrow X + Y \quad \Delta H° = D = \text{Bond dissociation energy}$$

When we say, for example, that the bond dissociation energy of Cl_2 is 243 kJ/mol, we mean that the standard enthalpy change for the reaction $Cl_2(g) \longrightarrow 2\, Cl(g)$ is $\Delta H° = 243$ kJ. Bond dissociation energies are always positive because energy must always be put into bonds to break them.

Remember...

Bond dissociation energy is the amount of energy that must be supplied to break a chemical bond in an isolated molecule in the gaseous state and is thus the amount of energy released when the bond forms. (Section 7.2)

Applying Hess's law, we can calculate an approximate enthalpy change for any reaction by subtracting the sum of the bond dissociation energies in the products from the sum of the bond dissociation energies in the reactants:

$$\Delta H° = D(\text{Reactant bonds}) - D(\text{Product bonds})$$

In the reaction of H_2 with Cl_2 to yield HCl, for example, the reactants have one Cl—Cl bond and one H—H bond, while the product has two H—Cl bonds.

$$H_2(g) + Cl_2(g) \longrightarrow 2\,HCl(g)$$

According to the data in Table 7.1 on page 219, the bond dissociation energy of Cl_2 is 243 kJ/mol, that of H_2 is 436 kJ/mol, and that of HCl is 432 kJ/mol. We can thus calculate an approximate standard enthalpy change for the reaction.

$$\begin{aligned}
\Delta H° &= D(\text{Reactant bonds}) - D(\text{Product bonds}) \\
&= (D_{Cl-Cl} + D_{H-H}) - (2\,D_{H-Cl}) \\
&= [(1\text{ mol})(243\text{ kJ/mol}) + (1\text{ mol})(436\text{ kJ/mol})] - (2\text{ mol})(432\text{ kJ/mol}) \\
&= -185\text{ kJ}
\end{aligned}$$

The reaction is exothermic by approximately 185 kJ.

WORKED EXAMPLE 8.10

USING BOND DISSOCIATION ENERGIES TO CALCULATE $\Delta H°$

Use the data in Table 7.1 on page 219 to find an approximate $\Delta H°$ in kilojoules for the industrial synthesis of chloroform by reaction of methane with Cl_2.

$$CH_4(g) + 3\,Cl_2(g) \longrightarrow CHCl_3(g) + 3\,HCl(g)$$

STRATEGY

Identify all the bonds in the reactants and products, and look up the appropriate bond dissociation energies in Table 7.1. Then subtract the sum of the bond dissociation energies in the products from the sum of the bond dissociation energies in the reactants to find the enthalpy change for the reaction.

SOLUTION

The reactants have four C—H bonds and three Cl—Cl bonds; the products have one C—H bond, three C—Cl bonds, and three H—Cl bonds. The bond dissociation energies from Table 7.1 are:

C—H	$D = 410$ kJ/mol	Cl—Cl	$D = 243$ kJ/mol
C—Cl	$D = 330$ kJ/mol	H—Cl	$D = 432$ kJ/mol

Subtracting the product bond dissociation energies from the reactant bond dissociation energies gives the enthalpy change for the reaction:

$$\begin{aligned}
\Delta H° &= [3\,D_{Cl-Cl} + 4\,D_{C-H}] - [D_{C-H} + 3\,D_{H-Cl} + 3\,D_{C-Cl}] \\
&= [(3\text{ mol})(243\text{ kJ/mol}) + (4\text{ mol})(410\text{ kJ/mol})] - [(1\text{ mol})(410\text{ kJ/mol}) \\
&\qquad + (3\text{ mol})(432\text{ kJ/mol}) + (3\text{ mol})(330\text{ kJ/mol})] \\
&= -327\text{ kJ}
\end{aligned}$$

The reaction is exothermic by approximately 330 kJ.

▶ **PROBLEM 8.17**   Use the data in Table 7.1 on page 219 to calculate an approximate $\Delta H°$ in kilojoules for the industrial synthesis of ethyl alcohol from ethylene: $C_2H_4(g) + H_2O(g) \longrightarrow C_2H_5OH(g)$.

▶ **PROBLEM 8.18**   Use the data in Table 7.1 to calculate an approximate $\Delta H°$ in kilojoules for the synthesis of hydrazine from ammonia: $2\,NH_3(g) + Cl_2(g) \longrightarrow N_2H_4(g) + 2\,HCl(g)$.

Ethyl alcohol

8.11 FOSSIL FUELS, FUEL EFFICIENCY, AND HEATS OF COMBUSTION

Surely the most familiar of all exothermic reactions is the one that takes place every time you turn up a thermostat, drive a car, or light a match: the burning of a carbon-based fuel by reaction with oxygen to yield H_2O, CO_2, and heat. The amount of energy released on burning a substance is called its **heat of combustion**, or *combustion enthalpy*, ΔH°_c, and is simply the standard enthalpy change for the reaction of 1 mol of the substance with oxygen. Hydrogen, for instance, has $\Delta H^\circ_c = -285.8$ kJ/mol, and methane has $\Delta H^\circ_c = -890.3$ kJ/mol. Note that the H_2O product in giving heats of combustion is $H_2O(l)$ rather than $H_2O(g)$.

$$H_2(g) + 1/2\, O_2(g) \longrightarrow H_2O(l) \qquad\qquad \Delta H^\circ_c = -285.8 \text{ kJ/mol}$$
$$CH_4(g) + 2\, O_2(g) \longrightarrow CO_2(g) + 2\, H_2O(l) \quad \Delta H^\circ_c = -890.3 \text{ kJ/mol}$$

To compare the efficiency of different fuels, it's more useful to calculate combustion enthalpies per gram or per milliliter of substance rather than per mole (Table 8.3). For applications where weight is important, as in rocket engines, hydrogen is ideal because its combustion enthalpy per gram is the highest of any known fuel. For applications where volume is important, as in automobiles, a mixture of *hydrocarbons*—compounds of carbon and hydrogen—such as those in gasoline is most efficient because hydrocarbon combustion enthalpies per milliliter are relatively high. Octane and toluene are representative examples.

TABLE 8.3   Thermochemical Properties of Some Fuels

Fuel	Combustion Enthalpy		
	kJ/mol	kJ/g	kJ/mL
Hydrogen, $H_2(l)$	−285.8	−141.8	−9.9*
Ethanol, $C_2H_5OH(l)$	−1366.8	−29.7	−23.4
Graphite, $C(s)$	−393.5	−32.8	−73.8
Methane, $CH_4(g)$	−890.3	−55.5	−30.8*
Methanol, $CH_3OH(l)$	−725.9	−22.7	−17.9
Octane, $C_8H_{18}(l)$	−5470	−47.9	−33.6
Toluene, $C_7H_8(l)$	−3910	−42.3	−36.7

*Calculated for the compressed liquid at 0 °C

With the exception of hydrogen, all common fuels are organic compounds, whose energy is derived ultimately from the sun through the photosynthesis of carbohydrates in green plants. Although the details are complex, the net result of the photosynthesis reaction is the conversion of carbon dioxide and water into glucose, $C_6H_{12}O_6$, plus oxygen. Glucose, once formed, is converted into cellulose and starch, which in turn act as structural materials for plants and as food sources for animals. The conversion is highly endothermic and therefore requires a large input of solar energy. It has been estimated that the total annual amount of solar energy absorbed by the Earth's vegetation is approximately 10^{19} kJ, an amount sufficient to synthesize 5×10^{14} kg of glucose per year.

$$6\, CO_2(g) + 6\, H_2O(l) \longrightarrow C_6H_{12}O_6(s) + 6\, O_2(g) \qquad \Delta H^\circ = 2803 \text{ kJ}$$

The fossil fuels we use most—coal, petroleum, and natural gas—are derived from the decayed remains of organisms from previous geologic eras. Both coal and petroleum are enormously complex mixtures of compounds. Coal is primarily of vegetable origin, and many of the compounds it contains are structurally similar to graphite (pure carbon). Petroleum is a viscous liquid mixture of hydrocarbons that are primarily of marine origin, and natural gas is primarily methane, CH_4.

▲ Much coal lies near the surface of the Earth and is obtained by strip mining.

Coal is burned just as it comes from the mine, but petroleum must be *refined* before use. Refining begins with *distillation*, the separation of crude liquid oil into fractions on the basis of their boiling points (bp). So-called straight-run gasoline (bp 30–200 °C) consists of compounds with 5–11 carbon atoms per molecule; kerosene (bp 175–300 °C) contains compounds in the C_{11}–C_{14} range; gas oil (bp 275–400 °C) contains C_{14}–C_{25} substances; and lubricating oils contain whatever remaining compounds will distill. Left over is a tarry residue of asphalt (**Figure 8.11**).

Figure 8.11
The products of petroleum refining.

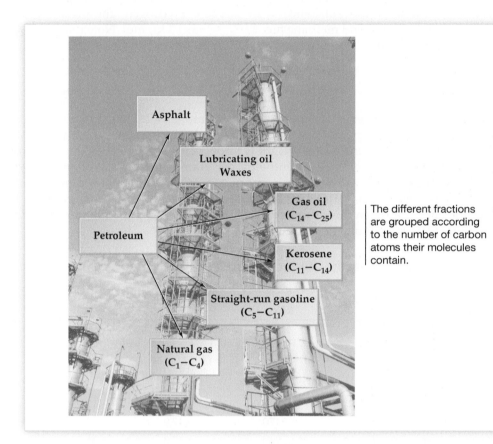

The different fractions are grouped according to the number of carbon atoms their molecules contain.

As the world's petroleum deposits become more scarce, other sources of energy will have to be found to replace them. Hydrogen, although it burns cleanly and is relatively nonpolluting, has numerous drawbacks: low availability, difficulty in transport and storage, and low combustion enthalpy per milliliter, to name a few. Ethanol and methanol look like potential choices for alternative fuels because both can be produced relatively cheaply and have reasonable combustion enthalpies. At present, ethanol is produced largely by fermentation of corn or cane sugar, but methods are being developed to produce it from waste wood by the breakdown of cellulose to glucose and subsequent fermentation. Methanol is produced directly from natural gas in a two-step process:

$$CH_4(g) + H_2O(g) \longrightarrow CO(g) + 3\,H_2(g)$$
$$CO(g) + 2\,H_2(g) \longrightarrow CH_3OH(l)$$

▶ **PROBLEM 8.19** Liquid butane (C_4H_{10}), the fuel used in many disposable lighters, has $\Delta H^\circ_f = -147.5$ kJ/mol and a density of 0.579 g/mL. Write a balanced equation for the combustion of butane, and use Hess's law to calculate the enthalpy of combustion in kJ/mol, kJ/g, and kJ/mL.

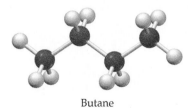

Butane

8.12 AN INTRODUCTION TO ENTROPY

We said in the introduction to this chapter that chemical reactions (and physical processes) occur when the final state is more stable than the initial state. Because less stable substances generally have higher internal energy and are converted into more stable substances with lower internal energy, energy is generally released in chemical reactions. At the same time, though, we've seen that some reactions and processes occur even though they absorb rather than release energy. The endothermic reaction of barium hydroxide octahydrate with ammonium chloride shown previously in Figure 8.6, for example, absorbs 80.3 kJ of heat ($\Delta H° = +80.3$ kJ) and leaves the surroundings so cold that the temperature drops below 0 °C.

$$Ba(OH)_2 \cdot 8\,H_2O(s) + 2\,NH_4Cl(s) \longrightarrow BaCl_2(aq) + 2\,NH_3(aq) + 10\,H_2O(l)$$
$$\Delta H° = +80.3 \text{ kJ}$$

An example of a physical process that takes place spontaneously yet absorbs energy takes place every time an ice cube melts. At a temperature of 0 °C, ice spontaneously absorbs heat from the surroundings to turn from solid into liquid water.

What's going on? Because the reaction of barium hydroxide octahydrate with ammonium chloride and the melting ice cube absorb heat yet still take place spontaneously, there must be some other factor in addition to energy that determines whether a reaction or process will occur. We'll take only a brief look at this additional factor now and return for a more in-depth study in Chapter 16.

Before exploring the situation further, it's important to understand what the word *spontaneous* means in chemistry, for it's not quite the same as in everyday language. In chemistry, a **spontaneous process** is one that, once started, proceeds on its own without a continuous external influence. The change need not happen quickly, like a spring uncoiling or a sled going downhill. It can also happen slowly, like the gradual rusting away of an iron bridge or abandoned car. A *nonspontaneous* process, by contrast, takes place only in the presence of a continuous external influence. Energy must be continuously expended to re-coil a spring or to push a sled uphill. When the external influence stops, the process also stops.

What do the reaction of barium hydroxide octahydrate and the melting of an ice cube have in common that allows the two processes to take place spontaneously even though they absorb heat? The common feature of these and all other processes that absorb heat yet occur spontaneously is an increase in the amount of molecular randomness of the system. The eight water molecules rigidly held in the $Ba(OH)_2 \cdot 8\,H_2O$ crystal break loose and become free to move about randomly in the aqueous liquid product. Similarly, the rigidly held H_2O molecules in the ice lose their crystalline ordering and move around freely in liquid water.

The amount of molecular randomness in a system is called the system's **entropy (S)**. Entropy has the units J/K (not kJ/K) and is a quantity that can be determined for pure substances, as we'll see in Section 16.5. The larger the value of S, the greater the molecular randomness of the particles in the system. Gases, for example, have more randomness and higher entropy than liquids, and liquids have more randomness and higher entropy than solids (**Figure 8.12**).

A change in entropy is represented as $\Delta S = S_{final} - S_{initial}$. When randomness increases, as it does when barium hydroxide octahydrate reacts or ice melts, ΔS has a positive value because $S_{final} > S_{initial}$. The reaction of $Ba(OH)_2 \cdot 8\,H_2O(s)$ with $NH_4Cl(s)$ has $\Delta S° = +428$ J/K, and the melting of ice has $\Delta S° = +22.0$ J/(K·mol). When randomness decreases, ΔS is negative because $S_{final} < S_{initial}$. The freezing of water, for example, has $\Delta S° = -22.0$ J/(K·mol). (As with $\Delta H°$, the superscript ° is used in $\Delta S°$ to refer to the standard entropy change in a reaction where products and reactants are in their standard states.)

Thus, two factors determine the spontaneity of a chemical or physical change in a system: a release or absorption of heat (ΔH) and an increase or decrease in molecular

▲ Sledding downhill is a spontaneous process that, once started, continues on its own. Dragging the sled back uphill is a nonspontaneous process that requires a continuous input of energy.

Figure 8.12

Entropy is a measure of molecular randomness.

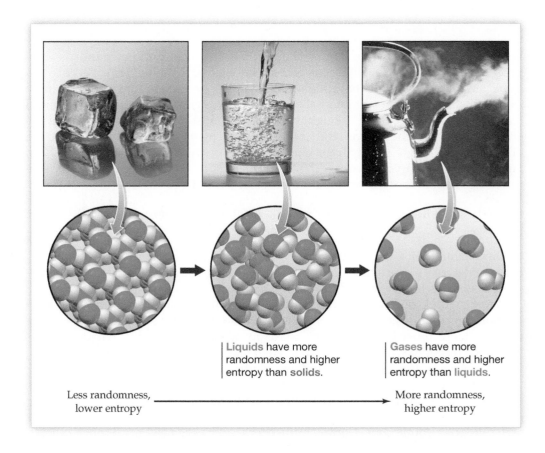

Liquids have more randomness and higher entropy than **solids**.

Gases have more randomness and higher entropy than **liquids**.

Less randomness, lower entropy ⟶ More randomness, higher entropy

randomness (ΔS). To decide whether a process is spontaneous, both enthalpy and entropy changes must be taken into account:

Spontaneous process: Favored by decrease in H (negative ΔH)
Favored by increase in S (positive ΔS)

Nonspontaneous process: Favored by increase in H (positive ΔH)
Favored by decrease in S (negative ΔS)

Note that the two factors don't have to operate in the same direction. Thus, it's possible for a process to be *disfavored* by enthalpy (endothermic, positive ΔH) yet still be spontaneous because it is strongly *favored* by entropy (positive ΔS). The melting of ice [$\Delta H° = +6.01$ kJ/mol; $\Delta S° = +22.0$ J/(K·mol)] is just such a process, as is the reaction of barium hydroxide octahydrate with ammonium chloride ($\Delta H° = +80.3$ kJ; $\Delta S° = +428$ J/K). In the latter case, 3 mol of solid reactants produce 10 mol of liquid water, 2 mol of dissolved ammonia, and 3 mol of dissolved ions (1 mol of Ba^{2+} and 2 mol of Cl^-), with a consequent large increase in molecular randomness:

$$\underbrace{Ba(OH)_2 \cdot 8\,H_2O(s) \; + \; 2\,NH_4Cl(s)}_{\text{3 mol solid reactants}} \longrightarrow \underset{\substack{\uparrow \\ \text{3 mol} \\ \text{dissolved ions}}}{BaCl_2(aq)} \; + \; \underset{\substack{\uparrow \\ \text{2 mol dissolved} \\ \text{molecules}}}{2\,NH_3(aq)} \; + \; \underset{\substack{\uparrow \\ \text{10 mol} \\ \text{liquid} \\ \text{water molecules}}}{10\,H_2O(l)}$$

$$\Delta H° \; = \; +80.3 \text{ kJ} \longleftarrow \text{Unfavorable}$$

$$\Delta S° \; = \; +428 \text{ J/K} \longleftarrow \text{Favorable}$$

Conversely, it's also possible for a process to be favored by enthalpy (exothermic, negative ΔH) yet be nonspontaneous because it is strongly disfavored by entropy (negative ΔS). The conversion of liquid water to ice is nonspontaneous above 0 °C, for example, because the process is disfavored by entropy [$\Delta S° = -22.0\ \text{J}/(\text{K}\cdot\text{mol})$] even though it is favored by enthalpy ($\Delta H° = -6.01\ \text{kJ}/\text{mol}$).

WORKED EXAMPLE 8.11

PREDICTING THE SIGN OF ΔS FOR A REACTION

Predict whether $\Delta S°$ is likely to be positive or negative for each of the following reactions:

(a) $H_2C{=}CH_2(g) + Br_2(g) \longrightarrow BrCH_2CH_2Br(l)$
(b) $2\ C_2H_6(g) + 7\ O_2(g) \longrightarrow 4\ CO_2(g) + 6\ H_2O(g)$

STRATEGY

Look at each reaction, and try to decide whether molecular randomness increases or decreases. Reactions that increase the number of gaseous molecules generally have a positive ΔS, while reactions that decrease the number of gaseous molecules have a negative ΔS.

SOLUTION

(a) The amount of molecular randomness in the system decreases when 2 mol of gaseous reactants combine to give 1 mol of liquid product, so the reaction has a negative $\Delta S°$.

(b) The amount of molecular randomness in the system increases when 9 mol of gaseous reactants give 10 mol of gaseous products, so the reaction has a positive $\Delta S°$.

▶ **PROBLEM 8.20** Ethane, C_2H_6, can be prepared by the reaction of acetylene, C_2H_2, with hydrogen. Is $\Delta S°$ for the reaction likely to be positive or negative? Explain.

$$C_2H_2(g) + 2\ H_2(g) \longrightarrow C_2H_6(g)$$

CONCEPTUAL PROBLEM 8.21 Is the reaction represented in the following drawing likely to have a positive or a negative value of $\Delta S°$? Explain.

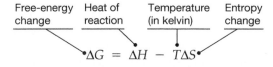

8.13 AN INTRODUCTION TO FREE ENERGY

How do we weigh the relative contributions of enthalpy changes (ΔH) and entropy changes (ΔS) to the overall spontaneity of a process? To take both factors into account when deciding the spontaneity of a chemical reaction or other process, we define a quantity called the **Gibbs free-energy change (ΔG)**, which is related to ΔH and ΔS by the equation $\Delta G = \Delta H - T\Delta S$.

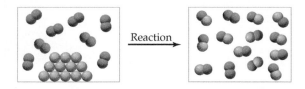

Free-energy change   Heat of reaction   Temperature (in kelvin)   Entropy change

$$\Delta G = \Delta H - T\Delta S$$

   The value of the free-energy change ΔG determines whether a chemical or physical process will occur spontaneously. If ΔG has a negative value, free energy is released and the process is spontaneous. If ΔG has a value of 0, the process is neither spontaneous nor nonspontaneous but is instead at an equilibrium. And if ΔG has a positive value, free energy is absorbed and the process is nonspontaneous.

$\Delta G < 0$ Process is spontaneous

$\Delta G = 0$ Process is at equilibrium—neither spontaneous nor nonspontaneous

$\Delta G > 0$ Process is nonspontaneous

The fact that the $T\Delta S$ term in the free-energy equation is temperature dependent implies that some processes might be either spontaneous or nonspontaneous, depending on the temperature. At low temperature, for instance, an unfavorable (positive) ΔH term might be larger than a favorable (positive) $T\Delta S$ term, but at higher temperature, the $T\Delta S$ term might be larger. Thus, an endothermic process that is nonspontaneous at low temperature can become spontaneous at higher temperature. This, in fact, is exactly what happens in the ice/water transition. At a temperature below 0 °C, the melting of ice is nonspontaneous because the unfavorable ΔH term outweighs the favorable $T\Delta S$ term. At a temperature above 0 °C, however, the melting of ice is spontaneous because the favorable $T\Delta S$ term outweighs the unfavorable ΔH term (Figure 8.13). At exactly 0 °C, the two terms are balanced.

$$\Delta G° = \Delta H° - T\Delta S°$$

At -10 °C (263 K): $\quad \Delta G° = 6.01 \dfrac{kJ}{mol} - (263\ K)\left(0.0220 \dfrac{kJ}{K\cdot mol}\right) = +0.22\ kJ/mol$

At 0 °C (273 K): $\quad \Delta G° = 6.01 \dfrac{kJ}{mol} - (273\ K)\left(0.0220 \dfrac{kJ}{K\cdot mol}\right) = 0.00\ kJ/mol$

At $+10$ °C (283 K): $\quad \Delta G° = 6.01 \dfrac{kJ}{mol} - (283\ K)\left(0.0220 \dfrac{kJ}{K\cdot mol}\right) = -0.22\ kJ/mol$

Figure 8.13
Melting and freezing. The melting of ice is disfavored by enthalpy ($\Delta H > 0$) but favored by entropy ($\Delta S > 0$). The freezing of water is favored by enthalpy ($\Delta H < 0$) but disfavored by entropy ($\Delta S < 0$).

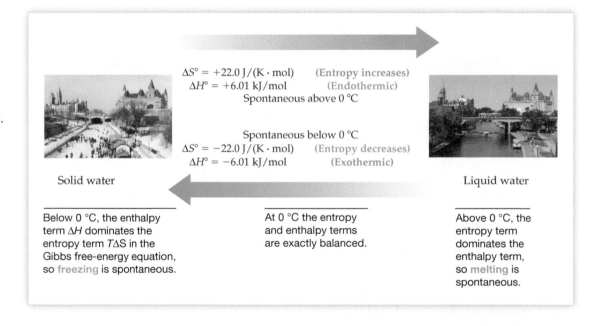

$\Delta S° = +22.0\ J/(K\cdot mol)$ (Entropy increases)
$\Delta H° = +6.01\ kJ/mol$ (Endothermic)
Spontaneous above 0 °C

Spontaneous below 0 °C
$\Delta S° = -22.0\ J/(K\cdot mol)$ (Entropy decreases)
$\Delta H° = -6.01\ kJ/mol$ (Exothermic)

Solid water

Liquid water

Below 0 °C, the enthalpy term ΔH dominates the entropy term $T\Delta S$ in the Gibbs free-energy equation, so freezing is spontaneous.

At 0 °C the entropy and enthalpy terms are exactly balanced.

Above 0 °C, the entropy term dominates the enthalpy term, so melting is spontaneous.

An example of a chemical reaction in which temperature controls spontaneity is that of carbon with water to yield carbon monoxide and hydrogen. The reaction has an unfavorable ΔH term (positive) but a favorable $T\Delta S$ term (positive) because randomness increases when a solid and 1 mol of gas are converted into 2 mol of gas:

$$C(s) + H_2O(g) \longrightarrow CO(g) + H_2(g) \qquad \Delta H° = +131\ kJ \qquad \text{Unfavorable}$$
$$\Delta S° = +134\ J/K \qquad \text{Favorable}$$

No reaction occurs if carbon and water are mixed at room temperature because the unfavorable ΔH term outweighs the favorable $T\Delta S$ term. At approximately 978 K (705 °C), however, the reaction becomes spontaneous because the favorable $T\Delta S$ term becomes larger than the unfavorable ΔH term. Below 978 K, ΔG has a positive value; at 978 K, $\Delta G = 0$; and above 978 K, ΔG has a negative value. (The calculation is not exact because values of ΔH and ΔS themselves vary somewhat with temperature.)

$$\Delta G° = \Delta H° - T\Delta S°$$

At 695 °C (968 K): $\Delta G° = 131 \text{ kJ} - (968 \text{ K})\left(0.134 \dfrac{\text{kJ}}{\text{K}}\right) = +1 \text{ kJ}$

At 705 °C (978 K): $\Delta G° = 131 \text{ kJ} - (978 \text{ K})\left(0.134 \dfrac{\text{kJ}}{\text{K}}\right) = 0 \text{ kJ}$

At 715 °C (988 K): $\Delta G° = 131 \text{ kJ} - (988 \text{ K})\left(0.134 \dfrac{\text{kJ}}{\text{K}}\right) = -1 \text{ kJ}$

The reaction of carbon with water is, in fact, the first step of an industrial process for manufacturing methanol (CH_3OH). As supplies of natural gas and oil diminish, this reaction may become important for the manufacture of synthetic fuels.

A process is at equilibrium when it is balanced between spontaneous and nonspontaneous—that is, when $\Delta G = 0$ and it is energetically unfavorable to go either from reactants to products or from products to reactants. Thus, at the equilibrium point, we can set up the equation

$$\Delta G = \Delta H - T\Delta S = 0 \quad \text{At equilibrium}$$

Solving this equation for T gives

$$T = \frac{\Delta H}{\Delta S}$$

which makes it possible to calculate the temperature at which a changeover in behavior between spontaneous and nonspontaneous occurs. Using the known values of $\Delta H°$ and $\Delta S°$ for the melting of ice, for instance, we find that the point at which liquid water and solid ice are in equilibrium is

$$T = \frac{\Delta H°}{\Delta S°} = \frac{6.01 \text{ kJ}}{0.0220 \dfrac{\text{kJ}}{\text{K}}} = 273 \text{ K} = 0 \text{ °C}$$

Not surprisingly, the ice/water equilibrium point is 273 K, or 0 °C, the melting point of ice.

In the same way, the temperature at which the reaction of carbon with water changes between spontaneous and nonspontaneous is 978 K, or 705 °C:

$$T = \frac{\Delta H°}{\Delta S°} = \frac{131 \text{ kJ}}{0.134 \dfrac{\text{kJ}}{\text{K}}} = 978 \text{ K}$$

This section and the preceding one serve only as an introduction to entropy and free energy. We'll return in Chapter 16 for a more in-depth look at these two important topics.

WORKED EXAMPLE 8.12

USING THE FREE-ENERGY EQUATION TO CALCULATE EQUILIBRIUM TEMPERATURE

Lime (CaO) is produced by heating limestone ($CaCO_3$) to drive off CO_2 gas, a reaction used to make Portland cement. Is the reaction spontaneous under standard conditions at 25 °C? Calculate the temperature at which the reaction becomes spontaneous.

$$CaCO_3(s) \longrightarrow CaO(s) + CO_2(g) \quad \Delta H° = 179.2 \text{ kJ}; \ \Delta S° = 160.0 \text{ J/K}$$

STRATEGY

The spontaneity of the reaction at a given temperature can be found by determining whether ΔG is positive or negative at that temperature. The changeover point between spontaneous and nonspontaneous can be found by setting $\Delta G = 0$ and solving for T.

SOLUTION

At 25 °C (298 K), we have

$$\Delta G = \Delta H - T\Delta S = 179.2 \text{ kJ} - (298 \text{ K})\left(0.1600 \dfrac{\text{kJ}}{\text{K}}\right) = +131.5 \text{ kJ}$$

Because ΔG is positive at this temperature, the reaction is nonspontaneous.

continued on next page

The changeover point between spontaneous and nonspontaneous is approximately

$$T = \frac{\Delta H}{\Delta S} = \frac{179.2 \text{ kJ}}{0.1600 \frac{\text{kJ}}{\text{K}}} = 1120 \text{ K}$$

The reaction becomes spontaneous above approximately 1120 K (847 °C).

WORKED CONCEPTUAL EXAMPLE 8.13

PREDICTING THE SIGNS OF ΔH, ΔS, AND ΔG FOR A REACTION

What are the signs of ΔH, ΔS, and ΔG for the following nonspontaneous transformation?

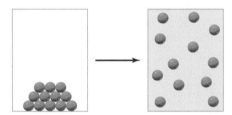

STRATEGY

First, decide what kind of process is represented in the drawing. Then decide whether the process increases or decreases the entropy of the system and whether it is exothermic or endothermic.

SOLUTION

The drawing shows ordered particles in a solid subliming to give a gas. Formation of a gas from a solid increases molecular randomness, so ΔS is positive. Furthermore, because we're told that the process is nonspontaneous, ΔG is also positive. Because the process is favored by ΔS (positive) yet still nonspontaneous, ΔH must be unfavorable (positive). This makes sense, because conversion of a solid to a liquid or gas requires energy and is always endothermic.

▶ **PROBLEM 8.22**   Which of the following reactions are spontaneous under standard conditions at 25 °C, and which are nonspontaneous?

(a) $AgNO_3(aq) + NaCl(aq) \longrightarrow AgCl(s) + NaNO_3(aq)$ $\Delta G° = -55.7$ kJ

(b) $2 C(s) + 2 H_2(g) \longrightarrow C_2H_4(g)$ $\Delta G° = 68.1$ kJ

▶ **PROBLEM 8.23**   Is the Haber process for the industrial synthesis of ammonia spontaneous or nonspontaneous under standard conditions at 25 °C? At what temperature (°C) does the changeover occur?

$$N_2(g) + 3 H_2(g) \longrightarrow 2 NH_3(g) \quad \Delta H° = -92.2 \text{ kJ}; \Delta S° = -199 \text{ J/K}$$

CONCEPTUAL PROBLEM 8.24   The following reaction is exothermic:

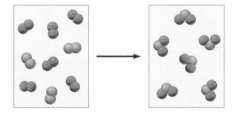

(a) Write a balanced equation for the reaction.

(b) What are the signs of ΔH and ΔS for the reaction?

(c) Is the reaction likely to be spontaneous at low temperatures only, at high temperatures only, or at all temperatures? Explain.

INQUIRY WHAT ARE BIOFUELS?

The petroleum era began in August 1859, when the world's first oil well was drilled near Titusville, Pennsylvania. Since that time, approximately 1.2×10^{12} barrels of petroleum have been used throughout the world, primarily as fuel for automobiles (1 barrel = 42 gallons).

No one really knows how much petroleum remains on Earth. Current world consumption is approximately 3.1×10^{10} barrels per year, and currently known recoverable reserves are estimated at 1.1×10^{12} barrels. Thus, the world's known petroleum reserves will be exhausted in approximately 35 years at the current rate of consumption. Additional petroleum reserves will surely be found, but consumption is also increasing, making any prediction of the amount of time remaining highly inaccurate. Only two things are certain: The amount of petroleum remaining *is* finite, and we *will* run out at some point, whenever that might be. Thus, alternative energy sources are needed.

Of the various alternative energy sources now being explored, *biofuels*—fuels derived from recently living organisms such as trees, corn, sugar cane, and rapeseed—look promising because they are renewable and because they are more nearly *carbon neutral* than fossil fuels, meaning that the amount of CO_2 released to the environment during the manufacture and burning of a biofuel is similar to the amount of CO_2 removed from the environment by photosynthesis during the plant's growth. Note that the phrase *carbon neutral* doesn't mean that biofuels don't release CO_2 when burned; they release just as much CO_2 as any other fuel.

The two biofuels receiving the most attention at present are ethanol and biodiesel. Ethanol, sometimes called bioethanol to make it sound more attractive, is simply ethyl alcohol, the same substance found in alcoholic drinks and produced in the same way: by yeast-catalyzed fermentation of carbohydrate.

▲ Vegetable oil from the bright yellow rapeseed plant is a leading candidate for large-scale production of biodiesel fuel.

Glucose
($C_6H_{12}O_6$)

$\xrightarrow{\text{Yeast enzymes}}$

Ethanol
(C_2H_5OH)

$2 \cdots \text{OH} + 2\, CO_2$

The only difference between beverage ethanol and fuel ethanol is the source of the sugar. Beverage ethanol comes primarily from fermentation of sugar in grapes (for wine) or grains (for distilled liquors), while fuel ethanol comes primarily from fermentation of cane sugar or corn. Much current work is being done, however, on developing economical methods of converting cheap cellulose-based agricultural and logging wastes into fermentable sugars.

Biodiesel consists primarily of organic compounds called *long-chain methyl esters*, which are produced by reaction of common vegetable oils with methyl alcohol in the presence of an acid catalyst. Any vegetable oil can be used, but rapeseed oil and soybean oil are the most common. (*Canola* oil, of which you may have heard, is a specific cultivar of generic rapeseed.) Once formed, the biodiesel is typically mixed in up to 30% concentration with petroleum-based diesel fuel for use in automobiles and trucks.

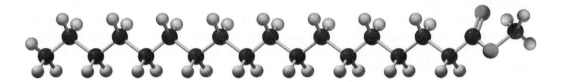

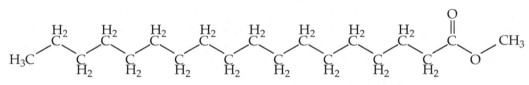

A typical long-chain methyl ester in biodiesel

▶ **PROBLEM 8.25** Write balanced equations for the combustion reactions of ethanol (C_2H_6O) and biodiesel ($C_{19}H_{38}O_2$) with oxygen to give CO_2 and H_2O.

▶ **PROBLEM 8.26** Biodiesel has a more favorable (more negative) combustion enthalpy per gram than ethanol. Explain, in light of your answer to Problem 8.25.

SUMMARY

Energy is either *kinetic* or *potential*. Kinetic energy (E_K) is the energy of motion. Its value depends on both the mass m and velocity v of an object according to the equation $E_K = (1/2)mv^2$. Potential energy (E_P) is the energy stored in an object because of its position or in a chemical substance because of its composition. **Heat** is the thermal energy transferred between two objects as the result of a temperature difference, whereas **temperature** is a measure of the kinetic energy of molecular motion.

According to the **conservation of energy law**, also known as the **first law of thermodynamics**, energy can be neither created nor destroyed. Thus, the total energy of an isolated system is constant. The total **internal energy (E)** of a system—the sum of all kinetic and potential energies for each particle in the system—is a **state function** because its value depends only on the present condition of the system, not on how that condition was reached.

Work (w) is defined as the distance moved times the force that produces the motion. In chemistry, most work is expansion work (*PV* work) done as the result of a volume change during a reaction when air molecules are pushed aside. The amount of work done by an expanding gas is given by the equation $w = -P\Delta V$, where P is the pressure against which the system must push and ΔV is the change in volume of the system.

The total internal energy change that takes place during a reaction is the sum of the heat transferred (q) and the work done ($-P\Delta V$). The equation

$$\Delta E = q + (-P\Delta V) \quad \text{or} \quad q = \Delta E + P\Delta V = \Delta H$$

where ΔH is the **enthalpy change** of the system, is a fundamental equation of thermochemistry. In general, the $P\Delta V$ term is much smaller than the ΔE term, so that the total internal energy change of a reacting system is approximately equal to ΔH, also called the **heat of reaction**. Reactions that have a negative ΔH are **exothermic** because heat is lost by the system, and reactions that have a positive ΔH are **endothermic** because heat is absorbed by the system.

Because enthalpy is a state function, ΔH is the same regardless of the path taken between reactants and products. Thus, the sum of the enthalpy changes for the individual steps in a reaction is equal to the overall enthalpy change for the entire reaction, a relationship known as **Hess's law**. Using this law, it is possible to calculate overall enthalpy changes for individual steps that can't be measured directly. Hess's law also makes it possible to calculate the enthalpy change of any reaction if the standard heats of formation ($\Delta H°_f$) are known for the reactants and products. The **standard heat of formation** is the enthalpy change for the hypothetical formation of 1 mol of a substance in its **thermodynamic standard state** from the most stable forms of the constituent elements in their standard states (1 atm pressure and a specified temperature, usually 25 °C).

In addition to enthalpy, **entropy (S)**—a measure of the amount of molecular randomness in a system—is also important in determining whether a process will occur spontaneously. Together, changes in enthalpy and entropy define a quantity called the **Gibbs free-energy change (ΔG)** according to the equation $\Delta G = \Delta H - T\Delta S$. If ΔG is negative, the reaction is **spontaneous**; if ΔG is positive, the reaction is nonspontaneous.

KEY WORDS

CONCEPTUAL PROBLEMS

Problems 8.1–8.26 appear within the chapter.

8.27 The following reaction is exothermic:

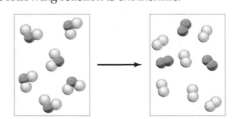

(a) Write a balanced equation for the reaction (red spheres represent A atoms and ivory spheres represent B atoms).

(b) What are the signs (+ or −) of ΔH and ΔS for the reaction?

(c) Is the reaction likely to be spontaneous at lower temperatures only, at higher temperatures only, or at all temperatures?

8.28 Imagine a reaction that results in a change in both volume and temperature:

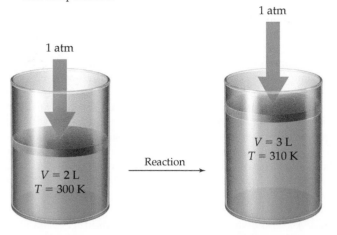

(a) Has any work been done? If so, is its sign positive or negative?

(b) Has there been an enthalpy change? If so, what is the sign of ΔH? Is the reaction exothermic or endothermic?

8.29 Redraw the following diagram to represent the situation (a) when work has been gained by the system and (b) when work has been lost by the system:

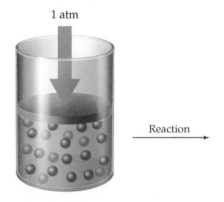

8.30 Acetylene, C_2H_2, reacts with H_2 in two steps to yield ethane, CH_3CH_3:

(1) $HC\equiv CH + H_2 \longrightarrow H_2C=CH_2$ $\Delta H° = -175.1$ kJ
(2) $H_2C=CH_2 + H_2 \longrightarrow CH_3CH_3$ $\Delta H° = -136.3$ kJ
Net $HC\equiv CH + 2\,H_2 \longrightarrow CH_3CH_3$ $\Delta H° = -311.4$ kJ

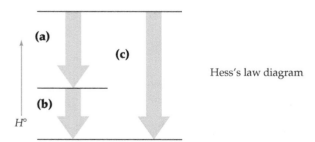

Hess's law diagram

Which arrow (a, b, c) in the Hess's law diagram corresponds to which step, and which arrow corresponds to the net reaction? Where are the reactants located on the diagram, and where are the products located?

8.31 Draw a Hess's law diagram similar to the one in Problem 8.30 for the reaction of ethyl alcohol (CH_3CH_2OH) with oxygen to yield acetic acid (CH_3CO_2H).

(1) $CH_3CH_2OH(l) + 1/2\,O_2(g) \longrightarrow$
     $\qquad\qquad CH_3CHO(g) + H_2O(l)$ $\Delta H° = -174.2$ kJ

(2) $CH_3CHO(g) + 1/2\,O_2(g) \longrightarrow$
     $\qquad\qquad CH_3CO_2H(l)$ $\Delta H° = -318.4$ kJ

Net $CH_3CH_2OH(l) + O_2(g) \longrightarrow$
     $\qquad\qquad CH_3CO_2H(l) + H_2O(l)$ $\Delta H° = -492.6$ kJ

8.32 A reaction is carried out in a cylinder fitted with a movable piston. The starting volume is $V = 5.00$ L, and the apparatus is held at constant temperature and pressure. Assuming that $\Delta H = -35.0$ kJ and $\Delta E = -34.8$ kJ, redraw the piston to show its position after reaction. Does V increase, decrease, or remain the same?

8.33 The following drawing portrays a reaction of the type $A \longrightarrow B + C$, where the different colored spheres represent different molecular structures. Assume that the reaction has $\Delta H° = +55$ kJ. Is the reaction likely to be spontaneous at all temperatures, nonspontaneous at all temperatures, or spontaneous at some but nonspontaneous at others? Explain.

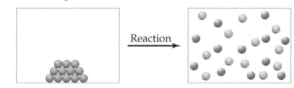

Reaction

8.34 What are the signs of ΔH, ΔS, and ΔG for the following spontaneous change? Explain.

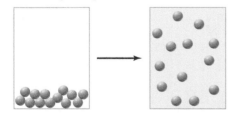

8.35 The following reaction of A_3 molecules is spontaneous:

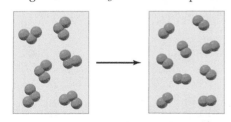

(a) Write a balanced equation for the reaction.

(b) What are the signs of ΔH, ΔS, and ΔG for the reaction? Explain.

SECTION PROBLEMS

Heat, Work, and Energy (Sections 8.1–8.3)

8.36 What is the difference between heat and temperature? Between work and energy? Between kinetic energy and potential energy?

8.37 What is internal energy?

8.38 Which has more kinetic energy, a 1400 kg car moving at 115 km/h or a 12,000 kg truck moving at 38 km/h?

8.39 Assume that the kinetic energy of a 1400 kg car moving at 115 km/h (Problem 8.38) could be converted entirely into heat. What amount of water could be heated from 20 °C to 50 °C by the car's energy?

8.40 Calculate the work done in joules by a chemical reaction if the volume increases from 3.2 L to 3.4 L against a constant external pressure of 3.6 atm. What is the sign of the energy change?

8.41 The addition of H_2 to C=C double bonds is an important reaction used in the preparation of margarine from vegetable oils. If 50.0 mL of H_2 and 50.0 mL of ethylene (C_2H_4) are allowed to react at 1.5 atm, the product ethane (C_2H_6) has a volume of 50.0 mL. Calculate the amount of PV work done, and tell the direction of the energy flow.

$$C_2H_4(g) + H_2(g) \longrightarrow C_2H_6(g)$$

8.42 Assume that the nutritional content of an apple—say 50 Cal (1 Cal = 1000 cal)—could be used to light a lightbulb. For how many minutes would there be light from each of the following?
(a) a 100 watt incandescent bulb (1 W = 1 J/s)
(b) a 23 watt compact fluorescent bulb, which provides a similar amount of light

8.43 A double cheeseburger has a caloric content of 440 Cal (1 Cal = 1000 cal). If this energy could be used to operate a television set, for how many hours would the following sets run?
(a) a 275 watt 46 in. plasma TV (1 W = 1 J/s)
(b) a 175 watt 46 in. LCD TV

8.44 A reaction inside a cylindrical container with a movable piston causes the volume to change from 12.0 L to 18.0 L while the pressure outside the container remains constant at 0.975 atm. (The volume of a cylinder is $V = \pi r^2 h$, where h is the height; 1 L · atm = 101.325 J.)
(a) What is the value in joules of the work w done during the reaction?
(b) The diameter of the piston is 17.0 cm. How far does the piston move?

8.45 At a constant pressure of 0.905 atm, a chemical reaction takes place in a cylindrical container with a movable piston having a diameter of 40.0 cm. During the reaction, the height of the piston drops by 65.0 cm. (The volume of a cylinder is $V = \pi r^2 h$, where h is the height; 1 L · atm = 101.325 J.)
(a) What is the change in volume in liters during the reaction?
(b) What is the value in joules of the work w done during the reaction?

Energy and Enthalpy (Sections 8.4–8.6)

8.46 What is the difference between the internal energy change ΔE and the enthalpy change ΔH? Which of the two is measured at constant pressure, and which at constant volume?

8.47 What is the sign of ΔH for an exothermic reaction? For an endothermic reaction?

8.48 Under what circumstances are ΔE and ΔH essentially equal?

8.49 Which of the following has the highest enthalpy content, and which the lowest at a given temperature: $H_2O(s)$, $H_2O(l)$, or $H_2O(g)$? Explain.

8.50 The enthalpy change for the reaction of 50.0 mL of ethylene with 50.0 mL of H_2 at 1.5 atm pressure (Problem 8.41) is $\Delta H = -0.31$ kJ. What is the value of ΔE?

8.51 Assume that a particular reaction evolves 244 kJ of heat and that 35 kJ of PV work is gained by the system. What are the values of ΔE and ΔH for the system? For the surroundings?

8.52 What is the enthalpy change (ΔH) for a reaction at a constant pressure of 1.00 atm if the internal energy change (ΔE) is 44.0 kJ and the volume increase is 14.0 L? (1 L · atm = 101.325 J.)

8.53 A reaction takes place at a constant pressure of 1.10 atm with an internal energy change (ΔE) of 71.5 kJ and a volume decrease of 13.6 L. What is the enthalpy change (ΔH) for the reaction? (1 L · atm = 101.325 J.)

8.54 Used in welding metals, the reaction of acetylene with oxygen has $\Delta H° = -1256.2$ kJ:

$$C_2H_2(g) + 5/2\ O_2(g) \longrightarrow H_2O(g) + 2\ CO_2(g)$$
$$\Delta H° = -1256.2 \text{ kJ}$$

How much PV work is done in kilojoules and what is the value of ΔE in kilojoules for the reaction of 6.50 g of acetylene at atmospheric pressure if the volume change is −2.80 L?

8.55 Ethyl chloride (C_2H_5Cl), a substance used as a topical anesthetic, is prepared by reaction of ethylene with hydrogen chloride:

$$C_2H_4(g) + HCl(g) \longrightarrow C_2H_5Cl(g) \quad \Delta H° = -72.3 \text{ kJ}$$

Ethyl chloride

How much PV work is done in kilojoules, and what is the value of ΔE in kilojoules if 89.5 g of ethylene and 125 g of HCl are allowed to react at atmospheric pressure and the volume change is −71.5 L?

8.56 The familiar "ether" used as an anesthetic agent is diethyl ether, $C_4H_{10}O$. Its heat of vaporization is +26.5 kJ/mol at its boiling point. How much energy in kilojoules is required to convert 100 mL of diethyl ether at its boiling point from liquid to vapor if its density is 0.7138 g/mL?

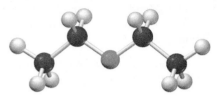

Diethyl ether

8.57 How much energy in kilojoules is required to convert 100 mL of water at its boiling point from liquid to vapor, and how does this compare with the result calculated in Problem 8.56 for diethyl ether? [$\Delta H_{vap}(H_2O)$ = +40.7 kJ/mol]

8.58 Aluminum metal reacts with chlorine with a spectacular display of sparks:

$$2\,Al(s) + 3\,Cl_2(g) \longrightarrow 2\,AlCl_3(s) \quad \Delta H° = -1408.4 \text{ kJ}$$

How much heat in kilojoules is released on reaction of 5.00 g of Al?

8.59 How much heat in kilojoules is evolved or absorbed in the reaction of 1.00 g of Na with H_2O? Is the reaction exothermic or endothermic?

$$2\,Na(s) + 2\,H_2O(l) \longrightarrow 2\,NaOH(aq) + H_2(g)$$
$$\Delta H° = -368.4 \text{ kJ}$$

8.60 How much heat in kilojoules is evolved or absorbed in the reaction of 2.50 g of Fe_2O_3 with enough carbon monoxide to produce iron metal? Is the process exothermic or endothermic?

$$Fe_2O_3(s) + 3\,CO(g) \longrightarrow 2\,Fe(s) + 3\,CO_2(g)$$
$$\Delta H° = -24.8 \text{ kJ}$$

8.61 How much heat in kilojoules is evolved or absorbed in the reaction of 233.0 g of calcium oxide with enough carbon to produce calcium carbide? Is the process exothermic or endothermic?

$$CaO(s) + 3\,C(s) \longrightarrow CaC_2(s) + CO(g) \quad \Delta H° = 464.6 \text{ kJ}$$

Calorimetry and Heat Capacity (Section 8.7)

8.62 What is the difference between heat capacity and specific heat?

8.63 Does a measurement carried out in a bomb calorimeter give a value for ΔH or ΔE? Explain.

8.64 Sodium metal is sometimes used as a cooling agent in heat-exchange units because of its relatively high molar heat capacity of 28.2 J/(mol·°C). What is the specific heat of sodium in J/(g·°C)?

8.65 Titanium metal is used as a structural material in many high-tech applications, such as in jet engines. What is the specific heat of titanium in J/(g·°C) if it takes 89.7 J to raise the temperature of a 33.0 g block by 5.20 °C? What is the molar heat capacity of titanium in J/(mol·°C)?

8.66 When 1.045 g of CaO is added to 50.0 mL of water at 25.0 °C in a calorimeter, the temperature of the water increases to 32.3 °C. Assuming that the specific heat of the solution is 4.18 J/(g·°C) and that the calorimeter itself absorbs a negligible amount of heat, calculate ΔH in kilojoules for the reaction

$$CaO(s) + H_2O(l) \longrightarrow Ca(OH)_2(aq)$$

8.67 When 0.187 g of benzene, C_6H_6, is burned in a bomb calorimeter, the surrounding water bath rises in temperature by 7.48 °C. Assuming that the bath contains 250.0 g of water and that the calorimeter itself absorbs a negligible amount of heat, calculate combustion energies (ΔE) for benzene in both kJ/g and kJ/mol.

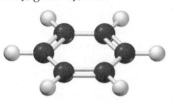

Benzene

8.68 When a solution containing 8.00 g of NaOH in 50.0 g of water at 25.0 °C is added to a solution of 8.00 g of HCl in 250.0 g of water at 25.0 °C in a calorimeter, the temperature of the solution increases to 33.5 °C. Assuming that the specific heat of the solution is 4.18 J/(g·°C) and that the calorimeter absorbs a negligible amount of heat, calculate ΔH in kilojoules for the reaction

$$NaOH(aq) + HCl(aq) \longrightarrow NaCl(aq) + H_2O(l)$$

When the experiment is repeated using a solution of 10.00 g of HCl in 248.0 g of water, the same temperature increase is observed. Explain.

8.69 Instant cold packs used to treat athletic injuries contain solid NH_4NO_3 and a pouch of water. When the pack is squeezed, the pouch breaks and the solid dissolves, lowering the temperature because of the endothermic reaction

$$NH_4NO_3(s) \xrightarrow{H_2O} NH_4NO_3(aq) \quad \Delta H = +25.7 \text{ kJ}$$

What is the final temperature in a squeezed cold pack that contains 50.0 g of NH_4NO_3 dissolved in 125 mL of water? Assume a specific heat of 4.18 J/(g·°C) for the solution, an initial temperature of 25.0 °C, and no heat transfer between the cold pack and the environment.

Hess's Law and Heats of Formation (Sections 8.8 and 8.9)

8.70 How is the standard state of an element defined?

8.71 What is a compound's standard heat of formation?

8.72 What is Hess's law, and why does it "work"?

8.73 Why do elements always have $\Delta H°_f = 0$?

8.74 What phase of matter is associated with the standard states of the following elements and compounds?

  (a) Cl_2 **(b)** Hg   **(c)** CO_2 **(d)** Ga

8.75 What is the phase of the standard states of the following elements and compounds?

  (a) NH_3 **(b)** Fe   **(c)** N_2 **(d)** Br_2

8.76 Write balanced equations for the formation of the following compounds from their elements:

  (a) iron(III) oxide

  (b) sucrose (table sugar, $C_{12}H_{22}O_{11}$)

  (c) uranium hexafluoride (a solid at 25 °C)

8.77 Write balanced equations for the formation of the following compounds from their elements:

(a) ethanol (C_2H_6O)

(b) sodium sulfate

(c) dichloromethane (a liquid, CH_2Cl_2)

8.78 Sulfuric acid (H_2SO_4), the most widely produced chemical in the world, is made by a two-step oxidation of sulfur to sulfur trioxide, SO_3, followed by reaction with water. Calculate $\Delta H°_f$ for SO_3 in kJ/mol, given the following data:

$$S(s) + O_2(g) \longrightarrow SO_2(g) \qquad \Delta H° = -296.8 \text{ kJ}$$
$$SO_2(g) + 1/2\, O_2(g) \longrightarrow SO_3(g) \quad \Delta H° = -98.9 \text{ kJ}$$

8.79 Calculate $\Delta H°_f$ in kJ/mol for benzene, C_6H_6, from the following data:

$$2\, C_6H_6(l) + 15\, O_2(g) \longrightarrow 12\, CO_2(g) + 6\, H_2O(l)$$
$$\Delta H° = -6534 \text{ kJ}$$
$$\Delta H°_f\, (CO_2) = -393.5 \text{ kJ/mol}$$
$$\Delta H°_f\, (H_2O) = -285.8 \text{ kJ/mol}$$

8.80 The standard enthalpy change for the reaction of $SO_3(g)$ with $H_2O(l)$ to yield $H_2SO_4(aq)$ is $\Delta H° = -227.8$ kJ. Use the information in Problem 8.78 to calculate $\Delta H°_f$ for $H_2SO_4(aq)$ in kJ/mol. [For $H_2O(l)$, $\Delta H°_f = -285.8$ kJ/mol.]

8.81 Acetic acid (CH_3CO_2H), whose aqueous solutions are known as *vinegar*, is prepared by reaction of ethyl alcohol (CH_3CH_2OH) with oxygen:

$$CH_3CH_2OH(l) + O_2(g) \longrightarrow CH_3CO_2H(l) + H_2O(l)$$

Use the following data to calculate $\Delta H°$ in kilojoules for the reaction:

$$\Delta H°_f\, [CH_3CH_2OH(l)] = -277.7 \text{ kJ/mol}$$
$$\Delta H°_f\, [CH_3CO_2H(l)] = -484.5 \text{ kJ/mol}$$
$$\Delta H°_f\, [H_2O(l)] = -285.8 \text{ kJ/mol}$$

8.82 Styrene (C_8H_8), the precursor of polystyrene polymers, has a standard heat of combustion of -4395 kJ/mol. Write a balanced equation for the combustion reaction, and calculate $\Delta H°_f$ for styrene in kJ/mol.

$$\Delta H°_f\, [CO_2(g)] = -393.5 \text{ kJ/mol};$$
$$\Delta H°_f\, [H_2O(l)] = -285.8 \text{ kJ/mol}$$

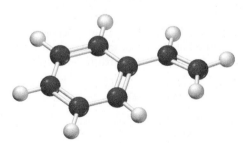

Styrene

8.83 Methyl *tert*-butyl ether (MTBE), $C_5H_{12}O$, a gasoline additive used to boost octane ratings, has $\Delta H°_f = -313.6$ kJ/mol. Write a balanced equation for its combustion reaction, and calculate its standard heat of combustion in kilojoules.

8.84 Methyl *tert*-butyl ether (Problem 8.83) is prepared by reaction of methanol(l) ($\Delta H°_f = -239.2$ kJ/mol) with 2-methyl-propene(g), according to the equation

$$CH_3-\underset{\underset{2\text{-Methylpropene}}{}}{C}=CH_2 + CH_3OH \longrightarrow$$

with CH_3 on top of the C.

$$CH_3-\overset{CH_3}{\underset{CH_3}{C}}-O-CH_3 \qquad \Delta H° = -57.5 \text{ kJ}$$

Methyl *tert*-butyl ether

Calculate $\Delta H°_f$ in kJ/mol for 2-methylpropene.

8.85 One possible use for the cooking fat left over after making french fries is to burn it as fuel. Write a balanced equation, and use the following data to calculate the amount of energy released in kJ/mL from the combustion of cooking fat:

$$\text{Formula} = C_{51}H_{88}O_6 \qquad \Delta H°_f = -1310 \text{ kJ/mol}$$
$$\text{Density} = 0.94 \text{ g/ml}$$

8.86 Given the standard heats of formation shown in Appendix B, what is $\Delta H°$ in kilojoules for the reaction $CaCO_3(s) \longrightarrow CaO(s) + CO_2(g)$?

8.87 Given the standard heats of formation shown in Appendix B, what is $\Delta H°$ in kilojoules for the reaction $3\, N_2O_4(g) + 2\, H_2O(l) \longrightarrow 4\, HNO_3(aq) + 2\, NO(g)$.

Bond Dissociation Energies (Section 8.10)

8.88 Use the bond dissociation energies in Table 7.1 on page 219 to calculate an approximate $\Delta H°$ in kilojoules for the reaction of ethylene with hydrogen to yield ethane.

$$H_2C=CH_2(g) + H_2(g) \longrightarrow CH_3CH_3(g)$$

8.89 Use the bond dissociation energies in Table 7.1 to calculate an approximate $\Delta H°$ in kilojoules for the industrial synthesis of isopropyl alcohol (rubbing alcohol) by reaction of water with propene.

$$\underset{\text{Propene}}{CH_3CH=CH_2} + H_2O \longrightarrow \underset{\text{Isopropyl alcohol}}{CH_3\overset{OH}{C}HCH_3}$$

8.90 Calculate an approximate heat of combustion for butane in kilojoules by using the bond dissociation energies in Table 7.1. (The strength of the $O=O$ bond is 498 kJ/mol, and that of a $C=O$ bond in CO_2 is 804 kJ/mol.)

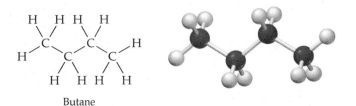

Butane

8.91 Use the bond dissociation energies in Table 7.1 to calculate an approximate heat of reaction, $\Delta H°$ in kilojoules, for the industrial reaction of ethanol with acetic acid to yield ethyl acetate (used as nail-polish remover) and water.

$$H-\underset{\underset{H}{|}}{\overset{\overset{H}{|}}{C}}-\overset{\overset{O}{\|}}{C}-O-H \;+\; H-\underset{\underset{H}{|}}{\overset{\overset{H}{|}}{C}}-\underset{\underset{H}{|}}{\overset{\overset{H}{|}}{C}}-O-H \longrightarrow$$

Acetic acid   Ethanol

$$H-\underset{\underset{H}{|}}{\overset{\overset{H}{|}}{C}}-\overset{\overset{O}{\|}}{C}-O-\underset{\underset{H}{|}}{\overset{\overset{H}{|}}{C}}-\underset{\underset{H}{|}}{\overset{\overset{H}{|}}{C}}-H \;+\; H_2O$$

Ethyl acetate

Free Energy and Entropy (Sections 8.12 and 8.13)

8.92 What does entropy measure?

8.93 What are the two terms that make up the free-energy change for a reaction, ΔG, and which of the two is usually more important?

8.94 How is it possible for a reaction to be spontaneous yet endothermic?

8.95 Is it possible for a reaction to be nonspontaneous yet exothermic? Explain.

8.96 Tell whether the entropy changes for the following processes are likely to be positive or negative:
(a) The fizzing of a newly opened can of soda
(b) The growth of a plant from seed

8.97 Tell whether the entropy changes, ΔS, for the following processes are likely to be positive or negative:
(a) The conversion of liquid water to water vapor at 100 °C
(b) The freezing of liquid water to ice at 0 °C
(c) The eroding of a mountain by a glacier

8.98 Tell whether the free-energy changes, ΔG, for the processes listed in Problem 8.97 are likely to be positive, negative, or zero.

8.99 When a bottle of perfume is opened, odorous molecules mix with air and slowly diffuse throughout the entire room. Is ΔG for the diffusion process positive, negative, or zero? What about ΔH and ΔS for the diffusion?

8.100 One of the steps in the cracking of petroleum into gasoline involves the thermal breakdown of large hydrocarbon molecules into smaller ones. For example, the following reaction might occur:

$$C_{11}H_{24} \longrightarrow C_4H_{10} + C_4H_8 + C_3H_6$$

Is ΔS for this reaction likely to be positive or negative? Explain.

8.101 The commercial production of 1,2-dichloroethane, a solvent used in dry cleaning, involves the reaction of ethylene with chlorine:

$$C_2H_4(g) + Cl_2(g) \longrightarrow C_2H_4Cl_2(l)$$

Is ΔS for this reaction likely to be positive or negative? Explain.

8.102 Tell whether reactions with the following values of ΔH and ΔS are spontaneous or nonspontaneous and whether they are exothermic or endothermic:
(a) $\Delta H = -48$ kJ; $\Delta S = +135$ J/K at 400 K
(b) $\Delta H = -48$ kJ; $\Delta S = -135$ J/K at 400 K
(c) $\Delta H = +48$ kJ; $\Delta S = +135$ J/K at 400 K
(d) $\Delta H = +48$ kJ; $\Delta S = -135$ J/K at 400 K

8.103 Tell whether reactions with the following values of ΔH and ΔS are spontaneous or nonspontaneous and whether they are exothermic or endothermic:
(a) $\Delta H = -128$ kJ; $\Delta S = 35$ J/K at 500 K
(b) $\Delta H = +67$ kJ; $\Delta S = -140$ J/K at 250 K
(c) $\Delta H = +75$ kJ; $\Delta S = 95$ J/K at 800 K

8.104 Suppose that a reaction has $\Delta H = -33$ kJ and $\Delta S = -58$ J/K. At what temperature will it change from spontaneous to nonspontaneous?

8.105 Suppose that a reaction has $\Delta H = +41$ kJ and $\Delta S = -27$ J/K. At what temperature, if any, will it change between spontaneous and nonspontaneous?

8.106 Which of the reactions (a)–(d) in Problem 8.102 are spontaneous at all temperatures, which are nonspontaneous at all temperatures, and which have an equilibrium temperature?

8.107 Vinyl chloride ($H_2C{=}CHCl$), the starting material used in the industrial preparation of poly(vinyl chloride), is prepared by a two-step process that begins with the reaction of Cl_2 with ethylene to yield 1,2-dichloroethane:

$$Cl_2(g) + H_2C{=}CH_2(g) \longrightarrow ClCH_2CH_2Cl(l)$$

$$\Delta H° = -217.5 \text{ kJ}$$
$$\Delta S° = -233.9 \text{ J/K}$$

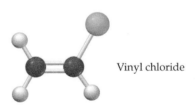

Vinyl chloride

(a) Tell whether the reaction is favored by entropy, by enthalpy, by both, or by neither, and then calculate $\Delta G°$ at 298 K.
(b) Tell whether the reaction has an equilibrium temperature between spontaneous and nonspontaneous. If yes, calculate the equilibrium temperature.

8.108 Ethyl alcohol has $\Delta H_{fusion} = 5.02$ kJ/mol and melts at -114.1 °C. What is the value of ΔS_{fusion} for ethyl alcohol?

8.109 Chloroform has $\Delta H_{vaporization} = 29.2$ kJ/mol and boils at 61.2 °C. What is the value of $\Delta S_{vaporization}$ for chloroform?

CHAPTER PROBLEMS

8.110 When 1.50 g of magnesium metal is allowed to react with 200 mL of 6.00 M aqueous HCl, the temperature rises from 25.0 °C to 42.9 °C. Calculate ΔH in kilojoules for the reaction, assuming that the heat capacity of the calorimeter is 776 J/°C, that the specific heat of the final solution is the same as that of water [(4.18 J/(g·°C)], and that the density of the solution is 1.00 g/mL.

8.111 Use the data in Appendix B to find standard enthalpies of reaction in kilojoules for the following processes:

(a) $C(s) + CO_2(g) \longrightarrow 2\,CO(g)$

(b) $2\,H_2O_2(aq) \longrightarrow 2\,H_2O(l) + O_2(g)$

(c) $Fe_2O_3(s) + 3\,CO(g) \longrightarrow 2\,Fe(s) + 3\,CO_2(g)$

8.112 Find $\Delta H°$ in kilojoules for the reaction of nitric oxide with oxygen, $2\,NO(g) + O_2(g) \longrightarrow N_2O_4(g)$, given the following data:

$$N_2O_4(g) \longrightarrow 2\,NO_2(g) \qquad \Delta H° = 55.3 \text{ kJ}$$
$$NO(g) + 1/2\,O_2(g) \longrightarrow NO_2(g) \quad \Delta H° = -58.1 \text{ kJ}$$

8.113 The boiling point of a substance is defined as the temperature at which liquid and vapor coexist in equilibrium. Use the heat of vaporization ($\Delta H_{vap} = 30.91$ kJ/mol) and the entropy of vaporization [$\Delta S_{vap} = 93.2$ J/(K·mol)] to calculate the boiling point (°C) of liquid bromine.

8.114 What is the melting point of benzene in kelvin if $\Delta H_{fusion} = 9.95$ kJ/mol and $\Delta S_{fusion} = 35.7$ J/(K·mol)?

8.115 Metallic mercury is obtained by heating the mineral cinnabar (HgS) in air:

$$HgS(s) + O_2(g) \longrightarrow Hg(l) + SO_2(g)$$

(a) Use the data in Appendix B to calculate $\Delta H°$ in kilojoules for the reaction.

(b) The entropy change for the reaction is $\Delta S° = +36.7$ J/K. Is the reaction spontaneous at 25 °C?

(c) Under what conditions, if any, is the reaction nonspontaneous? Explain.

8.116 Use the average bond dissociation energies in Table 7.1 to calculate approximate reaction enthalpies in kilojoules for the following processes:

(a) $2\,CH_4(g) \longrightarrow C_2H_6(g) + H_2(g)$

(b) $C_2H_6(g) + F_2(g) \longrightarrow C_2H_5F(g) + HF(g)$

(c) $N_2(g) + 3\,H_2(g) \longrightarrow 2\,NH_3(g)$

8.117 Methanol (CH_3OH) is made industrially in two steps from CO and H_2. It is so cheap to make that it is being considered for use as a precursor to hydrocarbon fuels, such as methane (CH_4):

Step 1. $CO(g) + 2\,H_2(g) \longrightarrow CH_3OH(l)$
$$\Delta S° = -332 \text{ J/K}$$

Step 2. $CH_3OH(l) \longrightarrow CH_4(g) + 1/2\,O_2(g)$
$$\Delta S° = 162 \text{ J/K}$$

(a) Calculate $\Delta H°$ in kilojoules for step 1.

(b) Calculate $\Delta G°$ in kilojoules for step 1.

(c) Is step 1 spontaneous at 298 K?

(d) Which term is more important, $\Delta H°$ or $\Delta S°$?

(e) In what temperature range is step 1 spontaneous?

(f) Calculate $\Delta H°$ for step 2.

(g) Calculate $\Delta G°$ for step 2.

(h) Is step 2 spontaneous at 298 K?

(i) Which term is more important, $\Delta H°$ or $\Delta S°$?

(j) In what temperature range is step 2 spontaneous?

(k) Calculate an overall $\Delta G°$, $\Delta H°$, and $\Delta S°$ for the formation of CH_4 from CO and H_2.

(l) Is the overall reaction spontaneous at 298 K?

(m) If you were designing a production facility, would you plan on carrying out the reactions in separate steps or together? Explain.

8.118 Isooctane, C_8H_{18}, is the component of gasoline from which the term *octane rating* derives.

Isooctane

(a) Write a balanced equation for the combustion of isooctane(l) with O_2 to yield $CO_2(g)$ and $H_2O(l)$.

(b) The standard molar heat of combustion for isooctane(l) is -5461 kJ/mol. Calculate $\Delta H°_f$ for isooctane(l).

8.119 We said in Section 8.1 that the potential energy of water at the top of a dam or waterfall is converted into heat when the water dashes against rocks at the bottom. The potential energy of the water at the top is equal to $E_P = mgh$, where m is the mass of the water, g is the acceleration of the falling water due to gravity ($g = 9.81$ m/s^2), and h is the height of the water. Assuming that all the energy is converted to heat, calculate the temperature rise of the water in degrees Celsius after falling over California's Yosemite Falls, a distance of 739 m. The specific heat of water is 4.18 J/(g·K).

8.120 For a process to be spontaneous, the total entropy of the system *and its surroundings* must increase; that is

$$\Delta S_{total} = \Delta S_{system} + \Delta S_{surr} > 0 \quad \text{For a spontaneous process}$$

Furthermore, the entropy change in the surroundings, ΔS_{surr}, is related to the enthalpy change for the process by the equation $\Delta S_{surr} = -\Delta H/T$.

(a) Since both ΔG and ΔS_{total} offer criteria for spontaneity, they must be related. Derive a relationship between them.

(b) What is the value of ΔS_{surr} for the photosynthesis of glucose from CO_2 at 298 K?

$$6\,CO_2(g) + 6\,H_2O(l) \longrightarrow C_6H_{12}O_6(s) + 6\,O_2(g)$$
$$\Delta G° = 2879 \text{ kJ}$$
$$\Delta S° = -262 \text{ J/K}$$

8.121 Set up a Hess's law cycle, and use the following information to calculate ΔH°_f for aqueous nitric acid, $HNO_3(aq)$. You will need to use fractional coefficients for some equations.

$$3\,NO_2(g) + H_2O(l) \longrightarrow 2\,HNO_3(aq) + NO(g)$$
$$\Delta H^\circ = -137.3\ kJ$$
$$2\,NO(g) + O_2(g) \longrightarrow 2\,NO_2(g) \qquad \Delta H^\circ = -116.2\ kJ$$
$$4\,NH_3(g) + 5\,O_2(g) \longrightarrow 4\,NO(g) + 6\,H_2O(l)$$
$$\Delta H^\circ = -1165.2\ kJ$$

$NH_3(g) \qquad \Delta H^\circ_f = -46.1\ kJ/mol$
$H_2O(l) \qquad \Delta H^\circ_f = -285.8\ kJ/mol$

8.122 Hess's law can be used to calculate reaction enthalpies for hypothetical processes that can't be carried out in the laboratory. Set up a Hess's law cycle that will let you calculate ΔH° for the conversion of methane to ethylene:

$$2\,CH_4(g) \longrightarrow C_2H_4(g) + 2\,H_2(g)$$

You can use the following information:

$$2\,C_2H_6(g) + 7\,O_2(g) \longrightarrow 4\,CO_2(g) + 6\,H_2O(l)$$
$$\Delta H^\circ = -3120.8\ kJ$$
$$CH_4(g) + 2\,O_2(g) \longrightarrow CO_2(g) + 2\,H_2O(l)$$
$$\Delta H^\circ = -890.3\ kJ$$
$$C_2H_4(g) + H_2(g) \longrightarrow C_2H_6(g) \qquad \Delta H^\circ = -136.3\ kJ$$

$H_2O(l) \qquad \Delta H^\circ_f = -285.8\ kJ/mol$

8.123 A 110.0 g piece of molybdenum metal is heated to 100.0 °C and placed in a calorimeter that contains 150.0 g of water at 24.6 °C. The system reaches equilibrium at a final temperature of 28.0 °C. Calculate the specific heat of molybdenum metal in $J/(g \cdot {}^\circ C)$. The specific heat of water is 4.184 $J/(g \cdot {}^\circ C)$.

8.124 Given 400.0 g of hot tea at 80.0 °C, what mass of ice at 0 °C must be added to obtain iced tea at 10.0 °C? The specific heat of the tea is 4.18 $J/(g \cdot {}^\circ C)$, and ΔH_{fusion} for ice is +6.01 kJ/mol.

8.125 Citric acid has three dissociable hydrogens. When 5.00 mL of 0.64 M citric acid and 45.00 mL of 0.77 M NaOH are mixed at an initial temperature of 26.0 °C, the temperature rises to 27.9 °C as the citric acid is neutralized. The combined mixture has a

mass of 51.6 g and a specific heat of 4.0 $J/(g \cdot {}^\circ C)$. Assuming that no heat is transferred to the surroundings, calculate the enthalpy change for the reaction of 1.00 mol of citric acid in kJ. Is the reaction exothermic or endothermic?

Citric acid

8.126 Assume that 100.0 mL of 0.200 M CsOH and 50.0 mL of 0.400 M HCl are mixed in a calorimeter. The solutions start out at 22.50 °C, and the final temperature after reaction is 24.28 °C. The densities of the solutions are all 1.00 g/mL, and the specific heat of the mixture is 4.2 $J/(g \cdot {}^\circ C)$. What is the enthalpy change for the neutralization reaction of 1.00 mol of CsOH in kJ?

8.127 Imagine that you dissolve 10.0 g of a mixture of $NaNO_3$ and KF in 100.0 g of water and find that the temperature rises by 2.22 °C. Using the following data, calculate the mass of each compound in the original mixture. Assume that the specific heat of the solution is 4.18 $J/(g \cdot {}^\circ C)$.

$$NaNO_3(s) \longrightarrow NaNO_3(aq) \quad \Delta H = +20.4\ kJ/mol$$
$$KF(s) \longrightarrow KF(aq) \qquad \Delta H = -17.7\ kJ/mol$$

8.128 Consider the reaction: $4\,CO(g) + 2\,NO_2(g) \longrightarrow 4\,CO_2(g) + N_2(g)$. Using the following information, determine ΔH° for the reaction at 25 °C.

$NO(g) \qquad\qquad\qquad\qquad\qquad \Delta H^\circ_f = +91.3\ kJ/mol$
$CO_2(g) \qquad\qquad\qquad\qquad\qquad \Delta H^\circ_f = -393.5\ kJ/mol$
$2\,NO(g) + O_2(g) \longrightarrow 2\,NO_2(g) \quad \Delta H^\circ = -116.2\ kJ$
$2\,CO(g) + O_2(g) \longrightarrow 2\,CO_2(g) \quad \Delta H^\circ = -566.0\ kJ$

MULTICONCEPT PROBLEMS

8.129 The reaction $S_8(g) \longrightarrow 4\,S_2(g)$ has $\Delta H^\circ = +237\ kJ$

(a) The S_8 molecule has eight sulfur atoms arranged in a ring. What is the hybridization and geometry around each sulfur atom in S_8?

(b) The average S—S bond dissociation energy is 225 kJ/mol. Using the value of ΔH° given above, what is the S=S double bond energy in $S_2(g)$?

(c) Assuming that the bonding in S_2 is similar to the bonding in O_2, give a molecular orbital description of the bonding in S_2. Is S_2 likely to be paramagnetic or diamagnetic?

8.130 Phosgene, $COCl_2(g)$, is a toxic gas used as an agent of warfare in World War I.

(a) Draw an electron-dot structure for phosgene.

(b) Using the table of bond dissociation energies (Table 7.1) and the value $\Delta H^\circ_f = 716.7\ kJ/mol$ for C(g), estimate ΔH°_f for $COCl_2(g)$ at 25 °C. Compare your answer to

the actual ΔH°_f given in Appendix B, and explain why your calculation is only an estimate.

8.131 Acid spills are often neutralized with sodium carbonate or sodium hydrogen carbonate. For neutralization of acetic acid, the unbalanced equations are

(1) $CH_3CO_2H(l) + Na_2CO_3(s) \longrightarrow$
$$CH_3CO_2Na(aq) + CO_2(g) + H_2O(l)$$
(2) $CH_3CO_2H(l) + NaHCO_3(s) \longrightarrow$
$$CH_3CO_2Na(aq) + CO_2(g) + H_2O(l)$$

(a) Balance both equations.

(b) How many kilograms of each substance is needed to neutralize a 1.000 gallon spill of pure acetic acid (density = 1.049 g/mL)?

(c) How much heat in kilojoules is absorbed or liberated in each reaction? See Appendix B for standard heats of formation; $\Delta H^\circ_f = -726.1\ kJ/mol$ for $CH_3CO_2Na(aq)$.

8.132 **(a)** Write a balanced equation for the reaction of potassium metal with water.

(b) Use the data in Appendix B to calculate $\Delta H°$ for the reaction of potassium metal with water.

(c) Assume that a chunk of potassium weighing 7.55 g is dropped into 400.0 g of water at 25.0 °C. What is the final temperature of the water if all the heat released is used to warm the water?

(d) What is the molarity of the KOH solution prepared in part **(c)**, and how many milliliters of 0.554 M H_2SO_4 are required to neutralize it?

8.133 Hydrazine, a component of rocket fuel, undergoes combustion to yield N_2 and H_2O:

$$N_2H_4(l) + O_2(g) \longrightarrow N_2(g) + 2\,H_2O(l)$$

(a) Draw an electron-dot structure for hydrazine, predict the geometry about each nitrogen atom, and tell the hybridization of each nitrogen.

(b) Use the following information to set up a Hess's law cycle, and then calculate $\Delta H°$ for the combustion reaction. You will need to use fractional coefficients for some equations.

$$2\,NH_3(g) + 3\,N_2O(g) \longrightarrow 4\,N_2(g) + 3\,H_2O(l)$$
$$\Delta H° = -1011.2 \text{ kJ}$$

$$N_2O(g) + 3\,H_2(g) \longrightarrow N_2H_4(l) + H_2O(l)$$
$$\Delta H° = -317.2 \text{ kJ}$$

$$4\,NH_3(g) + O_2(g) \longrightarrow 2\,N_2H_4(l) + 2\,H_2O(l)$$
$$\Delta H° = -286.0 \text{ kJ}$$

$$H_2O(l) \qquad \Delta H°_f = -285.8 \text{ kJ/mol}$$

(c) How much heat is released on combustion of 100.0 g of hydrazine?

8.134 Reaction of gaseous fluorine with compound **X** yields a single product **Y**, whose mass percent composition is 61.7% F and 38.3% Cl.

(a) What is a probable molecular formula for product **Y**, and what is a probable formula for **X**?

(b) Draw an electron-dot structure for **Y**, and predict the geometry around the central atom.

(c) Calculate $\Delta H°$ for the synthesis of **Y** using the following information:

$$2\,CIF(g) + O_2(g) \longrightarrow Cl_2O(g) + OF_2(g)$$
$$\Delta H° = +205.4 \text{ kJ}$$

$$2\,CIF_3(l) + 2\,O_2(g) \longrightarrow Cl_2O(g) + 3\,OF_2(g)$$
$$\Delta H° = +532.8 \text{ kJ}$$

$$OF_2(g) \qquad \Delta H°_f = +24.5 \text{ kJ/mol}$$

(d) How much heat in kilojoules is released or absorbed in the reaction of 25.0 g of **X** with a stoichiometric amount of F_2, assuming 87.5% yield for the reaction?

CHAPTER

9

Gases: Their Properties and Behavior

Without the invisible blanket of air surrounding us, balloons like Mr. Peanut couldn't float.

CONTENTS

A quick look around tells you that matter takes many forms. Most of the things around you are *solids*, substances whose constituent atoms, molecules, or ions are held rigidly together in a definite way, giving the solid a definite volume and shape. Other substances are *liquids*, whose constituent atoms or molecules are held together less strongly, giving the liquid a definite volume but a changeable and indefinite shape. Still other substances are *gases*, whose constituent atoms or molecules have little attraction for one another and are therefore free to move about in whatever volume is available.

Although gases are few in number—only about a hundred substances are gases at room temperature—their study was enormously important in the historical development of chemical theories. We'll look briefly at this historical development in the present chapter, and we'll see how the behavior of gases can be described.

9.1 GASES AND GAS PRESSURE

We live surrounded by a blanket of air—the mixture of gases that make up the Earth's atmosphere. As shown in Table 9.1, nitrogen and oxygen account for more than 99% by volume of dry air. The remaining 1% is largely argon, with trace amounts of several other substances also present. Carbon dioxide, about which there is so much current concern because of its relationship to global warming, is present in air only to the extent of about 0.0385%, or 385 parts per million (ppm). Although small, this value has risen in the past 160 years from an estimated 290 ppm in 1850, as the burning of fossil fuels and the deforestation of tropical rain forests have increased.

TABLE 9.1 Composition of Dry Air at Sea Level

Constituent	% Volume	% Mass
N_2	78.08	75.52
O_2	20.95	23.14
Ar	0.93	1.29
CO_2	0.0385	0.059
Ne	1.82×10^{-3}	1.27×10^{-3}
He	5.24×10^{-4}	7.24×10^{-5}
CH_4	1.7×10^{-4}	9.4×10^{-5}
Kr	1.14×10^{-4}	3.3×10^{-4}

Air is typical of gases in many respects, and its behavior illustrates several important points about gases. For instance, gas mixtures are always *homogeneous*, meaning that they are uniform in composition. Unlike liquids, which often fail to mix with one another and which may separate into distinct layers—oil and water, for example—gases always mix completely. Furthermore, gases are *compressible*. When pressure is applied, the volume of a gas contracts proportionately. Solids and liquids, however, are nearly incompressible, and even the application of great pressure changes their volume only slightly.

Homogeneous mixing and compressibility both occur because the molecules in gases are far apart (**Figure 9.1**). Mixing occurs because individual gas molecules have little interaction with their neighbors and the chemical identities of those neighbors are therefore irrelevant. In solids and liquids, by contrast, molecules are packed closely together, where they are affected by various attractive and repulsive forces that can inhibit their mixing. Compressibility is possible in gases because less than 0.1% of the volume of a typical gas is taken up by the molecules themselves under normal circumstances; the remaining 99.9% is empty space. By contrast, approximately 70% of a solid's or liquid's volume is taken up by the molecules.

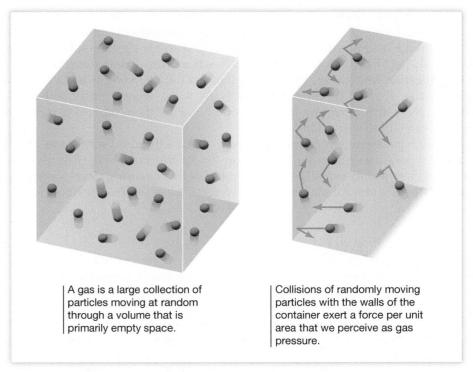

Figure 9.1
Molecular view of a gas.

One of the most obvious characteristics of gases is that they exert a measurable *pressure* on the walls of their container (Figure 9.1). We're all familiar with inflating a balloon or pumping up a bicycle tire and feeling the hardness that results from the pressure inside. In scientific terms, **pressure (*P*)** is defined as a force (*F*) exerted per unit area (*A*). Force, in turn, is defined as mass (*m*) times acceleration (*a*), which, on Earth, is usually the acceleration due to gravity, $a = 9.81$ m/s^2.

$$\text{Pressure } (P) = \frac{F}{A} = \frac{m \times a}{A}$$

The SI unit for force is the **newton (N)**, where $1\ \text{N} = 1\ (\text{kg} \cdot \text{m})/\text{s}^2$, and the SI unit for pressure is the **pascal (Pa)**, where $1\ \text{Pa} = 1\ \text{N/m}^2 = 1\ \text{kg}/(\text{m} \cdot \text{s}^2)$. Expressed in more familiar units, a pascal is actually a very small amount—the pressure exerted by a mass of 10.2 mg resting on an area of 1.00 cm^2. In rough terms, a penny sitting on the tip of your finger exerts a pressure of about 250 Pa.

$$P = \frac{m \times a}{A} = \frac{(10.2\ \text{mg})\left(\dfrac{1\ \text{kg}}{10^6\ \text{mg}}\right)\left(9.81\ \dfrac{\text{m}}{\text{s}^2}\right)}{(1.00\ \text{cm}^2)\left(\dfrac{1\ \text{m}^2}{10^4\ \text{cm}^2}\right)} = \frac{1.00 \times 10^{-4}\ \dfrac{\text{kg} \cdot \text{m}}{\text{s}^2}}{1.00 \times 10^{-4}\ \text{m}^2} = 1.00\ \text{Pa}$$

Just as the air in a tire and a penny on your finger exert pressure, the mass of air in the atmosphere pressing down on the Earth's surface exerts what we call *atmospheric pressure*. In fact, a 1 m^2 column of air extending from the Earth's surface through the upper atmosphere has a mass of about 10,300 kg, producing an atmospheric pressure of approximately 101,000 Pa, or 101 kPa (Figure 9.2).

$$P = \frac{m \times a}{A} = \frac{10,300\ \text{kg} \times 9.81\ \dfrac{\text{m}}{\text{s}^2}}{1.00\ \text{m}^2} = 101,000\ \text{Pa} = 101\ \text{kPa}$$

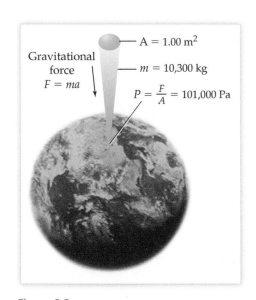

Gravitational force
$F = ma$

$A = 1.00$ m^2
$m = 10,300$ kg
$P = \dfrac{F}{A} = 101,000$ Pa

Figure 9.2
Atmospheric pressure. A column of air 1 m^2 in cross-sectional area extending from the Earth's surface through the upper atmosphere has a mass of about 10,300 kg, producing an atmospheric pressure of approximately 101,000 Pa.

As is frequently the case with SI units, which must serve many disciplines, the pascal is an inconvenient size for most chemical measurements. Thus, the alternative pressure units *millimeter of mercury (mm Hg)*, *atmosphere (atm)*, and *bar* are more often used.

The **millimeter of mercury**, also called a *torr* after the 17th-century Italian scientist Evangelista Torricelli (1608–1647), is based on atmospheric pressure measurements using a mercury *barometer*. As shown in Figure 9.3, a barometer consists of a long, thin tube that is sealed at one end, filled with mercury, and then inverted into a dish of mercury. Some mercury runs from the tube into the dish until the downward pressure of the mercury inside the column is exactly balanced by the outside atmospheric pressure, which presses on the mercury in the dish and pushes it up the column. The height of the mercury column varies slightly from day to day depending on the altitude and weather conditions, but atmospheric pressure at sea level was originally defined as exactly 760 mm Hg.

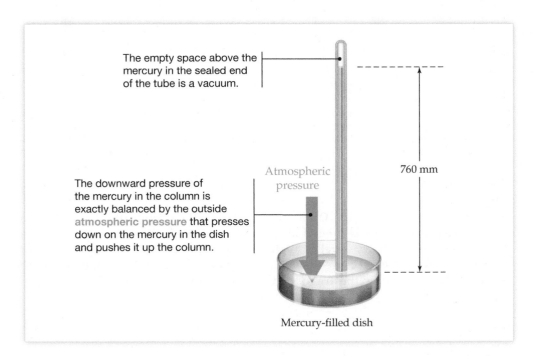

The empty space above the mercury in the sealed end of the tube is a vacuum.

The downward pressure of the mercury in the column is exactly balanced by the outside atmospheric pressure that presses down on the mercury in the dish and pushes it up the column.

Atmospheric pressure

760 mm

Mercury-filled dish

Figure 9.3
A mercury barometer. The barometer measures atmospheric pressure by determining the height of a mercury column supported in a sealed glass tube.

Knowing the density of mercury ($1.359\ 51 \times 10^4$ kg/m^3 at 0 °C) and the acceleration due to gravity ($9.806\ 65$ m/s^2), it's possible to calculate the pressure exerted by the column of mercury 760 mm (0.760 m) in height. Thus, 1 standard **atmosphere** of pressure (1 atm) is now defined as exactly 101,325 Pa:

$$P = (0.760\ \text{m})\left(1.359\ 51 \times 10^4\ \frac{\text{kg}}{\text{m}^3} \right)\left(9.806\ 65\ \frac{\text{m}}{\text{s}^2} \right) = 101{,}325\ \text{Pa}$$

$$\textbf{1 atm} = \textbf{760 mm Hg} = \textbf{101,325 Pa}$$

Although not strictly an SI unit, the **bar** is quickly gaining popularity as a unit of pressure because it is a particularly convenient power of 10 of the SI unit pascal and because it differs from 1 atm by only about 1%:

$$1\ \text{bar} = 100{,}000\ \text{Pa} = 100\ \text{kPa} = 0.986\ 923\ \text{atm}$$

Gas pressure inside a container is often measured using an open-end **manometer**, a simple instrument similar in principle to the mercury barometer. As shown in Figure 9.4, an open-end manometer consists of a U-tube filled with mercury, with one end connected to a gas-filled container and the other end open to the atmosphere. The difference between the pressure of the gas in the container and the pressure

Figure 9.4

Open-end manometers for measuring pressure in a gas-filled bulb.

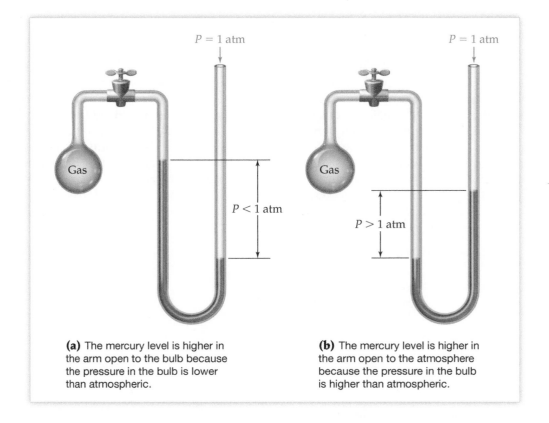

(a) The mercury level is higher in the arm open to the bulb because the pressure in the bulb is lower than atmospheric.

(b) The mercury level is higher in the arm open to the atmosphere because the pressure in the bulb is higher than atmospheric.

of the atmosphere is equal to the difference between the heights of the mercury levels in the two arms of the U-tube. If the gas pressure inside the container is less than atmospheric, the mercury level is higher in the arm connected to the container (Figure 9.4a). If the gas pressure inside the container is greater than atmospheric, the mercury level is higher in the arm open to the atmosphere (Figure 9.4b).

WORKED EXAMPLE 9.1

CONVERTING BETWEEN DIFFERENT UNITS OF PRESSURE

Typical atmospheric pressure on top of Mt. Everest (29,035 ft) is 265 mm Hg. Convert this value to pascals, atmospheres, and bars.

STRATEGY

Use the conversion factors 101,325 Pa/760 mm Hg, 1 atm/760 mm Hg, and 1 bar/10^5 Pa to carry out the necessary calculations.

SOLUTION

$$(265 \text{ mm Hg})\left(\frac{101,325 \text{ Pa}}{760 \text{ mm Hg}}\right) = 3.53 \times 10^4 \text{ Pa}$$

$$(265 \text{ mm Hg})\left(\frac{1 \text{ atm}}{760 \text{ mm Hg}}\right) = 0.349 \text{ atm}$$

$$(3.53 \times 10^4 \text{ Pa})\left(\frac{1 \text{ bar}}{10^5 \text{ Pa}}\right) = 0.353 \text{ bar}$$

BALLPARK CHECK

One atmosphere equals 760 mm Hg pressure. Since 265 mm Hg is about 1/3 of 760 mm Hg, the air pressure on Mt. Everest is about 1/3 of standard atmospheric pressure—approximately 30,000 Pa, 0.3 atm, or 0.3 bar.

▲ Atmospheric pressure decreases as altitude increases. On the top of Mt. Everest, typical atmospheric pressure is 265 mm Hg.

WORKED EXAMPLE 9.2

USING AN OPEN-END MANOMETER

Assume that you are using an open-end manometer (Figure 9.4) filled with mineral oil rather than mercury. What is the gas pressure in the bulb in millimeters of mercury if the level of mineral oil in the arm connected to the bulb is 237 mm higher than the level in the arm connected to the atmosphere and atmospheric pressure is 746 mm Hg? The density of mercury is 13.6 g/mL, and the density of mineral oil is 0.822 g/mL.

STRATEGY

The gas pressure in the bulb equals the difference between the outside pressure and the manometer reading. The manometer reading indicates that the pressure of the gas in the bulb is less than atmospheric because the liquid level is higher on the side connected to the sample. Because mercury is more dense than mineral oil by a factor of 13.6/0.822, or 16.5, a given pressure will hold a column of mercury only 1/16.5 times the height of a column of mineral oil.

SOLUTION

$$P_{manometer} = 237 \text{ mm mineral oil} \times \frac{0.822 \text{ mm Hg}}{13.6 \text{ mm mineral oil}} = 14.3 \text{ mm Hg}$$

$$P_{bulb} = P_{outside} - P_{manometer} = 746 \text{ mm Hg} - 14.3 \text{ mm Hg} = 732 \text{ mm Hg}$$

▶ **PROBLEM 9.1** Yet another common measure of pressure is the unit pounds per square inch (psi). How many pounds per square inch correspond to 1.00 atm? To 1.00 mm Hg?

▶ **PROBLEM 9.2** If the density of water is 1.00 g/mL and the density of mercury is 13.6 g/mL, how high a column of water in meters can be supported by standard atmospheric pressure? By 1 bar?

▶ **PROBLEM 9.3** What is the pressure in atmospheres in a container of gas connected to a mercury-filled, open-end manometer if the level in the arm connected to the container is 24.7 cm higher than in the arm open to the atmosphere and atmospheric pressure is 0.975 atm?

CONCEPTUAL PROBLEM 9.4 What is the pressure of the gas inside the apparatus shown on the right in mm Hg if the outside pressure is 750 mm Hg?

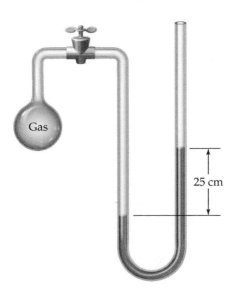

Gas

25 cm

9.2 THE GAS LAWS

Unlike solids and liquids, different gases show remarkably similar physical behavior regardless of their chemical makeup. Helium and fluorine, for example, are vastly different in their chemical properties yet are almost identical in much of their physical behavior. Numerous observations made in the late 1600s showed that the physical properties of any gas can be defined by four variables: pressure (P), temperature (T), volume (V), and amount, or number of moles (n). The specific relationships among these four variables are called the **gas laws**, and a gas whose behavior follows the laws exactly is called an **ideal gas**.

Boyle's Law: The Relationship between Gas Volume and Pressure

Imagine that you have a sample of gas inside a cylinder with a movable piston at one end (Figure 9.5). What would happen if you were to increase the pressure on the gas by pushing down on the piston? Experience probably tells you that the volume of gas in the cylinder would decrease as you increase the pressure. According to **Boyle's law**, the volume of a fixed amount of gas at a constant temperature varies inversely with its pressure. If the gas pressure is doubled, the volume is halved; if the pressure is halved, the gas volume doubles.

◄── Boyle's law $V \propto 1/P$ or $PV = k$ at constant n and T

The volume of an ideal gas varies inversely with pressure. That is, P times V is constant when n and T are kept constant. (The symbol $\propto$ means "is proportional to," and k denotes a constant.)

Figure 9.5
Boyle's law.

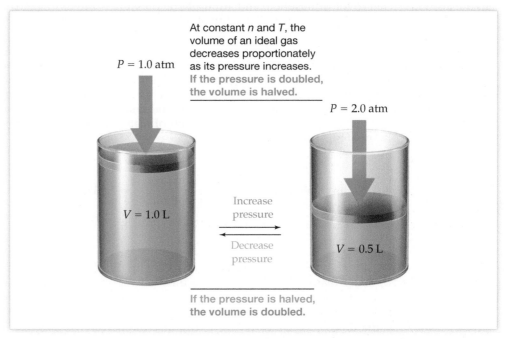

At constant n and T, the volume of an ideal gas decreases proportionately as its pressure increases.
If the pressure is doubled, the volume is halved.

$P = 1.0$ atm $P = 2.0$ atm

$V = 1.0$ L $V = 0.5$ L

Increase pressure

Decrease pressure

If the pressure is halved, the volume is doubled.

The validity of Boyle's law can be demonstrated by making a simple series of pressure–volume measurements on a gas sample (Table 9.2) and plotting them as in Figure 9.6. When V is plotted versus P, the result is a curve in the form of a hyperbola. When V is plotted versus $1/P$, however, the result is a straight line. Such graphical behavior is characteristic of mathematical equations of the form $y = mx + b$. In this case, $y = V$, $m = $ the slope of the line (the constant k in the present instance), $x = 1/P$, and $b = $ the y-intercept (a constant; 0 in the present instance). (See Appendix A.3 for a review of linear equations.)

$$V = k\left(\frac{1}{P}\right) + 0 \quad (\text{or } PV = k)$$
$$y = m \quad x \quad + b$$

TABLE 9.2 Pressure–Volume Measurements on a Gas Sample at Constant n, T

Pressure (mm Hg)	Volume (L)
760	1
380	2
253	3
190	4
152	5
127	6
109	7
95	8
84	9
76	10

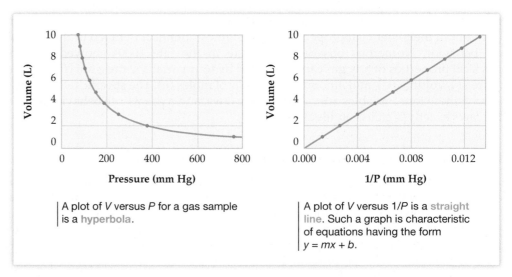

A plot of V versus P for a gas sample is a hyperbola.

A plot of V versus $1/P$ is a straight line. Such a graph is characteristic of equations having the form $y = mx + b$.

Figure 9.6
Boyle's law plot.

Charles's Law: The Relationship between Gas Volume and Temperature

Imagine that you again have a gas sample inside a cylinder with a movable piston at one end (Figure 9.7). What would happen if you were to raise the temperature of the sample while letting the piston move freely to keep the pressure constant? Experience tells you that the piston would move up because the volume of the gas in the cylinder would expand. According to **Charles's law**, the volume of a fixed amount of an ideal gas at a constant pressure varies directly with its absolute temperature. If the gas temperature in kelvin is doubled, the volume is doubled; if the gas temperature is halved, the volume is halved.

> **Charles's law** $V \propto T$ or $V/T = k$ at constant n and P
>
> The volume of an ideal gas varies directly with absolute temperature. That is, V divided by T is constant when n and P are held constant.

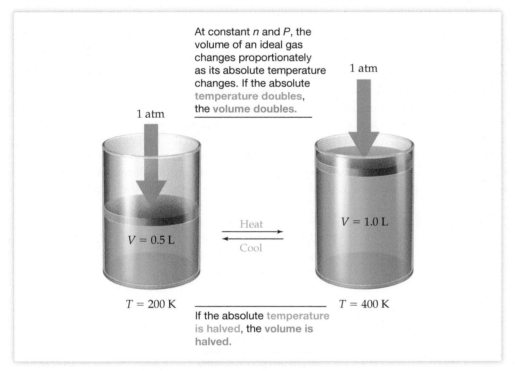

At constant n and P, the volume of an ideal gas changes proportionately as its absolute temperature changes. If the absolute temperature doubles, the volume doubles.

1 atm

1 atm

$V = 1.0$ L

Heat

Cool

$V = 0.5$ L

$T = 200$ K

$T = 400$ K

If the absolute temperature is halved, the volume is halved.

Figure 9.7
Charles's law.

The validity of Charles's law can be demonstrated by making a series of temperature–volume measurements on a gas sample, giving the results listed in Table 9.3. Like Boyle's law, Charles's law takes the mathematical form $y = mx + b$, where $y = V$, $m = $ the slope of the line (the constant k in the present instance), $x = T$, and $b = $ the y-intercept (0 in the present instance). A plot of V versus T is therefore a straight line whose slope is the constant k (Figure 9.8).

$$V = kT + 0 \quad \left(\text{or } \frac{V}{T} = k \right)$$
$$\uparrow \quad \uparrow\uparrow \quad \uparrow$$
$$y = mx + b$$

The plots of volume versus temperature demonstrate an interesting point. When temperature is plotted on the Celsius scale, the straight line can be extrapolated to $V = 0$ at $T = -273$ °C (Figure 9.8a). But because matter can't have a negative volume, this extrapolation suggests that -273 °C must be the lowest possible temperature, or *absolute zero* on the Kelvin scale (Figure 9.8b). In fact, the approximate value of absolute zero was first determined using this simple method.

TABLE 9.3	Temperature–Volume Measurements on a Gas Sample at Constant n and P
Temperature (K)	**Volume (L)**
123	0.45
173	0.63
223	0.82
273	1.00
323	1.18
373	1.37

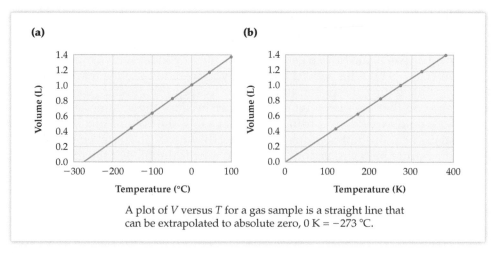

(a)

(b)

A plot of V versus T for a gas sample is a straight line that can be extrapolated to absolute zero, 0 K = −273 °C.

Figure 9.8
Charles's law plot.

Avogadro's Law: The Relationship between Volume and Amount

Imagine that you have two more gas samples inside cylinders with movable pistons (Figure 9.9). One cylinder contains 1 mol of a gas and the other contains 2 mol of gas at the same temperature and pressure as the first. Common sense says that the gas in the second cylinder will have twice the volume of the gas in the first cylinder because there is twice as much of it. According to **Avogadro's law**, the volume of an ideal gas at a fixed pressure and temperature depends on its molar amount. If the amount of the gas is doubled, the gas volume is doubled; if the amount is halved, the volume is halved.

Avogadro's law $V \propto n$ or $V/n = k$ at constant T and P

The volume of an ideal gas varies directly with its molar amount. That is, V divided by n is constant when T and P are held constant.

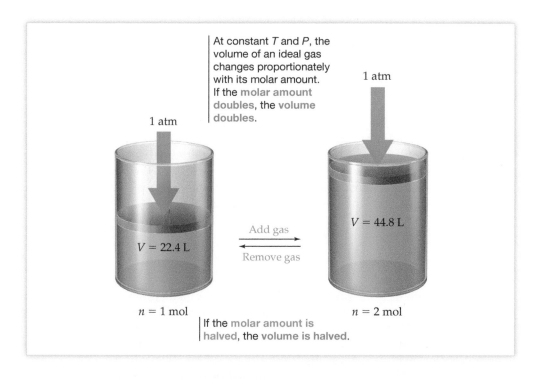

At constant T and P, the volume of an ideal gas changes proportionately with its molar amount. If the molar amount doubles, the volume doubles.

1 atm

1 atm

$V = 44.8$ L

Add gas

Remove gas

$V = 22.4$ L

$n = 1$ mol

$n = 2$ mol

If the molar amount is halved, the volume is halved.

Figure 9.9
Avogadro's law.

Put another way, Avogadro's law also says that equal volumes of different gases at the same temperature and pressure contain the same molar amounts. A 1 L container of oxygen contains the same number of moles as a 1 L container of helium, fluorine, argon, or any other gas at the same T and P. Furthermore, 1 mol of an ideal gas occupies a volume, called the **standard molar volume**, of 22.414 L at 0 °C and exactly 1 atm pressure. For comparison, the standard molar volume is nearly identical to the volume of three basketballs.

WORKED CONCEPTUAL EXAMPLE 9.3

VISUAL REPRESENTATIONS OF GAS LAWS

Show the approximate level of the movable piston in drawings **(a)** and **(b)** after the indicated changes have been made to the initial gas sample.

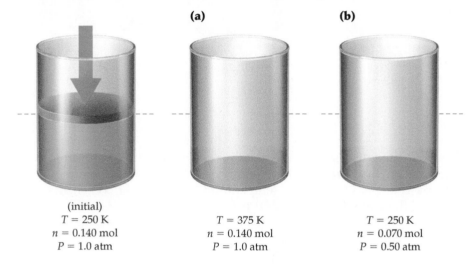

	(a)	**(b)**

(initial)
$T = 250$ K
$n = 0.140$ mol
$P = 1.0$ atm

$T = 375$ K
$n = 0.140$ mol
$P = 1.0$ atm

$T = 250$ K
$n = 0.070$ mol
$P = 0.50$ atm

STRATEGY

Identify which of the variables P, n, and T have changed, and calculate the effect of each change on the volume according to the appropriate gas law.

SOLUTION

(a) The temperature T has increased by a factor of $375/250 = 1.5$, while the molar amount n and the pressure P are unchanged. According to Charles's law, the volume will increase by a factor of 1.5.

(b) The temperature T is unchanged, while both the molar amount n and the pressure P are halved. According to Avogadro's law, halving the molar amount will halve the volume, and according to Boyle's law, halving the pressure will double the volume. The two changes cancel, so the volume is unchanged.

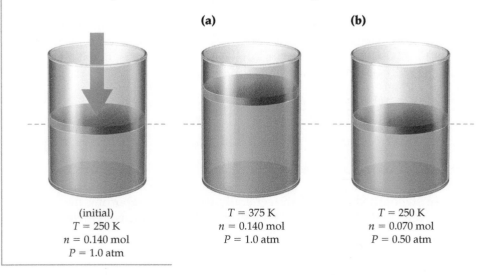

	(a)	**(b)**

(initial)
$T = 250$ K
$n = 0.140$ mol
$P = 1.0$ atm

$T = 375$ K
$n = 0.140$ mol
$P = 1.0$ atm

$T = 250$ K
$n = 0.070$ mol
$P = 0.50$ atm

CONCEPTUAL PROBLEM 9.5 Show the approximate level of the movable piston in drawings **(a)** and **(b)** after the indicated changes have been made to the initial gas sample at a constant pressure of 1.0 atm.

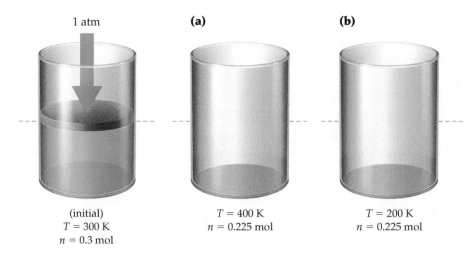

1 atm	**(a)**	**(b)**
(initial)	$T = 400$ K	$T = 200$ K
$T = 300$ K	$n = 0.225$ mol	$n = 0.225$ mol
$n = 0.3$ mol		

9.3 THE IDEAL GAS LAW

All three gas laws discussed in the previous section can be combined into a single statement called the **ideal gas law**, which describes how the volume of a gas is affected by changes in pressure, temperature, and amount. When the values of any three of the variables P, V, T, and n are known, the value of the fourth can be calculated using the ideal gas law. The proportionality constant R in the equation is called the **gas constant** and has the same value for all gases.

Ideal gas law $\quad V = \dfrac{nRT}{P} \quad$ or $\quad PV = nRT$

The ideal gas law can be rearranged in different ways to take the form of Boyle's law, Charles's law, or Avogadro's law.

Boyle's law: $\quad\quad PV = nRT = k \quad\quad$ (When n and T are constant)

Charles's law: $\quad\quad \dfrac{V}{T} = \dfrac{nR}{P} = k \quad\quad$ (When n and P are constant)

Avogadro's law: $\quad\quad \dfrac{V}{n} = \dfrac{RT}{P} = k \quad\quad$ (When T and P are constant)

The value of the gas constant R can be calculated from knowledge of the standard molar volume of a gas. Since 1 mol of a gas occupies a volume of 22.414 L at 0 °C (273.15 K) and 1 atm pressure, the gas constant R is equal to 0.082 058 $(\text{L} \cdot \text{atm})/(\text{K} \cdot \text{mol})$, or 8.3145 $\text{J}/(\text{K} \cdot \text{mol})$ in SI units:

$$R = \frac{P \cdot V}{n \cdot T} = \frac{(1 \text{ atm})(22.414 \text{ L})}{(1 \text{ mol})(273.15 \text{ K})} = 0.082\ 058 \, \frac{\text{L} \cdot \text{atm}}{\text{K} \cdot \text{mol}}$$

$$= 8.3145 \, \text{J}/(\text{K} \cdot \text{mol}) \quad\quad \text{(When } P \text{ is in pascals and } V \text{ is in cubic meters)}$$

The specific conditions used in the calculation—0 °C (273.15 K) and 1 atm pressure—are said to represent **standard temperature and pressure**, abbreviated **STP**. These standard conditions are generally used when reporting measurements on gases. Note that the standard temperature for gas measurements (0 °C, or

273.15 K) is different from that usually assumed for thermodynamic measurements (25 °C, or 298.15 K; Section 8.5).

🔑 **Standard Temperature and Pressure (STP) for Gases** $T = 0\,°C$ $P = 1\,atm$

We should also point out that the standard pressure for gas measurements, still listed here and in most other books as 1 atm (101,325 Pa), has actually been redefined to be 1 bar, or 100,000 Pa. This new standard pressure is now 0.986 923 atm, making the newly defined standard molar volume 22.711 L rather than 22.414 L. Like most other books, we'll continue for the present using 1 atm as the standard pressure.

The name *ideal* gas law implies that there must be some gases whose behavior is *nonideal*. In fact, there is no such thing as an ideal gas that obeys the equation perfectly under all circumstances. All real gases are nonideal to some extent and deviate slightly from the behavior predicted by the gas laws. As Table 9.4 shows, for example, the actual molar volume of a real gas often differs slightly from the 22.414 L ideal value. Under most conditions, though, the deviations from ideal behavior are so slight as to make little difference. We'll discuss circumstances in Section 9.8 where the deviations are greater.

TABLE 9.4   Molar Volumes of Some Real Gases at 0 °C and 1 atm

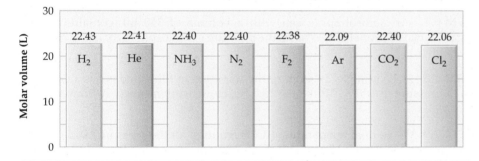

WORKED EXAMPLE 9.4

GAS LAW CALCULATIONS

How many moles of gas (air) are in the lungs of an average adult with a lung capacity of 3.8 L? Assume that the lungs are at 1.00 atm pressure and a normal body temperature of 37 °C.

STRATEGY

This problem asks for a value of n when V, P, and T are given. Rearrange the ideal gas law to the form $n = PV/RT$, convert the temperature from degrees Celsius to kelvin, and substitute the given values of P, V, and T into the equation.

SOLUTION

$$n = \frac{PV}{RT} = \frac{(1.00\ \text{atm})(3.8\ \text{L})}{\left(0.082\ 06\ \dfrac{\text{L} \cdot \text{atm}}{\text{K} \cdot \text{mol}}\right)(310\ \text{K})} = 0.15\ \text{mol}$$

The lungs of an average adult hold 0.15 mol of air.

BALLPARK CHECK

A lung volume of 4 L is about 1/6 of 22.4 L, the standard molar volume of an ideal gas. Thus, the lungs have a capacity of about 1/6 mol, or 0.17 mol.

GAS LAW CALCULATIONS

In a typical automobile engine, the mixture of gasoline and air in a cylinder is compressed from 1.0 atm to 9.5 atm prior to ignition. If the uncompressed volume of the cylinder is 410 mL, what is the volume in milliliters when the mixture is fully compressed?

STRATEGY

This is a Boyle's law problem because only P and V are changing, while n and T remain fixed. We can therefore set up the following equation and solve for V_{final}.

$$(PV)_{initial} = (PV)_{final} = nRT$$

SOLUTION

$$V_{final} = \frac{(PV)_{initial}}{P_{final}} = \frac{(1.0 \text{ atm})(410 \text{ mL})}{9.5 \text{ atm}} = 43 \text{ mL}$$

BALLPARK CHECK

Because the pressure in the cylinder increases about 10-fold, the volume must decrease about 10-fold according to Boyle's law, from approximately 400 mL to 40 mL.

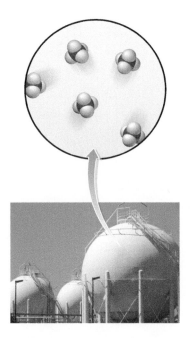

▲ How many moles of methane are in these tanks?

▶ **PROBLEM 9.6**   How many moles of methane gas, CH_4, are in a storage tank with a volume of 1.000×10^5 L at STP? How many grams?

▶ **PROBLEM 9.7**   An aerosol spray can with a volume of 350 mL contains 3.2 g of propane gas (C_3H_8) as propellant. What is the pressure in atmospheres of gas in the can at 20 °C?

▶ **PROBLEM 9.8**   A helium gas cylinder of the sort used to fill balloons has a volume of 43.8 L and a pressure of 1.51×10^4 kPa at 25.0 °C. How many moles of helium are in the tank?

▶ **PROBLEM 9.9**   What final temperature (°C) is required for the pressure inside an automobile tire to increase from 2.15 atm at 0 °C to 2.37 atm, assuming the volume remains constant?

CONCEPTUAL PROBLEM 9.10   Show the approximate level of the movable piston in drawings **(a)**, **(b)**, and **(c)** after the indicated changes have been made to the gas.

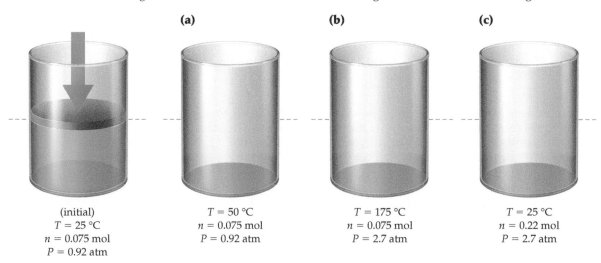

(a)   **(b)**   **(c)**

(initial)
$T = 25$ °C
$n = 0.075$ mol
$P = 0.92$ atm

$T = 50$ °C
$n = 0.075$ mol
$P = 0.92$ atm

$T = 175$ °C
$n = 0.075$ mol
$P = 2.7$ atm

$T = 25$ °C
$n = 0.22$ mol
$P = 2.7$ atm

9.4   STOICHIOMETRIC RELATIONSHIPS WITH GASES

Many chemical reactions, including some of the most important processes in the chemical industry, involve gases. Approximately 120 million metric tons of ammonia, for instance, is manufactured each year worldwide by the reaction of hydrogen with nitrogen according to the equation $3 H_2 + N_2 \longrightarrow 2 NH_3$. Thus, it's necessary to be able to calculate amounts of gaseous reactants just as it's necessary to calculate amounts of solids, liquids, and solutions (Sections 3.3–3.8).

Most gas calculations are just applications of the ideal gas law in which three of the variables P, V, T, and n are known and the fourth variable must be calculated. The reaction used in the deployment of automobile air bags, for instance, is the high-temperature decomposition of sodium azide, NaN_3, to produce N_2 gas. (The sodium is then removed by a subsequent reaction.) How many liters of N_2 gas at 1.15 atm and 30 °C are produced by decomposition of 45.0 g of NaN_3?

$$2 NaN_3(s) \longrightarrow 2 Na(s) + 3 N_2(g)$$

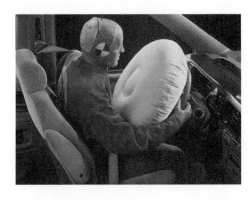

▲ Automobile air bags are inflated with N_2 gas produced by decomposition of sodium azide.

Values for P and T are given, the value of n can be calculated, and the ideal gas law will then let us find V. To find n, the number of moles of N_2 gas produced, we first need to find how many moles of NaN_3 are in 45.0 g:

Molar mass of NaN_3 = 65.0 g/mol

$$\text{Moles of } NaN_3 = (45.0 \text{ g } NaN_3)\left(\frac{1 \text{ mol } NaN_3}{65.0 \text{ g } NaN_3}\right) = 0.692 \text{ mol } NaN_3$$

Next, find how many moles of N_2 are produced in the decomposition reaction. According to the balanced equation, 2 mol of NaN_3 yields 3 mol of N_2, so 0.692 mol of NaN_3 yields 1.04 mol of N_2:

$$\text{Moles of } N_2 = (0.692 \text{ mol } NaN_3)\left(\frac{3 \text{ mol } N_2}{2 \text{ mol } NaN_3}\right) = 1.04 \text{ mol } N_2$$

Finally, use the ideal gas law to calculate the volume of N_2. Remember to use the Kelvin temperature (303 K) rather than the Celsius temperature (30 °C) in the calculation.

$$V = \frac{nRT}{P} = \frac{(1.04 \text{ mol } N_2)\left(0.082\,06 \dfrac{\text{L} \cdot \text{atm}}{\text{K} \cdot \text{mol}}\right)(303 \text{ K})}{1.15 \text{ atm}} = 22.5 \text{ L}$$

Worked Example 9.6 illustrates another gas stoichiometry calculation.

Still other applications of the ideal gas law make it possible to calculate such properties as density and molar mass. Densities are calculated by weighing a known volume of a gas at a known temperature and pressure, as shown in **Figure 9.10**. Using the ideal gas law to find the volume at STP and then dividing the measured mass by the volume gives the density at STP. Worked Example 9.7 gives a sample calculation.

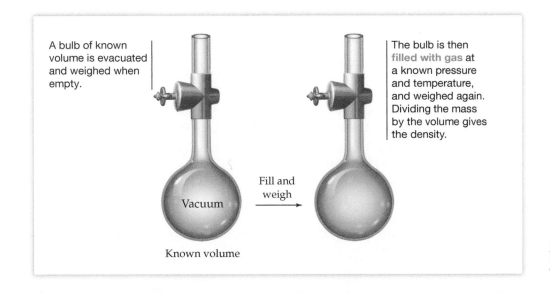

A bulb of known volume is evacuated and weighed when empty.

The bulb is then filled with gas at a known pressure and temperature, and weighed again. Dividing the mass by the volume gives the density.

Vacuum

Fill and weigh

Known volume

Figure 9.10
Determining the density of an unknown gas.

Molar masses, and therefore molecular masses, can also be calculated using the ideal gas law. Imagine, for instance, that an unknown gas found bubbling up in a swamp is collected, placed in a glass bulb, and found to have a density of 0.714 g/L at STP. What is the molecular mass of the gas?

Let's assume that we have 1.00 L of sample, which has a mass of 0.714 g. Since the density is measured at STP, we know T, P, and V, and we need to find n, the molar amount of gas that has a mass of 0.714 g:

$$n = \frac{PV}{RT} = \frac{(1.00\ \text{atm})(1.00\ \text{L})}{\left(0.082\ 06\ \dfrac{\text{L} \cdot \text{atm}}{\text{K} \cdot \text{mol}}\right)(273\ \text{K})} = 0.0446\ \text{mol}$$

Dividing the mass of the sample by the number of moles then gives the molar mass:

$$\text{Molar mass} = \frac{0.714\ \text{g}}{0.0446\ \text{mol}} = 16.0\ \text{g/mol}$$

Thus, the molar mass of the unknown gas (actually methane, CH_4) is 16.0 g/mol, and the molecular mass is 16.0 amu.

It's often true in chemistry, particularly in gas-law calculations, that a problem can be solved in more than one way. As an alternative method for calculating the molar mass of the unknown swamp gas, you might recognize that 1 mol of an ideal gas has a volume of 22.4 L at STP. Since 1.00 L of the unknown gas has a mass of 0.714 g, 22.4 L of the gas (1 mol) has a mass of 16.0 g:

$$\text{Molar mass} = \left(0.714\ \frac{\text{g}}{\text{L}}\right)\left(22.4\ \frac{\text{L}}{\text{mol}}\right) = 16.0\ \text{g/mol}$$

Worked Example 9.8 illustrates another calculation of the molar mass of an unknown gas.

WORKED EXAMPLE 9.6

FINDING A MASS USING GAS LAW CALCULATIONS

A typical high-pressure tire on a bicycle might have a volume of 365 mL and a pressure of 7.80 atm at 25 °C. Suppose the rider filled the tire with helium to minimize weight. What is the mass of the helium in the tire?

STRATEGY

We are given V, P, and T, and we need to use the ideal gas law to calculate n, the number of moles of helium in the tire. With n known, we then do a mole-to-mass conversion.

SOLUTION

$$n = \frac{PV}{RT} = \frac{(7.80\ \text{atm})(0.365\ \text{L})}{\left(0.082\ 06\ \dfrac{\text{L} \cdot \text{atm}}{\text{K} \cdot \text{mol}}\right)(298\ \text{K})} = 0.116\ \text{mol}$$

$$\text{Grams of helium} = 0.116\ \text{mol He} \times \frac{4.00\ \text{g He}}{1\ \text{mol He}} = 0.464\ \text{g}$$

WORKED EXAMPLE 9.7

FINDING A DENSITY USING GAS LAW CALCULATIONS

What is the density in g/L of ammonia at STP if the gas in a 1.000 L bulb weighs 0.672 g at 25 °C and 733.4 mm Hg pressure?

STRATEGY

The density of any substance is mass divided by volume. For the ammonia sample, the mass is 0.672 g but the volume of the gas is given under nonstandard conditions and must first be converted to STP. Because the amount of sample n is constant, we can set the quantity PV/RT measured under nonstandard conditions equal to PV/RT at STP and then solve for V at STP.

SOLUTION

$$n = \left(\frac{PV}{RT}\right)_{measured} = \left(\frac{PV}{RT}\right)_{STP} \quad \text{or} \quad V_{STP} = \left(\frac{PV}{RT}\right)_{measured}\left(\frac{RT}{P}\right)_{STP}$$

$$V_{STP} = \left(\frac{733.4 \text{ mm Hg} \times 1.000 \text{ L}}{298 \text{ K}}\right)\left(\frac{273 \text{ K}}{760 \text{ mm Hg}}\right) = 0.884 \text{ L}$$

The amount of gas in the 1.000 L bulb under the measured nonstandard conditions would have a volume of only 0.884 L at STP. Dividing the given mass by this volume gives the density of ammonia at STP:

$$\text{Density} = \frac{\text{Mass}}{\text{Volume}} = \frac{0.672 \text{ g}}{0.884 \text{ L}} = 0.760 \text{ g/L}$$

WORKED EXAMPLE 9.8

IDENTIFYING AN UNKNOWN USING GAS LAW CALCULATIONS

To identify the contents of an unlabeled cylinder of gas, a sample was collected and found to have a density of 5.380 g/L at 15 °C and 736 mm Hg pressure. What is the molar mass of the gas?

STRATEGY

Let's assume we have a 1.000 L sample of the gas, which weighs 5.380 g. We know the temperature, volume, and pressure of the gas and can therefore use the ideal gas law to find n, the number of moles in the sample. Dividing the mass by the number of moles then gives the molar mass.

SOLUTION

$$PV = nRT \quad \text{or} \quad n = \frac{PV}{RT}$$

$$n = \frac{\left(736 \text{ mm Hg} \times \dfrac{1 \text{ atm}}{760 \text{ mm Hg}}\right)(1.000 \text{ L})}{\left(0.082\,06 \dfrac{\text{L} \cdot \text{atm}}{\text{K} \cdot \text{mol}}\right)(288 \text{ K})} = 0.0410 \text{ mol}$$

$$\text{Molar mass} = \frac{5.380 \text{ g}}{0.0410 \text{ mol}} = 131 \text{ g/mol}$$

The gas is probably xenon (atomic mass = 131.3 amu).

▶ **PROBLEM 9.11** Carbonate-bearing rocks like limestone ($CaCO_3$) react with dilute acids such as HCl to produce carbon dioxide, according to the equation

$$CaCO_3(s) + 2\,HCl(aq) \longrightarrow CaCl_2(aq) + CO_2(g) + H_2O(l)$$

How many grams of CO_2 are formed by complete reaction of 33.7 g of limestone? What is the volume in liters of this CO_2 at STP?

▶ **PROBLEM 9.12** Propane gas (C_3H_8) is used as a fuel in rural areas. How many liters of CO_2 are formed at STP by the complete combustion of the propane in a container with a volume of 15.0 L and a pressure of 4.5 atm at 25 °C? The unbalanced equation is

$$C_3H_8(g) + O_2(g) \longrightarrow CO_2(g) + H_2O(l)$$

▶ **PROBLEM 9.13** A foul-smelling gas produced by the reaction of HCl with Na_2S was collected, and a 1.00 L sample was found to have a mass of 1.52 g at STP. What is the molecular mass of the gas? What is its likely formula and name?

▲ Carbonate-bearing rocks like limestone ($CaCO_3$) react with dilute acids such as HCl to produce bubbles of carbon dioxide.

9.5 PARTIAL PRESSURE AND DALTON'S LAW

Just as the gas laws apply to all pure gases, regardless of chemical identity, they also apply to *mixtures* of gases, such as air. The pressure, volume, temperature, and amount of a gas mixture are all related by the ideal gas law.

What is responsible for the pressure in a gas mixture? Because the pressure of a pure gas at constant temperature and volume is proportional to its amount ($P = nRT/V$), the pressure contribution from each individual gas in a mixture is also proportional to *its* amount in the mixture. In other words, the total pressure exerted by a mixture of gases in a container at constant V and T is equal to the sum of the pressures of each individual gas in the container, a statement known as **Dalton's law of partial pressures**.

▷ **Dalton's law of partial pressures** $P_{total} = P_1 + P_2 + P_3 + \ldots$ at constant V and T, where P_1, P_2, ... refer to the pressures each individual gas would have if it were alone.

The individual pressure contributions of the various gases in the mixture, P_1, P_2, and so forth, are called *partial pressures* and refer to the pressure each individual gas would exert if it were alone in the container. That is,

$$P_1 = n_1\left(\frac{RT}{V}\right) \qquad P_2 = n_2\left(\frac{RT}{V}\right) \qquad P_3 = n_3\left(\frac{RT}{V}\right) \qquad \ldots \text{ and so forth}$$

But because all the gases in the mixture have the same temperature and volume, we can rewrite Dalton's law to indicate that the total pressure depends only on the total molar amount of gas present and not on the chemical identities of the individual gases:

$$P_{total} = (n_1 + n_2 + n_3 + \cdots)\left(\frac{RT}{V}\right)$$

The concentration of any individual component in a gas mixture is usually expressed as a **mole fraction (X)**, which is defined simply as the number of moles of the component divided by the total number of moles in the mixture:

▷ **Mole fraction (X)** $= \dfrac{\text{Moles of component}}{\text{Total moles in mixture}}$

The mole fraction of component 1, for example, is

$$X_1 = \frac{n_1}{n_1 + n_2 + n_3 + \cdots} = \frac{n_1}{n_{total}}$$

But because $n = PV/RT$, we can also write

$$X_1 = \frac{P_1\left(\dfrac{V}{RT}\right)}{P_{total}\left(\dfrac{V}{RT}\right)} = \frac{P_1}{P_{total}}$$

which can be rearranged to solve for P_1, the partial pressure of component 1:

$$P_1 = X_1 \cdot P_{total}$$

This equation says that the partial pressure exerted by each component in a gas mixture is equal to the mole fraction of that component times the total pressure. In air, for example, the mole fractions of N_2, O_2, Ar, and CO_2 are 0.7808, 0.2095, 0.0093, and 0.000 38, respectively (Table 9.1), and the total pressure of the air is the sum of the individual partial pressures:

$$P_{air} = P_{N_2} + P_{O_2} + P_{Ar} + P_{CO_2} + \cdots$$

Thus, at a total air pressure of 1 atm (760 mm Hg), the partial pressures of the individual components are

$$
\begin{aligned}
P_{N_2} &= 0.780\ 8 \text{ atm N}_2 &&= 593.4 \text{ mm Hg} \\
P_{O_2} &= 0.209\ 5 \text{ atm O}_2 &&= 159.2 \text{ mm Hg} \\
P_{Ar} &= 0.009\ 3 \text{ atm Ar} &&= 7.1 \text{ mm Hg} \\
P_{CO_2} &= 0.000\ 38 \text{ atm CO}_2 &&= 0.3 \text{ mm Hg} \\
\hline
P_{air} &= 1.000\ 0 \text{ atm air} &&= 760.0 \text{ mm Hg}
\end{aligned}
$$

There are numerous practical applications of Dalton's law, ranging from the use of anesthetic agents in hospital operating rooms, where partial pressures of both oxygen and anesthetic in the patient's lungs must be constantly monitored, to the composition of diving gases used for underwater exploration. Worked Example 9.9 gives an illustration.

WORKED EXAMPLE 9.9

USING PARTIAL PRESSURES AND MOLE FRACTIONS

At an underwater depth of 250 ft, the pressure is 8.38 atm. What should the mole percent of oxygen in the diving gas be for the partial pressure of oxygen in the gas to be 0.21 atm, the same as in air at 1.0 atm?

STRATEGY

The partial pressure of a gas in a mixture is equal to the mole fraction of the gas times the total pressure. Rearranging this equation lets us solve for mole fraction of O_2.

SOLUTION

$$\text{Since}\quad P_{O_2} = X_{O_2} \cdot P_{total}, \quad \text{then} \quad X_{O_2} = \frac{P_{O_2}}{P_{total}}$$

$$X_{O_2} = \frac{0.21 \text{ atm}}{8.38 \text{ atm}} = 0.025$$

$$\text{Percent } O_2 = 0.025 \times 100\% = 2.5\% \ O_2$$

▲ The partial pressure of oxygen in the scuba tanks must be the same underwater as in air at atmospheric pressure.

The diving gas should contain 2.5% O_2 for the partial pressure of O_2 to be the same at 8.38 atm as it is in air at 1.0 atm.

BALLPARK CHECK

Because the pressure underwater is about 8 times atmospheric pressure, the percentage of O_2 in the diving gas should be about 1/8 times the percentage of O_2 in air (20%), or about 2.5%.

▶ **PROBLEM 9.14** What is the mole fraction of each component in a mixture of 12.45 g of H_2, 60.67 g of N_2, and 2.38 g of NH_3?

▶ **PROBLEM 9.15** What is the total pressure in atmospheres and what is the partial pressure of each component if the gas mixture in Problem 9.14 is in a 10.00 L steel container at 90 °C?

▶ **PROBLEM 9.16** On a humid day in summer, the mole fraction of gaseous H_2O (water vapor) in the air at 25 °C can be as high as 0.0287. Assuming a total pressure of 0.977 atm, what is the partial pressure in atmospheres of H_2O in the air?

CONCEPTUAL PROBLEM 9.17   What is the partial pressure of each gas—red, yellow, and green—if the total pressure inside the following container is 600 mm Hg?

9.6   THE KINETIC–MOLECULAR THEORY OF GASES

Thus far, we've concentrated on just describing the behavior of gases rather than on understanding the reasons for that behavior. Actually, the reasons are straightforward and were explained more than a century ago using a model called the **kinetic–molecular theory**. The kinetic–molecular theory is based on the following assumptions:

1. A gas consists of tiny particles, either atoms or molecules, moving about at random.

2. The volume of the particles themselves is negligible compared with the total volume of the gas. Most of the volume of a gas is empty space.

3. The gas particles act independently of one another; there are no attractive or repulsive forces between particles.

4. Collisions of the gas particles, either with other particles or with the walls of a container, are elastic. That is, the total kinetic energy of the gas particles is constant at constant T.

5. The average kinetic energy of the gas particles is proportional to the Kelvin temperature of the sample.

Beginning with these assumptions, it's possible not only to understand the behavior of gases but also to derive quantitatively the ideal gas law (though we'll not do so here). For example, let's look at how the individual gas laws follow from the five postulates of kinetic–molecular theory:

- Boyle's law ($P \propto 1/V$): Gas pressure is a measure of the number and forcefulness of collisions between gas particles and the walls of their container. The smaller the volume at constant n and T, the more crowded together the particles are and the greater the frequency of collisions. Thus, pressure increases as volume decreases (Figure 9.11a).

- Charles's law ($V \propto T$): Temperature is a measure of the average kinetic energy of the gas particles. The higher the temperature at constant n and P, the faster the gas particles move and the more room they need to move around in to avoid increasing their collisions with the walls of the container. Thus, volume increases as temperature increases (Figure 9.11b).

- Avogadro's law ($V \propto n$): The more particles there are in a gas sample, the more volume the particles need at constant P and T to avoid increasing their collisions with the walls of the container. Thus, volume increases as amount increases (Figure 9.11c).

- Dalton's law ($P_{total} = P_1 + P_2 + \cdots$): The chemical identity of the particles in a gas is irrelevant. Total pressure of a fixed volume of gas depends only on the temperature T and the total number of moles of gas n. The pressure exerted by a specific kind of particle thus depends on the mole fraction of that kind of particle in the mixture (Figure 9.11d).

One of the more important conclusions from kinetic–molecular theory comes from assumption 5—the relationship between temperature and E_K, the kinetic energy of molecular motion. It can be shown that the total kinetic energy of a mole of

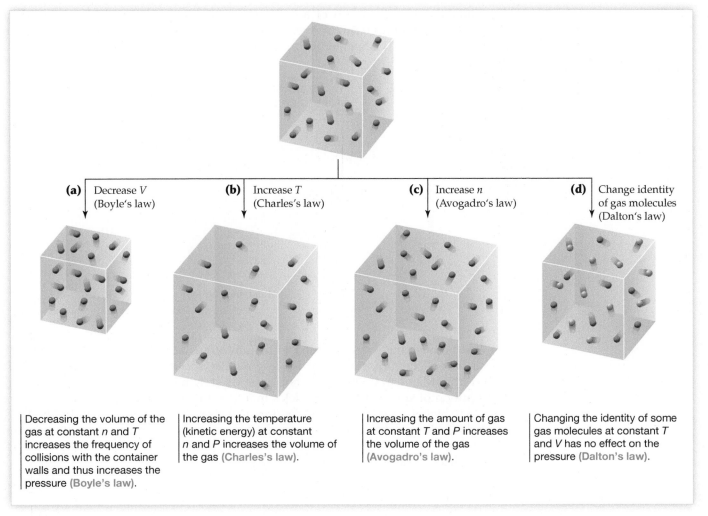

Figure 9.11
A kinetic–molecular view of the gas laws.

gas particles equals $3RT/2$ and that the average kinetic energy per particle is thus $3RT/2N_A$ where N_A is Avogadro's number. Knowing this relationship makes it possible to calculate the average speed u of a gas particle at a given temperature. To take a helium atom at room temperature (298 K), for instance, we can write

$$E_K = \frac{3}{2}\frac{RT}{N_A} = \frac{1}{2}mu^2$$

which can be rearranged to give

$$u^2 = \frac{3RT}{mN_A}$$

$$\text{or} \quad u = \sqrt{\frac{3RT}{mN_A}} = \sqrt{\frac{3RT}{M}} \quad \text{where } M \text{ is the molar mass}$$

Substituting appropriate values for R [8.314 J/(K · mol)] and for M, the molar mass of helium (4.00 × 10^{-3} kg/mol), we have

$$u = \sqrt{\frac{(3)\left(8.314\ \frac{\text{J}}{\text{K}\cdot\text{mol}}\right)(298\ \text{K})}{4.00 \times 10^{-3}\ \frac{\text{kg}}{\text{mol}}}} = \sqrt{1.86 \times 10^6\ \frac{\text{J}}{\text{kg}}}$$

$$= \sqrt{1.86 \times 10^6\ \frac{\frac{\text{kg}\cdot\text{m}^2}{\text{s}^2}}{\text{kg}}} = 1.36 \times 10^3\ \text{m/s}$$

Thus, the average speed of a helium atom at room temperature is more than 1.3 km/s, or about 3000 mi/h! Average speeds of some other molecules at 25 °C are given in Table 9.5. The heavier the molecule, the slower the average speed.

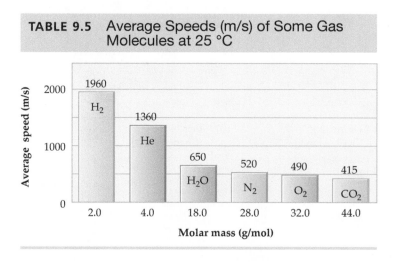

TABLE 9.5 Average Speeds (m/s) of Some Gas Molecules at 25 °C

Just because the average speed of helium atoms at 298 K is 1.36 km/s doesn't mean that all helium atoms are moving at that speed or that a given atom will travel from Maine to California in one hour. As shown in **Figure 9.12**, there is a broad distribution of speeds among particles in a gas, a distribution that flattens out and moves to higher speeds as the temperature increases. Furthermore, an individual gas particle is likely to travel only a very short distance before it collides with another particle and bounces off in a different direction. Thus, the actual path followed by a gas particle is a random zigzag.

Figure 9.12

The distribution of speeds for helium atoms at different temperatures.

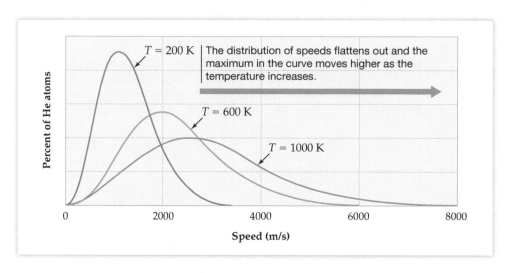

For helium at room temperature and 1 atm pressure, the average distance between collisions, called the *mean free path*, is only about 2×10^{-7} m, or 1000 atomic diameters, and there are approximately 10^{10} collisions per second. For a larger O_2 molecule, the mean free path is about 6×10^{-8} m.

▶ **PROBLEM 9.18**   Calculate the average speed of a nitrogen molecule in m/s on a hot day in summer ($T = 37$ °C) and on a cold day in winter ($T = -25$ °C).

▶ **PROBLEM 9.19**   At what temperature does the average speed of an oxygen molecule equal that of an airplane moving at 580 mph?

9.7 GRAHAM'S LAW: DIFFUSION AND EFFUSION OF GASES

The constant motion and high velocities of gas particles have some important practical consequences. One such consequence is that gases mix rapidly when they come in contact. Take the stopper off a bottle of perfume, for instance, and the odor will spread rapidly through a room as perfume molecules mix with the molecules in the air. This mixing of different molecules by random molecular motion with frequent collisions is called **diffusion**. A similar process in which gas molecules escape without collisions through a tiny hole into a vacuum is called **effusion** (Figure 9.13).

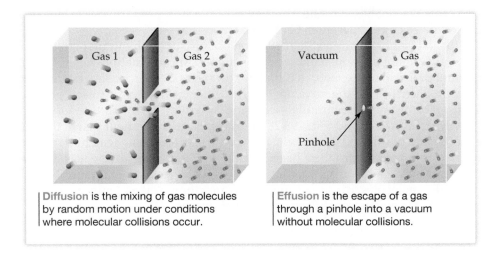

| **Diffusion** is the mixing of gas molecules by random motion under conditions where molecular collisions occur. | **Effusion** is the escape of a gas through a pinhole into a vacuum without molecular collisions. |

Figure 9.13
Diffusion and effusion of gases.

According to **Graham's law**, formulated in the mid-1800s by the Scottish chemist Thomas Graham (1805–1869), the rate of effusion of a gas is inversely proportional to the square root of its mass. In other words, the lighter the molecule, the more rapidly it effuses.

Graham's law Rate of effusion $\propto \dfrac{1}{\sqrt{m}}$

The rate of effusion of a gas is inversely proportional to the square root of its mass, m.

In comparing two gases at the same temperature and pressure, we can set up an equation showing that the ratio of the effusion rates of the two gases is inversely proportional to the ratio of the square roots of their masses:

$$\frac{\text{Rate}_1}{\text{Rate}_2} = \frac{\sqrt{m_2}}{\sqrt{m_1}} = \sqrt{\frac{m_2}{m_1}}$$

The inverse relationship between the rate of effusion and the square root of the mass follows directly from the connection between temperature and kinetic energy described in the previous section. Because temperature is a measure of average kinetic energy and is independent of the gas's chemical identity, different gases at the same temperature have the same average kinetic energy:

Since $\dfrac{1}{2}mu^2 = \dfrac{3\,RT}{2\,N_A}$ for any gas

then $\left(\dfrac{1}{2}mu^2\right)_{\text{gas 1}} = \left(\dfrac{1}{2}mu^2\right)_{\text{gas 2}}$ at the same T

Canceling the factor of 1/2 from both sides and rearranging, we find that the average speeds of the molecules in two gases vary as the inverse ratio of the square roots of their masses:

$$\text{Since} \quad \left(\frac{1}{2}mu^2\right)_{\text{gas 1}} = \left(\frac{1}{2}mu^2\right)_{\text{gas 2}}$$

$$\text{then} \quad (mu^2)_{\text{gas 1}} = (mu^2)_{\text{gas 2}} \quad \text{and} \quad \frac{(u_{\text{gas 1}})^2}{(u_{\text{gas 2}})^2} = \frac{m_2}{m_1}$$

$$\text{so} \quad \frac{u_{\text{gas 1}}}{u_{\text{gas 2}}} = \frac{\sqrt{m_2}}{\sqrt{m_1}} = \sqrt{\frac{m_2}{m_1}}$$

If, as seems reasonable, the rate of effusion of a gas is proportional to the average speed of the gas molecules, then Graham's law results.

Diffusion is more complex than effusion because of the molecular collisions that occur, but Graham's law usually works as a good approximation. One of the most important practical consequences is that mixtures of gases can be separated into their pure components by taking advantage of the different rates of diffusion of the components. For example, naturally occurring uranium is a mixture of isotopes, primarily ^{235}U (0.72%) and ^{238}U (99.28%). In uranium enrichment plants that purify the fissionable uranium-235 used for fuel in nuclear reactors, elemental uranium is converted into volatile uranium hexafluoride (bp 56 °C), and UF_6 gas is allowed to diffuse from one chamber to another through a permeable membrane. The $^{235}UF_6$ and $^{238}UF_6$ molecules diffuse through the membrane at slightly different rates according to the square root of the ratio of their masses:

$$\text{For } ^{235}UF_6, m = 349.03 \text{ amu}$$

$$\text{For } ^{238}UF_6, m = 352.04 \text{ amu}$$

$$\text{so} \quad \frac{\text{Rate of } ^{235}UF_6 \text{ diffusion}}{\text{Rate of } ^{238}UF_6 \text{ diffusion}} = \sqrt{\frac{352.04 \text{ amu}}{349.03 \text{ amu}}} = 1.0043$$

▲ Much of the uranium-235 used as a fuel in nuclear reactors is obtained by gas diffusion of UF_6 in these cylinders.

The UF_6 gas that passes through the membrane is thus very slightly enriched in the lighter, faster-moving isotope. After repeating the process many thousands of times, a separation of isotopes can be achieved. Approximately 35% of the Western world's nuclear fuel supply—some 5000 tons per year—is produced by this gas diffusion method, although the percentage is dropping because better methods are now available.

WORKED EXAMPLE 9.10

USING GRAHAM'S LAW TO CALCULATE DIFFUSION RATES

Assume that you have a sample of hydrogen gas containing H_2, HD, and D_2 that you want to separate into pure components (H = ^{1}H and D = ^{2}H). What are the relative rates of diffusion of the three molecules according to Graham's law?

STRATEGY

First, find the masses of the three molecules: for H_2, $m = 2.016$ amu; for HD, $m = 3.022$ amu; for D_2, $m = 4.028$ amu. Then apply Graham's law to different pairs of gas molecules.

SOLUTION

Because D_2 is the heaviest of the three molecules, it will diffuse most slowly. If we call its relative rate 1.000, we can then compare HD and H_2 with D_2:

Comparing HD with D_2, we have

$$\frac{\text{Rate of HD diffusion}}{\text{Rate of } D_2 \text{ diffusion}} = \sqrt{\frac{\text{mass of } D_2}{\text{mass of HD}}} = \sqrt{\frac{4.028 \text{ amu}}{3.022 \text{ amu}}} = 1.155$$

Comparing H_2 with D_2, we have

$$\frac{\text{Rate of } H_2 \text{ diffusion}}{\text{Rate of } D_2 \text{ diffusion}} = \sqrt{\frac{\text{mass of } D_2}{\text{mass of } H_2}} = \sqrt{\frac{4.028 \text{ amu}}{2.016 \text{ amu}}} = 1.414$$

Thus, the relative rates of diffusion are H_2 (1.414) > HD (1.154) > D_2 (1.000).

▶ **PROBLEM 9.20** Which gas in each of the following pairs diffuses more rapidly, and what are the relative rates of diffusion?

(a) Kr and O_2 (b) N_2 and acetylene (C_2H_2)

▶ **PROBLEM 9.21** What are the relative rates of diffusion of the three naturally occurring isotopes of neon, ^{20}Ne, ^{21}Ne, and ^{22}Ne?

9.8 THE BEHAVIOR OF REAL GASES

Before ending this discussion of gases, it's worthwhile expanding on a point made earlier: The behavior of a real gas is often a bit different from that of an ideal gas. For instance, kinetic–molecular theory assumes that the volume of the gas particles themselves is negligible compared with the total gas volume. The assumption is valid at STP, where the volume taken up by molecules of a typical gas is only about 0.05% of the total volume, but the assumption is not valid at 500 atm and 0 °C, where the volume of the molecules is about 20% of the total volume (**Figure 9.14**). As a result, the volume of a real gas at high pressure is larger than predicted by the ideal gas law.

Figure 9.14
The volume of a real gas.

At lower pressure, the volume of the gas particles is negligible compared to the total volume.

At higher pressure, the volume of the gas particles is more significant compared to the total volume. As a result, the volume of a real gas at high pressure is somewhat larger than the ideal value.

A second issue arising with real gases is the assumption that there are no attractive forces between particles. At lower pressures, this assumption is reasonable because the gas particles are so far apart. At higher pressures, however, the particles are much closer together and the attractive forces between them become more important. In general, intermolecular attractions become significant at a distance of about 10 molecular diameters and increase rapidly as the distance diminishes (**Figure 9.15**). The result is to draw the molecules of real gases together slightly, decreasing the volume at a given pressure (or decreasing the pressure for a given volume).

Note that the effect of molecular volume—to increase V—is opposite that of intermolecular attractions—to decrease V. The two factors therefore tend to cancel at intermediate pressures, but the effect of molecular volume dominates above about 350 atm.

Both ways in which the behavior of real gases deviates from the ideal gas law can be dealt with mathematically by a modification of the ideal gas law called the **van der Waals equation**, which uses two correction factors, called a and b. The increase in V, caused by the effect of molecular volume, is corrected by subtracting an amount nb from the observed volume. The decrease in V (or, equivalently, the decrease in P),

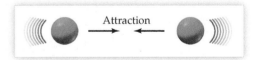

Figure 9.15
Molecules attract one another at distances up to about 10 molecular diameters. The result is a decrease in the actual volume of most real gases when compared with ideal gases at pressures up to 300 atm.

caused by the effect of intermolecular attractions, is best corrected by adding an amount an^2/V^2 to the pressure.

Correction for intermolecular attractions

Correction for molecular volume

van der Waals equation: $\left(P + \dfrac{an^2}{V^2}\right)(V - nb) = nRT$

or $P = \dfrac{nRT}{V - nb} - \dfrac{an^2}{V^2}$

▶ **PROBLEM 9.22** Assume that you have 0.500 mol of N_2 in a volume of 0.600 L at 300 K. Calculate the pressure in atmospheres using both the ideal gas law and the van der Waals equation. For N_2, $a = 1.35$ $(L^2 \cdot atm)/mol^2$, and $b = 0.0387$ L/mol.

9.9 THE EARTH'S ATMOSPHERE

The mantle of gases surrounding the Earth is far from the uniform mixture you might expect. Although atmospheric pressure decreases in a regular way at higher altitudes, the profile of temperature versus altitude is much more complex (Figure 9.16). Four regions of the atmosphere have been defined based on this temperature curve. The temperature in the *troposphere*, the region nearest the Earth's surface, decreases regularly up to about 12 km altitude, where it reaches a minimum value, and then increases in the *stratosphere*, up to about 50 km. Above the stratosphere, in the *mesosphere*, (50–85 km), the temperature again decreases but then again increases in the *thermosphere*. To give you a feeling for these altitudes, passenger jets normally fly near the top of the troposphere at altitudes of 10 to 12 km, and the world altitude record for jet aircraft is 37.65 km—roughly in the middle of the stratosphere.

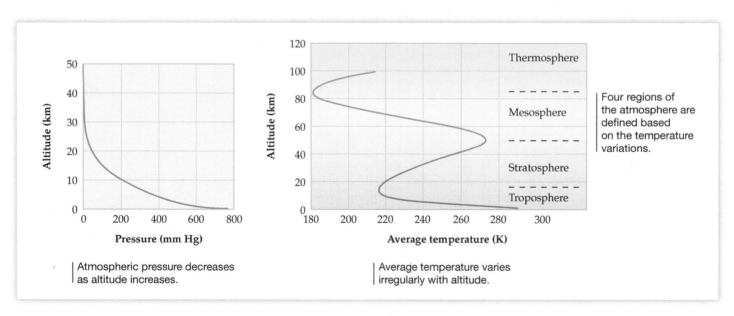

Figure 9.16
Variations of atmospheric pressure and average temperature with altitude.

Chemistry of the Troposphere

Not surprisingly, it's the layer nearest the Earth's surface—the troposphere—that is the most easily disturbed by human activities and has the greatest effect on the Earth's surface conditions. Among those effects, air pollution, acid rain, and global warming are particularly important.

Air Pollution Air pollution has appeared in the last two centuries as an unwanted by-product of industrialized societies. Its causes are relatively straightforward; its control is difficult. The main causes of air pollution are the release of unburned hydrocarbon molecules and the production of nitric oxide, NO, during combustion of petroleum products in older industrial plants and the approximately 750 million automobile and truck engines presently in use worldwide. The NO is further oxidized by reaction with air to yield nitrogen dioxide, NO_2, which splits into NO plus free oxygen atoms in the presence of sunlight (symbolized by $h\nu$). Reaction of the oxygen atoms with O_2 molecules then yields ozone, O_3, a highly reactive substance that can further combine with unburned hydrocarbons in the air. The end result is the production of so-called photochemical smog, the hazy, brownish layer lying over many cities.

$$NO_2(g) + h\nu \longrightarrow NO(g) + O(g)$$
$$O(g) + O_2(g) \longrightarrow O_3(g)$$

▲ The photochemical smog over many cities is the end result of pollution from automobile exhausts.

Acid Rain Acid rain, a second major environmental problem, results primarily from the production of sulfur dioxide, SO_2, that accompanies the burning of sulfur-containing coal in power-generating plants. Sulfur dioxide is slowly converted to SO_3 by reaction with oxygen in air, and SO_3 dissolves in rainwater to yield dilute sulfuric acid, H_2SO_4.

$$S\,(\text{in coal}) + O_2(g) \longrightarrow SO_2(g)$$
$$2\,SO_2(g) + O_2(g) \longrightarrow 2\,SO_3(g)$$
$$SO_3(g) + H_2O(l) \longrightarrow H_2SO_4(aq)$$

Among the many dramatic effects of acid rain are the extinction of fish in acidic lakes throughout parts of the northeastern United States, Canada, and Scandinavia, the damage to forests throughout much of central and eastern Europe, and the deterioration everywhere of marble buildings and statuary. Marble is a form of calcium carbonate, $CaCO_3$, and, like all metal carbonates, reacts with acid to produce CO_2. The result is a slow eating away of the stone.

$$CaCO_3(s) + H_2SO_4(aq) \longrightarrow CaSO_4(aq) + H_2O(l) + CO_2(g)$$

▲ The details on this marble statue have been eaten away over the years by acid rain.

Global Warming The third major atmospheric problem, global warming, is more complicated and less well understood than either air pollution or acid rain. The fundamental cause of the problem is that human activities over the past century appear to have disturbed the Earth's delicate thermal balance. One component of that balance is the radiant energy the Earth's surface receives from the sun, some of which is radiated back into space as infrared energy. Although much of this radiation passes out through the atmosphere, some is absorbed by atmospheric gases, particularly water vapor, carbon dioxide, and methane. This absorbed radiation warms the atmosphere and acts to maintain a relatively stable temperature at the Earth's surface. Should increasing amounts of radiation be absorbed, however, increased atmospheric heating would result and global temperatures would rise.

Careful measurements show that concentrations of atmospheric carbon dioxide have been rising in the last 160 years, largely because of the increased use of fossil fuels, from an estimated 290 parts per million (ppm) in 1850 to 385 ppm in 2009 (**Figure 9.17**). Thus, there is concern among atmospheric scientists that increased absorption of infrared radiation and widespread global warming will follow. Most atmospheric scientists believe, in fact, that global warming has begun, with current measurements showing a warming of the mid-troposphere by about 0.4 °C in the last 25 yrs. In addition, some computer models predict a potential warming of as much as 3 °C by the year 2050. Should this occur, the result would be a significant increase in melting of glacial ice and a consequent rise in ocean levels.

Figure 9.17
Annual concentration of atmospheric CO_2 since 1850.

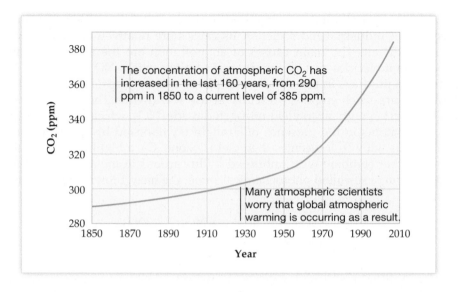

The concentration of atmospheric CO_2 has increased in the last 160 years, from 290 ppm in 1850 to a current level of 385 ppm.

Many atmospheric scientists worry that global atmospheric warming is occurring as a result.

Chemistry of the Upper Atmosphere

Relatively little of the atmosphere's mass is located above the troposphere, but the chemistry that occurs there is nonetheless crucial to maintaining life on Earth. Particularly important is what takes place in the *ozone layer*, an atmospheric band stretching from about 20–40 km above the Earth's surface. Ozone (O_3) is a severe pollutant at low altitudes but is critically important in the upper atmosphere because it absorbs intense ultraviolet radiation from the sun. Even though it is present in very small amounts in the stratosphere, ozone acts as a shield to prevent high-energy solar radiation from reaching the Earth's surface, where it can cause such health problems as eye cataracts and skin cancer.

Around 1976, a disturbing decrease in the amount of ozone present over the South Pole began showing up (Figure 9.18), and more recently a similar phenomenon has been found over the North Pole. Ozone levels drop to below 50% of normal in the polar spring before returning to near normal in the autumn.

Figure 9.18
A false-color satellite image of the ozone hole over Antarctica on September 24, 2009.

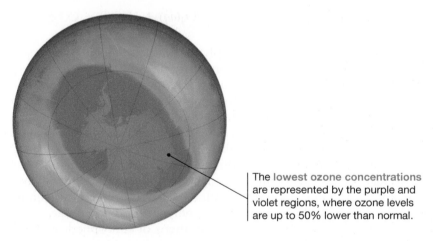

The lowest ozone concentrations are represented by the purple and violet regions, where ozone levels are up to 50% lower than normal.

The principal cause of ozone depletion is the presence in the stratosphere of *chlorofluorocarbons* (CFCs), such as CF_2Cl_2 and $CFCl_3$. Because they are inexpensive and stable, yet not toxic, flammable, or corrosive, CFCs are ideal as propellants in aerosol cans, as refrigerants, as solvents, and as fire-extinguishing agents. In addition, they are used for blowing bubbles into foamed plastic insulation. Unfortunately, the chemical stability that makes CFCs so useful also causes them to persist in the environment. Molecules released at ground level slowly diffuse into the stratosphere, where they undergo a complex series of reactions that ultimately result in ozone destruction.

Several different mechanisms of ozone destruction predominate under different stratospheric conditions. All are multistep processes that begin when ultraviolet light ($h\nu$) strikes a CFC molecule, breaking a carbon–chlorine bond and generating a chlorine atom:

$$CFCl_3 + h\nu \longrightarrow CFCl_2 + Cl$$

The resultant chlorine atom reacts with ozone to yield O_2 and ClO, and two ClO molecules then give Cl_2O_2. Further reaction occurs when Cl_2O_2 is struck by more ultraviolet light to generate O_2 and two more chlorine atoms.

$$(1) \quad 2\,[Cl + O_3 \longrightarrow O_2 + ClO]$$
$$(2) \quad 2\,ClO \longrightarrow Cl_2O_2$$
$$(3) \quad Cl_2O_2 + h\nu \longrightarrow 2\,Cl + O_2$$
$$\text{Net:} \quad 2\,O_3 + h\nu \longrightarrow 3\,O_2$$

Look at the overall result of the above reaction sequence. Chlorine atoms are used up in the first step but are regenerated in the third step, so they don't appear in the net equation. Thus, the net sequence is a never-ending *chain reaction*, in which the generation of just a few chlorine atoms from a few CFC molecules leads to the continuing destruction of a great many ozone molecules.

Recognition of the problem led the U.S. government in 1980 to ban the use of CFCs for aerosol propellants and, more recently, for refrigerants. Worldwide action to reduce CFC use began in September 1987, and an international ban on the industrial production and release of CFCs took effect in 1996. The ban has not been wholly successful, however, because of a substantial black market that has developed, particularly in Russia and China, where up to $300 million per year of illegal CFCs are thought to be manufactured. Even with these stringent efforts, amounts of CFCs in the stratosphere won't return to pre-1980 levels until the middle of this century.

▸ **PROBLEM 9.23**   The ozone layer is about 20 km thick, has an average total pressure of 10 mm Hg (1.3×10^{-2} atm), and has an average temperature of 230 K. The partial pressure of ozone in the layer is only about 1.2×10^{-6} mm Hg (1.6×10^{-9} atm). How many meters thick would the layer be if all the ozone contained in it were compressed into a thin layer of pure O_3 at STP?

▲ On April 7, 1853, Queen Victoria of England gave birth to her eighth child, while anesthetized by chloroform, changing forever the practice of obstetrics.

INQUIRY HOW DO INHALED ANESTHETICS WORK?

William Morton's demonstration in 1846 of ether-induced anesthesia during dental surgery ranks as one of the most important medical breakthroughs of all time. Before then, all surgery had been carried out with the patient conscious. Use of chloroform as an anesthetic quickly followed Morton's work, made popular by Queen Victoria of England, who in 1853 gave birth to a child while anesthetized by chloroform.

Literally hundreds of substances in addition to ether and chloroform have subsequently been shown to act as inhaled anesthetics. Halothane, isoflurane, sevoflurane, and desflurane are among the most commonly used agents at present. All four are nontoxic, nonflammable, and potent at relatively low doses.

Despite their importance, surprisingly little is known about how inhaled anesthetics work in the body. Even the definition of anesthesia as a behavioral state is imprecise, and the nature of the changes in brain function leading to anesthesia are unknown. Remarkably, the potency of different inhaled anesthetics correlates well with their solubility in olive oil: the more soluble in olive oil, the more potent as an anesthetic. This unusual observation has led many scientists to believe that anesthetics act by dissolving in the fatty membranes surrounding nerve cells. The resultant changes in the fluidity and shape of the membranes apparently decrease the ability of sodium ions to pass into the nerve cells, thereby blocking the firing of nerve impulses.

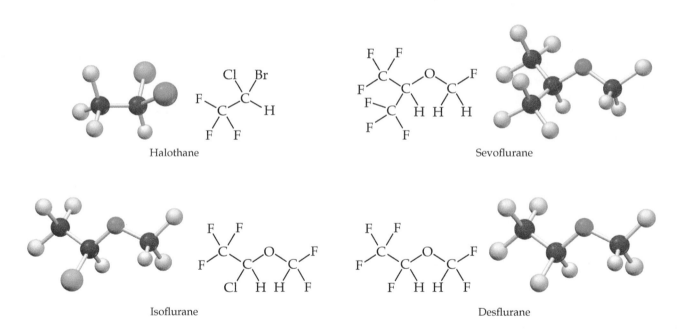

Depth of anesthesia is determined by the concentration of anesthetic agent that reaches the brain. Brain concentration, in turn, depends on the solubility and transport of the anesthetic agent in the bloodstream and on its partial pressure in inhaled air. Anesthetic potency is usually expressed as a *minimum alveolar concentration (MAC)*, defined as the percent concentration of anesthetic in inhaled air that results in anesthesia in 50% of patients. As shown in Table 9.6, nitrous oxide, N_2O, is the least potent of the common anesthetics. Fewer than 50% of patients are immobilized by breathing an 80:20 mix of nitrous oxide and oxygen. Halothane is the most potent agent; a partial pressure of only 5.7 mm Hg is sufficient to anesthetize 50% of patients.

TABLE 9.6 Relative Potency of Inhaled Anesthetics

Anesthetic	MAC (%)	MAC (partial pressure, mm Hg)
Nitrous oxide	—	>760
Desflurane	6.2	47
Sevoflurane	2.5	19
Isoflurane	1.4	11
Halothane	0.75	5.7

▶ PROBLEM 9.24   For ether, a partial pressure of 15 mm Hg results in anesthesia in 50% of patients. What is the MAC for ether?

▶ PROBLEM 9.25   Chloroform has an MAC of 0.77%.

(a) What partial pressure of chloroform is required to anesthetize 50% of patients?

(b) What mass of chloroform in 10.0 L of air at STP will produce the appropriate MAC?

SUMMARY

A gas is a collection of atoms or molecules moving independently through a volume that is largely empty space. Collisions of the randomly moving particles with the walls of their container exert a force per unit area that we perceive as **pressure**. The SI unit for pressure is the **pascal**, but the **atmosphere**, the **millimeter of mercury**, and the **bar** are more commonly used.

The physical condition of any gas is defined by four variables: pressure (P), temperature (T), volume (V), and molar amount (n). The specific relationships among these variables are called the **gas laws**:

Boyle's law:	The volume of a gas varies inversely with its pressure. That is, $V \propto 1/P$ or $PV = k$ at constant n, T.
Charles's law:	The volume of a gas varies directly with its Kelvin temperature. That is, $V \propto T$ or $V/T = k$ at constant n, P.
Avogadro's law:	The volume of a gas varies directly with its molar amount. That is, $V \propto n$ or $V/n = k$ at constant T, P.

The three individual gas laws can be combined into a single **ideal gas law**, $PV = nRT$. If any three of the four variables P, V, T, and n are known, the fourth can be calculated. The constant R in the equation is called the **gas constant** and has the same value for all gases. At **standard temperature and pressure** (**STP**; 1 atm and 0 °C), the **standard molar volume** of an ideal gas is 22.414 L.

The gas laws apply to mixtures of gases as well as to pure gases. According to **Dalton's law of partial pressures**, the total pressure exerted by a mixture of gases in a container is equal to the sum of the pressures each individual gas would exert alone.

The behavior of gases can be accounted for using a model called the **kinetic–molecular theory**, a group of five postulates:

1. A gas consists of tiny particles moving at random.
2. The volume of the gas particles is negligible compared with the total volume.
3. There are no forces between particles, either attractive or repulsive.
4. Collisions of gas particles are elastic.
5. The average kinetic energy of gas particles is proportional to their absolute temperature.

The connection between temperature and kinetic energy obtained from the kinetic–molecular theory makes it possible to calculate the average speed of a gas particle at any temperature. An important practical consequence of this relationship is **Graham's law**, which states that the rate of a gas's **effusion**, or spontaneous passage through a pinhole in a membrane, depends inversely on the square root of the gas's mass.

Real gases differ in their behavior from that predicted by the ideal gas law, particularly at high pressure, where gas particles are forced close together and intermolecular attractions become significant. The deviations from ideal behavior can be dealt with mathematically by the **van der Waals equation**.

KEY WORDS

CONCEPTUAL PROBLEMS

Problems 9.1–9.25 appear within the chapter.

9.26 A 1 : 1 mixture of helium (red) and argon (blue) at 300 K is portrayed below on the left. Draw the same mixture when the temperature is lowered to 150 K.

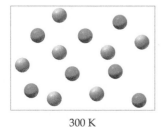

300 K

150 K

9.27 The following drawing represents a container holding a mixture of four gases, red, blue, green, and black. If the total pressure inside the container is 420 mm Hg, what is the partial pressure of each individual component?

9.28 Assume that you have a sample of gas in a cylinder with a movable piston, as shown in the following drawing:

Redraw the apparatus to show what the sample will look like after **(a)** the temperature is increased from 300 K to 450 K at constant pressure, **(b)** the pressure is increased from 1 atm to 2 atm at constant temperature, and **(c)** the temperature is decreased from 300 K to 200 K and the pressure is decreased from 3 atm to 2 atm.

9.29 Assume that you have a sample of gas at 350 K in a sealed container, as represented in **(a)**. Which of the drawings **(b)**–**(d)** represents the gas after the temperature is lowered from 350 K to 150 K?

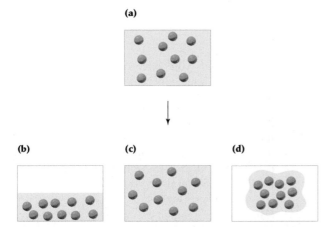

(a)

(b)   **(c)**   **(d)**

9.30 Assume that you have a mixture of He (atomic mass = 4 amu) and Xe (atomic mass = 131 amu) at 300 K. Which of the drawings best represents the mixture (blue = He; red = Xe)?

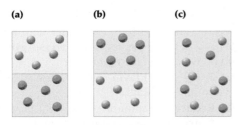

(a)   **(b)**   **(c)**

9.31 Three bulbs, two of which contain different gases and one of which is empty, are connected as shown in the following drawing. Redraw the apparatus to represent the gases after the stopcocks are opened and the system is allowed to come to equilibrium.

9.32 The apparatus shown is called a *closed-end* manometer because the arm not connected to the gas sample is closed to the atmosphere and is under vacuum. Explain how you can read the gas pressure in the bulb.

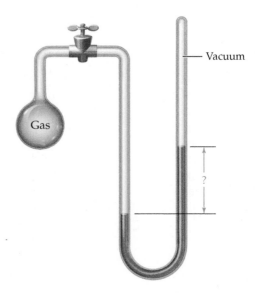

9.33 Redraw the following open-end manometer to show what it would look like when stopcock A is opened.

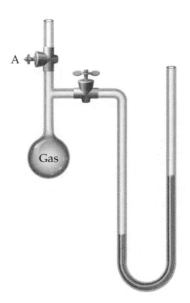

9.34 Effusion of a 1:1 mixture of two gases through a small pinhole produces the results shown below.
   (a) Which gas molecules—yellow or blue—have a higher average speed?
   (b) If the yellow molecules have a molecular mass of 25 amu, what is the molecular mass of the blue molecules?

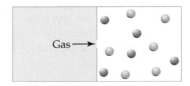

9.35 A glass tube has one end in a dish of mercury and the other end closed by a stopcock. The distance from the surface of the mercury to the bottom of the stopcock is 850 mm. The apparatus is at 25 °C, and the mercury level in the tube is the same as that in the dish.

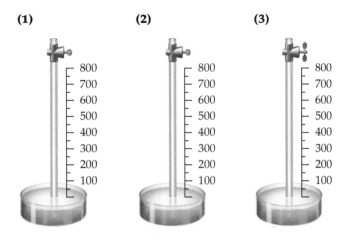

(1)   (2)   (3)

(a) Show on drawing **(1)** what the approximate level of mercury in the tube will be when the temperature of the entire apparatus is lowered from +25 °C to −25 °C.

(b) Show on drawing **(2)** what the approximate level of mercury in the tube will be when a vacuum pump is connected to the top of the tube, the stopcock is opened, the tube is evacuated, the stopcock is closed, and the pump is removed.

(c) Show on drawing **(3)** what the approximate level of mercury in the tube will be when the stopcock in drawing **(2)** is opened.

SECTION PROBLEMS

Gases and Gas Pressure (Section 9.1)

9.36 What is temperature a measure of?

9.37 Why are gases so much more compressible than solids or liquids?

9.38 Atmospheric pressure at the top of Pikes Peak in Colorado is approximately 480 mm Hg. Convert this value to atmospheres and to pascals.

9.39 Carry out the following conversions:

(a) 352 torr to kPa

(b) 0.255 atm to mm Hg

(c) 0.0382 mm Hg to Pa

9.40 What is the pressure in millimeters of mercury inside a container of gas connected to a mercury-filled open-end manometer of the sort shown in Figure 9.4 when the level in the arm connected to the container is 17.6 cm lower than the level in the arm open to the atmosphere and the atmospheric pressure reading outside the apparatus is 754.3 mm Hg?

9.41 What is the pressure in atmospheres inside a container of gas connected to a mercury-filled open-end manometer when the level in the arm connected to the container is 28.3 cm higher than the level in the arm open to the atmosphere and the atmospheric pressure reading outside the apparatus is 1.021 atm?

9.42 Assume that you have an open-end manometer filled with ethyl alcohol (density = 0.7893 g/mL at 20 °C) rather than mercury (density = 13.546 g/mL at 20 °C). What is the pressure in pascals if the level in the arm open to the atmosphere is 55.1 cm higher than the level in the arm connected to the gas sample and the atmospheric pressure reading is 752.3 mm Hg?

Ethyl alcohol

9.43 Assume that you have an open-end manometer filled with chloroform (density = 1.4832 g/mL at 20 °C) rather than mercury (density = 13.546 g/mL at 20 °C). What is the difference in height between the liquid in the two arms if the pressure in the arm connected to the gas sample is 0.788 atm and the atmospheric pressure reading is 0.849 atm? In which arm is the chloroform level higher?

Chloroform

9.44 Calculate the average molecular mass of air from the data given in Table 9.1.

9.45 What is the average molecular mass of a diving-gas mixture that contains 2.0% by volume O_2 and 98.0% by volume He?

The Gas Laws (Sections 9.2 and 9.3)

9.46 Assume that you have a cylinder with a movable piston. What would happen to the gas pressure inside the cylinder if you were to do the following?

(a) Triple the Kelvin temperature while holding the volume constant

(b) Reduce the amount of gas by 1/3 while holding the temperature and volume constant

(c) Decrease the volume by 45% at constant T

(d) Halve the Kelvin temperature, and triple the volume

9.47 Assume that you have a cylinder with a movable piston. What would happen to the gas volume of the cylinder if you were to do the following?

(a) Halve the Kelvin temperature while holding the pressure constant

(b) Increase the amount of gas by 1/4 while holding the temperature and pressure constant

(c) Decrease the pressure by 75% at constant T

(d) Double the Kelvin temperature, and double the pressure

9.48 Which sample contains more molecules: 1.00 L of O_2 at STP, 1.00 L of air at STP or 1.00 L of H_2 at STP?

9.49 Which sample contains more molecules: 2.50 L of air at 50 °C and 750 mm Hg pressure or 2.16 L of CO_2 at −10 °C and 765 mm Hg pressure?

9.50 Oxygen gas is commonly sold in 49.0 L steel containers at a pressure of 150 atm. What volume in liters would the gas occupy at a pressure of 1.02 atm if its temperature remained unchanged? If its temperature was raised from 20.0 °C to 35.0 °C at constant $P = 150$ atm?

9.51 A compressed air tank carried by scuba divers has a volume of 8.0 L and a pressure of 140 atm at 20 °C. What is the volume of air in the tank in liters at STP?

9.52 If 15.0 g of CO_2 gas has a volume of 0.30 L at 300 K, what is its pressure in millimeters of mercury?

9.53 If 2.00 g of N_2 gas has a volume of 0.40 L and a pressure of 6.0 atm, what is its Kelvin temperature?

9.54 The matter in interstellar space consists almost entirely of hydrogen atoms at a temperature of 100 K and a density of approximately 1 atom/cm^3. What is the gas pressure in millimeters of mercury?

9.55 Methane gas, CH_4, is sold in a 43.8 L cylinder containing 5.54 kg. What is the pressure inside the cylinder in kilopascals at 20 °C?

9.56 Many laboratory gases are sold in steel cylinders with a volume of 43.8 L. What mass in grams of argon is inside a cylinder whose pressure is 17,180 kPa at 20 °C?

9.57 A small cylinder of helium gas used for filling balloons has a volume of 2.30 L and a pressure of 13,800 kPa at 25 °C. How many balloons can you fill if each one has a volume of 1.5 L and a pressure of 1.25 atm at 25 °C?

Gas Stoichiometry (Section 9.4)

9.58 Which sample contains more molecules, 15.0 L of steam (gaseous H_2O) at 123.0 °C and 0.93 atm pressure or a 10.5 g ice cube at −5.0 °C?

9.59 Which sample contains more molecules, 3.14 L of Ar at 85.0 °C and 1111 mm Hg pressure or 11.07 g of Cl_2?

9.60 Imagine that you have two identical flasks, one containing hydrogen at STP and the other containing oxygen at STP. How can you tell which is which without opening them?

9.61 Imagine that you have two identical flasks, one containing chlorine gas and the other containing argon at the same temperature and pressure. How can you tell which is which without opening them?

9.62 What is the total mass in grams of oxygen in a room measuring 4.0 m by 5.0 m by 2.5 m? Assume that the gas is at STP and that air contains 20.95% oxygen by volume.

9.63 The average oxygen content of arterial blood is approximately 0.25 g of O_2 per liter. Assuming a body temperature of 37 °C, how many moles of oxygen are transported by each liter of arterial blood? How many milliliters?

9.64 One mole of an ideal gas has a volume of 22.414 L at STP. Assuming ideal behavior, what are the densities of the following gases in g/L at STP?

(a) CH_4 (b) CO_2 (c) O_2

9.65 What is the density in g/L of a gas mixture that contains 27.0% F_2 and 73.0% He by volume at 714 mm Hg and 27.5 °C?

9.66 An unknown gas is placed in a 1.500 L bulb at a pressure of 356 mm Hg and a temperature of 22.5 °C, and is found to weigh 0.9847 g. What is the molecular mass of the gas?

9.67 What are the molecular masses of the gases with the following densities:

(a) 1.342 g/L at STP

(b) 1.053 g/L at 25 °C and 752 mm Hg

9.68 Pure oxygen gas was first prepared by heating mercury(II) oxide, HgO:

$$2\,HgO(s) \longrightarrow 2\,Hg(l) + O_2(g)$$

What volume in liters of oxygen at STP is released by heating 10.57 g of HgO?

9.69 How many grams of HgO would you need to heat if you wanted to prepare 0.0155 mol of O_2 according to the equation in Problem 9.68?

9.70 Hydrogen gas can be prepared by reaction of zinc metal with aqueous HCl:

$$Zn(s) + 2\,HCl(aq) \longrightarrow ZnCl_2(aq) + H_2(g)$$

(a) How many liters of H_2 would be formed at 742 mm Hg and 15 °C if 25.5 g of zinc was allowed to react?

(b) How many grams of zinc would you start with if you wanted to prepare 5.00 L of H_2 at 350 mm Hg and 30.0 °C?

9.71 Ammonium nitrate can decompose explosively when heated according to the equation

$$2\,NH_4NO_3(s) \longrightarrow 2\,N_2(g) + 4\,H_2O(g) + O_2(g)$$

How many liters of gas would be formed at 450 °C and 1.00 atm pressure by explosion of 450 g of NH_4NO_3?

9.72 The reaction of sodium peroxide (Na_2O_2) with CO_2 is used in space vehicles to remove CO_2 from the air and generate O_2 for breathing:

$$2\,Na_2O_2(s) + 2\,CO_2(g) \longrightarrow 2\,Na_2CO_3(s) + O_2(g)$$

(a) Assuming that air is breathed at an average rate of 4.50 L/min (25 °C; 735 mm Hg) and that the concentration of CO_2 in expelled air is 3.4% by volume, how many grams of CO_2 are produced in 24 h?

(b) How many days would a 3.65 kg supply of Na_2O_2 last?

9.73 Titanium(III) chloride, a substance used in catalysts for preparing polyethylene, is made by high-temperature reaction of $TiCl_4$ vapor with H_2:

$$2\,TiCl_4(g) + H_2(g) \longrightarrow 2\,TiCl_3(s) + 2\,HCl(g)$$

(a) How many grams of $TiCl_4$ are needed for complete reaction with 155 L of H_2 at 435 °C and 795 mm Hg pressure?

(b) How many liters of HCl gas at STP will result from the reaction described in part (a)?

Dalton's Law and Mole Fraction (Section 9.5)

9.74 Use the information in Table 9.1 to calculate the partial pressure in atmospheres of each gas in dry air at STP.

9.75 Natural gas is a mixture of many substances, primarily CH_4, C_2H_6, C_3H_8, and C_4H_{10}. Assuming that the total pressure of the gases is 1.48 atm and that their mole ratio is 94 : 4.0 : 1.5 : 0.50, calculate the partial pressure in atmospheres of each gas.

9.76 A special gas mixture used in bacterial growth chambers contains 1.00% by weight CO_2 and 99.0% O_2. What is the partial pressure in atmospheres of each gas at a total pressure of 0.977 atm?

9.77 A gas mixture for use in some lasers contains 5.00% by weight HCl, 1.00% H_2, and 94% Ne. The mixture is sold in cylinders that have a volume of 49.0 L and a pressure of 13,800 kPa at 21.0 °C. What is the partial pressure in kilopascals of each gas in the mixture?

9.78 What is the mole fraction of each gas in the mixture described in Problem 9.77?

9.79 A mixture of Ar and N_2 gases has a density of 1.413 g/L at STP. What is the mole fraction of each gas?

9.80 A mixture of 14.2 g of H_2 and 36.7 g of Ar is placed in a 100.0 L container at 290 K.
   (a) What is the partial pressure of H_2 in atmospheres?
   (b) What is the partial pressure of Ar in atmospheres?

9.81 A 20.0 L flask contains 0.776 g of He and 3.61 g of CO_2 at 300 K.
   (a) What is the partial pressure of He in mm Hg?
   (b) What is the partial pressure of CO_2 in mm Hg?

9.82 A sample of magnesium metal reacts with aqueous HCl to yield H_2 gas:

$$Mg(s) + 2\,HCl(aq) \longrightarrow MgCl_2(aq) + H_2(g)$$

The gas that forms is found to have a volume of 3.557 L at 25 °C and a pressure of 747 mm Hg. Assuming that the gas is saturated with water vapor at a partial pressure of 23.8 mm Hg, what is the partial pressure in millimeters of mercury of the H_2? How many grams of magnesium metal were used in the reaction?

9.83 Chlorine gas was first prepared in 1774 by the oxidation of NaCl with MnO_2:

$$2\,NaCl(s) + 2\,H_2SO_4(l) + MnO_2(s) \longrightarrow$$
$$Na_2SO_4(s) + MnSO_4(s) + 2\,H_2O(g) + Cl_2(g)$$

Assume that the gas produced is saturated with water vapor at a partial pressure of 28.7 mm Hg and that it has a volume of 0.597 L at 27 °C and 755 mm Hg pressure.

   (a) What is the mole fraction of Cl_2 in the gas?
   (b) How many grams of NaCl were used in the experiment, assuming complete reaction?

Kinetic–Molecular Theory and Graham's Law (Sections 9.6 and 9.7)

9.84 What are the basic assumptions of the kinetic–molecular theory?

9.85 What is the difference between effusion and diffusion?

9.86 What is the difference between heat and temperature?

9.87 Why does a helium-filled balloon lose pressure faster than an air-filled balloon?

9.88 The average temperature at an altitude of 20 km is 220 K. What is the average speed in m/s of an N_2 molecule at this altitude?

9.89 At what temperature (°C) will xenon atoms have the same average speed that Br_2 molecules have at 20 °C?

9.90 Which has a higher average speed, H_2 at 150 K or He at 375 °C?

9.91 Which has a higher average speed, a Ferrari at 145 mph or a gaseous UF_6 molecule at 145 °C?

9.92 An unknown gas is found to diffuse through a porous membrane 2.92 times more slowly than H_2. What is the molecular mass of the gas?

9.93 What is the molecular mass of a gas that diffuses through a porous membrane 1.86 times faster than Xe? What might the gas be?

9.94 Rank the following gases in order of their speed of diffusion through a membrane, and calculate the ratio of their diffusion rates: HCl, F_2, Ar.

9.95 Which will diffuse through a membrane more rapidly, CO or N_2? Assume that the samples contain only the most abundant isotopes of each element, ^{12}C, ^{16}O, and ^{14}N.

9.96 A big-league fastball travels at about 45 m/s. At what temperature (°C) do helium atoms have this same average speed?

9.97 Traffic on the German autobahns reaches speeds of up to 230 km/h. At what temperature (°C) do oxygen molecules have this same average speed?

CHAPTER PROBLEMS

9.98 What is the greatest atmospheric concern—air pollution, acid rain, global warming, or ozone depletion—for each of the following?
   (a) $CFCl_3$ **(b)** S (in coal)   **(c)** CO_2 **(d)** NO

9.99 What is the role or effect of ozone in the troposphere and in the stratosphere?

9.100 Chlorine occurs as a mixture of two isotopes, ^{35}Cl and ^{37}Cl. What is the ratio of the diffusion rates of the three species $(^{35}Cl)_2$, $^{35}Cl^{37}Cl$, and $(^{37}Cl)_2$?

9.101 What would the atmospheric pressure be in millimeters of mercury if our atmosphere were composed of pure CO_2 gas?

9.102 The surface temperature of Venus is about 1050 K, and the pressure is about 75 Earth atmospheres. Assuming that these conditions represent a Venusian "STP," what is the standard molar volume in liters of a gas on Venus?

9.103 When you look directly up at the sky, you are actually looking through a very tall, transparent column of air that extends from the surface of the Earth thousands of kilometers into space. If the air in this column were liquefied, how tall would it be? The density of liquid air is 0.89 g/mL.

9.104 Uranium hexafluoride, a molecular solid used for purification of the uranium isotope needed to fuel nuclear power plants, sublimes at 56.5 °C. Assume that you have a 22.9 L vessel that contains 512.9 g of UF_6 at 70.0 °C.
   (a) What is the pressure in the vessel calculated using the ideal gas law?
   (b) What is the pressure in the vessel calculated using the van der Waals equation? (For UF_6, $a = 15.80$ $(L^2 \cdot atm)/mol^2$; $b = 0.1128$ L/mol.)

9.105 A driver with a nearly empty fuel tank may say she is "running on fumes." If a 15.0 gallon automobile gas tank had only gasoline vapor remaining in it, what is the farthest the vehicle could travel if it gets 20.0 miles per gallon on liquid gasoline? Assume the average molar mass of molecules in gasoline is 105 g/mol, the density of liquid gasoline is 0.75 g/mL, the pressure is 743 mm Hg, and the temperature is 25 °C.

9.106 Two 112 L tanks are filled with gas at 330 K. One contains 5.00 mol of Kr, and the other contains 5.00 mol of O_2. Considering the assumptions of kinetic–molecular theory, rank the gases from low to high for each of the following properties:

(a) collision frequency   (b) density (g/L)

(c) average speed   (d) pressure

9.107 Two identical 732.0 L tanks each contain 212.0 g of gas at 293 K, with neon in one tank and nitrogen in the other. Based on the assumptions of kinetic–molecular theory, rank the gases from low to high for each of the following properties:

(a) average speed   (b) pressure

(c) collision frequency   (d) density (g/L)

9.108 Pakistan's K2 is the world's second tallest mountain, with an altitude of 28,251 ft. Its base camp, where climbers stop to acclimate, is located about 16,400 ft above sea level.

(a) Approximate atmospheric pressure P at different altitudes is given by the equation $P = e^{-h/7000}$, where P is in atmospheres and h is the altitude in meters. What is the approximate atmospheric pressure in mm Hg at K2 base camp?

(b) What is the atmospheric pressure in mm Hg at the summit of K2?

(c) Assuming the mole fraction of oxygen in air is 0.2095, what is the partial pressure of oxygen in mm Hg at the summit of K2?

9.109 When a 10.00 L vessel containing 42.189 g of I_2 is heated to 1173 K, some I_2 dissociates: $I_2(g) \rightarrow 2\, I(g)$. If the final pressure in the vessel is 1.733 atm, what are the mole fractions of the two components $I_2(g)$ and $I(g)$ after the reaction?

9.110 Assume that you take a flask, evacuate it to remove all the air, and find its mass to be 478.1 g. You then fill the flask with argon to a pressure of 2.15 atm and reweigh it. What would the balance read in grams if the flask has a volume of 7.35 L and the temperature is 20.0 °C?

9.111 The apparatus shown consists of three bulbs connected by stopcocks. What is the pressure inside the system when the stopcocks are opened? Assume that the lines connecting the bulbs have zero volume and that the temperature remains constant.

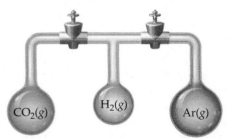

$CO_2(g)$	$H_2(g)$	$Ar(g)$
$P = 2.13$ atm	$P = 0.861$ atm	$P = 1.15$ atm
$V = 1.50$ L	$V = 1.00$ L	$V = 2.00$ L

9.112 The apparatus shown consists of three temperature-jacketed 1.000 L bulbs connected by stopcocks. Bulb **A** contains a mixture of $H_2O(g)$, $CO_2(g)$, and $N_2(g)$ at 25 °C and a total pressure of 564 mm Hg. Bulb **B** is empty and is held at a temperature of −70 °C. Bulb **C** is also empty and is held at a temperature of −190 °C. The stopcocks are closed, and the volume of the lines connecting the bulbs is zero. CO_2 sublimes at −78 °C, and N_2 boils at −196 °C.

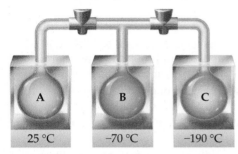

(a) The stopcock between **A** and **B** is opened, and the system is allowed to come to equilibrium. The pressure in **A** and **B** is now 219 mm Hg. What do bulbs **A** and **B** contain?

(b) How many moles of H_2O are in the system?

(c) Both stopcocks are opened, and the system is again allowed to come to equilibrium. The pressure throughout the system is 33.5 mm Hg. What do bulbs **A**, **B**, and **C** contain?

(d) How many moles of N_2 are in the system?

(e) How many moles of CO_2 are in the system?

9.113 Assume that you have 1.00 g of nitroglycerin in a 500.0 mL steel container at 20.0 °C and 1.00 atm pressure. An explosion occurs, raising the temperature of the container and its contents to 425 °C. The balanced equation is

$$4\, C_3H_5N_3O_9(l) \longrightarrow$$
$$12\, CO_2(g) + 10\, H_2O(g) + 6\, N_2(g) + O_2(g)$$

Nitroglycerin

(a) How many moles of nitroglycerin and how many moles of gas (air) were in the container originally?

(b) How many moles of gas are in the container after the explosion?

(c) What is the pressure in atmospheres inside the container after the explosion according to the ideal gas law?

9.114 Use both the ideal gas law and the van der Waals equation to calculate the pressure in atmospheres of 45.0 g of NH_3 gas in a 1.000 L container at 0 °C, 50 °C, and 100 °C. For NH_3, $a = 4.17$ (L$^2 \cdot$ atm)/mol^2 and $b = 0.0371$ L/mol.

9.115 When solid mercury(I) carbonate, Hg_2CO_3, is added to nitric acid, HNO_3, a reaction occurs to give mercury(II) nitrate, $Hg(NO_3)_2$, water, and two gases **A** and **B**:

$$Hg_2CO_3(s) + HNO_3(aq) \longrightarrow$$
$$Hg(NO_3)_2(aq) + H_2O(l) + A(g) + B(g)$$

(a) When the gases are placed in a 500.0 mL bulb at 20 °C, the pressure is 258 mm Hg. How many moles of gas are present?

(b) When the gas mixture is passed over CaO(s), gas **A** reacts, forming $CaCO_3(s)$:

$$CaO(s) + A(g) + B(g) \longrightarrow CaCO_3(s) + B(g)$$

The remaining gas **B** is collected in a 250.0 mL container at 20 °C and found to have a pressure of 344 mm Hg. How many moles of **B** are present?

(c) The mass of gas **B** collected in part **(b)** was found to be 0.218 g. What is the density of **B** in g/L?

(d) What is the molecular mass of **B**, and what is its formula?

(e) Write a balanced equation for the reaction of mercury(I) carbonate with nitric acid.

9.116 Dry ice (solid CO_2) has occasionally been used as an "explosive" in mining. A hole is drilled, dry ice and a small amount of gunpowder are placed in the hole, a fuse is added, and the hole is plugged. When lit, the exploding gunpowder rapidly vaporizes the dry ice, building up an immense pressure. Assume that 500.0 g of dry ice is placed in a cavity with a volume of 0.800 L and the ignited gunpowder heats the CO_2 to 700 K. What is the final pressure inside the hole?

9.117 Consider the combustion reaction of 0.148 g of a hydrocarbon having formula C_nH_{2n+2} with an excess of O_2 in a 400.0 mL steel container. Before reaction, the gaseous mixture had a temperature of 25.0 °C and a pressure of 2.000 atm. After complete combustion and loss of considerable heat, the mixture of products and excess O_2 had a temperature of 125.0 °C and a pressure of 2.983 atm.

(a) What is the formula and molar mass of the hydrocarbon?

(b) What are the partial pressures in atmospheres of the reactants?

(c) What are the partial pressures in atmospheres of the products and the excess O_2?

9.118 Natural gas is a mixture of hydrocarbons, primarily methane (CH_4) and ethane (C_2H_6). A typical mixture might have $X_{methane} = 0.915$ and $X_{ethane} = 0.085$. Let's assume that we have a 15.50 g sample of natural gas in a volume of 15.00 L at a temperature of 20.00 °C.

(a) How many total moles of gas are in the sample?

(b) What is the pressure of the sample in atmospheres?

(c) What is the partial pressure of each component in the sample in atmospheres?

(d) When the sample is burned in an excess of oxygen, how much heat in kilojoules is liberated?

9.119 A mixture of $CS_2(g)$ and excess $O_2(g)$ is placed in a 10.0 L reaction vessel at 100.0 °C and a pressure of 3.00 atm. A spark causes the CS_2 to ignite, burning it completely, according to the equation

$$CS_2(g) + 3 O_2(g) \longrightarrow CO_2(g) + 2 SO_2(g)$$

After reaction, the temperature returns to 100.0 °C, and the mixture of product gases (CO_2, SO_2, and unreacted O_2) is found to have a pressure of 2.40 atm. What is the partial pressure of each gas in the product mixture?

9.120 Gaseous compound **Q** contains only xenon and oxygen. When 0.100 g of **Q** is placed in a 50.0 mL steel vessel at 0 °C, the pressure is 0.229 atm.

(a) What is the molar mass of **Q**, and what is a likely formula?

(b) When the vessel and its contents are warmed to 100 °C, Q decomposes into its constituent elements. What is the total pressure, and what are the partial pressures of xenon and oxygen in the container?

9.121 When 10.0 g of a mixture of $Ca(ClO_3)_2$ and $Ca(ClO)_2$ is heated to 700 °C in a 10.0 L vessel, both compounds decompose, forming $O_2(g)$ and $CaCl_2(s)$. The final pressure inside the vessel is 1.00 atm.

(a) Write balanced equations for the decomposition reactions.

(b) What is the mass of each compound in the original mixture?

9.122 A 5.00 L vessel contains 25.0 g of PCl_3 and 3.00 g of O_2 at 15 °C. The vessel is heated to 200.0 °C, and the contents react to give $POCl_3$. What is the final pressure in the vessel, assuming that the reaction goes to completion and that all reactants and products are in the gas phase?

9.123 When 2.00 mol of NOCl(g) was heated to 225 °C in a 400.0 L steel reaction vessel, the NOCl partially decomposed according to the equation $2\,NOCl(g) \rightarrow 2\,NO(g) + Cl_2(g)$. The pressure in the vessel after reaction is 0.246 atm.

(a) What is the partial pressure of each gas in the vessel after reaction?

(b) What percent of the NOCl decomposed?

9.124 Ozone (O_3) can be prepared in the laboratory by passing an electrical discharge through oxygen gas: $3 O_2(g) \rightarrow 2 O_3(g)$. Assume that an evacuated steel vessel with a volume of 10.00 L is filled with 32.00 atm of O_2 at 25 °C and an electric discharge is passed through the vessel, causing some of the oxygen to be converted into ozone. As a result, the pressure inside the vessel drops to 30.64 atm at 25.0 °C. What is the final mass percent of ozone in the vessel?

9.125 A steel container with a volume of 500.0 mL is evacuated, and 25.0 g of $CaCO_3$ is added. The container and contents are then heated to 1500 K, causing the $CaCO_3$ to decompose completely, according to the equation $CaCO_3(s) \rightarrow CaO(s) + CO_2(g)$.

(a) Using the ideal gas law and ignoring the volume of any solids remaining in the container, calculate the pressure inside the container at 1500 K.

(b) Now make a more accurate calculation of the pressure inside the container. Take into account the volume of solid CaO (density $= 3.34$ g/mL) in the container, and use the van der Waals equation to calculate the pressure. The van der Waals constants for $CO_2(g)$ are: $a = 3.59$ ($L^2 \cdot$ atm)/mol^2, and $b = 0.0427$ L/mol.

9.126 Nitrogen dioxide dimerizes to give dinitrogen tetroxide: $2 NO_2(g) \rightarrow N_2O_4(g)$. At 298 K, 9.66 g of an NO_2/N_2O_4 mixture exerts a pressure of 0.487 atm in a volume of 6.51 L. What are the mole fractions of the two gases in the mixture?

9.127 A certain nonmetal reacts with hydrogen at 440 °C to form a poisonous, foul-smelling gas. The density of the gas at 25 °C and 1.00 atm is 3.309 g/L. What is the formula of the gas?

MULTICONCEPT PROBLEMS

9.128 An empty 4.00 L steel vessel is filled with 1.00 atm of $CH_4(g)$ and 4.00 atm of $O_2(g)$ at 300 °C. A spark causes the CH_4 to burn completely, according to the equation:

$$CH_4(g) + 2\,O_2(g) \longrightarrow CO_2(g) + 2\,H_2O(g) \qquad \Delta H° = -802 \text{ kJ}$$

(a) What mass of $CO_2(g)$ is produced in the reaction?

(b) What is the final temperature inside the vessel after combustion, assuming that the steel vessel has a mass of 14.500 kg, the mixture of gases has an average molar heat capacity of 21 J/(mol · °C), and the heat capacity of steel is 0.449 J/(g · °C)?

(c) What is the partial pressure of $CO_2(g)$ in the vessel after combustion?

9.129 When a gaseous compound **X** containing only C, H, and O is burned in O_2, 1 volume of the unknown gas reacts with 3 volumes of O_2 to give 2 volumes of CO_2 and 3 volumes of gaseous H_2O. Assume all volumes are measured at the same temperature and pressure.

(a) Calculate a formula for the unknown gas, and write a balanced equation for the combustion reaction.

(b) Is the formula you calculated an empirical formula or a molecular formula? Explain.

(c) Draw two different possible electron-dot structures for the compound **X**.

(d) Combustion of 5.000 g of **X** releases 144.2 kJ heat. Look up $\Delta H°_f$ values for $CO_2(g)$ and $H_2O(g)$ in Appendix B, and calculate $\Delta H°_f$ for compound **X**.

9.130 Isooctane, C_8H_{18}, is the component of gasoline from which the term *octane rating* derives.

(a) Write a balanced equation for the combustion of isooctane to yield CO_2 and H_2O.

(b) Assuming that gasoline is 100% isooctane, that isooctane burns to produce only CO_2 and H_2O, and that the density of isooctane is 0.792 g/mL, what mass of CO_2 in kilograms is produced each year by the annual U.S. gasoline consumption of 4.6×10^{10} L?

(c) What is the volume in liters of this CO_2 at STP?

(d) How many moles of air are necessary for the combustion of 1 mol of isooctane, assuming that air is 21.0% O_2 by volume? What is the volume in liters of this air at STP?

9.131 The *Rankine* temperature scale used in engineering is to the Fahrenheit scale as the Kelvin scale is to the Celsius scale. That is, 1 Rankine degree is the same size as 1 Fahrenheit degree, and 0 °R = absolute zero.

(a) What temperature corresponds to the freezing point of water on the Rankine scale?

(b) What is the value of the gas constant R on the Rankine scale in (L · atm)/(°R · mol)?

(c) Use the van der Waals equation to determine the pressure inside a 400.0 mL vessel that contains 2.50 mol of CH_4 at a temperature of 525 °R. For CH_4, $a = 2.253$ (L^2 · atm)/mol²; $b = 0.04278$ L/mol.

9.132 Chemical explosions are characterized by the instantaneous release of large quantities of hot gases, which set up a shock wave of enormous pressure (up to 700,000 atm)

and velocity (up to 20,000 mi/h). For example, explosion of nitroglycerin ($C_3H_5N_3O_9$) releases four gases, **A**, **B**, **C**, and **D**:

$$n\,C_3H_5N_3O_9(l) \longrightarrow a\,A(g) + b\,B(g) + c\,C(g) + d\,D(g)$$

Assume that the explosion of 1 mol (227 g) of nitroglycerin releases gases with a temperature of 1950 °C and a volume of 1323 L at 1.00 atm pressure.

(a) How many moles of hot gas are released by the explosion of 0.004 00 mol of nitroglycerin?

(b) When the products released by explosion of 0.004 00 mol of nitroglycerin were placed in a 500.0 mL flask and the flask was cooled to −10 °C, product **A** solidified, and the pressure inside the flask was 623 mm Hg. How many moles of **A** were present, and what is its likely identity?

(c) When gases **B**, **C**, and **D** were passed through a tube of powdered Li_2O, gas **B** reacted to form Li_2CO_3. The remaining gases, **C** and **D**, were collected in another 500.0 mL flask and found to have a pressure of 260 mm Hg at 25 °C. How many moles of **B** were present, and what is its likely identity?

(d) When gases **C** and **D** were passed through a hot tube of powdered copper, gas **C** reacted to form CuO. The remaining gas, **D**, was collected in a third 500.0 mL flask and found to have a mass of 0.168 g and a pressure of 223 mm Hg at 25 °C. How many moles each of **C** and **D** were present, and what are their likely identities?

(e) Write a balanced equation for the explosion of nitroglycerin.

9.133 Combustion analysis of 0.1500 g of methyl *tert*-butyl ether, an octane booster used in gasoline, gave 0.3744 g of CO_2 and 0.1838 g of H_2O. When a flask having a volume of 1.00 L was evacuated and then filled with methyl *tert*-butyl ether vapor at a pressure of 100.0 kPa and a temperature of 54.8 °C, the mass of the flask increased by 3.233 g.

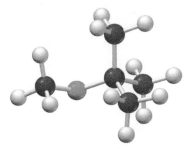

Methyl *tert*-butyl ether

(a) What is the empirical formula of methyl *tert*-butyl ether?

(b) What is the molecular mass and molecular formula of methyl *tert*-butyl ether?

(c) Write a balanced equation for the combustion reaction.

(d) The enthalpy of combustion for methyl *tert*-butyl ether is $\Delta H°_{combustion} = -3368.7$ kJ/mol. What is its standard enthalpy of formation, $\Delta H°_f$?

CHAPTER

10

Liquids, Solids, and Phase Changes

The three phases of water—solid, liquid, and vapor—are all present in winter at this hot spring in Yellowstone National Park

CONTENTS

The kinetic–molecular theory developed in the previous chapter accounts for the properties of gases by assuming that gas particles act independently of one another. Because the attractive forces between them are so weak, the particles in gases are free to move about at random and occupy whatever volume is available. The same is not true in liquids and solids, however. Liquids and solids are distinguished from gases by the presence of substantial attractive forces between particles. In liquids, these attractive forces are strong enough to hold the particles in close contact while still letting them slip and slide over one another. In solids, the forces are so strong that they hold the particles in place and prevent their movement (Figure 10.1).

Figure 10.1
A molecular comparison of gases, liquids, and solids.

In **gases**, the particles feel little attraction for one another and are free to move about randomly.

In **liquids**, the particles are held close together by attractive forces but are free to move around one another.

In **solids**, the particles are held in an ordered arrangement.

In this chapter, we'll examine the nature of the forces responsible for the properties of liquids and solids, paying particular attention to the ordering of particles in solids and to the different kinds of solids that result. In addition, we'll look at what happens during transitions between solid, liquid, and gaseous states and at the effects of temperature and pressure on these transitions.

10.1 POLAR COVALENT BONDS AND DIPOLE MOMENTS

Before looking at the forces between molecules, it's first necessary to develop the ideas of *bond dipoles* and *dipole moments*. We saw in Section 7.4 that polar covalent bonds form between atoms of different electronegativity. Chlorine is more electronegative than carbon, for instance, so the chlorine atom in chloromethane (CH_3Cl) attracts the electrons in the C—Cl bond. The C—Cl bond is therefore polarized so that the chlorine atom is slightly electron-rich ($\delta-$) and the carbon atom is slightly electron-poor ($\delta+$).

Because the polar C—Cl bond in chloromethane has two polar ends—a positive end and a negative end—we describe it as being a bond **dipole**, and we often represent the dipole using an arrow with a cross at one end ($\mapsto$) to indicate the direction of electron displacement. The point of the arrow represents the negative end of the dipole ($\delta-$), and the crossed end (which looks like a plus sign) represents the positive end ($\delta+$). This polarity is clearly visible in an **electrostatic potential map** (Section 7.4), which shows the electron-rich chlorine atom as red and the electron-poor remainder of the molecule as blue-green.

Remember...

Polar covalent bonds are those in which the bonding electrons are shared unequally between two atoms but are not completely transferred. Thus, they are intermediate between nonpolar covalent bonds and ionic bonds.   (Section 7.4)

Remember...

An **electrostatic potential map** uses color to portray the calculated electron distribution in a molecule. Electron-rich regions are red, and electron-poor regions are blue. (Section 7.4)

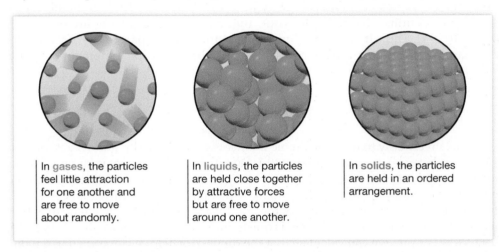

Chlorine is at the negative end of the bond dipole.

Carbon is at the positive end of the bond dipole.

Chloromethane, CH_3Cl

Just as individual bonds in molecules are often polar, molecules as a whole are also often polar because of the net sum of individual bond polarities and lone-pair contributions. The resultant *molecular dipoles* can be looked at in the following way: Assume that there is a center of mass of all positive charges (nuclei) in a molecule and a center of mass of all negative charges (electrons). If these two centers don't coincide, the molecule has a net polarity.

The measure of net molecular polarity is a quantity called the **dipole moment, μ** (Greek mu), which is defined as the magnitude of the charge Q at either end of the molecular dipole times the distance r between the charges: $\mu = Q \times r$. Dipole moments are expressed in *debyes* (D), where $1\,D = 3.336 \times 10^{-30}$ coulomb meters (C·m) in SI units. To calibrate your thinking, the charge on an electron is 1.60×10^{-19} C. Thus, if one proton and one electron were separated by 100 pm (a bit less than the length of a typical covalent bond), then the dipole moment would be 1.60×10^{-29} C·m, or 4.80 D:

$$\mu = Q \times r$$
$$\mu = (1.60 \times 10^{-19}\,C)(100 \times 10^{-12}\,m)\left(\frac{1\,D}{3.336 \times 10^{-30}\,C\cdot m}\right) = 4.80\,D$$

It's relatively easy to measure dipole moments experimentally, and values for some common substances are given in Table 10.1. Once the dipole moment is known, it's then possible to get an idea of the amount of charge separation in a molecule. In chloromethane, for example, the experimentally measured dipole moment is $\mu = 1.90$ D. If we assume that the contributions of the nonpolar C—H bonds are small, then most of the chloromethane dipole moment is due to the C—Cl bond. Since the C—Cl bond distance is 179 pm, we can calculate that the dipole moment of chloromethane would be $1.79 \times 4.80\,D = 8.59$ D if the C—Cl bond were ionic—that is, if a full negative charge on chlorine were separated from a full positive charge on carbon by a distance of 179 pm. But because the measured dipole moment of chloromethane is only 1.90 D, we can conclude that the C—Cl bond is only about $(1.90/8.59)(100\%) = 22\%$ ionic. Thus, the chlorine atom in chloromethane has an excess of about 0.2 electron, and the carbon atom has a deficiency of about 0.2 electron.

Not surprisingly, the largest dipole moment listed in Table 10.1 belongs to the ionic compound NaCl. Water and ammonia also have substantial dipole moments because both oxygen and nitrogen are electronegative relative to hydrogen and because both O and N have lone pairs of electrons that make substantial contributions to net molecular polarity:

TABLE 10.1	Dipole Moments of Some Common Compounds
Compound	**Dipole Moment (D)**
NaCl*	9.0
CH_3Cl	1.90
H_2O	1.85
NH_3	1.47
HCl	1.11
CO_2	0
CCl_4	0

* Measured in the gas phase

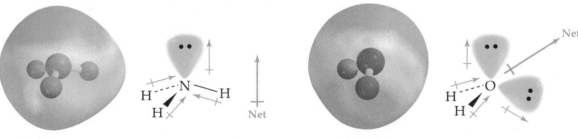

Ammonia ($\mu = 1.47$ D)   Water ($\mu = 1.85$ D)

In contrast with water and ammonia, carbon dioxide and tetrachloromethane (CCl_4) have zero dipole moments. Molecules of both substances contain *individual* polar covalent bonds, but because of the symmetry of their structures, the individual bond polarities exactly cancel.

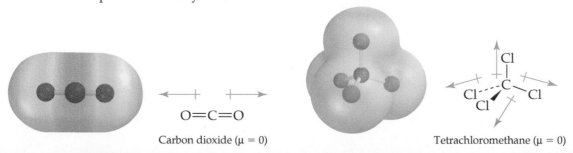

Carbon dioxide ($\mu = 0$)   Tetrachloromethane ($\mu = 0$)

CALCULATING PERCENT IONIC CHARACTER FROM A DIPOLE MOMENT

The dipole moment of HCl is 1.11 D, and the distance between atoms is 127 pm. What is the percent ionic character of the HCl bond?

STRATEGY

If HCl were 100% ionic, a negative charge (Cl^-) would be separated from a positive charge (H^+) by 127 pm. Calculate the expected dipole moment, and compare that calculated value to the actual value.

SOLUTION

The calculated dipole moment is

$$\mu = Q \times r$$

$$\mu = (1.60 \times 10^{-19}\,C)(127 \times 10^{-12}\,m)\left(\frac{1\,D}{3.336 \times 10^{-30}\,C \cdot m}\right) = 6.09\,D$$

The observed dipole moment of 1.11 D for HCl implies that the H—Cl bond is only about 18% ionic:

$$\frac{1.11\,D}{6.09\,D} \times 100\% = 18.2\%$$

PREDICTING THE PRESENCE OF A DIPOLE MOMENT

Would you expect vinyl chloride ($H_2C{=}CHCl$), the starting material used for preparation of poly(vinyl chloride) polymer, to have a dipole moment? If so, indicate the direction.

STRATEGY

First, use the VSEPR model described in Section 7.9 to predict the molecular shape of vinyl chloride. Then, assign polarities to the individual bonds according to the differences in electronegativity of the bonded atoms (Figure 7.4 on page 221), and make a reasonable guess about the overall polarity that would result by summing the individual contributions.

SOLUTION

Because both carbon atoms have three charge clouds, each has trigonal planar geometry and the molecule as a whole is planar:

Only the C—Cl bond has a substantial polarity, giving the molecule a net polarity:

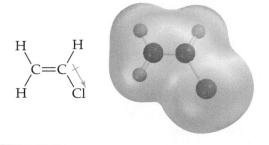

▶ **PROBLEM 10.1** The dipole moment of HF is $\mu = 1.83$ D, and the bond length is 92 pm. Calculate the percent ionic character of the H—F bond. Is HF more ionic or less ionic than HCl (Worked Example 10.1)?

▶ **PROBLEM 10.2** Tell which of the following compounds is likely to have a dipole moment, and show the direction of each.

(a) SF_6 (b) $H_2C=CH_2$ (c) $CHCl_3$ (d) CH_2Cl_2

CONCEPTUAL PROBLEM 10.3 The dipole moment of methanol is $\mu = 1.70$ D. Use arrows to indicate the direction in which electrons are displaced.

CONCEPTUAL PROBLEM 10.4 Methylamine, CH_3NH_2, is responsible for the odor of rotting fish. Look at the following electrostatic potential map of methylamine, and explain the observed polarity.

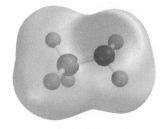

10.2 INTERMOLECULAR FORCES

Now that we know a bit about molecular polarities, let's see how they give rise to some of the forces that occur between molecules. The existence of such forces is easy to show. Take H_2O, for example. An individual H_2O molecule consists of two hydrogen atoms and one oxygen atom joined together in a specific way by the *intra*molecular forces that we call covalent bonds. But a visible sample of H_2O exists either as solid ice, liquid water, or gaseous vapor, depending on its temperature. Thus, there must also be some *intermolecular forces* that act between molecules to hold them close together at certain temperatures (**Figure 10.2**). (Strictly speaking, the term *intermolecular* refers only to molecular substances, but we'll use it generally to refer to interactions among all kinds of particles, including molecules, ions, and atoms.)

Intermolecular forces as a whole are usually called **van der Waals forces** after the Dutch scientist Johannes van der Waals (1837–1923). These forces are of several different types, including *dipole–dipole forces*, *London dispersion forces*, and *hydrogen bonds*. In addition, *ion–dipole forces* operate between ions and molecules. All these intermolecular forces are electrostatic in origin and result from the mutual attraction of unlike charges or the mutual repulsion of like charges. If the particles are ions, then full charges are present and the ion–ion attractions are so strong (energies on the order of 500–1000 kJ/mol) that they give rise to what we call ionic bonds (Section 6.7). If the particles are neutral, then only partial charges are present at best, but even so, the attractive forces can be substantial.

Remember...

Ionic bonds generally form between the cation of a metal and the anion of a reactive nonmetal. (Section 6.7)

Ion–Dipole Forces

We saw in the previous section that a molecule has a net polarity and an overall dipole moment if the sum of its individual bond dipoles is nonzero. One side of the molecule has a net excess of electrons and a partial negative charge ($\delta-$), while the

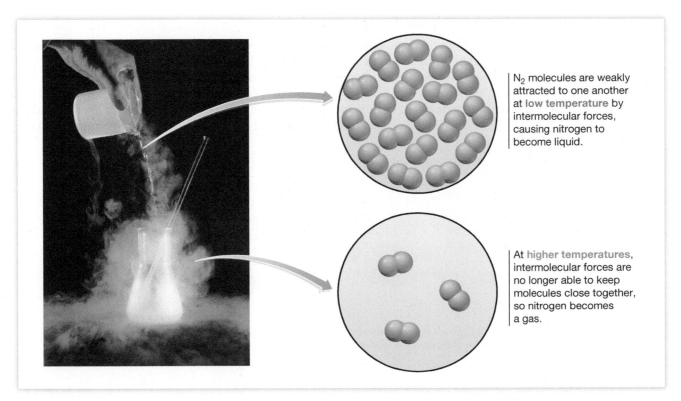

Figure 10.2
Intermolecular forces.

other side has a net deficiency of electrons and a partial positive charge ($\delta+$). An
ion–dipole force is the result of electrical interactions between an ion and the partial
charges on a polar molecule (Figure 10.3).

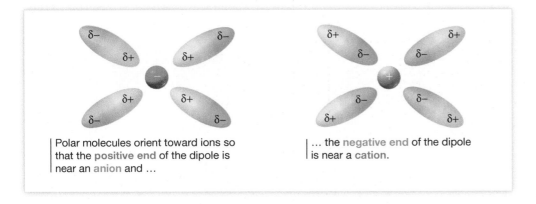

Polar molecules orient toward ions so that the **positive end** of the dipole is near an **anion** and …

… the **negative end** of the dipole is near a **cation**.

Figure 10.3
Ion–dipole forces.

As you might expect, the favored orientation of a polar molecule in the presence
of ions is one where the positive end of the dipole is near an anion and the negative
end of the dipole is near a cation. The magnitude of the interaction energy E depends
on the charge on the ion z, on the strength of the dipole as measured by its dipole
moment μ, and on the inverse square of the distance r from the ion to the dipole:
$E \propto z\mu/r^2$. Ion–dipole forces are particularly important in aqueous solutions of ionic
substances such as NaCl, in which polar water molecules surround the ions. We'll
explore this point in more detail in the next chapter.

Dipole–Dipole Forces

Neutral but polar molecules experience **dipole–dipole forces** as the result of electrical interactions among dipoles on neighboring molecules. The forces can be either attractive or repulsive, depending on the orientation of the molecules (**Figure 10.4**), and the net force in a large collection of molecules is a summation of many individual interactions of both types. The forces are generally weak, with energies on the order of 3–4 kJ/mol, and are significant only when molecules are in close contact.

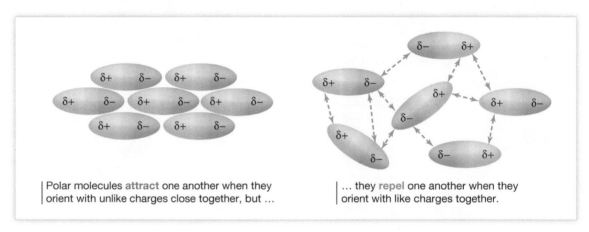

Polar molecules **attract** one another when they orient with unlike charges close together, but …

… they **repel** one another when they orient with like charges together.

Figure 10.4
Dipole–dipole forces.

Not surprisingly, the strength of a given dipole–dipole interaction depends on the sizes of the dipole moments involved. The more polar the substance, the greater the strength of its dipole–dipole interactions. Butane, for instance, is a nonpolar molecule with a molecular mass of 58 amu and a boiling point of $-0.5\,°C$, while acetone has the same molecular mass yet boils $57\,°C$ higher because it is polar.

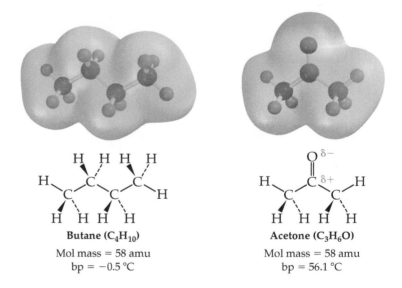

Butane (C_4H_{10})
Mol mass = 58 amu
bp = $-0.5\,°C$

Acetone (C_3H_6O)
Mol mass = 58 amu
bp = $56.1\,°C$

Table 10.2 lists several substances with similar molecular masses but different dipole moments and indicates that there is a rough correlation between dipole moment and boiling point. The larger the dipole moment, the stronger the intermolecular forces and the greater the amount of heat that must be added to overcome those forces. Thus, substances with higher dipole moments generally have higher boiling points.

TABLE 10.2 Comparison of Molecular Masses, Dipole Moments, and Boiling Points

Substance	Mol Mass (amu)	Dipole Moment (D)	bp (K)
$CH_3CH_2CH_3$	44.10	0.08	231
CH_3OCH_3	46.07	1.30	248
CH_3Cl	50.49	1.90	249
CH_3CN	41.05	3.93	355

London Dispersion Forces

The causes of intermolecular forces among charged and polar particles are easy to understand, but it's less obvious how attractive forces arise among nonpolar molecules or among the individual atoms of a noble gas. Benzene (C_6H_6), for instance, has zero dipole moment and therefore experiences no dipole–dipole forces. Nevertheless, there must be *some* intermolecular forces present among benzene molecules because the substance is a liquid rather than a gas at room temperature, with a melting point of 5.5 °C and a boiling point of 80.1 °C.

Benzene
$\mu = 0$
mp = 5.5 °C
bp = 80.1 °C

All atoms and molecules, regardless of structure, experience **London dispersion forces**, which result from the motion of electrons. Take even a simple nonpolar molecule like Br_2, for instance. Averaged over time, the distribution of electrons throughout the molecule is symmetrical, but at any given instant there may be more electrons at one end of the molecule than at the other, giving the molecule a short-lived dipole moment. This instantaneous dipole on one molecule can affect the electron distributions in neighboring molecules and *induce* temporary dipoles in those neighbors (Figure 10.5). As a result, weak attractive forces develop and Br_2 is a liquid at room temperature rather than a gas.

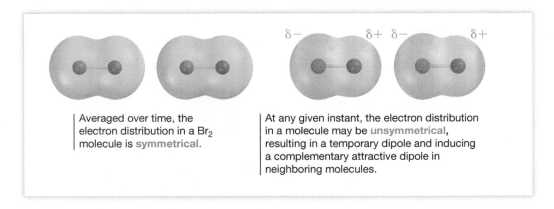

Averaged over time, the electron distribution in a Br_2 molecule is **symmetrical**.

At any given instant, the electron distribution in a molecule may be **unsymmetrical**, resulting in a temporary dipole and inducing a complementary attractive dipole in neighboring molecules.

Figure 10.5
London dispersion forces.

Dispersion forces are generally small, with energies in the range 1–10 kJ/mol, and their exact magnitude depends on the ease with which a molecule's electron cloud can be distorted by a nearby electric field, a property referred to as

TABLE 10.3	Melting Points and Boiling Points of the Halogens	
Halogen	mp (K)	bp (K)
F_2	53.5	85.0
Cl_2	171.6	239.1
Br_2	265.9	331.9
I_2	386.8	457.5

polarizability. A smaller molecule or lighter atom is less polarizable and has smaller dispersion forces because it has only a few, tightly held electrons. A larger molecule or heavier atom, however, is more polarizable and has larger dispersion forces because it has many electrons, some of which are less tightly held and are farther from the nucleus. Among the halogens, for instance, the F_2 molecule is small and less polarizable, while I_2 is larger and more polarizable. As a result, F_2 has smaller dispersion forces and is a gas at room temperature, while I_2 has larger dispersion forces and is a solid (Table 10.3).

Shape is also important in determining the magnitude of the dispersion forces affecting a molecule. More spread-out shapes, which maximize molecular surface area, allow greater contact between molecules and give rise to higher dispersion forces than do more compact shapes, which minimize molecular contact. Pentane, for example, boils at 309.2 K, whereas 2,2-dimethylpropane boils at 282.6 K. Both substances have the same molecular formula, C_5H_{12}, but pentane is longer and somewhat spread out, whereas 2,2-dimethylpropane is more spherical and compact (Figure 10.6).

Figure 10.6
The effect of molecular shape on London dispersion forces.

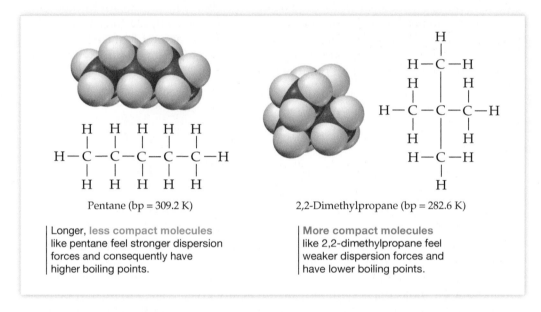

Pentane (bp = 309.2 K)

2,2-Dimethylpropane (bp = 282.6 K)

Longer, less compact molecules like pentane feel stronger dispersion forces and consequently have higher boiling points.

More compact molecules like 2,2-dimethylpropane feel weaker dispersion forces and have lower boiling points.

Hydrogen Bonds

In many ways, *hydrogen bonds* are responsible for life on Earth. They cause water to be a liquid rather than a gas at ordinary temperatures, and they are the primary intermolecular force that holds huge biomolecules in the shapes needed to play their essential roles in biochemistry. Deoxyribonucleic acid (DNA), for instance, contains two enormously long molecular strands that are coiled around each other and held together by hydrogen bonds.

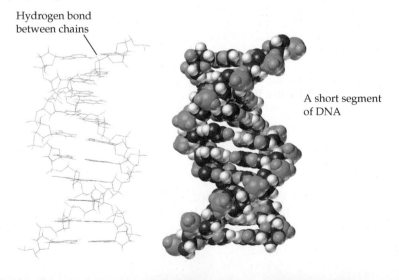

Hydrogen bond between chains

A short segment of DNA

A **hydrogen bond** is an attractive interaction between a hydrogen atom bonded to a very electronegative atom (O, N, or F) and an unshared electron pair on another electronegative atom. For example, hydrogen bonds occur in both water and ammonia:

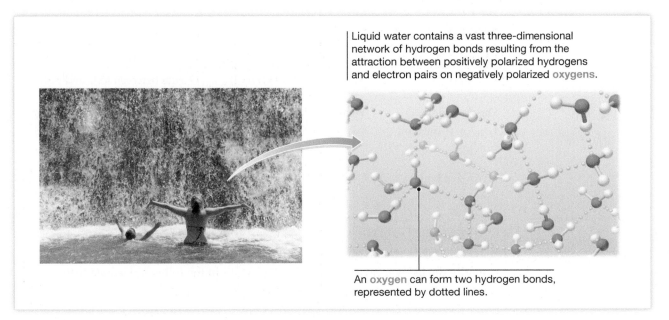

Water   Ammonia

Hydrogen bonds arise because O—H, N—H, and F—H bonds are highly polar, with a partial positive charge on the hydrogen and a partial negative charge on the electronegative atom. In addition, the hydrogen atom has no core electrons to shield its nucleus, and it has a small size so it can be approached closely by other molecules. As a result, the dipole–dipole attraction between the hydrogen and an unshared electron pair on a nearby atom is unusually strong, giving rise to a hydrogen bond. Water, in particular, is able to form a vast three-dimensional network of hydrogen bonds because each H_2O molecule has two hydrogens and two electron pairs (Figure 10.7).

Liquid water contains a vast three-dimensional network of hydrogen bonds resulting from the attraction between positively polarized hydrogens and electron pairs on negatively polarized oxygens.

An oxygen can form two hydrogen bonds, represented by dotted lines.

Figure 10.7
Hydrogen-bonding in water.

Hydrogen bonds can be quite strong, with energies up to 40 kJ/mol. To see one effect of hydrogen-bonding, look at Table 10.4, which plots the boiling points of the covalent binary hydrides for the group 4A–7A elements. As you might expect, the boiling points generally increase with molecular mass down a group of the periodic table as a result of increased London dispersion forces—for example, $CH_4 < SiH_4 < GeH_4 < SnH_4$. Three substances, however, are clearly anomalous: NH_3, H_2O, and HF. All three have higher boiling points than might be expected because of the hydrogen bonds they contain.

TABLE 10.4 Boiling Points of the Covalent Binary Hydrides of Groups 4A, 5A, 6A, and 7A

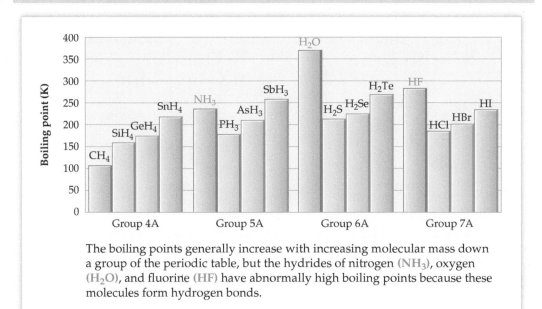

The boiling points generally increase with increasing molecular mass down a group of the periodic table, but the hydrides of nitrogen (NH_3), oxygen (H_2O), and fluorine (HF) have abnormally high boiling points because these molecules form hydrogen bonds.

A comparison of the various kinds of intermolecular forces is shown in Table 10.5.

TABLE 10.5 A Comparison of Intermolecular Forces

Force	Strength	Characteristics
Ion–dipole	Moderate (10–50 kJ/mol)	Occurs between ions and polar solvents
Dipole–dipole	Weak (3–4 kJ/mol)	Occurs between polar molecules
London dispersion	Weak (1–10 kJ/mol)	Occurs between all molecules; strength depends on size, polarizability
Hydrogen bond	Moderate (10–40 kJ/mol)	Occurs between molecules with O—H, N—H, and F—H bonds

WORKED EXAMPLE 10.3

IDENTIFYING INTERMOLECULAR FORCES

Identify the likely kinds of intermolecular forces in the following substances:

(a) HCl   (b) CH_3CH_3 (c) CH_3NH_2 (d) Kr

STRATEGY

Look at the structure of each substance, and decide what intermolecular forces are present. All molecules have dispersion forces; polar molecules have dipole–dipole forces; and molecules with O—H, N—H, or F—H bonds have hydrogen bonds.

SOLUTION

(a) HCl is a polar molecule but can't form hydrogen bonds. It has dipole–dipole forces and dispersion forces.

(b) CH_3CH_3 is a nonpolar molecule and has only dispersion forces.

(c) CH_3NH_2 is a polar molecule that can form hydrogen bonds. In addition, it has dipole–dipole forces and dispersion forces.

(d) Kr is nonpolar and has only dispersion forces.

▶ **PROBLEM 10.5** Of the substances Ar, Cl_2, CCl_4, and HNO_3, which has:

(a) The largest dipole–dipole forces?

(b) The largest hydrogen-bond forces?

(c) The smallest dispersion forces?

▶ **PROBLEM 10.6** Consider the kinds of intermolecular forces present in the following compounds, and rank the substances in likely order of increasing boiling point: H_2S (34 amu), CH_3OH (32 amu), C_2H_6 (30 amu), Ar (40 amu).

10.3 SOME PROPERTIES OF LIQUIDS

Many familiar and observable properties of liquids can be explained by the intermolecular forces just discussed. We all know, for instance, that some liquids, such as water or gasoline, flow easily when poured, whereas others, such as motor oil or maple syrup, flow sluggishly.

The measure of a liquid's resistance to flow is called its **viscosity**. Not surprisingly, viscosity is related to the ease with which individual molecules move around in the liquid and thus to the intermolecular forces present. Substances with small, nonpolar molecules, such as pentane and benzene, experience only weak intermolecular forces and have relatively low viscosities, whereas larger, more polar substances, such as glycerol [$C_3H_5(OH)_3$], experience stronger intermolecular forces and so have higher viscosities.

Another familiar property of liquids is **surface tension**, the resistance of a liquid to spread out and increase its surface area. Surface tension is caused by the difference in intermolecular forces experienced by molecules at the surface of a liquid and those experienced by molecules in the interior. Molecules at the surface feel attractive forces on only one side and are thus pulled in toward the liquid, while molecules in the interior are surrounded and are pulled equally in all directions (**Figure 10.8**). The ability of a water strider to walk on water and the beading up of water on a newly waxed car are both due to surface tension.

▲ Surface tension allows a water strider to walk on a pond without penetrating the surface.

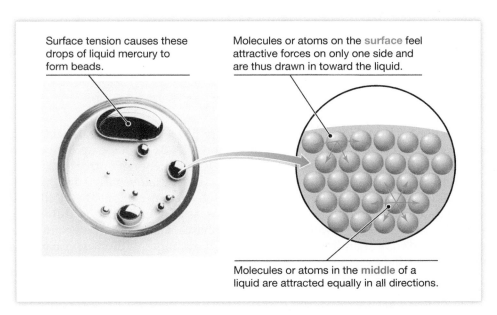

Surface tension causes these drops of liquid mercury to form beads.

Molecules or atoms on the surface feel attractive forces on only one side and are thus drawn in toward the liquid.

Molecules or atoms in the middle of a liquid are attracted equally in all directions.

Figure 10.8

Surface tension. Surface tension is the resistance of a liquid to spread out and increase its surface area.

Surface tension, like viscosity, is generally higher in liquids that have stronger intermolecular forces. Both properties are also temperature-dependent because molecules at higher temperatures have more kinetic energy to counteract the attractive forces holding them together. Data for some common substances are given in Table 10.6. Note that mercury has a particularly large surface tension, causing droplets to form beads (Figure 10.8) and giving the top of the mercury column in a barometer a rounded shape called a *meniscus*.

TABLE 10.6   Viscosities and Surface Tensions of Some Common Substances at 20 °C

Name	Formula	Viscosity $(N \cdot s/m^2)$	Surface Tension (J/m^2)
Pentane	C_5H_{12}	2.4×10^{-4}	1.61×10^{-2}
Benzene	C_6H_6	6.5×10^{-4}	2.89×10^{-2}
Water	H_2O	1.00×10^{-3}	7.29×10^{-2}
Ethanol	C_2H_5OH	1.20×10^{-3}	2.23×10^{-2}
Mercury	Hg	1.55×10^{-3}	4.6×10^{-1}
Glycerol	$C_3H_5(OH)_3$	1.49	6.34×10^{-2}

10.4 PHASE CHANGES

Solid ice melts to liquid water, liquid water freezes to solid ice or evaporates to gaseous steam, and gaseous steam condenses to liquid water. Such processes, in which the physical form but not the chemical identity of a substance changes, are called **phase changes**, or *changes of state*. Matter in any one state, or **phase**, can change into either of the other two. Solids can even change directly into gases, as occurs when dry ice (solid CO_2) sublimes. The names of the various phase changes are:

Fusion (melting)	solid $\rightarrow$ liquid
Freezing	liquid $\rightarrow$ solid
Vaporization	liquid $\rightarrow$ gas
Condensation	gas $\rightarrow$ liquid
Sublimation	solid $\rightarrow$ gas
Deposition	gas $\rightarrow$ solid

Remember...

The value of the **free-energy change** ΔG is a general criterion for the spontaneity of a chemical or physical process. If $\Delta G < 0$, the process is spontaneous; if $\Delta G = 0$, the process is at equilibrium; and if $\Delta G > 0$, the process is nonspontaneous. (Section 8.13)

Like all naturally occurring processes, every phase change has associated with it a **free-energy change,** ΔG. As we saw in Section 8.13, ΔG is made up of two contributions, an enthalpy part (ΔH) and a temperature-dependent entropy part ($T\Delta S$), according to the equation $\Delta G = \Delta H - T\Delta S$. The enthalpy part is the heat flow associated with making or breaking the intermolecular attractions that hold liquids and solids together, while the entropy part is associated with the difference in molecular randomness between the various phases. Gases are more random and have more entropy than liquids, which in turn are more random and have more entropy than solids.

The melting of a solid to a liquid, the sublimation of a solid to a gas, and the vaporization of a liquid to a gas all involve a change from a less random phase to a more random one, and all absorb heat energy to overcome the intermolecular forces holding particles together. Thus, both ΔS and ΔH are positive for these phase changes. By contrast, the freezing of a liquid to a solid, the deposition of a gas to a solid, and the condensation of a gas to a liquid all involve a change from a more random phase to a less random one, and all release heat energy as intermolecular attractions increase to hold particles more tightly together. Thus, both ΔS and ΔH have negative values for these phase changes. The situations are summarized in Figure 10.9.

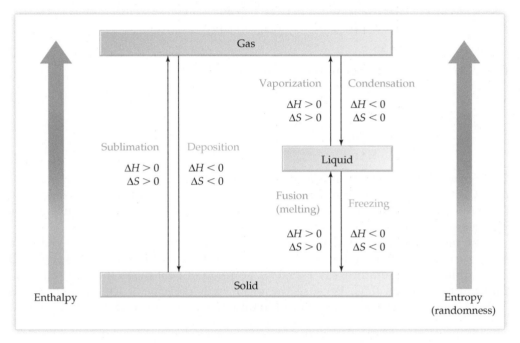

Figure 10.9
Phase changes and randomness. Changes from a less random phase to a more random one (up arrows) have positive values of ΔH and ΔS. Changes from a more random phase to a less random one (down arrows) have negative values of ΔH and ΔS.

Let's look at the transitions of solid ice to liquid water and liquid water to gaseous steam to see examples of energy relationships during phase changes. For the melting, or fusion, of ice to water, $\Delta H = +6.01$ kJ/mol and $\Delta S = +22.0$ J/(K·mol); for the vaporization of water to steam, $\Delta H = +40.67$ kJ/mol and $\Delta S = +109$ J/(K·mol). Both ΔH and ΔS are larger for the liquid $\rightarrow$ vapor change than for the solid $\rightarrow$ liquid change because many more intermolecular attractions need to be overcome and much more randomness is gained in the change of liquid to vapor. This highly endothermic conversion of liquid water to gaseous water vapor is used by many organisms as a cooling mechanism. When our bodies perspire on a warm day, evaporation of the perspiration absorbs heat and leaves the skin feeling cooler.

▲ Evaporation of perspiration carries away heat and cools the body after exertion.

▲ Why do citrus growers spray their trees with water on cold nights?

For phase changes in the opposite direction, the numbers have the same absolute values but opposite signs. That is, $\Delta H = -6.01$ kJ/mol and $\Delta S = -22.0$ J/(K·mol) for the freezing of liquid water to ice, and $\Delta H = -40.67$ kJ/mol and $\Delta S = -109$ J/(K·mol) for the condensation of water vapor to liquid water. Citrus growers take advantage of the exothermic freezing of water when they spray their trees with water on cold nights to prevent frost damage. As water freezes on the leaves, it releases heat that protects the tree.

Knowing the values of ΔH and ΔS for a phase transition makes it possible to calculate the temperature at which the change occurs. Recall from Section 8.13 that ΔG is negative for a spontaneous process, positive for a nonspontaneous process, and zero for a process at equilibrium. Thus, by setting $\Delta G = 0$ and solving for T in the free-energy equation, we can calculate the temperature at which two phases are in equilibrium. For the solid → liquid phase change in water, for instance, we have

$$\Delta G = \Delta H - T\Delta S = 0 \qquad \text{at equilibrium}$$

$$\text{or} \quad T = \Delta H / \Delta S$$

where $\Delta H = +6.01$ kJ/mol and $\Delta S = +22.0$ J/(K·mol)

$$\text{so} \quad T = \frac{6.01 \dfrac{\text{kJ}}{\text{mol}}}{0.0220 \dfrac{\text{kJ}}{\text{K·mol}}} = 273 \text{ K}$$

In other words, ice turns into liquid water, and liquid water turns into ice, at 273 K, or 0 °C, at 1 atm pressure—hardly a surprise. In practice, the calculation is more useful in the opposite direction. That is, the temperature at which a phase change occurs is measured and then used to calculate ΔS (= $\Delta H/T$).

The results of continuously adding heat to a substance can be displayed on a *heating curve* like that shown in **Figure 10.10** for H_2O. Beginning with solid H_2O at an arbitrary temperature, say -25.0 °C, addition of heat raises the ice's temperature until it reaches 0 °C. Because the molar heat capacity of ice (Section 8.7) is 36.57 J/(mol·°C), and because we need to raise the temperature 25.0 °C, 914 J/mol is required:

Remember...

The **molar heat capacity (C_m)** of a substance is the amount of heat necessary to raise the temperature of 1 mol of the substance by 1 °C.   (Section 8.7)

$$\text{Energy to heat ice from } -25 \text{ °C to } 0 \text{ °C} = \left(36.57 \frac{\text{J}}{\text{mol·°C}} \right)(25.0 \text{ °C}) = 914 \text{ J/mol}$$

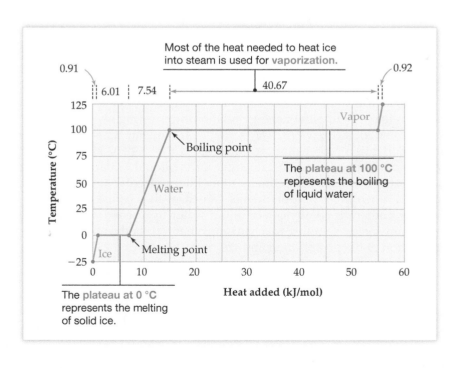

Figure 10.10
A heating curve for 1 mol of H_2O, showing the temperature changes and phase transitions that occur when heat is added.

Once the temperature of the ice reaches 0 °C, addition of further heat goes into disrupting hydrogen bonds and other intermolecular forces rather than into increasing the temperature, as indicated by the plateau at 0 °C on the heating curve in Figure 10.10. At this temperature—the melting point—solid and liquid coexist in equilibrium as molecules break free from their positions in the ice crystals and enter the liquid phase. Not until the solid turns completely to liquid does the temperature again rise. The amount of energy required to overcome enough intermolecular forces to convert a solid into a liquid is the *enthalpy of fusion*, or **heat of fusion**, ΔH_{fusion}. For ice, $\Delta H_{fusion} = +6.01$ kJ/mol.

Continued addition of heat to liquid water raises the temperature until it reaches 100 °C. Because the molar heat capacity of liquid water is 75.4 J/(mol·°C), 7.54 kJ/mol is required:

$$\text{Energy to heat water from 0 °C to 100 °C} = \left(75.4\ \frac{J}{mol \cdot °C}\right)(100\ °C) = 7.54 \times 10^3\ J/mol$$

Once the temperature of the water reaches 100 °C, addition of further heat again goes into overcoming intermolecular forces rather than into increasing the temperature, as indicated by the second plateau at 100 °C on the heating curve. At this temperature—the boiling point—liquid and vapor coexist in equilibrium as molecules break free from the surface of the liquid and enter the gas phase. The amount of energy necessary to convert a liquid into a gas is called the *enthalpy of vaporization*, or **heat of vaporization**, ΔH_{vap}. For water, $\Delta H_{vap} = +40.67$ kJ/mol. Only after the liquid has been completely vaporized does the temperature again rise.

Notice that the largest part (40.67 kJ/mol) of the 56.05 kJ/mol required to convert solid ice at −25 °C to gaseous steam at 125 °C is used for vaporization. The heat of vaporization for water is large because of the vast number of hydrogen bonds that must all be broken before molecules can escape from the liquid.

Table 10.7 gives further data on both heat of fusion and heat of vaporization for some common compounds. What is true for water is also true for other compounds: The heat of vaporization of a compound is always larger than its heat of fusion because all intermolecular forces must be overcome before vaporization can occur, but relatively fewer intermolecular forces must be overcome for a solid to change to a liquid.

TABLE 10.7 Heats of Fusion and Heats of Vaporization for Some Common Compounds

Name	Formula	ΔH_{fusion} (kJ/mol)	ΔH_{vap} (kJ/mol)
Ammonia	NH_3	5.66	23.33
Benzene	C_6H_6	9.87	30.72
Ethanol	C_2H_5OH	4.93	38.56
Helium	He	0.02	0.08
Mercury	Hg	2.30	59.11
Water	H_2O	6.01	40.67

WORKED EXAMPLE 10.4

CALCULATING AN ENTROPY OF VAPORIZATION

The boiling point of water is 100 °C, and the enthalpy change for the conversion of water to steam is $\Delta H_{vap} = 40.67$ kJ/mol. What is the entropy change for vaporization, ΔS_{vap}, in J/(K·mol)?

STRATEGY

At the temperature where a phase change occurs, the two phases coexist in equilibrium and ΔG, the free-energy difference between the phases, is zero: $\Delta G = \Delta H - T\Delta S = 0$.

continued on next page

Rearranging this equation gives $\Delta S = \Delta H/T$, where both ΔH and T are known. Remember that T must be expressed in kelvin.

SOLUTION

$$\Delta S_{vap} = \frac{\Delta H_{vap}}{T} = \frac{40.67 \frac{kJ}{mol}}{373.15 \text{ K}} = 0.1090 \text{ kJ/(K} \cdot \text{mol)} = 109.0 \text{ J/(K} \cdot \text{mol)}$$

As you might expect, there is a large positive entropy change, corresponding to a large increase in randomness, on converting water from a liquid to a gas.

▶ **PROBLEM 10.7** Which of the following processes would you expect to have a positive value of ΔS, and which a negative value?

(a) Sublimation of dry ice

(b) Formation of dew on a cold morning

(c) Mixing of cigarette smoke with air in a closed room

▶ **PROBLEM 10.8** Chloroform ($CHCl_3$) has $\Delta H_{vap} = 29.2$ kJ/mol and $\Delta S_{vap} = 87.5$ J/(K $\cdot$ mol). What is the boiling point of chloroform in kelvin?

10.5 EVAPORATION, VAPOR PRESSURE, AND BOILING POINT

Remember...

The gas pressure inside a container can be measured using an open-end **manometer**, which consists of a U-tube filled with mercury. The difference between the pressure of the gas and the pressure of the atmosphere is equal to the difference between the heights of the mercury levels in the two arms of the U-tube. (Section 9.1)

The conversion of a liquid to a vapor is visible when the liquid boils, but it occurs under other conditions as well. Let's imagine the two experiments illustrated in Figure 10.11. In one experiment, we place a liquid in an open container; in the other experiment, we place the liquid in a closed container connected to a mercury manometer (Section 9.1). After a certain amount of time has passed, the liquid in the first container has evaporated, while the liquid in the second container remains but the pressure has risen. At equilibrium and at a constant temperature, the pressure increase has a constant value called the **vapor pressure** of the liquid.

▲ Because bromine is colored, it's possible to see its reddish vapor above the liquid.

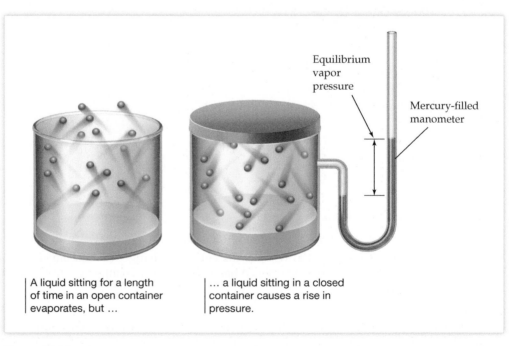

Equilibrium vapor pressure

Mercury-filled manometer

| A liquid sitting for a length of time in an open container evaporates, but ... | ... a liquid sitting in a closed container causes a rise in pressure. |

Figure 10.11
The origin of vapor pressure.

Evaporation and vapor pressure are both explained on a molecular level by the kinetic–molecular theory, developed in Section 9.6 to account for the behavior of gases. The molecules in a liquid are in constant motion but at a variety of speeds depending on the amount of kinetic energy they have. In considering a large sample, molecular kinetic energies follow a distribution curve like that shown in Figure 10.12, with the exact shape of the curve dependent on the temperature. The higher the temperature and the lower the boiling point of the substance, the greater the fraction of molecules in the sample that have sufficient kinetic energy to break free from the surface of the liquid and escape into the vapor.

Remember…
The **kinetic–molecular theory** is a group of five postulates that can be used to account for the behavior of gases and to derive the ideal gas law. Temperature and kinetic energy are related according to the equation $E_k = (3/2)RT$.   (Section 9.6)

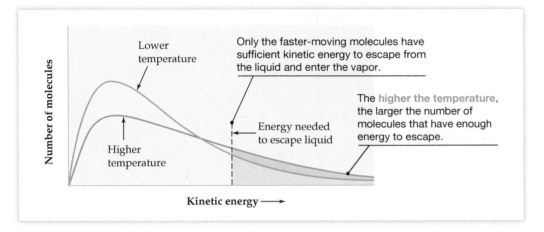

Figure 10.12
The distribution of molecular kinetic energies in a liquid.

Molecules that enter the vapor phase in an open container can escape from the liquid and drift away until the liquid evaporates entirely, but molecules in a closed container are trapped. As more and more molecules pass from the liquid to the vapor, the chances increase that random motion will cause some of them to return occasionally to the liquid. Ultimately, the number of molecules returning to the liquid and the number escaping become equal, at which point a dynamic equilibrium exists. Although *individual* molecules are constantly passing back and forth from one phase to the other, the *total numbers* of molecules in both liquid and vapor phases remain constant.

The numerical value of a liquid's vapor pressure depends on the magnitude of the intermolecular forces present and on the temperature. The smaller the intermolecular forces, the higher the vapor pressure, because loosely held molecules escape more easily. The higher the temperature, the higher the vapor pressure, because a larger fraction of molecules have sufficient kinetic energy to escape.

The Clausius–Clapeyron Equation

As indicated in Figure 10.13, the vapor pressure of a liquid rises with temperature in a nonlinear way. A linear relationship *is* found, however, when the natural logarithm of the vapor pressure, $\ln P_{vap}$, is plotted against the inverse of the Kelvin temperature, $1/T$. Table 10.8 gives the appropriate data for water, and Figure 10.13 shows the plot. As noted in Section 9.2, a linear graph is characteristic of mathematical equations of the form $y = mx + b$. In the present instance, $y = \ln P_{vap}$, $x = 1/T$, m is the slope of the line $(-\Delta H_{vap}/R)$, and b is the y-intercept (a constant, C). Thus, the data fit an expression known as the **Clausius–Clapeyron equation:**

natural
logarithm
↓

Clausius–Clapeyron equation $\ln P_{vap} = \left(-\dfrac{\Delta H_{vap}}{R}\right)\dfrac{1}{T} + C$

$\quad\quad\quad\quad y \quad = \quad\quad m \quad\quad x \; + \; b$

where ΔH_{vap} is the heat of vaporization of the liquid, R is the gas constant (Section 9.3), and C is a constant characteristic of each specific substance.

TABLE 10.8 Vapor Pressure of Water at Various Temperatures

Temp (K)	P_{vap} (mm Hg)	$\ln P_{vap}$	1/T	Temp (K)	P_{vap} (mm Hg)	$\ln P_{vap}$	1/T
273	4.58	1.522	0.003 66	333	149.4	5.007	0.003 00
283	9.21	2.220	0.003 53	343	233.7	5.454	0.002 92
293	17.5	2.862	0.003 41	353	355.1	5.872	0.002 83
303	31.8	3.459	0.003 30	363	525.9	6.265	0.002 75
313	55.3	4.013	0.003 19	373	760.0	6.633	0.002 68
323	92.5	4.527	0.003 10	378	906.0	6.809	0.002 65

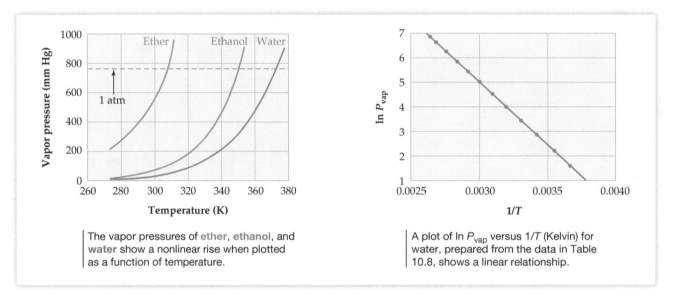

The vapor pressures of **ether**, **ethanol**, and **water** show a nonlinear rise when plotted as a function of temperature.

A plot of $\ln P_{vap}$ versus 1/T (Kelvin) for water, prepared from the data in Table 10.8, shows a linear relationship.

Figure 10.13
Vapor pressure of liquids at different temperatures.

▲ What is the vapor pressure of the liquid at its boiling point?

The Clausius–Clapeyron equation makes it possible to calculate the heat of vaporization of a liquid by measuring its vapor pressure at several temperatures and then plotting the results to obtain the slope of the line. Alternatively, once the heat of vaporization and the vapor pressure at one temperature are known, the vapor pressure of the liquid at any other temperature can be calculated, as shown in Worked Example 10.5.

When the vapor pressure of a liquid rises to the point where it becomes equal to the external pressure, the liquid boils and changes into vapor. On a molecular level, you might picture boiling in the following way: Imagine that a few molecules in the interior of the liquid momentarily break free from their neighbors and form a microscopic bubble. If the external pressure from the atmosphere is greater than the vapor pressure inside the bubble, the bubble is immediately crushed. At the temperature where the external pressure and the vapor pressure in the bubble are the same, however, the bubble is not crushed. Instead, it rises through the denser liquid, grows larger as more molecules join it, and appears as part of the vigorous action we associate with boiling.

The temperature at which a liquid boils when the external pressure is exactly 1 atm is called the **normal boiling point**. On the plots in Figure 10.13, the normal boiling points of the three liquids are reached when the curves cross the dashed line representing 760 mm Hg—for ether, 34.6 °C (307.8 K); for ethanol, 78.3 °C (351.5 K); and for water, 100.0 °C (373.15 K).

If the external pressure is less than 1 atm, then the vapor pressure necessary for boiling is reached earlier than 1 atm and the liquid boils at a lower than normal temperature. On top of Mt. Everest, for example, where the atmospheric pressure is only about 260 mm Hg, water boils at approximately 71 °C rather than 100 °C. Conversely, if the external pressure on a liquid is greater than 1 atm, the vapor pressure necessary for boiling is reached later and the liquid boils at a greater than normal temperature. Pressure cookers take advantage of this effect by causing water to boil at a higher temperature, thereby allowing food to cook more rapidly.

WORKED EXAMPLE 10.5

CALCULATING A VAPOR PRESSURE USING THE CLAUSIUS–CLAPEYRON EQUATION

The vapor pressure of ethanol at 34.7 °C is 100.0 mm Hg, and the heat of vaporization of ethanol is 38.6 kJ/mol. What is the vapor pressure of ethanol in millimeters of mercury at 65.0 °C?

STRATEGY

There are several ways to do this problem. One way is to use the vapor pressure at $T = 307.9$ K (34.7 °C) to find a value for C in the Clausius–Clapeyron equation. You could then use that value to solve for $\ln P_{vap}$ at $T = 338.2$ K (65.0 °C).

Alternatively, because C is a constant, its value is the same at any two pressures and temperatures. That is:

$$C = \ln P_1 + \frac{\Delta H_{vap}}{RT_1} = \ln P_2 + \frac{\Delta H_{vap}}{RT_2}$$

This equation can be rearranged to solve for the desired quantity, $\ln P_2$:

$$\ln P_2 = \ln P_1 + \left(\frac{\Delta H_{vap}}{R}\right)\left(\frac{1}{T_1} - \frac{1}{T_2}\right)$$

where $P_1 = 100.0$ mm Hg and $\ln P_1 = 4.6052$, $\Delta H_{vap} = 38.6$ kJ/mol, $R = 8.3145$ J/(K·mol), $T_2 = 338.2$ K (65.0 °C), and $T_1 = 307.9$ K (34.7 °C).

SOLUTION

$$\ln P_2 = 4.6052 + \left(\frac{38,600\ \dfrac{J}{mol}}{8.3145\ \dfrac{J}{K \cdot mol}}\right)\left(\frac{1}{307.9\ K} - \frac{1}{338.2\ K}\right)$$

$$\ln P_2 = 4.6052 + 1.3509 = 5.9561$$

$$P_2 = \text{antiln}\ (5.9561) = 386.1\ \text{mm Hg}$$

Antilogarithms are reviewed in Appendix A.2.

WORKED EXAMPLE 10.6

CALCULATING A HEAT OF VAPORIZATION USING THE CLAUSIUS–CLAPEYRON EQUATION

Ether has $P_{vap} = 400$ mm Hg at 17.9 °C and a normal boiling point of 34.6 °C. What is the heat of vaporization, ΔH_{vap}, for ether in kJ/mol?

STRATEGY

The heat of vaporization, ΔH_{vap}, of a liquid can be obtained either graphically from the slope of a plot of $\ln P_{vap}$ versus $1/T$ or algebraically from the Clausius–Clapeyron equation. As derived in Worked Example 10.5,

$$\ln P_2 = \ln P_1 + \left(\frac{\Delta H_{vap}}{R}\right)\left(\frac{1}{T_1} - \frac{1}{T_2}\right)$$

continued on next page

which can be solved for ΔH_{vap}:

$$\Delta H_{vap} = \frac{(\ln P_2 - \ln P_1)(R)}{\left(\dfrac{1}{T_1} - \dfrac{1}{T_2}\right)}$$

where $P_1 = 400$ mm Hg and $\ln P_1 = 5.991$, $P_2 = 760$ mm Hg at the normal boiling point and $\ln P_2 = 6.633$, $R = 8.3145$ J/(K·mol), $T_1 = 291.1$ K (17.9 °C), and $T_2 = 307.8$ K (34.6 °C).

SOLUTION

$$\Delta H_{vap} = \frac{(6.633 - 5.991)\left(8.3145\ \dfrac{J}{K \cdot mol}\right)}{\dfrac{1}{291.1\ K} - \dfrac{1}{307.8\ K}} = 28{,}600\ J/mol = 28.6\ kJ/mol$$

▶ **PROBLEM 10.9** The normal boiling point of benzene is 80.1 °C, and the heat of vaporization is $\Delta H_{vap} = 30.7$ kJ/mol. What is the boiling point of benzene in °C on top of Mt. Everest, where $P = 260$ mm Hg?

▶ **PROBLEM 10.10** Bromine has $P_{vap} = 400$ mm Hg at 41.0 °C and a normal boiling point of 331.9 K. What is the heat of vaporization, ΔH_{vap}, of bromine in kJ/mol?

10.6 KINDS OF SOLIDS

It's clear from a brief look around that most substances are solids rather than liquids or gases at room temperature. It's also clear that there are many different kinds of solids. Some solids, such as iron and aluminum, are hard and metallic. Others, such as sugar and table salt, are crystalline and easily broken. And still others, such as rubber and many plastics, are soft and amorphous.

The most fundamental distinction between kinds of solids is that some are crystalline and others are amorphous. **Crystalline solids** are those whose constituent particles—atoms, ions, or molecules—have an ordered arrangement extending over a long range. This order on the atomic level is also seen on the visible level because crystalline solids usually have flat faces and distinct angles (Figure 10.14a). **Amorphous solids**, by contrast, are those whose constituent particles are randomly arranged and have no ordered long-range structure (Figure 10.14b). Rubber is an example.

(a) A crystalline solid, such as this amethyst, has flat faces and distinct angles. These regular macroscopic features reflect a similarly ordered arrangement of particles at the atomic level.

(b) An amorphous solid like rubber has a disordered arrangement of its constituent particles.

Figure 10.14
Some different kinds of solids.

Crystalline solids can be further categorized as *ionic, molecular, covalent network,* or *metallic.*

Ionic solids are those like sodium chloride, whose constituent particles are ions. A crystal of sodium chloride is composed of alternating Na^+ and Cl^- ions ordered in a regular three-dimensional arrangement and held together by ionic bonds, as discussed in Sections 2.11 and 6.7.

Molecular solids are those like sucrose or ice, whose constituent particles are molecules held together by the intermolecular forces discussed in Section 10.2. A crystal of ice, for example, is composed of H_2O molecules held together in a regular way by hydrogen bonding (Figure 10.15a).

Covalent network solids are those like quartz (Figure 10.15b) or diamond, whose atoms are linked together by covalent bonds into a giant three-dimensional array. In effect, a covalent network solid is one *very* large molecule.

Metallic solids, such as silver or iron, also consist of large arrays of atoms, but their crystals have metallic properties such as electrical conductivity. We'll discuss metals in Chapter 21.

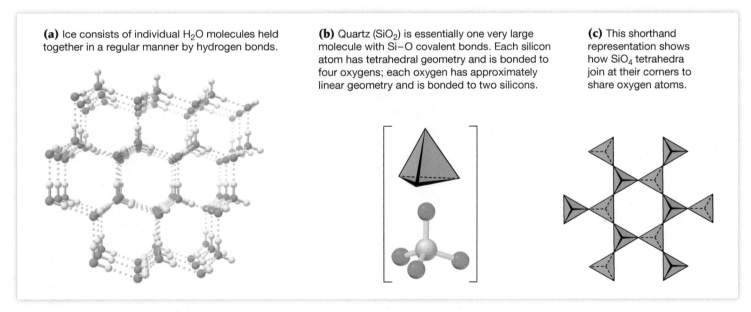

(a) Ice consists of individual H_2O molecules held together in a regular manner by hydrogen bonds.

(b) Quartz (SiO_2) is essentially one very large molecule with Si–O covalent bonds. Each silicon atom has tetrahedral geometry and is bonded to four oxygens; each oxygen has approximately linear geometry and is bonded to two silicons.

(c) This shorthand representation shows how SiO_4 tetrahedra join at their corners to share oxygen atoms.

Figure 10.15
Crystal structures of ice, a molecular solid, and quartz, a covalent network solid.

A summary of the different types of crystalline solids and their characteristics is given in Table 10.9.

TABLE 10.9   Types of Crystalline Solids and Their Characteristics

Type of Solid	Intermolecular Forces	Properties	Examples
Ionic	Ion–ion forces	Brittle, hard, high-melting	$NaCl$, KBr, $MgCl_2$
Molecular	Dispersion forces, dipole–dipole forces, hydrogen bonds	Soft, low-melting, nonconducting	H_2O, Br_2, CO_2, CH_4
Covalent network	Covalent bonds	Hard, high-melting	C (diamond), SiO_2
Metallic	Metallic bonds	Variable hardness and melting point, conducting	Na, Zn, Cu, Fe

10.7 PROBING THE STRUCTURE OF SOLIDS: X-RAY CRYSTALLOGRAPHY

How can the structure of a solid be found experimentally? According to a principle of optics, the wavelength of light used to observe an object must be less than twice the length of the object itself. Since atoms have diameters of around 2×10^{-10} m and the visible light detected by our eyes has wavelengths of $4-7 \times 10^{-7}$ m, it's impossible to see atoms using even the finest optical microscope. To "see" atoms, we must use "light" with a wavelength of approximately 10^{-10} m, which is in the X-ray region of the electromagnetic spectrum (Section 5.1).

The origins of X-ray crystallography go back to the work of Max von Laue in 1912. On passing X rays through a crystal of sodium chloride and letting them strike a photographic plate, Laue noticed that a pattern of spots was produced on the plate, indicating that the X rays were being *diffracted* by the atoms in the crystal. A typical diffraction pattern is shown in **Figure 10.16**.

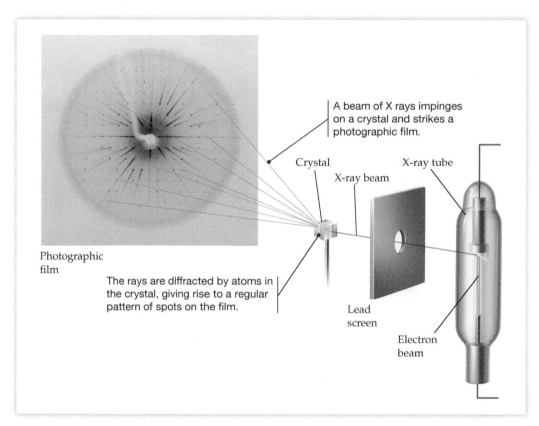

A beam of X rays impinges on a crystal and strikes a photographic film.

Crystal

X-ray tube

X-ray beam

Photographic film

The rays are diffracted by atoms in the crystal, giving rise to a regular pattern of spots on the film.

Lead screen

Electron beam

Figure 10.16
An X-ray diffraction experiment.

Diffraction of electromagnetic radiation occurs when a beam is scattered by an object containing regularly spaced lines (such as those in a diffraction grating) or points (such as the atoms in a crystal). This scattering can happen only if the spacing between the lines or points is comparable to the wavelength of the radiation.

As shown schematically in **Figure 10.17**, diffraction is due to *interference* between two waves passing through the same region of space at the same time. If the waves are in-phase, peak to peak and trough to trough, the interference is constructive and the combined wave is increased in intensity. If the waves are out-of-phase, however, the interference is destructive and the wave is canceled. Constructive interference gives rise to the intense spots observed on Laue's photographic plate, while destructive interference causes the surrounding light areas.

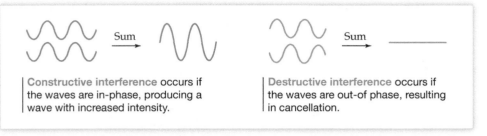

Constructive interference occurs if
the waves are in-phase, producing a
wave with increased intensity.

Destructive interference occurs if
the waves are out-of phase, resulting
in cancellation.

Figure 10.17
Interference of electromagnetic waves.

How does the diffraction of X rays by atoms in a crystal give rise to the observed pattern of spots on a photographic plate? According to an explanation advanced in 1913 by the English physicist William H. Bragg and his 22-year-old son, William L. Bragg, the X rays are diffracted by different layers of atoms in the crystal, leading to constructive interference in some instances but destructive interference in others.

To understand the Bragg analysis, imagine that incoming X rays with wavelength λ strike a crystal face at an angle θ and then bounce off at the same angle, just as light bounces off a mirror (**Figure 10.18**). Those rays that strike an atom in the top layer are all reflected at the same angle θ, and those rays that strike an atom in the second layer are also reflected at the angle θ. But because the second layer of atoms is farther from the X-ray source, the distance that the X rays have to travel to reach the second layer is farther than the distance they have to travel to reach the first layer by an amount indicated as BC in Figure 10.18. Using trigonometry, you can show that the extra distance BC is equal to the distance between atomic layers d (= AC) times the sine of the angle θ:

$$\sin \theta = \frac{BC}{d} \quad \text{so} \quad BC = d \sin \theta$$

The extra distance $BC = CB'$ must also be traveled again by the *reflected* rays as they exit the crystal, making the total extra distance traveled equal to $2d \sin \theta$.

$$BC + CB' = 2d \sin \theta$$

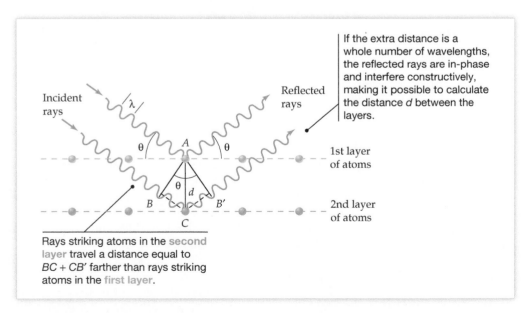

Incident
rays

Reflected
rays

If the extra distance is a
whole number of wavelengths,
the reflected rays are in-phase
and interfere constructively,
making it possible to calculate
the distance d between the
layers.

1st layer
of atoms

2nd layer
of atoms

Rays striking atoms in the second
layer travel a distance equal to
$BC + CB'$ farther than rays striking
atoms in the first layer.

Figure 10.18
Diffraction of X rays of wavelength λ from atoms in the top two layers of a crystal.

The key to the Bragg analysis is the realization that the different rays striking the two layers of atoms are in-phase initially but can be in-phase after reflection only if the extra distance $BC + CB'$ is equal to a whole number of wavelengths $n\lambda$, where n is an integer (1, 2, 3, ...). If the extra distance is not a whole number of wavelengths, then the reflected rays will be out-of-phase and will cancel. Setting the extra distance $2d \sin \theta = n\lambda$ and rearranging to solve for d gives the **Bragg equation**:

$$BC + CB' = 2d \sin \theta = n\lambda$$

Bragg equation $d = \dfrac{n\lambda}{2 \sin \theta}$

Of the variables in the Bragg equation, the value of the wavelength λ is known, the value of $\sin \theta$ can be measured, and the value of n is a small integer, usually 1. Thus, the distance d between layers of atoms in a crystal can be calculated. For their work, the Braggs shared the 1915 Nobel Prize in Physics. The younger Bragg was 25 years old at the time.

Computer-controlled X-ray diffractometers are now available that automatically rotate a crystal and measure the diffraction from all angles. Analysis of the X-ray diffraction pattern then makes it possible to measure the interatomic distance between any two nearby atoms in a crystal. For molecular substances, this knowledge of interatomic distances indicates which atoms are close enough to form a bond. X-ray analysis thus provides a means for determining the structures of molecules (Figure 10.19).

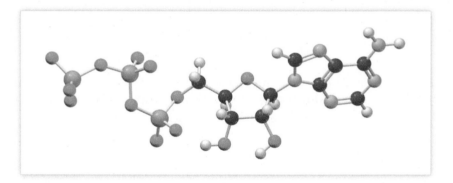

Figure 10.19
A computer-generated structure of adenosine triphosphate (ATP) as determined by X-ray crystallography. ATP has been called "the energy currency of the living cell" because it fuels many metabolic processes.

10.8 UNIT CELLS AND THE PACKING OF SPHERES IN CRYSTALLINE SOLIDS

How do particles—whether atoms, ions, or molecules—pack together in crystals? Let's look at metals, which are the simplest examples of crystal packing because the individual atoms are spheres. Not surprisingly, metal atoms (and other kinds of particles as well) generally pack together in crystals so that they can be as close as possible and maximize intermolecular attractions.

If you were to take a large number of uniformly sized marbles and arrange them in a box in some orderly way, there are four possibilities you might come up with. One way to arrange the marbles is in orderly rows and stacks, with the spheres in one layer sitting directly on top of those in the previous layer so that all layers are identical (Figure 10.20a). In this arrangement, called **simple cubic packing**, each sphere is touched by six neighbors—four in its own layer, one above, and one below—and is thus said to have a **coordination number** of 6. Only 52% of the available volume is occupied by the spheres in simple cubic packing, making inefficient use of space and minimizing attractive forces. Of all the metals in the periodic table, only polonium crystallizes in this way.

Alternatively, space could be used more efficiently if, instead of stacking the spheres directly on top of one another, you slightly separate the spheres in a given layer and offset alternating layers in an *a-b-a-b* arrangement so that the spheres in the *b* layers fit into the depressions between spheres in the *a* layers, and vice versa (**Figure 10.20b**). In this arrangement, called **body-centered cubic packing**, each sphere has a coordination number of 8—four neighbors above and four below—and space is used quite efficiently: 68% of the available volume is occupied. Iron, sodium, and 14 other metals crystallize in this way.

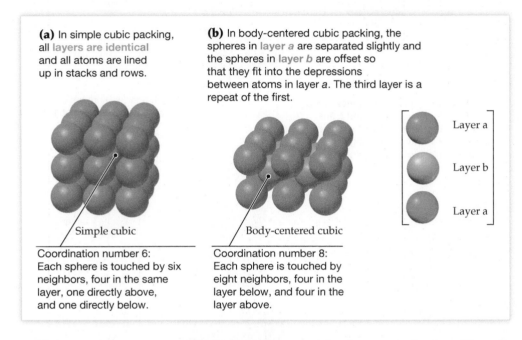

(a) In simple cubic packing, all layers are identical and all atoms are lined up in stacks and rows.

(b) In body-centered cubic packing, the spheres in layer *a* are separated slightly and the spheres in layer *b* are offset so that they fit into the depressions between atoms in layer *a*. The third layer is a repeat of the first.

Layer a

Layer b

Layer a

Simple cubic

Body-centered cubic

Coordination number 6: Each sphere is touched by six neighbors, four in the same layer, one directly above, and one directly below.

Coordination number 8: Each sphere is touched by eight neighbors, four in the layer below, and four in the layer above.

Figure 10.20
Simple cubic packing and body-centered cubic packing.

The remaining two packing arrangements of spheres are both said to be *closest-packed*. The **hexagonal closest-packed** arrangement (**Figure 10.21a**) has two alternating layers, *a-b-a-b*. Each layer has a hexagonal arrangement of touching spheres, which are offset so that spheres in a *b* layer fit into the small triangular depressions between spheres in an *a* layer. Zinc, magnesium, and 19 other metals crystallize in this way.

The **cubic closest-packed** arrangement (**Figure 10.21b**) has *three* alternating layers, *a-b-c-a-b-c*. The *a-b* layers are identical to those in the hexagonal closest-packed arrangement, but the third layer is offset from both *a* and *b* layers. Silver, copper, and 16 other metals crystallize with this arrangement.

In both kinds of closest-packed arrangements, each sphere has a coordination number of 12—six neighbors in the same layer, three above, and three below—and 74% of the available volume is filled. The next time you're in a grocery store, look to see how the oranges or apples are stacked in their display box. They'll almost certainly have a closest-packed arrangement.

◀ What kind of packing arrangement do these oranges have?

Figure 10.21
Hexagonal closest-packing and cubic closest-packing. In both kinds of packing, each sphere is touched by 12 neighbors, 6 in the same layer, 3 in the layer above, and 3 in the layer below.

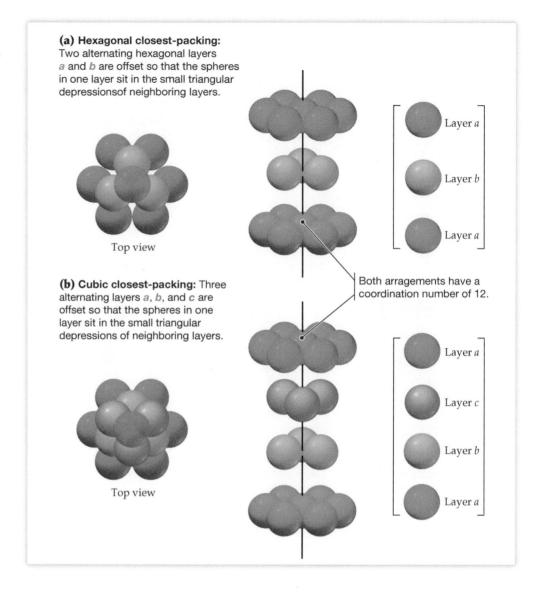

(a) Hexagonal closest-packing: Two alternating hexagonal layers *a* and *b* are offset so that the spheres in one layer sit in the small triangular depressionsof neighboring layers.

Top view

(b) Cubic closest-packing: Three alternating layers *a*, *b*, and *c* are offset so that the spheres in one layer sit in the small triangular depressions of neighboring layers.

Top view

Layer *a*

Layer *b*

Layer *a*

Both arragements have a coordination number of 12.

Layer *a*

Layer *c*

Layer *b*

Layer *a*

▲ Just as these bricks are stacked together in a regular way on the pallet, a crystal is made of many small repeating units called unit cells that stack together in a regular way.

Unit Cells

Having taken a bulk view of how spheres can pack in a crystal, let's now take a close-up view. Just as a large brick wall is made up of many identical bricks stacked together in a repeating pattern, a crystal is made up of many small repeat units called **unit cells** stacked together in three dimensions.

Fourteen different unit-cell geometries occur in crystalline solids. All are parallelepipeds—six-sided geometric solids whose faces are parallelograms. We'll be concerned here only with those unit cells that have cubic symmetry; that is, cells whose edges are equal in length and whose angles are 90°.

There are three kinds of cubic unit cells: *primitive-cubic, body-centered cubic*, and *face-centered cubic*. As shown in **Figure 10.22a**, a **primitive-cubic unit cell** for a metal has an atom at each of its eight corners, where it is shared with seven neighboring cubes that come together at the same point. As a result, only 1/8 of each corner atom "belongs" to a given cubic unit. This primitive-cubic unit cell, with all atoms arranged in orderly rows and stacks, is the repeat unit found in simple cubic packing.

A **body-centered cubic unit cell** has eight corner atoms plus an additional atom in the center of the cube (**Figure 10.22b**). This body-centered cubic unit cell, with two repeating offset layers and with the spheres in a given layer slightly separated, is the repeat unit found in body-centered cubic packing.

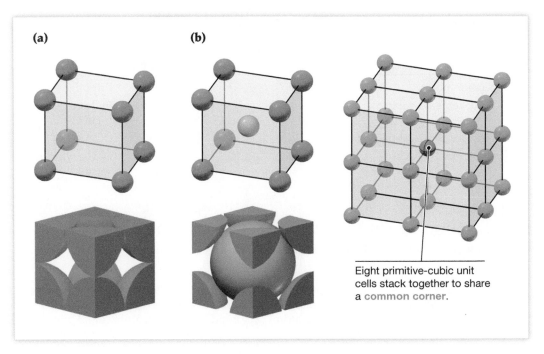

Figure 10.22
Geometries of (a) primitive-cubic and (b) body-centered cubic unit cells. Both skeletal (top) and space-filling views (bottom) are shown.

A **face-centered cubic unit cell** has eight corner atoms plus an additional atom in the center of each of its six faces, where it is shared with one other neighboring cube (Figure 10.23a). Thus, 1/2 of each face atom belongs to a given unit cell. This face-centered cubic unit cell is the repeat unit found in cubic closest-packing, as can be seen by looking down the body diagonal of a unit cell (Figure 10.23b). The faces of the unit-cell cube are at 54.7° angles to the layers of the atoms.

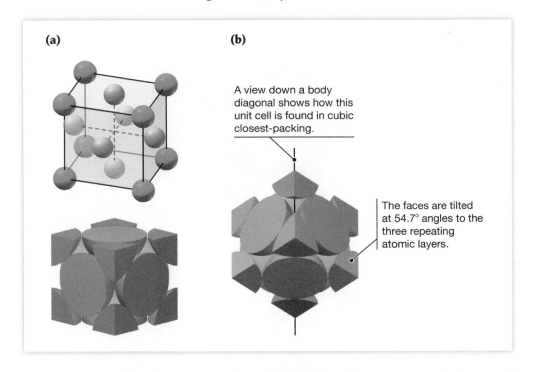

Figure 10.23
Geometry of a face-centered cubic unit cell.

A summary of stacking patterns, coordination numbers, amount of space used, and unit cells for the four kinds of packing of spheres is given in Table 10.10. Hexagonal closest-packing is the only one of the four that has a noncubic unit cell.

TABLE 10.10   Summary of the Four Kinds of Packing for Spheres

Structure	Stacking Pattern	Coordination Number	Space Used (%)	Unit Cell
Simple cubic	a-a-a-a-	6	52	Primitive cubic
Body-centered cubic	a-b-a-b-	8	68	Body-centered cubic
Hexagonal closest-packed	a-b-a-b-	12	74	(Noncubic)
Cubic closest-packed	a-b-c-a-b-c-	12	74	Face-centered cubic

WORKED EXAMPLE 10.7

CALCULATING THE NUMBER OF ATOMS IN A UNIT CELL

How many atoms are in one primitive-cubic unit cell of a metal?

STRATEGY AND SOLUTION

As shown in Figure 10.22a, a primitive-cubic unit cell has an atom at each of its eight corners. When unit cells are stacked together, each corner atom is shared by eight cubes, so that only 1/8 of each atom "belongs" to a given unit cell. Thus there is $1/8 \times 8 = 1$ atom per unit cell.

WORKED EXAMPLE 10.8

USING UNIT-CELL DIMENSIONS TO CALCULATE THE RADIUS OF AN ATOM

Silver metal crystallizes in a cubic closest-packed arrangement with the edge of the unit cell having a length $d = 407$ pm. What is the radius in picometers of a silver atom?

STRATEGY AND SOLUTION

Cubic closest-packing uses a face-centered cubic unit cell. Looking at any one face of the cube head-on shows that the face atoms touch the corner atoms along the diagonal of the face but that corner atoms do not touch one another along the edges. Each diagonal is therefore equal to four atomic radii, $4r$:

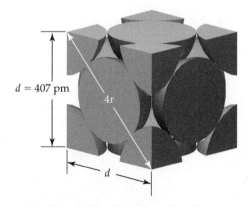

Because the diagonal and two edges of the cube form a right triangle, we can use the Pythagorean theorem to set the sum of the squares of the two edges equal to the square of the diagonal, $d^2 + d^2 = (4r)^2$ and then solve for r, the radius of one atom:

$$d^2 + d^2 = (4r)^2$$

$$2d^2 = 16r^2 \quad \text{and} \quad r^2 = \frac{d^2}{8}$$

$$\text{thus} \quad r = \sqrt{\frac{d^2}{8}} = \sqrt{\frac{(407 \text{ pm})^2}{8}} = 144 \text{ pm}$$

The radius of a silver atom is 144 pm.

WORKED EXAMPLE 10.9

USING UNIT-CELL DIMENSIONS TO CALCULATE THE DENSITY OF A METAL

Nickel has a face-centered cubic unit cell with a length of 352.4 pm along an edge. What is the density of nickel in g/cm^3?

STRATEGY

Density is mass divided by volume. The mass of a single unit cell can be calculated by counting the number of atoms in the cell and multiplying by the mass of a single atom. The volume of a single cubic unit cell with edge d is $d^3 = (3.524 \times 10^{-8}\,cm)^3 = 4.376 \times 10^{-23}\,cm^3$.

SOLUTION

Each of the eight corner atoms in a face-centered cubic unit cell is shared by eight unit cells, so that only $1/8 \times 8 = 1$ atom belongs to a single cell. In addition, each of the six face atoms is shared by two unit cells, so that $1/2 \times 6 = 3$ atoms belong to a single cell. Thus, a single cell has 1 corner atom and 3 face atoms, for a total of 4, and each atom has a mass equal to the molar mass of nickel (58.69 g/mol) divided by Avogadro's number (6.022×10^{23} atoms/mol). We can now calculate the density:

$$\text{Density} = \frac{\text{Mass}}{\text{Volume}} = \frac{(4\,\text{atoms})\left(\dfrac{58.69\,\dfrac{g}{mol}}{6.022 \times 10^{23}\,\dfrac{\text{atoms}}{mol}}\right)}{4.376 \times 10^{-23}\,cm^3} = 8.909\,g/cm^3$$

The calculated density of nickel is $8.909\,g/cm^3$. (The measured value is $8.90\,g/cm^3$.)

WORKED CONCEPTUAL EXAMPLE 10.10

IDENTIFYING A UNIT CELL

Imagine a tiled floor in the following pattern. Identify the smallest repeating rectangular unit, analogous to a two-dimensional unit cell.

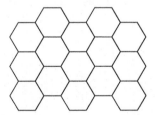

STRATEGY

Using trial and error, the idea is to draw two perpendicular sets of parallel lines that define a repeating rectangular unit. There may be more than one possibility.

SOLUTION

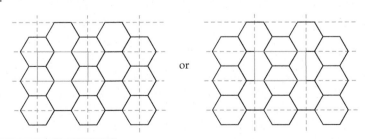

or

▶ **PROBLEM 10.11** How many atoms are in the following:

(a) One body-centered cubic unit cell of a metal

(b) One face-centered cubic unit cell of a metal

▶ **PROBLEM 10.12**   Polonium metal crystallizes in a simple cubic arrangement, with the edge of a unit cell having a length $d = 334$ pm. What is the radius in picometers of a polonium atom?

▶ **PROBLEM 10.13**   What is the density of polonium (Problem 10.12) in g/cm^3?

CONCEPTUAL PROBLEM 10.14   Imagine a tiled floor in the following pattern. Identify the smallest repeating unit, analogous to a two-dimensional unit cell.

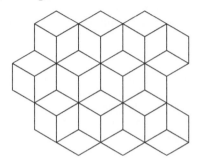

10.9   STRUCTURES OF SOME IONIC SOLIDS

Remember...

Atomic radius decreases when an atom is converted to a cation by loss of an electron and increases when the atom is converted to an anion by gain of an electron. (Section 6.2)

Simple ionic solids such as NaCl and KBr are like metals in that the individual ions are spheres that pack together in a regular way. They differ from metals, however, in that the spheres are not all the same size—anions generally have larger radii than cations (Section 6.2). As a result, ionic solids adopt a variety of different unit cells, depending on the size and charge of the ions. NaCl, KCl, and a number of other salts have a face-centered cubic unit cell in which the larger Cl^- anions occupy corners and faces while the smaller Na^+ cations fit into the holes between adjacent anions (Figure 10.24).

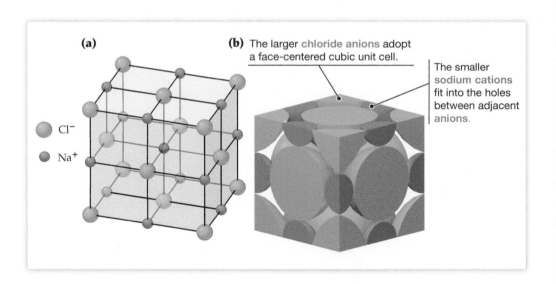

Figure 10.24
The unit cell of NaCl. Both a skeletal view **(a)** and a space-filling view **(b)** in which the unit cell is viewed edge-on are shown.

It's necessary, of course, that the unit cell of an ionic substance be electrically neutral, with equal numbers of positive and negative charges. In the NaCl unit cell, for instance, there are four Cl^- anions ($1/8 \times 8 = 1$ corner atom, plus $1/2 \times 6 = 3$ face atoms) and also four Na^+ cations ($1/4 \times 12 = 3$ edge atoms, plus 1 center atom). (Remember that each corner atom in a cubic unit cell is shared by eight cells, each face atom is shared by two cells, and each edge atom is shared by four cells.)

Two other common ionic unit cells are shown in Figure 10.25. Copper(I) chloride has a face-centered cubic arrangement of the larger Cl^- anions, with the smaller Cu^+ cations in holes so that each is surrounded by a tetrahedron of four anions. Barium

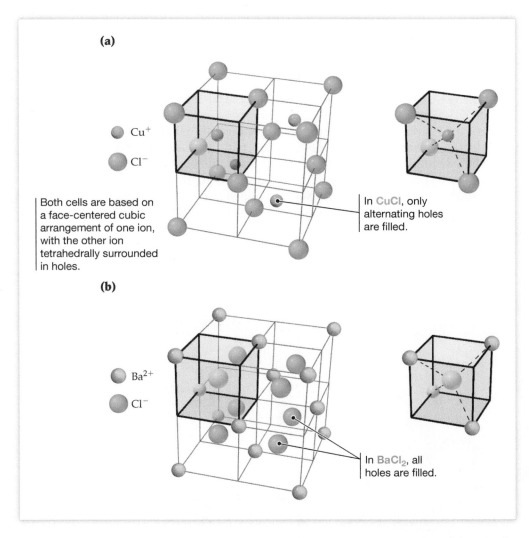

Figure 10.25
Unit cells of (a) CuCl and (b) BaCl$_2$.

(a)

Cu$^+$

Cl$^-$

Both cells are based on a face-centered cubic arrangement of one ion, with the other ion tetrahedrally surrounded in holes.

In CuCl, only alternating holes are filled.

(b)

Ba^{2+}

Cl$^-$

In BaCl$_2$, all holes are filled.

chloride, by contrast, has a face-centered cubic arrangement of the smaller Ba^{2+} *cations*, with the larger Cl$^-$ anions surrounded tetrahedrally. As required for charge neutrality, there are twice as many Cl$^-$ anions as Ba^{2+} cations.

▶ **PROBLEM 10.15** Count the numbers of + and − charges in the CuCl and BaCl$_2$ unit cells (Figure 10.25), and show that both cells are electrically neutral.

CONCEPTUAL PROBLEM 10.16 Rhenium oxide crystallizes in the following cubic unit cell:

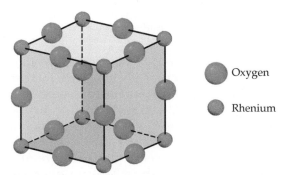

Oxygen

Rhenium

(a) How many rhenium atoms and how many oxygen atoms are in each unit cell?
(b) What is the formula of rhenium oxide?
(c) What is the oxidation state of rhenium?
(d) What is the geometry around each oxygen atom?
(e) What is the geometry around each rhenium atom?

10.10   STRUCTURES OF SOME COVALENT NETWORK SOLIDS

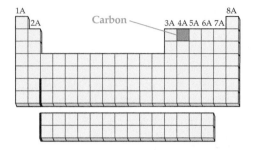

Carbon

Carbon exists in more than 40 known structural forms, or **allotropes,** several of which are crystalline but most of which are amorphous. Graphite, the most common allotrope of carbon and the most stable under normal conditions, is a crystalline covalent network solid that consists of two-dimensional sheets of fused six-membered rings (Figure 10.26a). Each carbon atom is sp^2-hybridized and is bonded with trigonal planar geometry to three other carbons. The diamond form of elemental carbon is a covalent network solid in which each carbon atom is sp^3-hybridized and is bonded with tetrahedral geometry to four other carbons (Figure 10.26b).

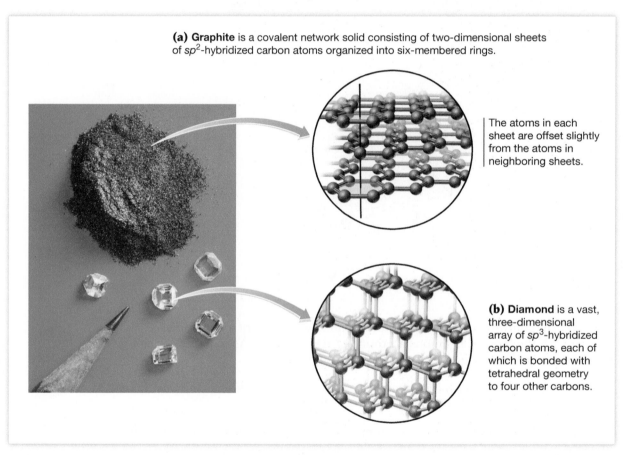

(a) **Graphite** is a covalent network solid consisting of two-dimensional sheets of sp^2-hybridized carbon atoms organized into six-membered rings.

The atoms in each sheet are offset slightly from the atoms in neighboring sheets.

(b) **Diamond** is a vast, three-dimensional array of sp^3-hybridized carbon atoms, each of which is bonded with tetrahedral geometry to four other carbons.

Figure 10.26
Two crystalline allotropes of carbon, (a) graphite and (b) diamond.

In addition to graphite and diamond, a third crystalline allotrope of carbon called *fullerene* was discovered in 1985 as a constituent of soot. Fullerene consists of spherical C_{60} molecules with the extraordinary shape of a soccer ball. The C_{60} ball has 12 pentagonal and 20 hexagonal faces, with each atom sp^2-hybridized and bonded to three other atoms (Figure 10.27a). Closely related to both graphite and fullerene are a group of carbon allotropes called *nanotubes*—tubular structures made of repeating six-membered carbon rings, as if a sheet of graphite were rolled up (Figure 10.27b). Typically, the tubes have a diameter of about 2–30 nm and a length of up to 1 mm.

The different structures of the carbon allotropes lead to widely different properties. Because of its three-dimensional network of strong single bonds that tie all atoms in a crystal together, diamond is the hardest known substance. In addition to its use in jewelry, diamond is widely used industrially for the tips of saw blades and drilling bits. It is an electrical insulator and has a melting point of about 8700 °C at a

Figure 10.27
Fullerene, C_{60}, and carbon nanotubes.

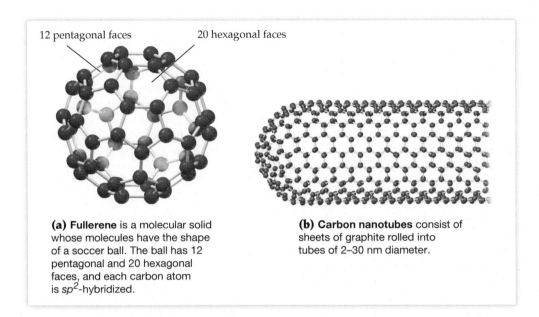

12 pentagonal faces   20 hexagonal faces

(a) Fullerene is a molecular solid whose molecules have the shape of a soccer ball. The ball has 12 pentagonal and 20 hexagonal faces, and each carbon atom is sp^2-hybridized.

(b) Carbon nanotubes consist of sheets of graphite rolled into tubes of 2–30 nm diameter.

pressure of 6–10 million atm. Clear, colorless, and highly crystalline, diamonds are very rare and are found in only a few places in the world, particularly in central and southern Africa.

Graphite is the black, slippery substance used as the "lead" in pencils, as an electrode material in batteries, and as a lubricant in locks. All these properties result from its sheetlike structure. Air and water molecules can adsorb onto the flat faces of the sheets, allowing the sheets to slide over one another and giving graphite its greasy feeling and lubricating properties. Graphite is more stable than diamond at normal pressures but can be converted into diamond at very high pressure and temperature. In fact, approximately 120,000 kg of industrial diamonds is synthesized annually by applying 150,000 atm pressure to graphite at high temperature.

Fullerene, black and shiny like graphite, is the subject of much current research because of its interesting electronic properties. When fullerene is allowed to react with rubidium metal, a superconducting material called rubidium fulleride, Rb_3C_{60}, is formed. (We'll discuss superconductors in more detail in Section 21.7.) Carbon nanotubes are being studied for use as fibers in the structural composites used to make golf clubs, bicycle frames, boats, and airplanes. Their tensile strength is approximately 50–60 times greater than that of steel.

Silica

Just as living organisms are based on carbon compounds, most rocks and minerals are based on silicon compounds. Quartz and much sand, for instance, are nearly pure *silica*, SiO_2. Silicon and oxygen together, in fact, make up nearly 75% of the mass of the Earth's crust. Considering that silicon and carbon are both in group 4A of the periodic table, you might expect SiO_2 to be similar in its properties to CO_2. In fact, though, CO_2 is a molecular substance and a gas at room temperature, whereas SiO_2 (Figure 10.15b on page 367) is a covalent network solid with a melting point over 1600 °C.

The dramatic difference in properties between CO_2 and SiO_2 is due primarily to the difference in electronic structure between carbon and silicon. The π part of a *carbon*–oxygen **double bond** is formed by sideways overlap of a carbon $2p$ orbital with an oxygen $2p$ orbital (Section 7.12). If a similar *silicon*–oxygen double bond were to form, it would require overlap of an oxygen $2p$ orbital and a silicon $3p$ orbital. But because the Si—O bond distance is longer than the C—O distance and a $3p$ orbital is larger than a $2p$ orbital, overlap between the two is not as favorable. As a result, silicon forms four single bonds to four oxygens in a covalent network structure rather than two double bonds to two oxygens in a molecular structure.

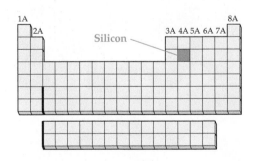

Remember...

Two atoms form a **double bond** when they approach each other with their hybrid orbitals aligned head-on for σ bonding and with their unhybridized p orbitals aligned in a parallel, sideways manner to form a π bond. (Section 7.12)

▲ Colored glasses contain transition metal ions.

Heating silica above about 1600 °C breaks many of its Si—O bonds and turns it from a crystalline solid into a viscous liquid. When this fluid is cooled, some of the Si—O bonds re-form in a random arrangement, and a noncrystalline, amorphous solid called *quartz glass* is formed. If additives are mixed in before cooling, a wide variety of glasses can be prepared. Common window glass, for instance, is prepared by adding $CaCO_3$ and Na_2CO_3. Addition of various transition metal ions results in the preparation of colored glasses, and addition of B_2O_3 produces a high-melting *borosilicate glass* that is sold under the trade name Pyrex. Borosilicate glass is particularly useful for cooking utensils and laboratory glassware because it expands very little when heated and is thus unlikely to crack.

10.11 PHASE DIAGRAMS

Now that we've looked at the three phases of matter individually, let's take an overall view. As noted previously, any one phase of matter can change spontaneously into either of the other two, depending on the temperature and pressure. A convenient way to picture this pressure–temperature dependency of a pure substance in a closed system without air present is to use what is called a **phase diagram**. As illustrated for water in Figure 10.28, a typical phase diagram shows which phase is stable at different combinations of pressure and temperature. When a boundary line between phases is crossed by changing either the temperature or the pressure, a phase change occurs.

Figure 10.28

A phase diagram for H_2O. Various features of the diagram are discussed in the text. Note that the pressure and temperature axes are not drawn to scale.

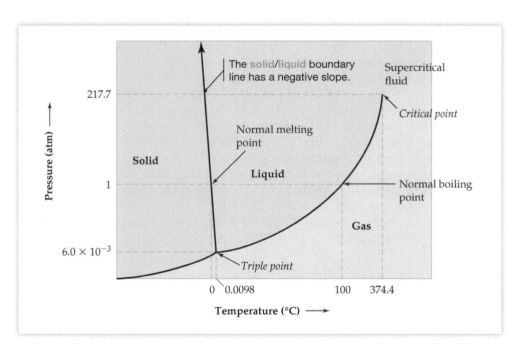

▲ At the triple point, solid exists in the boiling liquid. That is, solid, liquid, and gas coexist in equilibrium.

The simplest way to understand a phase diagram is to begin at the origin in the lower left corner of Figure 10.28 and travel up and right along the boundary line between solid on the left and gas on the right. Points on this line represent pressure/temperature combinations at which the two phases are in equilibrium in a closed system and a direct phase transition between solid ice and gaseous water vapor occurs. At some point along the solid/gas line, an intersection is reached where two lines diverge to form the bounds of the liquid region. The solid/liquid boundary for H_2O goes up and slightly left, while the liquid/gas boundary continues curving up and to the right. Called the **triple point**, this three-way intersection represents a unique combination of pressure and temperature at which all three phases coexist in equilibrium. For water, the triple-point temperature T_t is 0.0098 °C, and the triple-point pressure P_t is 6.0×10^{-3} atm.

Continuing up and slightly left from the triple point, the solid/liquid boundary line represents the melting point of solid ice (or the freezing point of liquid water) at various pressures. When the pressure is 1 atm, the melting point—called the **normal melting point**—is exactly 0 °C. There is a slight negative slope to the line, indicating that the melting point of ice decreases as pressure increases. Water is unusual in this respect, because most substances have a positive slope to their solid/liquid line, indicating that their melting points *increase* with pressure. We'll say more about this behavior shortly.

Continuing up and right from the triple point, the liquid/gas boundary line represents the pressure/temperature combinations at which liquid and gas coexist and water vaporizes (or steam condenses). In fact, the part of the curve up to 1 atm pressure is simply the vapor pressure curve we saw previously in Figure 10.13. When the pressure is 1 atm, water is at its normal boiling point of 100 °C. Continuing along the liquid/gas boundary line, we suddenly reach the **critical point**, where the line abruptly ends. The critical temperature T_c is the temperature beyond which a gas cannot be liquefied, no matter how great the pressure, and the critical pressure P_c is the pressure beyond which a liquid cannot be vaporized, no matter how high the temperature. For water, $T_c = 374.4$ °C and $P_c = 217.7$ atm.

We're all used to seeing solid/liquid and liquid/gas phase transitions, but behavior at the critical point lies so far outside our normal experiences that it's hard to imagine. Think of it this way: A *gas* at the critical point is under such high pressure, and its molecules are so close together, that it becomes indistinguishable from a liquid. A *liquid* at the critical point is at such a high temperature, and its molecules are so relatively far apart, that it becomes indistinguishable from a gas. Thus, the two phases simply become one and form a **supercritical fluid** that is neither true liquid nor true gas. No distinct physical phase change occurs on going beyond the critical point. Rather, a whitish, pearly sheen momentarily appears, and the visible boundary between liquid and gas suddenly vanishes. Frankly, you have to see it to believe it.

The phase diagram of CO_2 shown in **Figure 10.29** has many of the same features as that of water but differs in several interesting respects. First, the triple point is at $P_t = 5.11$ atm, meaning that CO_2 can't be a liquid below this pressure, no matter what the temperature. At 1 atm pressure, CO_2 is a solid below −78.5 °C but a gas above this temperature. Second, the slope of the solid/liquid boundary is positive, meaning that the solid phase is favored as the pressure rises and that the melting point of solid CO_2 therefore increases with pressure.

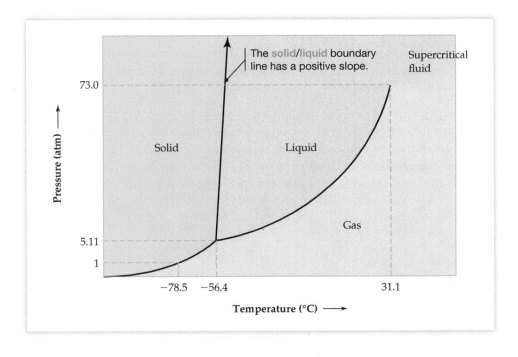

Figure 10.29
A phase diagram for CO_2. The pressure and temperature axes are not to scale.

Figure 10.30
Pressure and melting point. Why does the weighted wire cut through this block of ice?

The effect of pressure on the slope of the solid/liquid boundary line—negative for H_2O but positive for CO_2 and most other substances—depends on the relative densities of the solid and liquid phases. For CO_2 and most other substances, the solid phase is denser than the liquid because particles are packed closer together in the solid. Increasing the pressure pushes the molecules even closer together, thereby favoring the solid phase even more and giving the solid/liquid boundary line a positive slope. Water, however, becomes less dense when it freezes to a solid because large empty spaces are left between molecules due to the ordered three-dimensional network of hydrogen bonds in ice (Figure 10.15a). As a result, increasing the pressure favors the liquid phase, giving the solid/liquid boundary a negative slope.

Figure 10.30 shows a simple demonstration of the effect of pressure on melting point. If a thin wire with heavy weights at each end is draped over a block of ice near 0 °C, the wire rapidly cuts through the block because the increased pressure lowers the melting point of the ice under the wire, causing the ice to liquefy. If the same experiment is tried with a block of dry ice (solid CO_2), however, nothing happens. The dry ice is unaffected because the increased pressure under the wire makes melting more difficult rather than less difficult.

WORKED EXAMPLE 10.11

INTERPRETING A PHASE DIAGRAM

Freeze-dried foods are prepared by freezing the food and removing water by subliming the ice at low pressure. Look at the phase diagram of water in Figure 10.28, and tell the maximum pressure in mm Hg at which ice and water vapor are in equilibrium.

STRATEGY

Solid and vapor are in equilibrium only below the triple-point pressure, $P_t = 6.0 \times 10^{-3}$ atm, which needs to be converted to millimeters of mercury.

SOLUTION

$$6.0 \times 10^{-3} \text{ atm} \times \frac{760 \text{ mm Hg}}{1 \text{ atm}} = 4.6 \text{ mm Hg}$$

▶ **PROBLEM 10.17** Look at the phase diagram of CO_2 in Figure 10.29, and tell the minimum pressure in atmospheres at which liquid CO_2 can exist.

▶ **PROBLEM 10.18** Look at the phase diagram of CO_2 in Figure 10.29, and describe what happens to a CO_2 sample when the following changes are made:
 (a) The temperature is increased from −100 °C to 0 °C at a constant pressure of 2 atm.
 (b) The pressure is reduced from 72 atm to 5.0 atm at a constant temperature of 30 °C.
 (c) The pressure is first increased from 3.5 atm to 76 atm at −10 °C, and the temperature is then increased from −10 °C to 45 °C.

CONCEPTUAL PROBLEM 10.19 Gallium metal has the following phase diagram (the pressure axis is not to scale). In the region shown, gallium has two different solid phases.
 (a) Where on the diagram are the solid, liquid, and vapor regions?
 (b) How many triple points does gallium have? Circle each on the diagram.
 (c) At 1 atm pressure, which phase is more dense, solid or liquid? Explain.

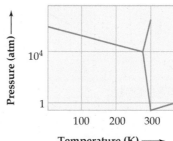

INQUIRY LIQUIDS MADE OF IONS?

When you think of ionic compounds, you probably think of crystalline, high-melting solids: sodium chloride (mp = 801 °C), magnesium oxide (mp = 2825 °C), lithium carbonate (mp = 732 °C), and so on. It's certainly true that many ionic compounds fit that description, but not all. Some ionic compounds are actually liquid at room temperature. Ionic liquids, in fact, have been known for nearly a century—the first such compound to be discovered was ethylammonium nitrate, $CH_3CH_2NH_3^+ NO_3^-$, with a melting point of just 12 °C.

Generally speaking, the ionic liquids used today are salts in which the cation has an irregular shape and in which one or both of the ions are large and bulky so that the charges are dispersed over a large volume. Both factors minimize the crystal lattice energy, thereby making the solid less stable and favoring the liquid. Typical cations are derived from nitrogen-containing organic compounds called *amines*, either 1,3-dialkylimidazolium ions or *N*-alkylpyridinium ions.

▲ As surprising as it sounds, the bottom liquid in this reactor is composed of ions.

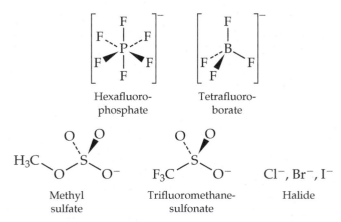

A 1,3-dialkylimidazolium ion   An *N*-alkylpyridium ion

Anions are just as varied as the cations, and more than 500 different ionic liquids with different anion/cation combinations are commercially available. Hexafluorophosphate, tetrafluoroborate, alkyl sulfates, trifluoromethanesulfonate, and halides are typical anions.

Hexafluoro-
phosphate   Tetrafluoroborate

Methyl
sulfate   Trifluoromethanesulfonate Cl^-, Br^-, I^-

Halide

For many years, ionic liquids were just laboratory curiosities. More recently, though, they have been found to be excellent solvents, particularly for use in green chemistry processes like those described in the Chapter 4 *Inquiry*. Among the properties of ionic liquids:

- They dissolve both polar and nonpolar compounds, giving highly concentrated solutions and thereby minimizing the amount of liquid needed.
- They can be fine-tuned for use in specific reactions by varying cation and anion structures.
- They are nonflammable.
- They are stable at high temperatures.
- They have negligible vapor pressures and don't evaporate.
- They are generally recoverable and can be reused many times.

Among their potential applications, ionic liquids are now being explored for use as electrolytes in high-temperature batteries, as solvents for the extraction of heavy organic materials from oil shale, and as replacements for toxic or flammable organic solvents in many industrial processes. We'll be hearing much more about ionic liquids in the coming years.

▶ **PROBLEM 10.20**   How does an ionic liquid differ from a typical molecular liquid, such as water?

▶ **PROBLEM 10.21**   What structural features do ionic liquids have that prevent them from forming solids easily?

SUMMARY

The presence of polar covalent bonds in a molecule can cause the molecule to have a net polarity, a property measured by the **dipole moment**.

Intermolecular forces, known collectively as **van der Waals forces**, are the attractions responsible for holding particles together in the liquid and solid phases. There are several kinds of intermolecular forces, all of which arise from electrical attractions. **Dipole–dipole forces** occur between two polar molecules. **London dispersion forces** are characteristic of all molecules and result from the presence of temporary dipole moments caused by momentarily unsymmetrical electron distributions. A **hydrogen bond** is the attraction between a positively polarized hydrogen atom bonded to O, N, or F and a lone pair of electrons on an O, N, or F atom of another molecule. In addition, **ion–dipole forces** occur between an ion and a polar molecule.

Matter in any one **phase**—solid, liquid, or gas—can undergo a **phase change** to either of the other two phases. Like all naturally occurring processes, a phase change has associated with it a free-energy change, $\Delta G = \Delta H - T \Delta S$. The enthalpy component, ΔH, is a measure of the change in intermolecular forces; the entropy component, ΔS, is a measure of the change in molecular randomness accompanying the phase transition. The enthalpy change for the solid–liquid transition is called the **heat of fusion**, and the enthalpy change for the liquid–vapor transition is the **heat of vaporization**.

The effects of temperature and pressure on phase changes can be displayed graphically on a **phase diagram**. A typical phase diagram has three regions—solid, liquid, and gas—separated by three boundary lines that represent pressure/temperature combinations

at which two phases are in equilibrium and phase changes occur. At exactly 1 atm pressure, the temperature at the solid/liquid boundary corresponds to the **normal melting point** of the substance, and the temperature at the liquid/gas boundary corresponds to the **normal boiling point**. The three lines meet at the **triple point**, a unique combination of temperature and pressure at which all three phases coexist in equilibrium. The liquid/gas line runs from the triple point to the **critical point**, a pressure/temperature combination beyond which liquid and gas phases become a **supercritical fluid** that is neither a true liquid nor a true gas.

Solids can be characterized as **amorphous** if their particles are randomly arranged or **crystalline** if their particles are ordered. Crystalline solids can be further characterized as **ionic solids** if their particles are ions, **molecular solids** if their particles are molecules, **covalent network solids** if they consist of a covalently bonded array of atoms without discrete molecules, or **metallic solids** if their particles are metal atoms.

The regular three-dimensional network of particles in a crystal is made up of small repeating units called **unit cells**. There are 14 kinds of unit cells, 3 of which have cubic symmetry. **Simple cubic packing** uses a **primitive-cubic** unit cell, with an atom at each corner of the cube. **Body-centered cubic packing** uses a **body-centered cubic** unit cell, with an atom at the center and at each corner of the cube. **Cubic closest-packing** uses a **face-centered cubic** unit cell, with an atom at the center of each face and at each corner of the cube. A fourth kind of packing, called **hexagonal closest-packing**, uses a noncubic unit cell.

KEY WORDS

CONCEPTUAL PROBLEMS

Problems 10.1–10.21 appear within the chapter.

10.22 Ethyl acetate, $CH_3CO_2CH_2CH_3$, is commonly used as a solvent and nail-polish remover. Look at the following electrostatic potential map of ethyl acetate, and explain the observed polarity.

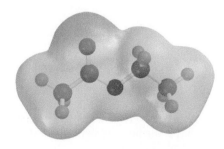

10.23 Identify each of the following kinds of packing:

(a)   **(b)**   **(c)**   **(d)**

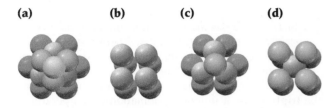

10.24 Zinc sulfide, or sphalerite, crystallizes in the following cubic unit cell:

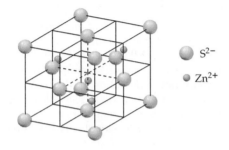

- S^{2-}
- Zn^{2+}

(a) What kind of packing do the sulfide ions adopt?

(b) How many S^{2-} ions and how many Zn^{2+} ions are in the unit cell?

10.25 Perovskite, a mineral containing calcium, oxygen, and titanium, crystallizes in the following cubic unit cell:

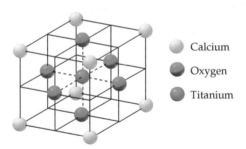

- Calcium
- Oxygen
- Titanium

(a) What is the formula of perovskite?

(b) What is the oxidation number of the titanium atom in perovskite?

10.26 The phase diagram of a substance is shown below.

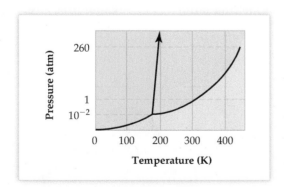

(a) Approximately what is the normal boiling point and what is the normal melting point of the substance?

(b) What is the physical state of the substance under the following conditions?

    (i) $T = 150\ K$, $P = 0.5$ atm

    (ii) $T = 325\ K$, $P = 0.9$ atm

    (iii) $T = 450\ K$, $P = 265$ atm

10.27 Boron nitride, BN, is a covalent network solid with a structure similar to that of graphite. Sketch a small portion of the boron nitride structure.

10.28 Imagine a tiled floor made of square and octagonal tiles in the following pattern. Identify the smallest repeating unit, analogous to a unit cell.

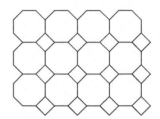

10.29 The following phase diagram of elemental carbon has three different solid phases in the region shown.

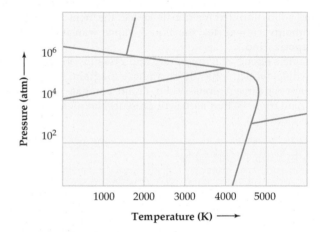

(a) Show where the solid, liquid, and vapor regions are on the diagram.

(b) How many triple points does carbon have? Circle each on the diagram.

(c) Graphite is the most stable solid phase under normal conditions. Identify the graphite phase on the diagram.

(d) On heating graphite to 2500 K at a pressure of 100,000 atm, it can be converted into diamond. Identify the diamond phase on the graph.

(e) Which phase is more dense, graphite or diamond? Explain.

10.30 Acetic acid, the principal nonaqueous constituent of vinegar, exists as a *dimer* in the liquid phase, with two acetic acid molecules joined together by two hydrogen bonds. Sketch the structure you would expect this dimer to have.

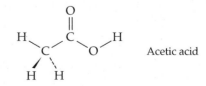

Acetic acid

10.31 Assume that you have a liquid in a cylinder equipped with a movable piston. There is no air in the cylinder, the volume of space above the liquid is 200 mL, and the equilibrium vapor pressure above the liquid is 28.0 mm Hg. What is the equilibrium pressure above the liquid when the volume of space is decreased from 200 mL to 100 mL at constant temperature?

$V = 200$ mL
$P = 28.0$ mm Hg

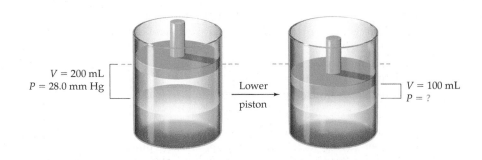

Lower
piston

$V = 100$ mL
$P = ?$

SECTION PROBLEMS

Dipole Moments and Intermolecular Forces (Sections 10.1 – 10.3)

10.32 Why don't all molecules with polar covalent bonds have dipole moments?

10.33 What is the difference between London dispersion forces and dipole–dipole forces?

10.34 What are the most important kinds of intermolecular forces present in each of the following substances?

(a) Chloroform, $CHCl_3$ (b) Oxygen, O_2

(c) Polyethylene, C_nH_{2n+2} (d) Methanol, CH_3OH

10.35 Of the substances Xe, CH_3Cl, HF, which has:

(a) The smallest dipole–dipole forces?

(b) The largest hydrogen bond forces?

(c) The largest dispersion forces?

10.36 Methanol (CH_3OH; bp = 65 °C) boils nearly 230 °C higher than methane (CH_4; bp = −164 °C), but 1-decanol ($C_{10}H_{21}OH$; bp = 231 °C) boils only 57 °C higher than decane ($C_{10}H_{22}$; bp = 174 °C). Explain.

Methanol

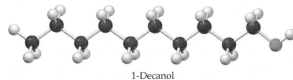

1-Decanol

10.37 Which substance in each of the following pairs would you expect to have larger dispersion forces?

(a) Ethane, C_2H_6, or octane, C_8H_{18}

(b) HCl or HI

(c) H_2O or H_2Se

10.38 Which of the following substances would you expect to have a nonzero dipole moment? Explain, and show the direction of each.

(a) Cl_2O (b) XeF_4

(c) Chloroethane, CH_3CH_2Cl (d) BF_3

10.39 Which of the following substances would you expect to have a nonzero dipole moment? Explain, and show the direction of each.

(a) NF_3 (b) CH_3NH_2 (c) XeF_2 (d) PCl_5

10.40 The dipole moment of BrCl is 0.518 D and the distance between atoms is 213.9 pm. What is the percent ionic character of the BrCl bond?

10.41 The dipole moment of ClF is 0.887 D and the distance between atoms is 162.8 pm. What is the percent ionic character of the ClF bond?

10.42 Why is the dipole moment of SO_2 1.63 D, but that of CO_2 is zero?

10.43 Draw three-dimensional structures of PCl_3 and PCl_5, and then explain why one of the molecules has a dipole moment and one does not.

10.44 The class of ions PtX_4^{2-}, where X is a halogen, has a square planar geometry.

(a) Draw a structure for a $PtBr_2Cl_2^{2-}$ ion that has no dipole moment.

(b) Draw a structure for a $PtBr_2Cl_2^{2-}$ ion that has a dipole moment.

10.45 Of the two compounds SiF_4 and SF_4, which is polar and which is nonpolar?

10.46 Draw a picture showing how hydrogen bonding takes place between two ammonia molecules.

10.47 1,3-Propanediol can form *intra*molecular as well as intermolecular hydrogen bonds. Draw a structure of 1,3-propanediol showing an intramolecular hydrogen bond.

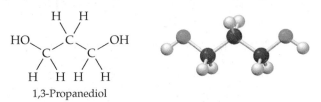

1,3-Propanediol

10.48 A magnetized needle gently placed on the surface of a glass of water acts like a makeshift compass. Is it water's viscosity or its surface tension that keeps the needle on top?

10.49 Water flows quickly through the narrow neck of a bottle, but maple syrup flows sluggishly. Is this different behavior due to a difference in viscosity or in surface tension for the liquids?

Vapor Pressure and Phase Changes (Sections 10.4 and 10.5)

10.50 Why is ΔH_{vap} usually larger than ΔH_{fusion}?

10.51 Why is the heat of sublimation, ΔH_{subl}, equal to the sum of ΔH_{vap} and ΔH_{fusion} at the same temperature?

10.52 Mercury has mp = −38.8 °C and bp = 356.6 °C. What, if any, phase changes take place under the following conditions at 1.0 atm pressure?

(a) The temperature of a sample is raised from −30 °C to 365 °C.

(b) The temperature of a sample is lowered from 291 K to 238 K.

(c) The temperature of a sample is lowered from 638 K to 231 K.

10.53 Iodine has mp = 113.7 °C and bp = 184.4 °C. What, if any, phase changes take place under the following conditions at 1.0 atm pressure?

(a) The temperature of a solid sample is held at 113.7 °C while heat is added.

(b) The temperature of a sample is lowered from 452 K to 389 K.

10.54 Water at room temperature is placed in a flask connected by rubber tubing to a vacuum pump, and the pump is turned on. After several minutes, the volume of the water has decreased and what remains has turned to ice. Explain.

10.55 Ether at room temperature is placed in a flask connected by a rubber tube to a vacuum pump, the pump is turned on, and the ether begins boiling. Explain.

10.56 How much energy in kilojoules is needed to heat 5.00 g of ice from −10.0 °C to 30.0 °C? The heat of fusion of water is 6.01 kJ/mol, and the molar heat capacity is 36.6 J/(K·mol) for ice and 75.3 J/(K·mol) for liquid water.

10.57 How much energy in kilojoules is released when 15.3 g of steam at 115.0 °C is condensed to give liquid water at 75.0 °C? The heat of vaporization of liquid water is 40.67 kJ/mol, and the molar heat capacity is 75.3 J/(K·mol) for the liquid and 33.6 J/(K·mol) for the vapor.

10.58 How much energy in kilojoules is released when 7.55 g of water at 33.5 °C is cooled to −10.0 °C? (See Problem 10.56 for the necessary data.)

10.59 How much energy in kilojoules is released when 25.0 g of ethanol vapor at 93.0 °C is cooled to −10.0 °C? Ethanol has mp = −114.1 °C, bp = 78.3 °C, ΔH_{vap} = 38.56 kJ/mol, and ΔH_{fusion} = 4.93 kJ/mol. The molar heat capacity is 112.3 J/(K·mol) for the liquid and 65.6 J/(K·mol) for the vapor.

10.60 Draw a molar heating curve for ethanol, C_2H_5OH, similar to that shown for water in Figure 10.10 on page 360. Begin with solid ethanol at its melting point, and raise the temperature to 100 °C. The necessary data are given in Problem 10.59.

10.61 Draw a molar heating curve for sodium similar to that shown for water in Figure 10.10. Begin with solid sodium at its melting point, and raise the temperature to 1000 °C. The necessary data are mp = 97.8 °C, bp = 883 °C, ΔH_{vap} = 89.6 kJ/mol, and ΔH_{fusion} = 2.64 kJ/mol. Assume that the molar heat capacity is 20.8 J/(K·mol) for both liquid and vapor phases and does not change with temperature.

10.62 Naphthalene, better known as "mothballs," has bp = 218 °C and ΔH_{vap} = 43.3 kJ/mol. What is the entropy of vaporization, ΔS_{vap} in J/(K·mol) for naphthalene?

10.63 What is the entropy of fusion, ΔS_{fusion} in J/(K·mol) for sodium? The necessary data are given in Problem 10.61.

10.64 Carbon disulfide, CS_2, has P_{vap} = 100 mm Hg at −5.1 °C and a normal boiling point of 46.5 °C. What is ΔH_{vap} for carbon disulfide in kJ/mol?

Carbon disulfide

10.65 The vapor pressure of $SiCl_4$ is 100 mm Hg at 5.4 °C, and the normal boiling point is 57.7 °C. What is ΔH_{vap} for $SiCl_4$ in kJ/mol?

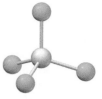

Silicon tetrachloride

10.66 What is the vapor pressure of CS_2 in mm Hg at 20.0 °C? (See Problem 10.64.)

10.67 What is the vapor pressure of $SiCl_4$ in mm Hg at 30.0 °C? (See Problem 10.65.)

10.68 Dichloromethane, CH_2Cl_2, is an organic solvent used for removing caffeine from coffee beans. The following table gives the vapor pressure of dichloromethane at various temperatures. Fill in the rest of the table, and use the data to plot curves of P_{vap} versus T and ln P_{vap} versus $1/T$.

Temp (K)	P_{vap} (mm Hg)	ln P_{vap}	1/T
263	80.1	?	?
273	133.6	?	?
283	213.3	?	?
293	329.6	?	?
303	495.4	?	?
313	724.4	?	?

10.69 The following table gives the vapor pressure of mercury at various temperatures. Fill in the rest of the table, and use the data to plot curves of P_{vap} versus T and ln P_{vap} versus $1/T$.

Temp (K)	P_{vap} (mm Hg)	ln P_{vap}	1/T
500	39.3	?	?
520	68.5	?	?
540	114.4	?	?
560	191.6	?	?
580	286.4	?	?
600	432.3	?	?

10.70 Use the plot you made in Problem 10.68 to find a value in kJ/mol for ΔH_{vap} for dichloromethane.

10.71 Use the plot you made in Problem 10.69 to find a value in kJ/mol for ΔH_{vap} for mercury. The normal boiling point of mercury is 630 K.

10.72 Choose any two temperatures and corresponding vapor pressures in the table given in Problem 10.68, and use those values to calculate ΔH_{vap} for dichloromethane in kJ/mol. How does the value you calculated compare to the value you read from your plot in Problem 10.70?

10.73 Choose any two temperatures and corresponding vapor pressures in the table given in Problem 10.69, and use those values to calculate ΔH_{vap} for mercury in kJ/mol. How does the value you calculated compare to the value you read from your plot in Problem 10.71?

Kinds and Structures of Solids (Sections 10.6 – 10.9)

10.74 List the four main classes of crystalline solids, and give a specific example of each.

10.75 What kinds of particles are present in each of the four main classes of crystalline solids?

10.76 Which of the substances Na_3PO_4, CBr_4, rubber, Au, and quartz best fits each of the following descriptions?
  (a) amorphous solid   (b) ionic solid
  (c) molecular solid   (d) covalent network solid
  (e) metallic solid

10.77 Which of the substances diamond, Hg, Cl_2, glass, and KCl best fits each of the following descriptions?
  (a) amorphous solid   (b) ionic solid
  (c) molecular solid   (d) covalent network solid
  (e) metallic solid

10.78 Silicon carbide is very hard, has no known melting point, and diffracts X rays. What type of solid is it: amorphous, ionic, molecular, covalent network, or metallic?

10.79 Arsenic tribromide melts at 31.1 °C, diffracts X rays, and does not conduct electricity in either the solid or liquid phase. What type of solid is it: amorphous, ionic, molecular, covalent network, or metallic?

10.80 Diffraction of X rays with $\lambda = 154.2$ pm occurred at an angle $\theta = 22.5°$ from a metal surface. What is the spacing (in pm) between the layers of atoms that diffracted the X rays?

10.81 Diffraction of X rays with $\lambda = 154.2$ pm occurred at an angle $\theta = 76.84°$ from a metal surface. What is the spacing (in pm) between layers of atoms that diffracted the X rays?

10.82 What is a unit cell?

10.83 Which of the four kinds of packing used by metals makes the most efficient use of space, and which makes the least efficient use?

10.84 Copper crystallizes in a face-centered cubic unit cell with an edge length of 362 pm. What is the radius of a copper atom in picometers? What is the density of copper in g/cm^3?

10.85 Lead crystallizes in a face-centered cubic unit cell with an edge length of 495 pm. What is the radius of a lead atom in picometers? What is the density of lead in g/cm^3?

10.86 Aluminum has a density of 2.699 g/cm^3 and crystallizes with a face-centered cubic unit cell. What is the edge length of a unit cell in picometers?

10.87 Tungsten crystallizes in a body-centered cubic unit cell with an edge length of 317 pm. What is the length in picometers of a unit-cell diagonal that passes through the center atom?

10.88 In light of your answer to Problem 10.87, what is the radius in picometers of a tungsten atom?

10.89 Sodium has a density of 0.971 g/cm^3 and crystallizes with a body-centered cubic unit cell. What is the radius of a sodium atom, and what is the edge length of the cell in picometers?

10.90 Titanium metal has a density of 4.506 g/cm^3 and an atomic radius of 144.8 pm. In what cubic unit cell does titanium crystallize?

10.91 Calcium metal has a density of 1.55 g/cm^3 and crystallizes in a cubic unit cell with an edge length of 558.2 pm.
  (a) How many Ca atoms are in one unit cell?
  (b) In which of the three cubic unit cells does calcium crystallize?

10.92 Sodium hydride, NaH, crystallizes in a face-centered cubic unit cell similar to that of NaCl (Figure 10.24; page 376). How many Na^+ ions touch each H^- ion, and how many H^- ions touch each Na^+ ion?

10.93 Cesium chloride crystallizes in a cubic unit cell with Cl^- ions at the corners and a Cs^+ ion in the center. Count the numbers of + and − charges, and show that the unit cell is electrically neutral.

10.94 If the edge length of an NaH unit cell is 488 pm, what is the length in picometers of an Na—H bond? (See Problem 10.92.)

10.95 The edge length of a CsCl unit cell (Problem 10.93) is 412.3 pm. What is the length in picometers of the Cs—Cl bond? If the ionic radius of a Cl^- ion is 181 pm, what is the ionic radius in picometers of a Cs^+ ion?

Phase Diagrams (Section 10.11)

10.96 Look at the phase diagram of CO_2 in Figure 10.29, and tell what phases are present under the following conditions:
  (a) $T = -60$ °C, $P = 0.75$ atm
  (b) $T = -35$ °C, $P = 18.6$ atm
  (c) $T = -80$ °C, $P = 5.42$ atm

10.97 Look at the phase diagram of H_2O in Figure 10.28, and tell what happens to an H_2O sample when the following changes are made:
  (a) The temperature is reduced from 48 °C to −4.4 °C at a constant pressure of 6.5 atm.
  (b) The pressure is increased from 85 atm to 226 atm at a constant temperature of 380 °C.

10.98 Bromine has $T_t = -7.3$ °C, $P_t = 44$ mm Hg, $T_c = 315$ °C, and $P_c = 102$ atm. The density of the liquid is 3.1 g/cm^3, and the density of the solid is 3.4 g/cm^3. Sketch a phase diagram for bromine, and label all points of interest.

10.99 Oxygen has $T_t = 54.3$ K, $P_t = 1.14$ mm Hg, $T_c = 154.6$ K, and $P_c = 49.77$ atm. The density of the liquid is 1.14 g/cm^3, and the density of the solid is 1.33 g/cm^3. Sketch a phase diagram for oxygen, and label all points of interest.

10.100 Refer to the bromine phase diagram you sketched in Problem 10.98, and tell what phases are present under the following conditions:
  (a) $T = -10$ °C, $P = 0.0075$ atm
  (b) $T = 25$ °C, $P = 16$ atm

10.101 Refer to the oxygen phase diagram you sketched in Problem 10.99, and tell what phases are present under the following conditions:
  (a) $T = -210$ °C, $P = 1.5$ atm
  (b) $T = -100$ °C, $P = 66$ atm

10.102 Does solid oxygen (Problem 10.99) melt when pressure is applied, as water does? Explain.

10.103 Assume that you have samples of the following three gases at 25 °C. Which of the three can be liquefied by applying pressure, and which cannot? Explain.
  Ammonia: $T_c = 132.5$ °C and $P_c = 112.5$ atm
  Methane: $T_c = -82.1$ °C and $P_c = 45.8$ atm
  Sulfur dioxide: $T_c = 157.8$ °C and $P_c = 77.7$ atm

10.104 Benzene has a melting point of 5.53 °C and a boiling point of 80.09 °C at atmospheric pressure. Its density is 0.8787 g/cm^3 when liquid and 0.899 g/cm^3 when solid; it has $T_c = 289.01$ °C, $P_c = 48.34$ atm, $T_t = 5.52$ °C, and $P_t = 0.0473$ atm. Starting from a point at 200 K and 66.5 atm, trace the following path on a phase diagram:
  (1) First, increase T to 585 K while keeping P constant.
  (2) Next, decrease P to 38.5 atm while keeping T constant.
  (3) Then, decrease T to 278.66 K while keeping P constant.
  (4) Finally, decrease P to 0.0025 atm while keeping T constant.
  What is your starting phase, and what is your final phase?

10.105 Refer to the oxygen phase diagram you drew in Problem 10.99, and trace the following path starting from a point at 0.0011 atm and −225 °C:

(1) First, increase P to 35 atm while keeping T constant.

(2) Next, increase T to −150 °C while keeping P constant.

(3) Then, decrease P to 1.0 atm while keeping T constant.

(4) Finally, decrease T to −215 °C while keeping P constant.

What is your starting phase, and what is your final phase?

10.106 How many phase transitions did you pass through in Problem 10.104, and what are they?

10.107 What phase transitions did you pass through in Problem 10.105?

CHAPTER PROBLEMS

10.108 Fluorine is more electronegative than chlorine (Figure 7.4), yet fluoromethane (CH_3F; $\mu = 1.86$ D) has a smaller dipole moment than chloromethane (CH_3Cl; $\mu = 1.90$ D). Explain.

10.109 What is the atomic radius in picometers of an argon atom if solid argon has a density of 1.623 g/cm^3 and crystallizes at low temperature in a face-centered cubic unit cell?

10.110 Mercury has mp = −38.8 °C, a molar heat capacity of 27.9 J/(K·mol) for the liquid and 28.2 J/(K·mol) for the solid, and $\Delta H_{fusion} = 2.33$ kJ/mol. Assuming that the heat capacities don't change with temperature, how much energy in kilojoules is needed to heat 7.50 g of Hg from a temperature of −50.0 °C to +50.0 °C?

10.111 Silicon carbide, SiC, is a covalent network solid with a structure similar to that of diamond. Sketch a small portion of the SiC structure.

10.112 In Denver, the Mile-High City, water boils at 95 °C. What is atmospheric pressure in atmospheres in Denver? ΔH_{vap} for H_2O is 40.67 kJ/mol.

10.113 There are three compounds with the formula $C_2H_2Br_2$. Two of the three have dipole moments, and one does not. Draw the structures of all three compounds, and tell which has no dipole moment.

10.114 If a protein can be induced to crystallize, its molecular structure can be determined by X-ray crystallography. Protein crystals, though solid, contain a large amount of water molecules along with the protein. The protein chicken egg-white lysozyme, for instance, crystallizes with a unit cell having angles of 90° and with edge lengths of 7.9×10^3 pm, 7.9×10^3 pm, and 3.8×10^3 pm. There are eight molecules in the unit cell. If the lysozyme molecule has a molecular mass of 1.44×10^4 amu and a density of 1.35 g/cm^3, what percent of the unit cell is occupied by the protein?

10.115 The molecular structure of a scorpion toxin, a small protein, was determined by X-ray crystallography. The unit cell has angles of 90°, contains 16 molecules, and has a volume of 1.019×10^2 nm^3. If the molecular mass of the toxin is 3336 amu and the density is about 1.35 g/cm^3, what percent of the unit cell is occupied by protein?

10.116 Magnesium metal has $\Delta H_{fusion} = 9.037$ kJ/mol and $\Delta S_{fusion} = 9.79$ J/(K·mol). What is the melting point in °C of magnesium?

10.117 Titanium tetrachloride, $TiCl_4$, has a melting point of −23.2 °C and has $\Delta H_{fusion} = 9.37$ kJ/mol. What is the entropy of fusion, ΔS_{fusion} in J/(K·mol), for $TiCl_4$?

10.118 Dichlorodifluoromethane, CCl_2F_2, one of the chlorofluoro-carbon refrigerants responsible for destroying part of the Earth's ozone layer, has $P_{vap} = 40.0$ mm Hg at −81.6 °C

and $P_{vap} = 400$ mm Hg at −43.9 °C. What is the normal boiling point of CCl_2F_2 in °C?

Dichlorodifluoromethane

10.119 The chlorofluorocarbon refrigerant trichlorofluoromethane, CCl_3F, has $P_{vap} = 100.0$ mm Hg at −23 °C and $\Delta H_{vap} = 24.77$ kJ/mol.

(a) What is the normal boiling point of trichlorofluoromethane in °C?

(b) What is ΔS_{vap} for trichlorofluoromethane?

10.120 Nitrous oxide, N_2O, occasionally used as an anesthetic by dentists under the name "laughing gas," has $P_{vap} = 100$ mm Hg at −110.3 °C and a normal boiling point of −88.5 °C. What is the heat of vaporization of nitrous oxide in kJ/mol?

10.121 Acetone, a common laboratory solvent, has $\Delta H_{vap} = 29.1$ kJ/mol and a normal boiling point of 56.1 °C. At what temperature in °C does acetone have $P_{vap} = 105$ mm Hg?

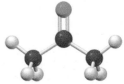

Acetone

10.122 Use the following data to sketch a phase diagram for krypton: $T_t = -169$ °C, $P_t = 133$ mm Hg, $T_c = -63$ °C, $P_c = 54$ atm, mp = −156.6 °C, bp = −152.3 °C. The density of solid krypton is 2.8 g/cm^3, and the density of the liquid is 2.4 g/cm^3. Can a sample of gaseous krypton at room temperature be liquefied by raising the pressure?

10.123 What is the physical phase of krypton (Problem 10.122) under the following conditions:

(a) $P = 5.3$ atm, $T = -153$ °C

(b) $P = 65$ atm, $T = 250$ K

10.124 Calculate the percent volume occupied by the spheres in a body-centered cubic unit cell.

10.125 Iron crystallizes in a body-centered cubic unit cell with an edge length of 287 pm. What is the radius of an iron atom in picometers?

10.126 Iron metal has a density of 7.86 g/cm^3 and a molar mass of 55.85 g. Use this information together with the data in Problem 10.125 to calculate a value for Avogadro's number.

10.127 Silver metal crystallizes in a face-centered cubic unit cell with an edge length of 408 pm. The molar mass of silver is 107.9 g/mol, and its density is 10.50 g/cm^3. Use these data to calculate a value for Avogadro's number.

10.128 A drawing of the NaCl unit cell is shown in Figure 10.24.

    (a) What is the edge length in picometers of the NaCl unit cell? The ionic radius of Na^+ is 97 pm, and the ionic radius of Cl^- is 181 pm.

    (b) What is the density of NaCl in g/cm^3?

10.129 Niobium oxide crystallizes in the following cubic unit cell:

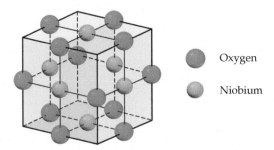

Oxygen

Niobium

    (a) How many niobium atoms and how many oxygen atoms are in each unit cell?

    (b) What is the formula of niobium oxide?

    (c) What is the oxidation state of niobium?

10.130 For each of the following substances, identify the intermolecular force or forces that predominate. Using your knowledge of the relative strengths of the various forces, rank the substances in order of their normal boiling points.

$$Al_2O_3, \; F_2, \; H_2O, \; Br_2, \; ICl, \; NaCl$$

10.131 One form of silver telluride (Ag_2Te) crystallizes with a cubic unit cell and a density of $7.70 \; g/cm^3$. X-ray crystal-lography shows that the edge of the cubic unit cell has a length of 529 pm. How many Ag atoms are in the unit cell?

10.132 Substance **X** has a vapor pressure of 100 mm Hg at its triple point (48 °C). When 1 mol of **X** is heated at 1 atm pressure with a constant rate of heat input, the following heating curve is obtained:

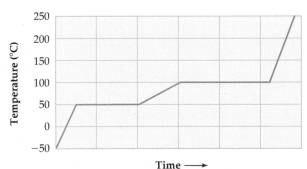

    (a) Sketch the phase diagram for **X**, including labels for different phases, triple point, melting point, and boiling point.

    (b) For each of the following, choose which phase of **X** (solid, liquid, or gas) fits the description:

        (i) Is the most dense at 50 °C

        (ii) Is the least dense at 50 °C

        (iii) Has the greatest specific heat

        (iv) Predominates at 80 °C and 1 atm

        (v) Can have a vapor pressure of 20 mm Hg

MULTICONCEPT PROBLEMS

10.133 Look up thermodynamic data for ethanol (C_2H_5OH) in Appendix B, estimate the normal boiling point of ethanol, and calculate the vapor pressure of ethanol at 25 °C.

10.134 The mineral *magnetite* is an iron oxide ore that has a density of $5.20 \; g/cm^3$. At high temperature, magnetite reacts with carbon monoxide to yield iron metal and carbon dioxide. When 2.660 g of magnetite is allowed to react with sufficient carbon monoxide, the CO_2 product is found to have a volume of 1.136 L at 298 K and 751 mm Hg pressure.

    (a) What mass of iron in grams is formed in the reaction?

    (b) What is the formula of magnetite?

    (c) Magnetite has a somewhat complicated cubic unit cell with an edge length of 839 pm. How many Fe and O atoms are present in each unit cell?

10.135 A group 3A metal has a density of $2.70 \; g/cm^3$ and a cubic unit cell with an edge length of 404 pm. Reaction of a $1.07 \; cm^3$ chunk of the metal with an excess of hydrochloric acid gives a colorless gas that occupies 4.00 L at 23.0 °C and a pressure of 740 mm Hg.

    (a) Identify the metal.

    (b) Is the unit cell primitive, body-centered, or face-centered?

    (c) What is the atomic radius of the metal atom in picometers?

10.136 A cube-shaped crystal of an alkali metal, 1.62 mm on an edge, was vaporized in a 500.0 mL evacuated flask. The resulting vapor pressure was 12.5 mm Hg at 802 °C. The structure of the solid metal is known to be body-centered cubic.

    (a) What is the atomic radius of the metal atom in picometers?

    (b) Use the data in Figure 5.18 on page 177 to identify the alkali metal.

    (c) What are the densities of the solid and the vapor in g/cm^3?

10.137 Assume that 1.588 g of an alkali metal undergoes complete reaction with the amount of gaseous halogen contained in a 0.500 L flask at 298 K and 755 mm Hg pressure. In the reaction, 22.83 kJ is released ($\Delta H = -22.83 \; kJ$). The product, a binary ionic compound, crystallizes in a unit cell with anions in a face-centered cubic arrangement and with cations centered along each edge between anions. In addition, there is a cation in the center of the cube.

    (a) What is the identity of the alkali metal?

    (b) The edge length of the unit cell is 535 pm. Find the radius of the alkali metal cation from the data in Figure 6.1 on page 189, and then calculate the radius of the halide anion. Identify the anion from the data in Figure 6.2 on page 189.

    (c) Sketch a space-filling, head-on view of the unit cell, labeling the ions. Are the anions in contact with one another?

    (d) What is the density of the compound in g/cm^3?

    (e) What is the standard heat of formation for the compound?

APPENDIX A

Mathematical Operations

A.1 SCIENTIFIC NOTATION

The numbers that you encounter in chemistry are often either very large or very small. For example, there are about 33,000,000,000,000,000,000,000 H_2O molecules in 1.0 mL of water, and the distance between the H and O atoms in an H_2O molecule is 0.000 000 000 095 7 m. These quantities are more conveniently written in scientific notation as 3.3×10^{22} molecules and 9.57×10^{-11} m, respectively. In scientific notation, numbers are written in the exponential format $A \times 10^n$, where A is a number between 1 and 10, and the exponent n is a positive or negative integer.

How do you convert a number from ordinary notation to scientific notation? If the number is greater than or equal to 10, shift the decimal point to the *left* by n places until you obtain a number between 1 and 10. Then, multiply the result by 10^n. For example, the number 8137.6 is written in scientific notation as 8.1376×10^3:

$$8137.6 = 8.1376 \times 10^3 \quad \text{Number of places decimal point was shifted to the left}$$

Shift decimal point to the left by 3 places to get a number between 1 and 10

When you shift the decimal point to the left by three places, you are in effect dividing the number by $10 \times 10 \times 10 = 1000 = 10^3$. Therefore, you must multiply the result by 10^3 so that the value of the number is unchanged.

To convert a number less than 1 to scientific notation, shift the decimal point to the *right* by n places until you obtain a number between 1 and 10. Then, multiply the result by 10^{-n}. For example, the number 0.012 is written in scientific notation as 1.2×10^{-2}:

$$0.012 = 1.2 \times 10^{-2} \quad \text{Number of places decimal point was shifted to the right}$$

Shift decimal point to the right by 2 places to get a number between 1 and 10

When you shift the decimal point to the right by two places, you are in effect multiplying the number by $10 \times 10 = 100 = 10^2$. Therefore, you must multiply the result by 10^{-2} so that the value of the number is unchanged. ($10^2 \times 10^{-2} = 10^0 = 1$.)

The following table gives some additional examples. To convert from scientific notation to ordinary notation, simply reverse the preceding process. Thus, to write the number 5.84×10^4 in ordinary notation, drop the factor of 10^4 and move the decimal point by 4 places to the *right* ($5.84 \times 10^4 = 58,400$). To write the number 3.5×10^{-1} in ordinary notation, drop the factor of 10^{-1} and move the decimal point by 1 place to the *left* ($3.5 \times 10^{-1} = 0.35$). Note that you don't need scientific notation for numbers between 1 and 10 because $10^0 = 1$.

Number	Scientific Notation
58,400	5.84×10^4
0.35	3.5×10^{-1}
7.296	$7.296 \times 10^0 = 7.296$

Addition and Subtraction

To add or subtract two numbers expressed in scientific notation, both numbers must have the same exponent. Thus, to add 7.16×10^3 and 1.32×10^2, first write the latter number as 0.132×10^3 and then add:

$$
\begin{array}{r}
7.16 \ \times 10^3 \\
+0.132 \times 10^3 \\
\hline
7.29 \ \times 10^3
\end{array}
$$

The answer has three significant figures. (Significant figures are discussed in Section 1.12.) Alternatively, you can write the first number as 71.6×10^2 and then add:

$$
\begin{array}{r}
71.6 \ \times 10^2 \\
+1.32 \times 10^2 \\
\hline
72.9 \ \times 10^2 = 7.29 \times 10^3
\end{array}
$$

Multiplication and Division

To multiply two numbers expressed in scientific notation, multiply the factors in front of the powers of 10 and then add the exponents:

$$(A \times 10^n)(B \times 10^m) = AB \times 10^{n+m}$$

For example,

$$(2.5 \times 10^4)(4.7 \times 10^7) = (2.5)(4.7) \times 10^{4+7} = 12 \times 10^{11} = 1.2 \times 10^{12}$$

$$(3.46 \times 10^5)(2.2 \times 10^{-2}) = (3.46)(2.2) \times 10^{5+(-2)} = 7.6 \times 10^3$$

Both answers have two significant figures.

To divide two numbers expressed in scientific notation, divide the factors in front of the powers of 10 and then subtract the exponent in the denominator from the exponent in the numerator:

$$\frac{A \times 10^n}{B \times 10^m} = \frac{A}{B} \times 10^{n-m}$$

For example,

$$\frac{3 \times 10^6}{7.2 \times 10^2} = \frac{3}{7.2} \times 10^{6-2} = 0.4 \times 10^4 = 4 \times 10^3 \qquad \text{(1 significant figure)}$$

$$\frac{7.50 \times 10^{-5}}{2.5 \times 10^{-7}} = \frac{7.50}{2.5} \times 10^{-5-(-7)} = 3.0 \times 10^2 \qquad \text{(2 significant figures)}$$

Powers and Roots

To raise a number $A \times 10^n$ to a power m, raise the factor A to the power m and then multiply the exponent n by the power m:

$$(A \times 10^n)^m = A^m \times 10^{n \times m}$$

For example, 3.6×10^2 raised to the 3rd power is 4.7×10^7:

$$(3.6 \times 10^2)^3 = (3.6)^3 \times 10^{2 \times 3} = 47 \times 10^6 = 4.7 \times 10^7 \qquad \text{(2 significant figures)}$$

To take the mth root of a number $A \times 10^n$, raise the number to the power $1/m$. That is, raise factor A to the power $1/m$ and then divide the exponent n by the root m:

$$\sqrt[m]{A \times 10^n} = (A \times 10^n)^{1/m} = A^{1/m} \times 10^{n/m}$$

For example, the square root of 9.0×10^8 is 3.0×10^4:

$$\sqrt[2]{9.0 \times 10^8} = (9.0 \times 10^8)^{1/2} = (9.0)^{1/2} \times 10^{8/2} = 3.0 \times 10^4 \quad \text{(2 significant figures)}$$

Because the exponent in the answer (n/m) is an integer, we must sometimes rewrite the original number by shifting the decimal point so that the exponent n is an integral multiple of the root m. For example, to take the cube root of 6.4×10^{10}, we first rewrite this number as 64×10^9 so that the exponent (9) is an integral multiple of the root 3:

$$\sqrt[3]{6.4 \times 10^{10}} = \sqrt[3]{64 \times 10^9} = (64)^{1/3} \times 10^{9/3} = 4.0 \times 10^3$$

Scientific Notation and Electronic Calculators

With a scientific calculator you can carry out calculations in scientific notation. You should consult the instruction manual for your particular calculator to learn how to enter and manipulate numbers expressed in an exponential format. On most calculators, you enter the number $A \times 10^n$ by (i) entering the number A, (ii) pressing a key labeled EXP or EE, and (iii) entering the exponent n. If the exponent is negative, you press a key labeled $+/-$ before entering the value of n. (Note that you do not enter the number 10.) The calculator displays the number $A \times 10^n$ with the number A on the left followed by some space and then the exponent n. For example,

$$4.625 \times 10^2 \quad \text{is displayed as} \quad 4.625 \quad 02$$

To add, subtract, multiply, or divide exponential numbers, use the same sequence of keystrokes as you would in working with ordinary numbers. When you add or subtract on a calculator, the numbers need not have the same exponent; the calculator automatically takes account of the different exponents. Remember, though, that the calculator often gives more digits in the answer than the allowed number of significant figures. It's sometimes helpful to outline the calculation on paper, as in the preceding examples, in order to keep track of the number of significant figures.

Most calculators have x^2 and $\sqrt{x}$ keys for squaring a number and finding its square root. Just enter the number and press the appropriate key. You probably have a y^x (or a^x) key for raising a number to a power. To raise 4.625×10^2 to the 3rd power, for example, use the following keystrokes: (i) enter the number 4.625×10^2 in the usual way, (ii) press the y^x key, (iii) enter the power 3, and (iv) press the $=$ key. The result is displayed as 9.8931641 07, but it must be rounded to 4 significant figures. Therefore, $(4.625 \times 10^2)^3 = 9.893 \times 10^7$.

To take the mth root of a number, raise the number to the power $1/m$. For example, to take the 5th root of 4.52×10^{11}, use the following keystrokes: (i) enter the number 4.52×10^{11}, (ii) press the y^x key, (iii) enter the number 5 (for the 5th root), (iv) press the $1/x$ key (to convert the 5th root to the power 1/5), and (v) press the $=$ key. The result is

$$\sqrt[5]{4.52 \times 10^{11}} = (4.52 \times 10^{11})^{1/5} = 2.14 \times 10^2$$

The calculator is able to handle the nonintegral exponent 11/5, and there is therefore no need to enter the number as 45.2×10^{10} so that the exponent is an integral multiple of the root 5.

▶ **PROBLEM A.1** Perform the following calculations, expressing the result in scientific notation with the correct number of significant figures. (You don't need a calculator for these.)

(a) $(1.50 \times 10^4) + (5.04 \times 10^3)$ (b) $(2.5 \times 10^{-2}) - (5.0 \times 10^{-3})$

(c) $(4.0 \times 10^4)^2$ (d) $\sqrt[3]{8 \times 10^{12}}$ (e) $\sqrt{2.5 \times 10^5}$

ANSWERS:

(a) 2.00×10^4 (b) 2.0×10^{-2} (c) 1.6×10^9 (d) 2×10^4 (e) $\pm 5.0 \times 10^2$

▶ **PROBLEM A.2** Perform the following calculations, expressing the result in scientific notation with the correct number of significant figures. (Use a calculator for these.)

(a) $(9.72 \times 10^{-1}) + (3.4823 \times 10^2)$ (b) $(3.772 \times 10^3) - (2.891 \times 10^4)$

(c) $(7.62 \times 10^{-3})^4$ (d) $\sqrt[3]{8.2 \times 10^7}$ (e) $\sqrt[5]{3.47 \times 10^{-12}}$

ANSWERS:

(a) 3.4920×10^2 (b) -2.514×10^4 (c) 3.37×10^{-9}

(d) 4.3×10^2 (e) 5.11×10^{-3}

A.2 LOGARITHMS

Common Logarithms

Any positive number x can be written as 10 raised to some power z—that is, $x = 10^z$. The exponent z is called the *common*, or *base 10*, *logarithm* of the number x and is denoted $\log_{10} x$, or simply $\log x$:

$$x = 10^z \qquad \log x = z$$

For example, 100 can be written as 10^2, and log 100 is therefore equal to 2:

$$100 = 10^2 \qquad \log 100 = 2$$

Similarly,

$$10 = 10^1 \qquad \log 10 = 1$$
$$1 = 10^0 \qquad \log 1 = 0$$
$$0.1 = 10^{-1} \qquad \log 0.1 = -1$$

In general, the logarithm of a number x is the power z to which 10 must be raised to equal the number x.

As **Figure A.1** shows, the logarithm of a number greater than 1 is positive, the logarithm of 1 is zero, and the logarithm of a positive number less than 1 is negative. The logarithm of a *negative* number is undefined because 10 raised to any power is always positive ($x = 10^z > 0$).

You can use a calculator to find the logarithm of a number that is not an integral power of 10. For example, to find the logarithm of 61.2, simply enter 61.2, and press the LOG key. The logarithm should be between 1 and 2 because 61.2 is between 10^1 and 10^2. The calculator gives a value of 1.786751422, which must be rounded to 1.787 because 61.2 has three significant figures.

Significant Figures and Common Logarithms

The only significant figures in a logarithm are the digits to the right of the decimal point; the number to the left of the decimal point is an exact number related to the integral power of 10 in the exponential expression for the number whose logarithm is

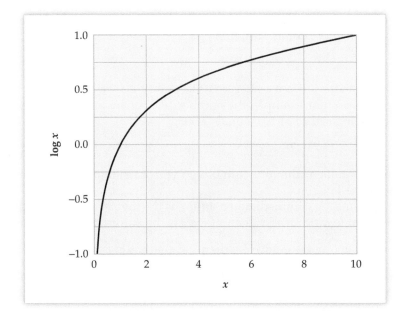

Values of log x for values of x in the range 0.1 to 10.

to be found. Thus, the logarithm of 61.2, which has three significant figures, can be written as follows:

$$\log \underbrace{61.2}_{} = \log (\underbrace{6.12}_{} \times 10^1) = \log 6.12 + \log 10^1 = \underbrace{0.787}_{} + 1 = 1.\underbrace{787}_{}$$

| 3 SF's | 3 SF's | Exact number | | 3 SF's | Exact number | Exact number | 3 SF's |

The digit (1) to the left of the decimal point in the logarithm (1.787) is an exact number and is not a significant figure; it merely indicates the location of the decimal point in the number 61.2. There are only three significant figures in the logarithm (7, 8, 7) because 61.2 has only three significant figures. Similarly, log 61 = 1.79 (2 significant figures), and log $(6 \times 10^1) = 1.8$ (1 significant figure).

Antilogarithms

The antilogarithm, denoted antilog, is the inverse of the common logarithm. If z is the logarithm of x, then x is the antilogarithm of z. But since x can be written as 10^z, the antilogarithm of z is 10^z:

$$\text{If} \quad z = \log x \quad \text{then} \quad x = \text{antilog } z = 10^z$$

In other words, the antilog of a number is 10 raised to a power equal to that number. For example, the antilog of 2 is $10^2 = 100$, and the antilog of 3.71 is $10^{3.71}$.

To find the value of antilog 3.71, use your calculator. If you have a 10^x key, enter 3.71 and press the 10^x key. If you have a y^x key, use the following keystrokes: (i) enter 10, (ii) press the y^x key, (iii) enter the exponent 3.71, and (iv) press the = key. If you have an INV (inverse) key, enter 3.71, press the INV key, and then press the LOG key. The calculator gives antilog 3.71 = 5.12861384×10^3, which must be rounded to 5.1×10^3 (2 significant figures) because the logarithm (3.71) has just two significant figures, the two digits to the right of the decimal point.

Natural Logarithms

The number $e = 2.718\ 28\ldots$, like $\pi = 3.141\ 59\ldots$, turns up in many scientific problems. It is therefore convenient to define a logarithm based on e, just as we defined a logarithm based on 10. Just as a number x can be written as 10^z, it can also be written as e^u. The exponent u is called the *natural*, or *base e, logarithm* of the number x and is denoted $\log_e x$, or more commonly, $\ln x$:

$$x = e^u \qquad \ln x = u$$

The natural logarithm of a number x is the power u to which e must be raised to equal the number x. For example, the number 10.0 can be written as $e^{2.303}$, and therefore the natural logarithm of 10.0 equals 2.303:

$$10.0 = e^{2.303} = (2.718\ 28...)^{2.303} \qquad \ln 10.0 = 2.303 \qquad \text{(3 significant figures)}$$

To find the natural logarithm of a number on your calculator, simply enter the number, and press the LN key.

The natural antilogarithm, denoted antiln, is the inverse of the natural logarithm. If u is the natural logarithm of x, then $x\,(=e^u)$ is the natural antilogarithm of u:

$$\text{If} \quad u = \ln x \qquad \text{then} \qquad x = \text{antiln } u = e^u$$

In other words, the natural antilogarithm of a number is e raised to a power equal to that number. For example, the natural antilogarithm of 3.71 is $e^{3.71}$, which equals 41:

$$\text{antiln } 3.71 = e^{3.71} = 41 \qquad \text{(2 significant figures)}$$

Your calculator probably has an INV (inverse) key or an e^x key. To find the natural antilogarithm of a number—say, 3.71—enter 3.71, press the INV key, and then press the LN key. Alternatively, you can enter 3.71, and press the e^x key.

Some Mathematical Properties of Logarithms

Because logarithms are exponents, the algebraic properties of exponents can be used to derive the following useful relationships involving logarithms:

1. The logarithm (either common or natural) of a product xy equals the sum of the logarithm of x and the logarithm of y:

$$\log xy = \log x + \log y \qquad \ln xy = \ln x + \ln y$$

2. The logarithm of a quotient x/y equals the difference between the logarithm of x and the logarithm of y :

$$\log \frac{x}{y} = \log x - \log y \qquad \ln \frac{x}{y} = \ln x - \ln y$$

It follows from these relationships that

$$\log \frac{y}{x} = -\log \frac{x}{y} \qquad \ln \frac{y}{x} = -\ln \frac{x}{y}$$

Because $\log 1 = \ln 1 = 0$, it also follows that

$$\log \frac{1}{x} = -\log x \qquad \ln \frac{1}{x} = -\ln x$$

3. The logarithm of x raised to a power a equals a times the logarithm of x:

$$\log x^a = a \log x \qquad \ln x^a = a \ln x$$

Similarly,

$$\log x^{1/a} = \frac{1}{a} \log x \qquad \ln x^{1/a} = \frac{1}{a} \ln x$$

where

$$x^{1/a} = \sqrt[a]{x}.$$

What is the numerical relationship between the common logarithm and the natural logarithm? To derive it, we begin with the definitions of $\log x$ and $\ln x$:

$$\log x = z \qquad \text{where} \qquad x = 10^z$$

$$\log x = u \qquad \text{where} \qquad x = e^u$$

We then write $\ln x$ in terms of 10^z and make use of the property that $\ln x^a = a \ln x$:

$$\ln x = \ln 10^z = z \ln 10$$

Because $z = \log x$ and $\ln 10.0 = 2.303$, we find that the natural logarithm is 2.303 times the common logarithm:

$$\ln x = 2.303 \log x$$

Since the natural and common logarithms differ by a factor of only 2.303, the same rule can be used to find the number of significant figures in both: The only digits that are significant figures in both natural and common logarithms are those to the right of the decimal point.

▶ **PROBLEM A.3**   Use a calculator to evaluate the following expressions, and round each result to the correct number of significant figures:

(a) $\log 705$ (b) $\ln (3.4 \times 10^{-6})$ (c) antilog (-2.56) (d) antiln 8.1

ANSWERS:

(a) 2.848   (b) −12.59   (c) 2.8×10^{-3} (d) 3×10^3

A.3 STRAIGHT-LINE GRAPHS AND LINEAR EQUATIONS

The results of a scientific experiment are often summarized in the form of a graph. Consider an experiment in which some property y is measured as a function of some variable x. (A real example would be measurement of the volume of a gas as a function of its temperature, but we'll use y and x to keep the discussion general.) Suppose that we obtain the following experimental data:

x	y
−1	−5
1	1
3	7
5	13

The graph in Figure A.2 shows values of x, called the independent variable, along the horizontal axis and values of y, the dependent variable, along the vertical axis. Each pair of experimental values of x and y is represented by a point on the graph. For this particular experiment, the four data points lie on a straight line.

The equation of a straight line can be written as

$$y = mx + b$$

where m is the slope of the line and b is the intercept, the value of y at the point where the line crosses the y axis—that is, the value of y when $x = 0$. The slope of the line is the change in $y(\Delta y)$ for a given change in $x(\Delta x)$:

$$m = \text{slope} = \frac{\Delta y}{\Delta x}$$

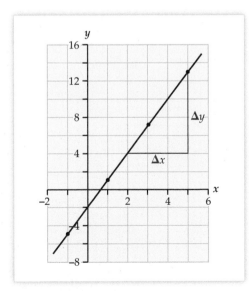

Figure A.2
A straight-line y versus x plot of the data in the table.

The right-triangle in Figure A.2 shows that y changes from 4 to 13 when x changes from 2 to 5. Therefore, the slope of the line is 3:

$$m = \text{slope} = \frac{\Delta y}{\Delta x} = \frac{13 - 4}{5 - 2} = \frac{9}{3} = 3$$

The graph shows a y intercept of $-2\,(b = -2)$, and the equation of the line is therefore

$$y = 3x - 2$$

An equation of the form $y = mx + b$ is called a *linear equation* because values of x and y that satisfy such an equation are the coordinates of points that lie on a straight line. We also say that y is a *linear function* of x, or that y is *directly proportional* to x. In our example, the rate of change of y is 3 times that of x.

A.4 QUADRATIC EQUATIONS

A quadratic equation is an equation that can be written in the form

$$ax^2 + bx + c = 0$$

where a, b, and c are constants. The equation contains only powers of x and is called quadratic because the highest power of x is 2. The solutions to a quadratic equation (values of x that satisfy the equation) are given by the *quadratic formula*:

$$x = \frac{-b \pm \sqrt{b^2 - 4ac}}{2a}$$

The $\pm$ indicates that there are two solutions, one given by the $+$ sign and the other given by the $-$ sign.

As an example, let's solve the equation

$$x^2 = \frac{2 - 6x}{3}$$

First, we put the equation into the form $ax^2 + bx + c = 0$ by multiplying it by 3 and moving $2 - 6x$ to the left side. The result is

$$3x^2 + 6x - 2 = 0$$

Then we apply the quadratic formula with $a = 3$, $b = 6$, and $c = -2$:

$$x = \frac{-6 \pm \sqrt{(6)^2 - 4(3)(-2)}}{2(3)}$$

$$= \frac{-6 \pm \sqrt{36 + 24}}{6} = \frac{-6 \pm \sqrt{60}}{6} = \frac{-6 \pm 7.746}{6}$$

The two solutions are

$$x = \frac{-6 + 7.746}{6} = \frac{1.746}{6} = 0.291 \quad \text{and} \quad x = \frac{-6 - 7.746}{6} = \frac{-13.746}{6} = -2.291$$

APPENDIX B

Thermodynamic Properties at 25 °C

TABLE B.1   Inorganic Substances

Substance and State	$\Delta H°_f$ (kJ/mol)	$\Delta G°_f$ (kJ/mol)	$S°$ [J/(K·mol)]	Substance and State	$\Delta H°_f$ (kJ/mol)	$\Delta G°_f$ (kJ/mol)	$S°$ [J/(K·mol)]
Aluminum				*Calcium*			
Al(s)	0	0	28.3	Ca(s)	0	0	41.4
Al(g)	330.0	289.4	164.5	Ca(g)	177.8	144.0	154.8
AlCl$_3$(s)	−704.2	−628.8	109.3	Ca^{2+}(aq)	−542.8	−553.6	−53.1
Al$_2$O$_3$(s)	−1676	−1582	50.9	CaF$_2$(s)	−1228.0	−1175.6	68.5
				CaCl$_2$(s)	−795.4	−748.8	108.4
Barium				CaH$_2$(s)	−181.5	−142.5	41.4
Ba(s)	0	0	62.5	CaC$_2$(s)	−59.8	−64.8	70.0
Ba(g)	180.0	146.0	170.1	CaO(s)	−634.9	−603.3	38.1
Ba^{2+}(aq)	−537.6	−560.8	9.6	Ca(OH)$_2$(s)	−985.2	−897.5	83.4
BaCl$_2$(s)	−855.0	−806.7	123.7	CaCO$_3$(s)	−1207.6	−1129.1	91.7
BaO(s)	−548.0	−520.3	72.1	CaSO$_4$(s)	−1434.1	−1321.9	107
BaCO$_3$(s)	−1213.0	−1134.4	112.1	Ca$_3$(PO$_4$)$_2$(s)	−4120.8	−3884.7	236.0
BaSO$_4$(s)	−1473.2	−1362.2	132.2				
Beryllium							
Be(s)	0	0	9.5	*Carbon*			
BeO(s)	−609.4	−580.1	13.8	C(s, graphite)	0	0	5.7
Be(OH)$_2$(s)	−902.5	−815.0	45.5	C(s, diamond)	1.9	2.9	2.4
				C(g)	716.7	671.3	158.0
Boron				CO(g)	−110.5	−137.2	197.6
B(s)	0	0	5.9	CO$_2$(g)	−393.5	−394.4	213.6
BF$_3$(g)	−1136.0	−1119.4	254.3	CO$_2$(aq)	−413.8	−386.0	117.6
BCl$_3$(g)	−403.8	−388.7	290.0	CO$_3^{2-}$(aq)	−677.1	−527.8	−56.9
B$_2$H$_6$(g)	36.4	87.6	232.0	HCO$_3^-$(aq)	−692.0	−586.8	91.2
B$_2$O$_3$(s)	−1273.5	−1194.3	54.0	H$_2$CO$_3$(aq)	−699.7	−623.2	187.4
H$_3$BO$_3$(s)	−1094.3	−968.9	90.0	HCN(l)	108.9	125.0	112.8
				HCN(g)	135.1	124.7	201.7
Bromine				CS$_2$(l)	89.0	64.6	151.3
Br(g)	111.9	82.4	174.9	CS$_2$(g)	116.7	67.1	237.7
Br$^-$(aq)	−121.5	−104.0	82.4	COCl$_2$(g)	−219.1	−204.9	283.4
Br$_2$(l)	0	0	152.2				
Br$_2$(g)	30.9	3.14	245.4				
HBr(g)	−36.3	−53.4	198.6				
Cadmium				*Cesium*			
Cd(s)	0	0	51.8	Cs(s)	0	0	85.2
Cd(g)	111.8	77.3	167.6	Cs(g)	76.5	49.6	175.6
Cd^{2+}(aq)	−75.9	−77.6	−73.2	Cs$^+$(aq)	−258.3	−292.0	133.1
CdCl$_2$(s)	−391.5	−343.9	115.3	CsF(s)	−553.5	−525.5	92.8
CdO(s)	−258.4	−228.7	54.8	CsCl(s)	−443.0	−414.5	101.2
CdS(s)	−161.9	−156.5	64.9	CsBr(s)	−405.8	−391.4	113.1
CdSO$_4$(s)	−933.3	−822.7	123.0	CsI(s)	−346.6	−340.6	123.1

(continued)

TABLE B.1   Inorganic Substances (*continued*)

Substance and State	$\Delta H°_f$ (kJ/mol)	$\Delta G°_f$ (kJ/mol)	$S°$ [J/(K · mol)]	Substance and State	$\Delta H°_f$ (kJ/mol)	$\Delta G°_f$ (kJ/mol)	$S°$ [J/(K · mol)]
Chlorine				*Iron*			
$Cl(g)$	121.3	105.3	165.1	$Fe(s)$	0	0	27.3
$Cl^-(aq)$	−167.2	−131.3	56.5	$Fe(g)$	416.3	370.3	180.5
$Cl_2(g)$	0	0	223.0	$FeCl_2(s)$	−341.8	−302.3	118.0
$HCl(g)$	−92.3	−95.3	186.8	$FeCl_3(s)$	−399.5	−334.0	142.3
$HCl(aq)$	−167.2	−131.2	56.5	$FeO(s)$	−272	−255	61
$ClO_2(g)$	102.5	120.5	256.7	$Fe_2O_3(s)$	−824.2	−742.2	87.4
$Cl_2O(g)$	80.3	97.9	266.1	$Fe_3O_4(s)$	−1118	−1015	146
Chromium				$FeS_2(s)$	−178.2	−166.9	52.9
$Cr(s)$	0	0	23.8	*Lead*			
$Cr(g)$	396.6	351.8	174.4	$Pb(s)$	0	0	64.8
$Cr_2O_3(s)$	−1140	−1058	81.2	$Pb(g)$	195.2	162.2	175.3
Cobalt				$PbCl_2(s)$	−359.4	−314.1	136.0
$Co(s)$	0	0	30.0	$PbBr_2(s)$	−278.7	−261.9	161.5
$Co(g)$	424.7	380.3	179.4	$PbO(s)$	−217.3	−187.9	68.7
$CoO(s)$	−237.9	−214.2	53.0	$PbO_2(s)$	−277	−217.4	68.6
Copper				$PbS(s)$	−100	−98.7	91.2
$Cu(s)$	0	0	33.1	$PbCO_3(s)$	−699.1	−625.5	131.0
$Cu(g)$	337.4	297.7	166.3	$PbSO_4(s)$	−919.9	−813.2	148.6
$Cu^{2+}(aq)$	64.8	65.5	−99.6	*Lithium*			
$CuCl(s)$	−137.2	−119.9	86.2	$Li(s)$	0	0	29.1
$CuCl_2(s)$	−220.1	−175.7	108.1	$Li(g)$	159.3	126.6	138.7
$CuO(s)$	−157.3	−129.7	42.6	$Li^+(aq)$	−278.5	−293.3	13
$Cu_2O(s)$	−168.6	−146.0	93.1	$LiF(s)$	−616.0	−587.7	35.7
$CuS(s)$	−53.1	−53.6	66.5	$LiCl(s)$	−408.6	−384.4	59.3
$Cu_2S(s)$	−79.5	−86.2	120.9	$LiBr(s)$	−351.2	−342.0	74.3
$CuSO_4(s)$	−771.4	−662.2	109.2	$LiI(s)$	−270.4	−270.3	86.8
Fluorine				$Li_2O(s)$	−597.9	−561.2	37.6
$F(g)$	79.4	62.3	158.7	$LiOH(s)$	−487.5	−441.5	42.8
$F^-(aq)$	−332.6	−278.8	−13.8	*Magnesium*			
$F_2(g)$	0	0	202.7	$Mg(s)$	0	0	32.7
$HF(g)$	−273.3	−275.4	173.7	$Mg(g)$	147.1	112.5	148.6
Hydrogen				$MgCl_2(s)$	−641.6	−591.8	89.6
$H(g)$	218.0	203.3	114.6	$MgO(s)$	−601.7	−569.4	26.9
$H^+(aq)$	0	0	0	$MgCO_3(s)$	−1096	−1012	65.7
$H_2(g)$	0	0	130.6	$MgSO_4(s)$	−1284.9	−1170.6	91.6
$OH^-(aq)$	−230.0	−157.3	−10.8	*Manganese*			
$H_2O(l)$	−285.8	−237.2	69.9	$Mn(s)$	0	0	32.0
$H_2O(g)$	−241.8	−228.6	188.7	$Mn(g)$	280.7	238.5	173.6
$H_2O_2(l)$	−187.8	−120.4	110	$MnO(s)$	−385.2	−362.9	59.7
$H_2O_2(g)$	−136.3	−105.6	232.6	$MnO_2(s)$	−520.0	−465.1	53.1
$H_2O_2(aq)$	−191.2	−134.1	144	*Mercury*			
Iodine				$Hg(l)$	0	0	76.0
$I(g)$	106.8	70.3	180.7	$Hg(g)$	61.32	31.85	174.8
$I^-(aq)$	−55.2	−51.6	111	$Hg^{2+}(aq)$	171.1	164.4	−32.2
$I_2(s)$	0	0	116.1	$Hg_2^{2+}(aq)$	172.4	153.5	84.5
$I_2(g)$	62.4	19.4	260.6	$HgCl_2(s)$	−224.3	−178.6	146.0
$HI(g)$	26.5	1.7	206.5	$Hg_2Cl_2(s)$	−265.4	−210.7	191.6

TABLE B.1   Inorganic Substances (*continued*)

Substance and State	$\Delta H°_f$ (kJ/mol)	$\Delta G°_f$ (kJ/mol)	$S°$ [J/(K·mol)]	Substance and State	$\Delta H°_f$ (kJ/mol)	$\Delta G°_f$ (kJ/mol)	$S°$ [J/(K·mol)]
$HgO(s)$	−90.8	−58.6	70.3	*Potassium*			
$HgS(s)$	−58.2	−50.6	82.4	$K(s)$	0	0	64.7
				$K(g)$	89.2	60.6	160.2
Nickel				$K^+(aq)$	−252.4	−283.3	102.5
$Ni(s)$	0	0	29.9	$KF(s)$	−567.3	−537.8	66.6
$Ni(g)$	429.7	384.5	182.1	$KCl(s)$	−436.5	−408.5	82.6
$NiCl_2(s)$	−305.3	−259.1	97.7	$KBr(s)$	−393.8	−380.7	95.9
$NiO(s)$	−240	−212	38.0	$KI(s)$	−327.9	−324.9	106.3
$NiS(s)$	−82.0	−79.5	53.0	$K_2O(s)$	−361.5		
				$K_2O_2(s)$	−494.1	−425.1	102.1
Nitrogen				$KO_2(s)$	−284.9	−239.4	116.7
$N(g)$	472.7	455.6	153.2	$KOH(s)$	−424.6	−379.4	81.2
$N_2(g)$	0	0	191.5	$KOH(aq)$	−482.4	−440.5	91.6
$NH_3(g)$	−46.1	−16.5	192.3	$KClO_3(s)$	−397.7	−296.3	143.1
$NH_3(aq)$	−80.3	−26.6	111	$KClO_4(s)$	−432.8	−303.1	151.0
$NH_4^+(aq)$	−132.5	−79.4	113	$KNO_3(s)$	−494.6	−394.9	133.1
$N_2H_4(l)$	50.6	149.2	121.2				
$N_2H_4(g)$	95.4	159.3	238.4	*Rubidium*			
$NO(g)$	91.3	87.6	210.7	$Rb(s)$	0	0	76.8
$NO_2(g)$	33.2	51.3	240.0	$Rb(g)$	80.9	53.1	170.0
$N_2O(g)$	82.0	104.2	219.7	$Rb^+(aq)$	−251.2	−284.0	121.5
$N_2O_4(g)$	11.1	99.8	304.3	$RbF(s)$	−557.7		
$N_2O_5(g)$	13.3	117.1	355.6	$RbCl(s)$	−435.4	−407.8	95.9
$NOCl(g)$	51.7	66.1	261.6	$RbBr(s)$	−394.6	−381.8	110.0
$NO_2Cl(g)$	12.6	54.4	272.1	$RbI(s)$	−333.8	−328.9	118.4
$HNO_3(l)$	−174.1	−80.8	155.6				
$HNO_3(g)$	−133.9	−73.5	266.8	*Selenium*			
$HNO_2(aq)$	−119	−50.6	136	$Se(s, black)$	0	0	42.44
$HNO_3(aq)$	−207.4	−111.3	146.4	$H_2Se(g)$	29.7	15.9	219.0
$NO_3^-(aq)$	−207.4	−111.3	146.4				
$NH_4Cl(s)$	−314.4	−202.9	94.6	*Silicon*			
$NH_4NO_3(s)$	−365.6	−184.0	151.1	$Si(s)$	0	0	18.8
				$Si(g)$	450.0	405.5	167.9
Oxygen				$SiF_4(g)$	−1615.0	−1572.8	282.7
$O(g)$	249.2	231.7	160.9	$SiCl_4(l)$	−687.0	−619.8	239.7
$O_2(g)$	0	0	205.0	$SiO_2(s, quartz)$	−910.7	−856.3	41.5
$O_3(g)$	143	163	238.8				
				Silver			
Phosphorus				$Ag(s)$	0	0	42.6
$P(s, white)$	0	0	41.1	$Ag(g)$	284.9	246.0	173.0
$P(s, red)$	−18	−12	22.8	$Ag^+(aq)$	105.6	77.1	72.7
$P_4(g)$	58.9	24.5	279.9	$AgF(s)$	−204.6		
$PH_3(g)$	5.4	13.5	210.1	$AgCl(s)$	−127.1	−109.8	96.2
$PCl_3(l)$	−319.7	−272.3	217.1	$AgBr(s)$	−100.4	−96.9	107.1
$PCl_3(g)$	−287.0	−267.8	311.7	$AgI(s)$	−61.8	−66.2	115.5
$PCl_5(s)$	−443.5			$Ag_2O(s)$	−31.1	−11.2	121.3
$PCl_5(g)$	−374.9	−305.0	364.5	$Ag_2S(s)$	−32.6	−40.7	144.0
$P_4O_{10}(s)$	−2984	−2698	228.9	$AgNO_3(s)$	−124.4	−33.4	140.9
$PO_4^{3-}(aq)$	−1277.4	−1018.7	−220.5				
$HPO_4^{2-}(aq)$	−1292.1	−1089.2	−33.5	*Sodium*			
$H_2PO_4^-(aq)$	−1296.3	−1130.2	90.4	$Na(s)$	0	0	51.2
$H_3PO_4(s)$	−1284.4	−1124.3	110.5	$Na(g)$	107.3	76.8	153.6

(*continued*)

TABLE B.1   Inorganic Substances (*continued*)

Substance and State	$\Delta H°_f$ (kJ/mol)	$\Delta G°_f$ (kJ/mol)	$S°$ [J/(K · mol)]	Substance and State	$\Delta H°_f$ (kJ/mol)	$\Delta G°_f$ (kJ/mol)	$S°$ [J/(K · mol)]
$Na^+(aq)$	−240.1	−261.9	59.0	*Tin*			
$NaF(s)$	−576.6	−546.3	51.1	$Sn(s, white)$	0	0	51.2
$NaCl(s)$	−411.2	−384.2	72.1	$Sn(s, gray)$	−2.1	0.1	44.1
$NaBr(s)$	−361.1	−349.0	86.8	$Sn(g)$	301.2	266.2	168.4
$NaI(s)$	−287.8	−286.1	98.5	$SnCl_4(l)$	−511.3	−440.1	258.6
$NaH(s)$	−56.3	−33.5	40.0	$SnCl_4(g)$	−471.5	−432.2	365.8
$Na_2O(s)$	−414.2	−375.5	75.1	$SnO(s)$	−280.7	−251.9	57.4
$Na_2O_2(s)$	−510.9	−447.7	95.0	$SnO_2(s)$	−577.6	−515.8	49.0
$NaO_2(s)$	−260.2	−218.4	115.9				
$NaOH(s)$	−425.6	−379.5	64.5	*Titanium*			
$NaOH(aq)$	−470.1	−419.2	48.2	$Ti(s)$	0	0	30.6
$Na_2CO_3(s)$	−1130.7	−1044.5	135.0	$Ti(g)$	473.0	428.4	180.2
$NaHCO_3(s)$	−950.8	−851.0	102	$TiCl_4(l)$	−804.2	−737.2	252.3
$NaNO_3(s)$	−467.9	−367.0	116.5	$TiCl_4(g)$	−763.2	−726.3	353.2
$NaNO_3(aq)$	−447.5	−373.2	205.4	$TiO_2(s)$	−944.0	−888.8	50.6
$Na_2SO_4(s)$	−1387.1	−1270.2	149.6				
				Tungsten			
Sulfur				$W(s)$	0	0	32.6
$S(s, rhombic)$	0	0	31.8	$W(g)$	849.4	807.1	174.0
$S(s, monoclinic)$	0.3			$WO_3(s)$	−842.9	−764.0	75.9
$S(g)$	277.2	236.7	167.7				
$S_2(g)$	128.6	79.7	228.2	*Zinc*			
$H_2S(g)$	−20.6	−33.6	205.7	$Zn(s)$	0	0	41.6
$H_2S(aq)$	−39.7	−27.9	121	$Zn(g)$	130.4	94.8	160.9
$HS^-(aq)$	−17.6	12.1	62.8	$Zn^{2+}(aq)$	−153.9	−147.1	−112.1
$SO_2(g)$	−296.8	−300.2	248.1	$ZnCl_2(s)$	−415.1	−369.4	111.5
$SO_3(g)$	−395.7	−371.1	256.6	$ZnO(s)$	−350.5	−320.5	43.7
$H_2SO_4(l)$	−814.0	−690.1	156.9	$ZnS(s)$	−206.0	−201.3	57.7
$H_2SO_4(aq)$	−909.3	−744.6	20	$ZnSO_4(s)$	−982.8	−871.5	110.5
$HSO_4^-(aq)$	−887.3	−756.0	132				
$SO_4^{2-}(aq)$	−909.3	−744.6	20				

TABLE B.2 Organic Substances

Substance and State	Formula	$\Delta H°_f$ (kJ/mol)	$\Delta G°_f$ (kJ/mol)	$S°$ [J/(K · mol)]
Acetaldehyde(g)	CH_3CHO	−166.2	−133.0	263.8
Acetic acid(l)	CH_3CO_2H	−484.5	−390	160
Acetylene(g)	C_2H_2	227.4	209.9	200.8
Benzene(l)	C_6H_6	49.1	124.5	173.4
Butane(g)	C_4H_{10}	−126	−17	310
Carbon tetrachloride(l)	CCl_4	−135.4	−65.3	216.4
Dichloroethane(l)	CH_2ClCH_2Cl	−165.2	−79.6	208.5
Ethane(g)	C_2H_6	−84.0	−32.0	229.1
Ethanol(l)	C_2H_5OH	−277.7	−174.9	161
Ethanol(g)	C_2H_5OH	−234.8	−167.9	281.5
Ethylene(g)	C_2H_4	52.3	68.1	219.5
Ethylene oxide(g)	C_2H_4O	−52.6	−13.1	242.4
Formaldehyde(g)	$HCHO$	−108.6	−102.5	218.8
Formic acid(l)	HCO_2H	−424.7	−361.4	129.0
Glucose(s)	$C_6H_{12}O_6$	−1273.3	−910	209.2
Methane(g)	CH_4	−74.8	−50.8	186.2
Methanol(l)	CH_3OH	−239.2	−166.6	127
Methanol(g)	CH_3OH	−201.0	−162.3	239.8
Propane(g)	C_3H_8	−103.8	−23.4	270.2
Vinyl chloride(g)	$CH_2{=}CHCl$	35	51.9	263.9

Properties of Water

Normal melting point	0 °C = 273.15 K
Normal boiling point	100 °C = 373.15 K
Heat of fusion	6.01 kJ/mol at 0 °C
Heat of vaporization	44.94 kJ/mol at 0 °C
	44.02 kJ/mol at 25 °C
	40.67 kJ/mol at 100 °C
Specific heat	4.179 J/(g · °C) at 25 °C
Ion-product constant, K_w	1.15×10^{-15} at 0 °C
	1.01×10^{-14} at 25 °C
	5.43×10^{-13} at 100 °C

TABLE E.1 Vapor Pressure of Water at Various Temperatures

Temp (°C)	P_{vap} (mm Hg)	Temp (°C)	P_{vap} (mm Hg)
0	4.58	60	149.4
10	9.21	70	233.7
20	17.5	80	355.1
30	31.8	90	525.9
40	55.3	100	760.0
50	92.5	105	906.0

Answers to Selected Problems

Chapter 1

1.1 (a) Cd; (b) Sb; (c) Am **1.2** (a) silver; (b) rhodium; (c) rhenium; (d) cesium; (e) argon; (f) arsenic **1.3** (a) Ti, metal; (b) Te, semimetal; (c) Se, nonmetal; (d) Sc, metal; (e) At, semimetal; (f) Ar, nonmetal **1.4** copper (Cu), silver (Ag), and gold (Au) **1.5** (a) 3.72×10^{-10} m; (b) 1.5×10^{11} m **1.6** (a) microgram; (b) decimeter; (c) picosecond; (d) kiloampere; (e) millimole **1.7** 37.0 °C; 310.2 K **1.8** (a) 195 K; (b) 316 °F; (c) 215 °F **1.9** 2.212 g/cm^3 **1.10** 6.32 mL **1.11** 428 kJ **1.12** (a) 2300 kJ; (b) 6.3 h **1.13** The results are both precise and accurate. **1.14** (a) 5 significant figures; (b) 6 significant figures; (c) 1, 2, 3, or 4 significant figures; (d) 3 significant figures; (e) 18 students is an exact number; (f) 1 significant figure; (g) 4 significant figures; (h) 3 or 4 significant figures **1.15** (a) 3.774 L; (b) 255 K; (c) 55.26 kg; (d) 906.40 kJ **1.16** (a) 24.612 g; (b) 1.26×10^3 g/L; (c) 41.1 mL **1.17** 32.6 °C (3 significant figures) **1.18** (a) 1947 °F; (b) 6×10^{-11} cm^3 **1.19** 8.88 g; 0.313 ounces **1.20** 2.52 cm^3; 4.45×10^{23} C atoms. **1.21** 300 g

Conceptual Problems

1.22

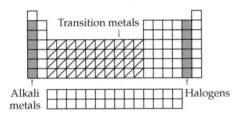

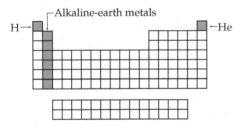

1.24 red—gas; blue—42; green—lithium, sodium, potassium or rubidium are possible answers **1.26** (a) good precision, poor accuracy; (b) good precision, good accuracy; (c) poor precision, poor accuracy **1.28** The 5 mL graduated cylinder will give more accurate measurements. *Section Problems* **1.30** 118 elements are presently known. About 90 elements occur naturally. **1.32** There are 18 groups in the periodic table. They are labeled as follows: 1A, 2A, 3B, 4B, 5B, 6B, 7B, 8B (3 groups), 1B, 2B, 3A, 4A, 5A, 6A, 7A, 8A.

1.34

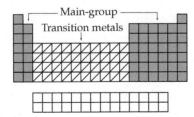

1.36

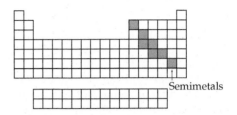

1.38 Li, Na, K, Rb, and Cs **1.40** F, Cl, Br, and I **1.42** a metal **1.44** All match in groups 2A and 7A. **1.46** (a) Gd; (b) Ge; (c) Tc; (d) As **1.48** (a) tellurium; (b) rhenium; (c) beryllium; (d) argon; (e) plutonium **1.50** (a) Tin is Sn, Ti is titanium; (b) Manganese is Mn, Mg is magnesium; (c) Potassium is K, Po is polonium; (d) The symbol for helium is He. **1.52** Mass measures the amount of matter in an object, whereas weight measures the pull of gravity on an object by the earth or other celestial body. **1.54** (a) kilogram, kg; (b) meter, m; (c) kelvin, K; (d) cubic meter, m^3; (e) joule, (kg·m^2)/s^2; (f) kg/m^3 or g/cm^3 **1.56** A Celsius degree is larger than a Fahrenheit degree by a factor of 9/5. **1.58** The volume of a cubic decimeter (dm^3) and a liter (L) are the same. **1.60** (a) and (b) **1.62** cL is centiliter (10^{-2} L) **1.64** (a) 6.02×10^1 km; (b) 46 μs; (c) 200,098 g **1.66** 1×10^9 pg/mg; 3.5×10^4 pg/35 ng **1.68** (a) 5 pm = 5×10^{-10} cm = 5×10^{-3} nm; (b) 8.5 cm^3 = 8.5×10^{-6} m^3 = 8.5×10^3 mm^3; (c) 65.2 mg = 0.0652 g = 6.52×10^{10} pg **1.70** (a) 6 significant figures; (b) 6 significant figures; (c) 4 significant figures; (d) 3 significant figures; (e) 2, 3, 4, or 5 significant figures; (f) 5 significant figures **1.72** 3.6665×10^6 m^3. **1.74** (a) 4.5332×10^2 mg; (b) 4.21×10^{-5} mL; (c) 6.67×10^5 g **1.76** (a) 3.567×10^4 m (4 significant figures); 35,670.1 m (6 significant figures); (b) 69 g (2 significant figures); 68.5 g (3 significant figures); (c) 4.99×10^3 cm (3 significant figures); (d) 2.3098×10^{-4} kg (5 significant figures) **1.78** (a) 10.0; (b) 26; (c) 0.039; (d) 5526; (e) 87.6; (f) 13 **1.80** 11.394 mi/hr **1.82** (a) 110 g; (b) 443.2 m; (c) 7.6181×10^{12} m^2 **1.84** (a) 43,560 ft^3; (b) 3.92×10^8 acre-ft **1.86** (a) 2000 mg/L; (b) 2000 μg/mL; (c) 2 g/L; (d) 2000 ng/μL; (e) 10 g **1.88** 0.61 cm/shake **1.90** 103.8 °F; 72.0 °F **1.92** 3422 °C; 3695 K **1.94** (a) 1.021 °E/°C; (b) 0.5675 °E/°F; (c) H$_2$O melting point = 119.8 °E; H$_2$O boiling point = 222.0 °E; (d) 157.6 °E; (e) Because the outside temperature is 50.0 °F, I would wear a sweater or light jacket. **1.96** 2500 kg **1.98** 0.18 cm^3; 162,000 cm^3 **1.100** 11 g/cm^3 **1.102** Car: 7.1×10^5 J; Truck: 6.7×10^5 J **1.104** 169 kcal *Chapter Problems* **1.106** 2.33 g/cm^3 **1.108** mp = 801 °C = 1474 °F; bp = 1413 °C = 2575 °F **1.110** 75.85 mL **1.112** (a) 0.958 61 g/mL; (b) 4047 m^2; (c) 1400 kg; (d) 140 kg; (e) 792 Cal from fat **1.114** (a) 200 kisses; (b) 3.3 mL; (c) 26 Cal/kiss; (d) 51% **1.116** The Celsius and Fahrenheit scales "cross" at −40 °C (−40 °F). **1.118** 5 tablets **1.120** 34.1 °C **1.122** 45.9 g **1.124** (a) metal; (b) indium; (c) 5.904 g/cm^3; (d) 355 °G

Chapter 2

2.1 3/2 **2.2** 2×10^4 Au atoms **2.3** 40 times **2.4** 34 p, 34 e$^-$, 41 n **2.5** $^{35}_{17}$Cl has 18 n; $^{37}_{17}$Cl has 20 n **2.6** $^{109}_{47}$Ag **2.7** 63.55 amu **2.8** 2.04×10^{22} Cu atoms **2.9** (a) 72.04 g Ti; (b) 7.75 g Na; (c) 614.8 g U

2.10 (a) 0.2405 mol Ti; (b) 1.2670 mol Na; (c) 6.205 mol U
2.11 (a) $^{106}_{44}Ru \rightarrow ^{0}_{-1}e + ^{106}_{45}Rh$; (b) $^{189}_{83}Bi \rightarrow ^{4}_{2}He + ^{185}_{81}Tl$;
(c) $^{204}_{84}Po + ^{0}_{-1}e \rightarrow ^{204}_{83}Bi$ **2.12** $^{4}_{2}He$ **2.13** $^{148}_{69}Tm$ decays to $^{148}_{68}Er$ by either
positron emission or electron capture. **2.14** (a) ^{199}Au decays by beta
emission. ^{173}Au decays by alpha emission; (b) ^{196}Pb decays by
positron emission. ^{206}Pb is nonradioactive.

2.15

$$
\begin{array}{c}
\quad\;\; H \quad\;\; H \\
\quad\;\; | \quad\;\;\; | \\
H-C-N-H \\
\quad\;\; | \\
\quad\;\; H
\end{array}
$$

2.16 $C_5H_{11}NO_2S$ **2.17** Figure (b) **2.18** $C_9H_{13}NO_3$ **2.19** (a) ionic;
(b) molecular; (c) molecular; (d) ionic **2.20** (a) ionic; (b) molecular
2.21 (a) cesium fluoride; (b) potassium oxide; (c) copper(II) oxide;
(d) barium sulfide; (e) beryllium bromide **2.22** (a) VCl_3; (b) MnO_2;
(c) CuS; (d) Al_2O_3 **2.23** red—potassium sulfide, K_2S;
green—strontium iodide, SrI_2; blue—gallium oxide, Ga_2O_3
2.24 (a) nitrogen trichloride; (b) tetraphosphorus hexoxide;
(c) disulfur difluoride; (d) selenium dioxide **2.25** (a) S_2Cl_2; (b) ICl;
(c) NI_3 **2.26** (a) phosphorus pentachloride; (b) dinitrogen monoxide
2.27 (a) calcium hypochlorite; (b) silver thiosulfate; (c) sodium
dihydrogen phosphate; (d) tin(II) nitrate; (e) lead(IV) acetate;
(f) ammonium sulfate **2.28** (a) Li_3PO_4; (b) $Mg(HSO_4)_2$;
(c) $Mn(NO_3)_2$; (d) $Cr_2(SO_4)_3$ **2.29** Drawing 1 $CaCl_2$; Drawing 2 LiBr
and $NaNO_2$ **2.30** H and He *Conceptual Problems* **2.32** Drawing
(a) represents a collection of SO_2 units. **2.34** Figures (b) and (d)
2.36 (a) $C_3H_7NO_2$; (b) $C_2H_6O_2$; (c) $C_2H_4O_2$ *Section Problems* **2.38**
The law of mass conservation in terms of Dalton's atomic theory
states that chemical reactions only rearrange the way that atoms are
combined; the atoms themselves are not changed. The law of
definite proportions in terms of Dalton's atomic theory states that
the chemical combination of elements to make different substances
occurs when atoms join together in small, whole-number ratios.
2.40 3.7 g

2.42

$$\frac{C:H \text{ mass ratio in benzene}}{C:H \text{ mass ratio in ethane}} = \frac{12}{4.00} = \frac{3}{1}$$

$$\frac{C:H \text{ mass ratio in benzene}}{C:H \text{ mass ratio in ethylene}} = \frac{12}{6.0} = \frac{2}{1}$$

$$\frac{C:H \text{ mass ratio in ethylene}}{C:H \text{ mass ratio in ethane}} = \frac{6.0}{4.00} = \frac{3}{2}$$

2.44 (a) benzene, CH; ethane, CH_3; ethylene, CH_2; (b) These
ratios are consistent with their modern formulas. **2.46** X g
2.48 5.27×10^{-4} x g **2.50** 1 Zn:1 S **2.52** The "other" compound
is not methane

$$\frac{C:H \text{ mass ratio in "other"}}{C:H \text{ mass ratio in methane}} = \frac{4}{3}$$

2.54 The atomic number is equal to the number of protons. The
mass number is equal to the sum of the number of protons and
the number of neutrons. **2.56** The subscript giving the atomic
number of an atom is often left off of an isotope symbol because
one can readily look up the atomic number in the periodic table.
2.58 ^{63}Cu **2.60** (a) carbon, C; (b) argon, Ar; (c) vanadium, V **2.62** (a)
$^{220}_{86}Rn$; (b) $^{210}_{84}Po$; (c) $^{197}_{79}Au$ **2.64** (a) 7 p, 7 e⁻, 8 n; (b) 27 p, 27 e⁻, 33 n;
(c) 53 p, 53 e⁻, 78 n; (d) 58 p, 58 e⁻, 84 n **2.66** (a) $^{24}_{12}Mg$, magnesium;
(b) $^{58}_{28}Ni$, nickel; (c) $^{104}_{46}Pd$, palladium; (d) $^{183}_{74}W$, tungsten **2.68** $^{12}_{5}C$;
$^{33}_{35}Br$; $^{11}_{5}Bo$ **2.70** 10.8 amu **2.72** 25.982 amu for ^{26}Mg;
2.74 Positron emission is the conversion of a proton in the nucleus
into a neutron plus an ejected positron. Electron capture is the
process in which a proton in the nucleus captures an inner-shell

electron and is thereby converted into a neutron. **2.76** In beta
emission a neutron is converted to a proton and the atomic number
increases. In positron emission a proton is converted to a neutron
and the atomic number decreases. **2.78** (a) $^{126}_{50}Sn \rightarrow ^{0}_{-1}e + ^{126}_{51}Sb$;
(b) $^{210}_{88}Ra \rightarrow ^{4}_{2}He + ^{206}_{86}Rn$; (c) $^{77}_{37}Rb \rightarrow ^{0}_{1}e + ^{77}_{36}Kr$;
(d) $^{76}_{36}Kr + ^{0}_{-1}e \rightarrow ^{76}_{35}Br$ **2.80** (a) $^{0}_{1}e$; (b) $^{4}_{2}He$; (c) $^{0}_{-1}e$
2.82 (a) $^{162}_{75}Re \rightarrow ^{158}_{73}Ta + ^{4}_{2}He$; (b) $^{138}_{62}Sm + ^{0}_{-1}e \rightarrow ^{138}_{61}Pm$;
(c) $^{188}_{74}W \rightarrow ^{188}_{73}Re + ^{0}_{-1}e$; (d) $^{165}_{73}Ta \rightarrow ^{165}_{72}Hf + ^{0}_{1}e$ **2.84** ^{160}W is neutron
poor and decays by alpha emission. ^{185}W is neutron rich and
decays by beta emission. **2.86** $^{237}_{93}Np$, $^{233}_{91}Pa$, $^{233}_{92}U$, $^{229}_{90}Th$, $^{225}_{88}Ra$, $^{225}_{89}Ac$,
$^{221}_{87}Fr$, $^{217}_{85}At$, $^{213}_{83}Bi$, $^{213}_{84}Po$, $^{209}_{82}Pb$, $^{209}_{83}Bi$ **2.88** 6 α, 4 β **2.90** A covalent
bond results when two atoms share several (usually two) of their
electrons. An ionic bond results from a complete transfer of one or
more electrons from one atom to another. The C—H bonds in
methane (CH_4) are covalent bonds. The bond in NaCl (Na^+Cl^-)
is an ionic bond. **2.92** Element symbols are composed of one or
two letters. If the element symbol is two letters, the first letter
is uppercase and the second is lowercase. CO stands for carbon
and oxygen in carbon monoxide. **2.94** (a) Be^{2+}, 4 p, 2 e⁻; (b) Rb^+,
37 p, 36 e⁻; (c) Se^{2-}, 34 p, 36 e⁻; (d) Au^{3+} 79 p, 76 e⁻ **2.96** C_3H_8O

2.98

$$
\begin{array}{c}
\;\; H \;\;\;\; H \;\;\;\; H \;\;\;\; H \\
\;\; | \;\;\;\;\; | \;\;\;\;\; | \;\;\;\;\; | \\
H-C-C-C-C-H \\
\;\; | \;\;\;\;\; | \;\;\;\;\; | \;\;\;\;\; | \\
\;\; H \;\;\;\; H \;\;\;\; H \;\;\;\; H
\end{array}
$$

2.100

$$
\begin{array}{c}
\;\;\;\;\;\; H \;\;\;\;\;\;\;\;\;\;\;\;\;\;\; H \\
\;\;\;\;\;\; | \;\;\;\;\;\;\;\;\;\;\;\;\;\;\; | \\
\;\; H-C-H \;\;\;\;\;\; H-C-H \\
\;\; H \;\;\; | \;\;\; H \;\;\;\;\;\;\; H \\
\;\; | \;\;\;\;\; | \;\;\; | \;\;\;\;\;\;\; | \\
H-C \;\;\;\; C \;\;\; C \;\;\;\; C \;\;\;\; C-H \\
\;\; | \;\;\;\;\; | \;\;\; | \;\;\;\;\;\;\; | \\
\;\; H \;\;\; | \;\;\; H \;\;\;\;\;\;\; H \\
\;\; H-C-H \\
\;\;\;\;\;\; | \\
\;\;\;\;\;\; H
\end{array}
$$

2.102 (a) KCl; (b) $SnBr_2$; (c) CaO; (d) $BaCl_2$; (e) AlH_3
2.104 (a) barium ion; (b) cesium ion; (c) vanadium(III) ion;
(d) hydrogen carbonate ion; (e) ammonium ion; (f) nickel(II) ion;
(g) nitrite ion; (h) chlorite ion; (i) manganese(II) ion; (j) perchlorate
ion **2.106** (a) $CaBr_2$; (b) $CaSO_4$; (c) $Al_2(SO_4)_3$ **2.108** (a) $CaCl_2$; (b) CaO;
(c) CaS **2.110** (a) SO_3^{2-}; (b) PO_4^{3-}; (c) Zr^{4+}; (d) CrO_4^{2-};
(e) $CH_3CO_2^-$; (f) $S_2O_3^{2-}$ **2.112** (a) NO, nitrogen monoxide; (b) N_2O,
dinitrogen monoxide; (c) NO_2, nitrogen dioxide; (d) N_2O_4,
dinitrogen tetroxide; (e) N_2O_5, dinitrogen pentoxide
2.114 (a) Na_2SO_4; (b) $Ba_3(PO_4)_2$; (c) $Ga_2(SO_4)_3$ *Chapter Problems*
2.116 72.6 amu **2.118** For NH_3, 0.505 g H; For N_2H_4, 0.337 g H
2.120 (a) I; (b) Kr **2.122** 12.0005 amu **2.124** 151.165 amu
2.126 $^{100}_{43}Tc \rightarrow ^{0}_{1}e + ^{100}_{42}Mo$ (positron emission); $^{100}_{43}Tc + ^{0}_{-1}e \rightarrow ^{100}_{42}Mo$
(electron capture)

2.128

$$
\begin{array}{c}
\;\; H \;\;\;\;\; O \;\;\;\;\; H \\
\;\;\; \backslash \;\;\; / \;\; \backslash \;\;\; / \\
\;\; H-C \;\;\;\;\;\;\;\; C-H \\
\;\;\;\;\; \backslash \;\;\;\;\;\;\;\; / \\
\;\;\;\;\;\; C-C \\
\;\; H \; / \;\;\;\; \backslash \; H \\
\;\;\;\; H \;\;\;\;\;\; H
\end{array}
$$

Chapter 3

3.1 $2 NaClO_3 \rightarrow 2 NaCl + 3 O_2$ **3.2** (a) $C_6H_{12}O_6 \rightarrow 2 C_2H_6O +$
$2 CO_2$; (b) $6 CO_2 + 6 H_2O \rightarrow C_6H_{12}O_6 + 6 O_2$; (c) $4 NH_3 + Cl_2 \rightarrow$
$N_2H_4 + 2 NH_4Cl$ **3.3** $3 A_2 + 2 B \rightarrow 2 BA_3$ **3.4** (a) 159.7 amu;
(b) 98.1 amu; (c) 192.1 amu; (d) 334.4 amu **3.5** 2.77×10^{-3} mol;
1.67×10^{21} molecules **3.6** (a) 3.33 g $C_4H_6O_3$; (b) 5.87 g $C_9H_8O_4$;

(c) 1.96 g CH_3CO_2H **3.7** 63% **3.8** 4220 g **3.9** Li_2O is the limiting reactant; 41 kg H_2O **3.10** 921 g CO_2 **3.11** (a) $A + B_2 \rightarrow AB_2$; A is the limiting reactant; (b) 1.0 mol of AB_2 **3.12** (a) 0.025 mol; (b) 1.62 mol **3.13** (a) 25.0 g; (b) 67.6 g **3.14** 690 mL **3.15** 1 g **3.16** 0.656 M **3.17** Dilute 6.94 mL of 18.0 M H_2SO_4 with enough water to make 250.0 mL of solution. **3.18** 10.0 mL **3.19** 5.47×10^{-2} M **3.20** 0.758 M **3.21** Because the two volumes are equal and the concentrations are proportional to the number of solute ions, $[OH^-] = 0.67$ M. **3.22** CH_4N; 39.9% C, 13.4% H, 46.6% N **3.23** $MgCO_3$ **3.24** 37.5% C, 4.21% H, 58.3% O **3.25** $C_{10}H_{20}O$ **3.26** $C_5H_{10}O_5$ **3.27** (a) B_2H_6; (b) $C_3H_6O_3$ **3.28** The assumptions that (i) the oil molecules are tiny cubes; (ii) the oil layer is one molecule thick; (iii) the molecular mass of 900 amu for the oil **3.29** 1.0×10^{24} molecules/mole *Conceptual Problems* **3.30** box (b) **3.32** 0.004 mol CO_2; 0.0025 mol H_2O **3.34** 309.36 amu **3.36** (a) $A_2 + 3B_2 \rightarrow 2AB_3$; B_2 is the limiting reactant; (b) 2/3 mol AB_3 *Section Problems* **3.38** Equation (b) is balanced, (a) is not balanced. **3.40** (a) $Mg + 2HNO_3 \rightarrow H_2 + Mg(NO_3)_2$; (b) $CaC_2 + 2H_2O \rightarrow Ca(OH)_2 + C_2H_2$; (c) $2S + 3O_2 \rightarrow 2SO_3$; (d) $UO_2 + 4HF \rightarrow UF_4 + 2H_2O$ **3.42** (a) $SiCl_4 + 2H_2O \rightarrow SiO_2 + 4HCl$; (b) $P_4O_{10} + 6H_2O \rightarrow 4H_3PO_4$; (c) $CaCN_2 + 3H_2O \rightarrow CaCO_3 + 2NH_3$; (d) $3NO_2 + H_2O \rightarrow 2HNO_3 + NO$ **3.44** (a) Hg_2Cl_2: 472.1 amu; (b) $C_4H_8O_2$: 88.1 amu; (c) CF_2Cl_2: 120.9 amu **3.46** (a) 558.7 amu; (b) 444.5 amu; (c) 321.8 amu **3.48** (a) 47.87 g; (b) 159.81 g; (c) 200.59 g; (d) 18.02 g **3.50** 0.867 mol **3.52** 119 amu **3.54** 1.97×10^{-3} mol $FeSO_4$; 1.19×10^{21} Fe(II) atoms **3.56** 6.44×10^{-4} mol; 3.88×10^{20} molecules **3.58** Ne **3.60** 166.8 kg **3.62** (a) $2Fe_2O_3 + 3C \rightarrow 4Fe + 3CO_2$; (b) 4.93 mol C; (c) 59.2 g C **3.64** (a) $2Mg + O_2 \rightarrow 2MgO$; (b) 16.5 g O_2, 41.5 g MgO; (c) 38.0 g Mg, 63.0 g MgO **3.66** (a) $2HgO \rightarrow 2Hg + O_2$; (b) 42.1 g Hg, 3.36 g O_2; (c) 451 g HgO **3.68** AgCl **3.70** (a) 581 g I_2; (b) 1847 g HI **3.72** 15.8 g NH_3, 83.3 g N_2 left over **3.74** 5.22 g $C_2H_4Cl_2$ **3.76** (a) 12.0 g H_2SO_4; (b) 14.9 g $NiSO_4$ **3.78** 0.526 L CO_2, $CaCO_3$ is the limiting reactant. **3.80** 3.2 g **3.82** 86.8% **3.84** (a) 0.0420 mol; (b) 0.12 mol **3.86** 160 mL **3.88** 0.0685 M **3.90** 0.958 M **3.92** 1.71 M **3.94** 15.5 g **3.96** 57.2 mL **3.98** 20.0% C, 6.72% H, 46.6% N, 26.6% O **3.100** C_7H_7Cl **3.102** SnF_2 **3.104** C_7H_8 **3.106** 13,000 amu **3.108** Disilane is Si_2H_6 **3.110** C_4H_6O **3.112** $C_{12}Br_{10}O$ *Chapter Problems* **3.114** Na^+, 0.147 M; Ca^{2+}, 0.002 98 M; K^+, 0.004 02 M; Cl^-, 0.157 M **3.116** (a) 5.1×10^{-11} mol/L; (b) 1.3×10^{13} g Au **3.118** (a) 39.99% C; 6.713% H; 53.27% O; (b) 2.055% H; 32.70% S; 65.25% O; (c) 24.75% K; 34.77% Mn; 40.51% O; (d) 45.89% C; 2.751% H; 7.647% N; 26.20% O; 17.51% S **3.120** (a) $6WCl_6 + 8Bi \rightarrow W_6Cl_{12} + 8BiCl_3$; (b) 105.4 g Bi; (c) 146 g W_6Cl_{12} **3.122** $C_{10}H_{10}Fe$ **3.124** Na^+, 0.295 M; Li^+, 0.0406 M; SO_4^{2-}, 0.0590 M; PO_4^{3-}, 0.0725 M **3.126** High resolution mass spectrometry is capable of measuring the mass of molecules with a particular isotopic composition. **3.128** 18.1 lb **3.130** $C_3H_{12}N_2Cl_2$ **3.132** The empirical formula is $C_7H_6O_3$; the molecular formula is $C_7H_6O_3$. **3.134** 0.63 g of benzoic acid and 0.37 g of gallic acid **3.136** 4.4 g Fe_2O_3; 5.6 g FeO **3.138** $C_6H_{12}O_6 + 6O_2 \rightarrow 6CO_2 + 6H_2O$; 97.2 g CO_2, 56.1 L CO_2 **3.140** (a) 79.91% Cu, 20.1% S; (b) Cu_2S; (c) 4.2×10^{22} Cu^+ ions/cm^3 **3.142** 5.32 g PCl_3, 4.68 g PCl_5 **3.144** The mass ratio of NH_4NO_3 to $(NH_4)_2HPO_4$ in the mixture is 2 to 1. **3.146** (a) 80 amu; Br; (b) 64 amu; Cu **3.148** (a) (i) $M_2O_3(s) + 3C(s) + 3Cl_2(g) \rightarrow 2MCl_3(l) + 3CO(g)$; (ii) $2MCl_3(l) + 3H_2(g) \rightarrow 2M(s) + 6HCl(g)$; (b) 10.8 amu; B; (c) 0.265 g

Chapter 4

4.1 (a) precipitation; (b) redox; (c) acid–base neutralization **4.2** 0.675 M **4.3** A_2Y is the strongest electrolyte because it is completely dissociated into ions. A_2X is the weakest electrolyte because it is the least dissociated. **4.4** (a) $2Ag^+(aq) + CrO_4^{2-}(aq) \rightarrow Ag_2CrO_4(s)$;

(b) $2H^+(aq) + MgCO_3(s) \rightarrow H_2O(l) + CO_2(g) + Mg^{2+}(aq)$; (c) $Hg^{2+}(aq) + 2I^-(aq) \rightarrow HgI_2(s)$ **4.5** (a) $CdCO_3$, insoluble; (b) MgO, insoluble; (c) Na_2S, soluble; (d) $PbSO_4$, insoluble; (e) $(NH_4)_3PO_4$, soluble; (f) $HgCl_2$, soluble **4.6** (a) $Ni^{2+}(aq) + S^{2-}(aq) \rightarrow NiS(s)$; (b) $Pb^{2+}(aq) + CrO_4^{2-}(aq) \rightarrow PbCrO_4(s)$; (c) $Ag^+(aq) + Br^-(aq) \rightarrow AgBr(s)$; (d) $Zn^{2+}(aq) + CO_3^{2-}(aq) \rightarrow ZnCO_3(s)$ **4.7** $3CaCl_2(aq) + 2Na_3PO_4(aq) \rightarrow Ca_3(PO_4)_2(s) + 6NaCl(aq)$; $3Ca^{2+}(aq) + 2PO_4^{3-}(aq) \rightarrow Ca_3(PO_4)_2(s)$ **4.8** The precipitate is either $Mg_3(PO_4)_2$ or $Zn_3(PO_4)_2$. **4.9** (a) periodic acid; (b) bromous acid; (c) chromic acid **4.10** (a) H_3PO_3; (b) H_2Se **4.11** (a) $2Cs^+(aq) + 2OH^-(aq) + 2H^+(aq) + SO_4^{2-}(aq) \rightarrow 2Cs^+(aq) + SO_4^{2-}(aq) + 2H_2O(l)$; $H^+(aq) + OH^-(aq) \rightarrow H_2O(l)$; (b) $Ca^{2+}(aq) + 2OH^-(aq) + 2CH_3CO_2H(aq) \rightarrow Ca^{2+}(aq) + 2CH_3CO_2^-(aq) + 2H_2O(l)$; $CH_3CO_2H(aq) + OH^-(aq) \rightarrow CH_3CO_2^-(aq) + H_2O(l)$ **4.12** HY is the strongest acid; HX is the weakest acid. **4.13** (a) Cl −1, Sn +4; (b) O −2, Cr +6; (c) O −2, Cl −1, V +5; (d) O −2, V +3; (e) O −2, H +1, N +5; (f) O −2, S +6, Fe +2 **4.14** $2Cu^{2+}(aq) + 4I^-(aq) \rightarrow 2CuI(s) + I_2(aq)$; Cu^{2+} +2; I^- −1; CuI: Cu +1, I −1; I_2: 0; oxidizing agent, Cu^{2+}; reducing agent, I^- **4.15** (a) C is oxidized. C is the reducing agent. The Sn in SnO_2 is reduced. SnO_2 is the oxidizing agent. (b) Sn^{2+} is oxidized. Sn^{2+} is the reducing agent. Fe^{3+} is reduced. Fe^{3+} is the oxidizing agent. (c) The N in NH_3 is oxidized. NH_3 is the reducing agent. Each O in O_2 is reduced. O_2 is the oxidizing agent. **4.16** (a) N. R.; (b) N. R. **4.17** Because B will reduce A^+, B is above A in the activity series. Because B will not reduce C^+, C is above B in the activity series. Therefore C must be above A in the activity series and C will reduce A^+. **4.18** A > D > B > C **4.19** (a) $MnO_4^-(aq) \rightarrow MnO_2(s)$; $IO_3^-(aq) \rightarrow IO_4^-(aq)$; (b) $NO_3^-(aq) \rightarrow NO_2(g)$; $SO_2(aq) \rightarrow SO_4^{2-}(aq)$ **4.20** $2NO_3^-(aq) + 8H^+(aq) + 3Cu(s) \rightarrow 3Cu^{2+}(aq) + 2NO(g) + 4H_2O(l)$ **4.21** $4Fe(OH)_2(s) + 2H_2O(l) + O_2(g) \rightarrow 4Fe(OH)_3(s)$ **4.22** 1.98 M **4.23** $Pb(s) + PbO_2(s) + 2HSO_4^-(aq) + 2H^+(aq) \rightarrow 2PbSO_4(s) + 2H_2O(l)$ **4.24** For a green process look for a solvent that is safe, non-toxic, non-polluting, and renewable. H_2O would be an excellent green solvent. *Conceptual Problems* **4.26** In the precipitate there are two cations (blue) for each anion (red), so the anion must have a −2 charge and the cation a +1 charge for charge neutrality of the precipitate. The cation must be Ag^+ because all Na^+ salts are soluble. Ag_2CrO_4 and Ag_2CO_3 are insoluble and consistent with the observed result. **4.28** The NaOCl concentration is 0.040 M. 67% of the I^- solution from the buret must be added to the flask to react with all of the OCl^-. **4.30** (a) No reaction. (b) Reaction would occur. (c) Reaction would occur. *Section Problems* **4.32** (a) precipitation; (b) redox; (c) acid–base neutralization **4.34** (a) $Hg^{2+}(aq) + 2I^-(aq) \rightarrow HgI_2(s)$; (b) $2HgO(s) \xrightarrow{\text{Heat}} 2Hg(l) + O_2(g)$; (c) $H_3PO_4(aq) + 3OH^-(aq) \rightarrow PO_4^{3-}(aq) + 3H_2O(l)$ **4.36** (a) bright; (b) dark; (c) dim **4.38** $Ba(OH)_2$ is soluble in aqueous solution, dissociates into $Ba^{2+}(aq)$ and $2OH^-(aq)$, and conducts electricity. H_2SO_4 dissociates into $H^+(aq)$ and $HSO_4^-(aq)$. H_2SO_4 solutions conduct electricity. When equal molar solutions of $Ba(OH)_2$ and H_2SO_4 are mixed, the insoluble $BaSO_4$ is formed along with two H_2O. In water, $BaSO_4$ does not produce any appreciable amount of ions and the mixture does not conduct electricity. **4.40** (a) strong; (b) weak; (c) strong; (d) strong; (e) weak; (f) nonelectrolyte **4.42** (a) 2.25 M; (b) 1.42 M **4.44** (a) insoluble; (b) soluble; (c) insoluble; (d) insoluble **4.46** (a) No precipitate will form; (b) $Fe(OH)_2(s)$ will precipitate; (c) No precipitate; (d) No precipitate. **4.48** (a) no precipitate; (b) $BaSO_4(s)$ will precipitate; (c) $AgCl(s)$ will precipitate. **4.50** (a) $Pb(NO_3)_2(aq) + Na_2SO_4(aq) \rightarrow PbSO_4(s) + 2NaNO_3(aq)$; (b) $3MgCl_2(aq) + 2K_3PO_4(aq) \rightarrow Mg_3(PO_4)_2(s) + 6KCl(aq)$;

(c) $ZnSO_4(aq) + Na_2CrO_4(aq) \rightarrow ZnCrO_4(s) + Na_2SO_4(aq)$
4.52 Add $HCl(aq)$; it will selectively precipitate $AgCl(s)$.
4.54 Cs^+ and/or NH_4^+ **4.56** Add the solution to an active metal, such as magnesium. Bubbles of H_2 gas indicate the presence of an acid. **4.58** (a) $2 H^+(aq) + 2 ClO_4^-(aq) + Ca^{2+}(aq) + 2 OH^-(aq) \rightarrow$ $Ca^{2+}(aq) + 2 ClO_4^-(aq) + 2 H_2O(l)$; (b) $CH_3CO_2H(aq) +$ $Na^+(aq) + OH^-(aq) \rightarrow CH_3CO_2^-(aq) + Na^+(aq) + H_2O(l)$
4.60 (a) $H^+(aq) + OH^-(aq) \rightarrow H_2O(l)$; (b) $H^+(aq) + OH^-(aq) \rightarrow$ $H_2O(l)$ **4.62** (a) basic because there is an excess of KOH; (b) basic because there is an excess of $Ba(OH)_2$. **4.64** (a) 9.0 mL; (b) 11.0 mL
4.66 best reducing agents, the bottom left; best oxidizing agents, top right; (excluding the noble gases) **4.68** (a) gains electrons; (b) loses electrons; (c) loses electrons; (d) gains electrons
4.70 (a) NO_2: O -2, N $+4$; (b) SO_3: O -2, S $+6$; (c) $COCl_2$: O -2, Cl -1, C $+4$; (d) CH_2Cl_2: Cl -1, H $+1$, C 0; (e) $KClO_3$: O -2, K $+1$, Cl $+5$; (f) HNO_3: O -2, H $+1$, N $+5$ **4.72** (a) ClO_3^-: O -2, Cl $+5$; (b) SO_3^{2-}: O -2, S $+4$; (c) $C_2O_4^{2-}$: O -2, C $+3$; (d) NO_2^-: O -2, N $+3$; (e) BrO^-: O -2, Br $+1$; (f) AsO_4^{3-}: O -2, As $+5$ **4.74** (a) $Ca(s)$ is oxidized; $Sn^{2+}(aq)$ is reduced; (b) not a redox reaction **4.76** (a) N. R.; (b) N. R.; (c) N. R.; (d) $Au^{3+}(aq) +$ $3 Ag(s) \rightarrow 3 Ag^+(aq) + Au(s)$ **4.78** (a) A > B > C > D; (b) (1) N. R.; (2) N. R. **4.80** (a) reduction; (b) oxidation; (c) oxidation; (d) reduction **4.82** (a) $3 e^- + 4 H^+(aq) +$ $NO_3^-(aq) \rightarrow NO(g) + 2 H_2O(l)$; (b) $Zn(s) \rightarrow Zn^{2+}(aq) + 2 e^-$; (c) $Ti^{3+}(aq) + 2 H_2O(l) \rightarrow TiO_2(s) + 4 H^+(aq) + e^-$; (d) $Sn^{4+}(aq) + 2 e^- \rightarrow Sn^{2+}(aq)$ **4.84** (a) oxidation: $Te(s) \rightarrow TeO_2(s)$; reduction: $NO_3^-(aq) \rightarrow NO(g)$; (b) oxidation: $Fe^{2+}(aq) \rightarrow Fe^{3+}(aq)$; reduction: $H_2O_2(aq) \rightarrow H_2O(l)$ **4.86** (a) $14 H^+(aq) +$ $Cr_2O_7^{2-}(aq) + 6 e^- \rightarrow 2 Cr^{3+}(aq) + 7 H_2O(l)$; (b) $4 H_2O(l) +$ $CrO_4^{2-}(aq) + 3 e^- \rightarrow Cr(OH)_4^-(aq) + 4 OH^-(aq)$; (c) $Bi^{3+}(aq) + 6 OH^-(aq) \rightarrow BiO_3^-(aq) + 3 H_2O(l) + 2 e^-$; (d) $H_2O(l) + ClO^-(aq) + 2 e^- \rightarrow Cl^-(aq) + 2 OH^-(aq)$
4.88 (a) $H_2O(l) + 2 MnO_4^-(aq) + 3 IO_3^-(aq) \rightarrow 2 MnO_2(s) +$ $3 IO_4^-(aq) + 2 OH^-(aq)$; (b) $2 Cu(OH)_2(s) + N_2H_4(aq) \rightarrow$ $2 Cu(s) + 4 H_2O(l) + N_2(g)$; (c) $3 Fe(OH)_2(s) + 4 H_2O(l) +$ $CrO_4^{2-}(aq) \rightarrow 3 Fe(OH)_3(s) + Cr(OH)_4^-(aq) + OH^-(aq)$; (d) $ClO_4^-(aq) + 2 H_2O_2(aq) \rightarrow ClO_2^-(aq) + 2 H_2O(l) + 2 O_2(g)$
4.90 (a) $Zn(s) + 2 VO^{2+}(aq) + 4 H^+(aq) \rightarrow Zn^{2+}(aq) +$ $2 V^{3+}(aq) + 2 H_2O(l)$; (b) $2 H^+(aq) + Ag(s) + NO_3^-(aq) \rightarrow$ $Ag^+(aq) + NO_2(g) + H_2O(l)$; (c) $3 Mg(s) + 16 H^+(aq) +$ $2 VO_4^{3-}(aq) \rightarrow 3 Mg^{2+}(aq) + 2 V^{2+}(aq) + 8 H_2O(l)$; (d) $6 H^+(aq) + IO_3^-(aq) + 8 I^-(aq) \rightarrow 3 I_3^-(aq) + 3 H_2O(l)$
4.92 0.670 g I_2 **4.94** 1.130 M **4.96** 0.134 M **4.98** 80.32% **4.100** 0.101%
Chapter Problems **4.102** (a) $4[Fe(CN)_6]^{3-}(aq) + N_2H_4(aq) +$ $4 OH^-(aq) \rightarrow 4[Fe(CN)_6]^{4-}(aq) + N_2(g) + 4 H_2O(l)$; (b) $SeO_3^{2-}(aq) + Cl_2(g) + 2 OH^-(aq) \rightarrow SeO_4^{2-}(aq) +$ $2 Cl^-(aq) + H_2O(l)$; (c) $2 Co^{2+}(aq) + H_2O(l) + HO_2^-(aq) +$ $3 OH^-(aq) \rightarrow 2 Co(OH)_3(s)$ **4.104** (a) C_2H_6: H $+1$, C -3; (b) $Na_2B_4O_7$: O -2, Na $+1$, B $+3$; (c) Mg_2SiO_4: O -2, Mg $+2$, Si $+4$ **4.106** (a) C > A > D > B; (b) (1) The reaction, $A^+ + C \rightarrow A + C^+$, will occur; (2) $A^+ + B \rightarrow A + B^+$, will not occur. **4.108** 0.4450% Cu **4.110** $K_{sp} = [Mg^{2+}][F^-]^2 = 7.0 \times 10^{-11}$ **4.112** (a) $Hg_2^{2+}(aq) +$ $2 Cl^-(aq) \rightarrow Hg_2Cl_2(s)$; (b) $Pb^{2+}(aq) + SO_4^{2-}(aq) \rightarrow PbSO_4(s)$; (c) $Ca^{2+}(aq) + CO_3^{2-}(aq) \rightarrow CaCO_3(s)$; (d) $Ba^{2+}(aq) +$ $SO_4^{2-}(aq) \rightarrow BaSO_4(s)$ **4.114** (a) $2 Mn(OH)_2(s) + H_2O_2(aq) \rightarrow$ $2 Mn(OH)_3(s)$; (b) $4 H^+(aq) + 3 MnO_4^{2-}(aq) \rightarrow MnO_2(s) +$ $2 MnO_4^-(aq) + 2 H_2O(l)$; (c) $8 I^-(aq) + IO_3^-(aq) + 6 H^+(aq) \rightarrow$ $3 I_3^-(aq) + 3 H_2O(l)$; (d) $2 H_2O(l) + 2 P(s) + 3 PO_4^{3-}(aq) +$ $OH^-(aq) \rightarrow 5 HPO_3^{2-}(aq)$ **4.116** (a) $20 H^+(aq) + S_4O_6^{2-}(aq) +$ $6 Al(s) \rightarrow 4 H_2S(aq) + 6 Al^{3+}(aq) + 6 H_2O(l)$; (b) $14 H^+(aq) +$ $6 S_2O_3^{2-}(aq) + Cr_2O_7^{2-} \rightarrow 3 S_4O_6^{2-}(aq) + 2 Cr^{3+}(aq) + 7 H_2O(l)$; (c) $18 H_2O(l) + 14 ClO_3^-(aq) + 3 As_2S_3(s) \rightarrow 14 Cl^-(aq) +$ $6 H_2AsO_4^-(aq) + 9 HSO_4^-(aq) + 15 H^+(aq)$; (d) $3 H_2O(l) +$

$7 IO_3^-(aq) + 6 Re(s) \rightarrow 7 I^-(aq) + 6 ReO_4^-(aq) + 6 H^+(aq)$; (e) $26 H^+(aq) + 30 HSO_4^-(aq) + As_4(s) + 10 Pb_3O_4(s) \rightarrow$ $4 H_2AsO_4^-(aq) + 30 PbSO_4(s) + 24 H_2O(l)$; (f) $3 HNO_2(aq) \rightarrow$ $NO_3^-(aq) + 2 NO(g) + H_2O(l) + H^+(aq)$ **4.118** 3.06 g Cu_2O; 7.44 g CuO **4.120** Al **4.122** (a) $2 H^+ + 2 Cl^- + H_2O_2 \rightarrow Cl_2 + 2 H_2O$, H_2O_2 reduced; (b) $6 H^+ + 2 MnO_4^- + 5 H_2O_2 \rightarrow 2 Mn^{2+} +$ $5 O_2 + 8 H_2O$, H_2O_2 oxidized; (c) $H_2O_2 + Cl_2 \rightarrow 2 H^+ + 2 Cl^- +$ O_2, H_2O_2 oxidized. **4.124** 63.68% *Multiconcept Problems* **4.126** 6.5 g $Ba(OH)_2$; 3.5 g NaOH **4.128** (a) $BaSO_4(s)$ and $AgCl(s)$; (b) 150 g $BaCl_2$, 50 g NaCl, 50 g KNO_3 **4.130** (a) $14 H^+(aq) +$ $Cr_2O_7^{2-}(aq) + 6 Cr^{2+}(aq) \rightarrow 8 Cr^{3+}(aq) + 7 H_2O(l)$; (b) K^+, 0.0833 M; NO_3^-, 0.617 M; H^+, 0.183 M; $Cr_2O_7^{2-}$, 0.0250 M; Cr^{3+}, 0.133 M
4.132 (a) (1) $3 Cu(s) + 8 H^+(aq) + 2 NO_3^-(aq) \rightarrow 3 Cu^{2+}(aq) +$ $2 NO(g) + 4 H_2O(l)$; (2) $2 Cu^{2+}(aq) + 2 SCN^-(aq) +$ $H_2O(l) + HSO_3^-(aq) \rightarrow 2 CuSCN(s) + HSO_4^-(aq) + 2 H^+(aq)$; (3) $10 Cu^+(aq) + 12 H^+(aq) + 2 IO_3^-(aq) \rightarrow 10 Cu^{2+}(aq) + I_2(aq) +$ $6 H_2O(l)$; (4) $I_2(aq) + 2 S_2O_3^{2-}(aq) \rightarrow 2 I^-(aq) + S_4O_6^{2-}(aq)$; (5) $2 ZnNH_4PO_4 \rightarrow Zn_2P_2O_7 + H_2O + 2 NH_3$; (b) 77.1% Cu; (c) 19.5% Zn **4.134** (a) $5 H_3MO_3(aq) + 2 MnO_4^-(aq) + 6 H^+(aq) \rightarrow$ $5 H_3MO_4(aq) + 2 Mn^{2+}(aq) + 3 H_2O(l)$; (b) 1.34×10^{-3} mol M_2O_3; 2.68×10^{-3} mol M (c) As.

Chapter 5

5.1 gamma ray, 8.43×10^{18} Hz; radar wave, 2.91×10^9 Hz
5.2 2.93 m; 3.14×10^{-10} m **5.3** (b) has the higher frequency. (b) represents the more intense beam of light. (b) represents blue light. (a) represents red light. **5.4** 397.0 nm **5.5** 1875 nm
5.6 820.4 nm **5.7** 1310 kJ/mol **5.8** IR, 77.2 kJ/mol; UV, 479 kJ/mol; X ray, 2.18×10^4 kJ/mol **5.9** 2.34×10^{-38} m

5.10

n	l	m_l	Orbital	No. of Orbitals
5	0	0	$5s$	1
	1	$-1, 0, +1$	$5p$	3
	2	$-2, -1, 0, +1, +2$	$5d$	5
	3	$-3, -2, -1, 0, +1, +2, +3$	$5f$	7
	4	$-4, -3, -2, -1, 0, +1, +2, +3, +4$	$5g$	9

There are 25 possible orbitals in the fifth shell.
5.11 (a) $2p$; (b) $4f$; (c) $3d$ **5.12** (a) $n = 3, l = 0, m_l = 0$; (b) $n = 2, l = 1$, $m_l = -1, 0, +1$; (c) $n = 4, l = 2, m_l = -2, -1, 0, +1, +2$
5.13 four nodal planes. **5.14** $n = 4$ and $l = 2$ **5.15** 1.31×10^3 kJ/mol
5.16 Cr, Cu, Nb, Mo, Ru, Rh, Pd, Ag, La, Ce, Gd, Pt, Au, Ac, Th, Pa, U, Np, Cm, Ds, Rg **5.17** (a) Ti, $1s^2 2s^2 2p^6 3s^2 3p^6 4s^2 3d^2$ or [Ar] $4s^2 3d^2$;

$$[Ar] \; \underset{4s}{\uparrow\downarrow} \quad \underset{3d}{\underline{\uparrow} \; \underline{\uparrow} \; \underline{} \; \underline{} \; \underline{}}$$

(b) Zn, $1s^2 2s^2 2p^6 3s^2 3p^6 4s^2 3d^{10}$ or [Ar] $4s^2 3d^{10}$;

$$[Ar] \; \underset{4s}{\uparrow\downarrow} \quad \underset{3d}{\underline{\uparrow\downarrow} \; \underline{\uparrow\downarrow} \; \underline{\uparrow\downarrow} \; \underline{\uparrow\downarrow} \; \underline{\uparrow\downarrow}}$$

(c) Sn, $1s^2 2s^2 2p^6 3s^2 3p^6 4s^2 3d^{10} 4p^6 5s^2 4d^{10} 5p^2$ or [Kr] $5s^2 4d^{10} 5p^2$;

$$[Kr] \; \underset{5s}{\uparrow\downarrow} \quad \underset{4d}{\underline{\uparrow\downarrow} \; \underline{\uparrow\downarrow} \; \underline{\uparrow\downarrow} \; \underline{\uparrow\downarrow} \; \underline{\uparrow\downarrow}} \quad \underset{5p}{\underline{\uparrow} \; \underline{\uparrow} \; \underline{}}$$

(d) Pb, [Xe] $6s^2 4f^{14} 5d^{10} 6p^2$
5.18 Na^+, $1s^2 2s^2 2p^6$; Cl^-, $1s^2 2s^2 2p^6 3s^2 3p^6$ **5.19** Ni **5.20** (a) Ba; (b) Hf; (c) Sn; (d) Lu **5.21** Excited mercury atoms in a fluorescent bulb emit photons, some in the visible but most in the ultraviolet region. Visible photons contribute to light we can see; ultraviolet

photons are invisible to our eyes. To utilize this ultraviolet energy, fluorescent bulbs are coated on the inside with a phosphor that absorbs ultraviolet photons and re-emits the energy as visible light. *Conceptual Problems*

5.22

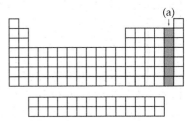

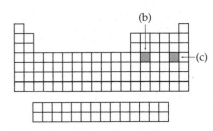

5.24 The green element, molybdenum, has an anomalous electron configuration. Its predicted configuration is $[Ar]\,5s^2\,4d^4$. Its anomalous configuration is $[Ar]\,5s^1\,4d^5$ because of the resulting half-filled d-orbitals. **5.26** Ga **5.28** Sr (215 pm) > Ca (197 pm) > Br (114 pm) *Section Problems* **5.30** Violet has the higher frequency and energy. Red has the higher wavelength. **5.32** visible; completely within this range; ultraviolet and infrared; partially in this range. **5.34** 5.5×10^{-8} m **5.36** (a) $\nu = 99.5$ MHz, $E = 3.97 \times 10^{-5}$ kJ/mol, $\nu = 1150$ kHz, $E = 4.589 \times 10^{-7}$ kJ/mol. The FM radio wave (99.5 MHz) has the higher energy. (b) $\lambda = 3.44 \times 10^{-9}$ m, $E = 3.48 \times 10^{4}$ kJ/mol, $\lambda = 6.71 \times 10^{-2}$ m, $E = 1.78 \times 10^{-3}$ kJ/mol. The X ray ($\lambda = 3.44 \times 10^{-9}$ m) has the higher energy. **5.38** (a) 36.4 cm; (b) 34.3 cm **5.40** (a) 1320 nm, near IR; (b) 0.149 m, radio wave; (c) 65.4 nm, UV **5.42** (a) 779 nm, 2.55×10^{-19} J; (b) 649 nm, 3.06×10^{-19} J; (c) 405 nm, 4.91×10^{-19} J **5.44** For $n = 3$, $E = 182.3$ kJ/mol; For $n = 4$, $E = 246.1$ kJ/mol; For $n = 5$, $E = 275.6$ kJ/mol **5.46** 2.45×10^{-12} m, γ ray **5.48** 1.06×10^{-34} m **5.50** 9.14×10^{-24} m/s **5.52** 8×10^{-31} m **5.54** n is the principal quantum number. The size and energy level of an orbital depends on n. l is the angular-momentum quantum number. l defines the three-dimensional shape of an orbital. m_l is the magnetic quantum number. m_l defines the spatial orientation of an orbital. m_s is the spin quantum number. m_s indicates the spin of the electron and can have either of two values, $+1/2$ or $-1/2$. **5.56** The probability of finding the electron drops off rapidly as distance from the nucleus increases, although it never drops to zero, even at large distances. As a result, there is no definite boundary or size for an orbital. However, we usually imagine the boundary surface of an orbital enclosing the volume where an electron spends 95% of its time. **5.58** Part of the electron–nucleus attraction is canceled by the electron–electron repulsion, an effect we describe by saying that the electrons are shielded from the nucleus by the other electrons. The net nuclear charge actually felt by an electron is called the effective nuclear charge, Z_{eff}, and is often substantially lower than the actual nuclear charge, Z_{actual}. $Z_{eff} = Z_{actual} -$ electron shielding **5.60** (a) $4s$: $n = 4$; $l = 0$; $m_l = 0$; $m_s = \pm1/2$; (b) $3p$: $n = 3$; $l = 1$; $m_l = -1, 0, +1$; $m_s = \pm1/2$; (c) $5f$: $n = 5$; $l = 3$; $m_l = -3, -2, -1, 0, +1, +2, +3$; $m_s = \pm1/2$; (d) $5d$: $n = 5$; $l = 2$; $m_l = -2, -1, 0, +1, +2$; $m_s = \pm1/2$ **5.62** (a) not allowed because for $l = 0$, $m_l = 0$ only; (b) allowed; (c) not allowed

because for $n = 4$, $l = 0, 1, 2,$ or 3 only **5.64** The maximum number of electrons will occur when the $5g$ orbital is filled: $[Rn]\,7s^2\,5f^{14}\,6d^{10}\,7p^6\,8s^2\,5g^{18} = 138$ electrons **5.66** $E = 328.1$ kJ/mol **5.68** 363 kJ/mol **5.70** The principal quantum number n increases by 1 from one period to the next. As the principal quantum number increases, the number of orbitals in a shell increases. The progression of elements parallels the number of electrons in a particular shell. **5.72** (a) $5d$; (b) $4s$; (c) $6s$ **5.74** (a) $3d$; (b) $4p$; (c) $6d$; (d) $6s$ **5.76** (a) $1s^2\,2s^2\,2p^6\,3s^2\,3p^6\,4s^2\,3d^2$; (b) $1s^2\,2s^2\,2p^6\,3s^2\,3p^6\,4s^2\,3d^{10}\,4p^6\,5s^2\,4d^6$; (c) $1s^2\,2s^2\,2p^6\,3s^2\,3p^6\,4s^2\,3d^{10}\,4p^6\,5s^2\,4d^{10}\,5p^2$; (d) $1s^2\,2s^2\,2p^6\,3s^2\,3p^6\,4s^2\,3d^{10}\,4p^6\,5s^2$; (e) $1s^2\,2s^2\,2p^6\,3s^2\,3p^6\,4s^2\,3d^{10}\,4p^4$

5.78

(a) Rb,　[Kr] ⥮ $5s$

(b) W,　[Xe] ⥮ $6s$　⥮ ⥮ ⥮ ⥮ ⥮ ⥮ ⥮ $4f$　↑ ↑ ↑ ↑ — $5d$

(c) Ge,　[Ar] ⥮ $4s$　⥮ ⥮ ⥮ ⥮ ⥮ $3d$　↑ ↑ — $4p$

(d) Zr,　[Kr] ⥮ $5s$　↑ ↑ — — — $4d$

5.80 $4s > 4d > 4f$ **5.82** (a) 2; (b) 2; (c) 1; (d) 3 **5.84** $Z = 121$ **5.86** Atomic radii increase down a group because the electron shells are farther away from the nucleus. **5.88** F < O < S **5.90** Mg has a higher ionization energy than Na because Mg has a higher Z_{eff} and a smaller size. **5.92** $[Rn]\,7s^2\,5f^{14}\,6d^{10}\,7p^4$ *Chapter Problems* **5.94** 164 nm **5.96** $\lambda = 410.2$ nm; $E = 291.6$ kJ/mol **5.98** 2279 nm **5.100** (a) 0.151 kJ/mol; (b) 2.17×10^{-8} kJ/mol; (c) 2.91 kJ/mol

5.102

(a) Ra, $[Rn]\,7s^2$　　[Rn] ⥮ $7s$

(b) Sc, $[Ar]\,4s^2\,3d^1$　　[Ar] ⥮ $4s$　↑ — — — — $3d$

(c) Lr, $[Rn]\,7s^2\,5f^{14}\,6d^1$

[Rn] ⥮ $7s$　⥮ ⥮ ⥮ ⥮ ⥮ ⥮ ⥮ $5f$　↑ — — — — $6d$

(d) B, $[He]\,2s^2\,2p^1$　　[He] ⥮ $2s$　↑ — — $2p$

(e) Te, $[Kr]\,5s^2\,4d^{10}\,5p^4$

[Kr] ⥮ $5s$　⥮ ⥮ ⥮ ⥮ ⥮ $4d$　⥮ ↑ ↑ $5p$

5.104 580 nm

5.106

(a) Sr,　[Kr] ⥮ $5s$

(b) Cd,　[Kr] ⥮ $5s$　⥮ ⥮ ⥮ ⥮ ⥮ $4d$

(c) Ti,　[Ar] ⥮ $4s$　↑ ↑ — — — $3d$

(d) Se,　[Ar] ⥮ $4s$　⥮ ⥮ ⥮ ⥮ ⥮ $3d$　⥮ ↑ ↑ $4p$

5.108 (a) 1.0×10^{-10} m; (b) 1.2×10^{6} kJ/mol; (c) X rays **5.110** K, $Z_{eff} = 2.26$; Kr, $Z_{eff} = 4.06$ **5.112** 8.3×10^{28} photons **5.114** 940 kJ/mol

5.116

$$\Delta E = \frac{Z^2 e^2}{2a_0}\left[\frac{1}{n_1^2} - \frac{1}{n_2^2}\right]$$

This equation shows that ΔE is proportional to

$$\left[\frac{1}{n_1^2} - \frac{1}{n_2^2}\right]$$

where n_1 and n_2 are integers with $n_2 > n_1$. This is similar to the Balmer–Rydberg equation where $1/\lambda$ or ν is proportional to

$$\left[\frac{1}{m^2} - \frac{1}{n^2}\right]$$

where m and n are integers with $n > m$. **5.118** (a) $3d$, n = 3, l = 2; (b) $2p$, n = 2, l = 1, m_l = −1, 0, +1; $3p$, n = 3, l = 1,m_l = −1, 0, +1; $3d$, n = 3, l = 2, m_l = −2, −1, 0, +1,+2; (c) N, $1s^2\,2s^2\,2p^3$ so the $3s$, $3p$, and $3d$ orbitals are empty; (d) C, $1s^2\,2s^2\,2p^2$ so the $1s$ and $2s$ orbitals are filled; (e) Be, $1s^2\,2s^2$ so the $2s$ orbital contains the outermost electrons; (f) $2p$ and $3p$ (↑ ↑ __) and $3d$ (↑ ↑ __ __ __). **5.120** (a) 1.09×10^{15} s^{-1}; (b) 1.8 nm

Multiconcept Problems **5.122** (a) $5f$ subshell: n = 5, l = 3, m_l = −3, −2, −1, 0, +1, +2, +3; $3d$ subshell: n = 3, l = 2, m_l = −2, −1, 0, +1, +2; (b) 1282 nm; (c) 146 kJ/mol

Chapter 6

6.1 [Rn]; (b) [Kr]; (c) [Ar]; (d) [Ne] **6.2** Zn^{2+} **6.3** (a) O^{2-}; (b) S; (c) Fe; (d) H^- **6.4** K^+, r = 133 pm; Cl^-, r = 184 pm; K, r = 227 pm **6.5** (a) Br; (b) S; (c) Se; (d) Ne **6.6** (a) Be; (b) Ga **6.7** (b) Cl has the highest E_{i1} and smallest E_{i4}. **6.8** Al < Kr < Ca **6.9** Cr can accept an electron into a $4s$ orbital. Both Mn and Fe accept the added electron into a $3d$ orbital that contains an electron, but Mn has a lower value of Z_{eff}. **6.10** The least favorable E_{ea} is for Kr. The most favorable E_{ea} is for Ge. **6.11** (a) [Kr]; (b) [Xe]; (c) [Ar]-like configuration (note that Ga^{3+} has ten $3d$ electrons in addition to the two $3s$ and six $3p$ electrons); (d) [Ne] **6.12** gain 2 electrons **6.13** −562 kJ/mol **6.14** (a) KCl; (b) CaF_2; (c) CaO **6.15** (b) MgO has the larger lattice energy. **6.16** (a) O^{2-}; (b) O_2^{2-}; (c) O_2^- **6.17** (a) $2\,Cs(s) + 2\,H_2O(l) \rightarrow 2\,Cs^+(aq) + 2\,OH^-(aq) + H_2(g)$; (b) $Rb(s) + O_2(g) \rightarrow RbO_2(s)$; (c) $2\,K(s) + 2\,NH_3(g) \rightarrow 2\,KNH_2(g) + H_2(g)$; **6.18** (a) $Be(s) + Br_2(l) \rightarrow BeBr_2(s)$; (b) $Sr(s) + 2\,H_2O(l) \rightarrow Sr(OH)_2(aq) + H_2(g)$; (c) $2\,Mg(s) + O_2(g) \rightarrow 2\,MgO(s)$ **6.19** MgS(s); −2 **6.20** evaporation of seawater; mining deposits of *halite*, or *rock salt* *Conceptual Problems* **6.22** (a) ionic compound; (b) covalent compound

6.24

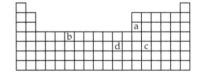

(a) Al^{3+}; (b) Cr^{3+}; (c) Sn^{2+}; (d) Ag^+ **6.26** (a) I_2; (b) Na; (c) NaCl; (d) Cl_2 **6.28** Green, CBr_4; Blue, SrF_2; Red, PbS or PbS_2 *Section Problems* **6.30** A covalent bond results when two atoms share several (usually two) of their electrons. An ionic bond results from a complete transfer of one or more electrons from one atom to another. The C—H bonds in methane (CH_4) are covalent bonds. The bond in NaCl (Na^+Cl^-) is an ionic bond. **6.32** (a) 4 p, 2 e$^-$, (b) 37 p, 36 e$^-$; (c) 34 p, 36 e$^-$; (d) 79 p, 76 e$^-$ **6.34** (a) La^{3+}, [Xe]; (b) Ag^+, [Kr] $4d^{10}$; (c) Sn^{2+}, [Kr] $5s^2\,4d^{10}$ **6.36** Ca^{2+}, [Ar]; Ti^{2+}, [Ar] $3d^2$ **6.38** Cr^{2+}; Fe^{2+} **6.40** Largest E_{i1} in group 8A because of the largest values of Z_{eff}; smallest E_{i1} in group 1A because of the

smallest values of Z_{eff}. **6.42** (a) Ca; (b) Ca **6.44** Ar has the highest E_{i2} and the lowest E_{i7}. **6.46** boron **6.48** (a) lowest: K; highest: Li; (b) lowest: B; highest: Cl; (c) lowest: Ca; highest: Cl **6.50** They have the same magnitude but opposite signs. **6.52** Na^+ has a more negative electron affinity than either Na or Cl. **6.54** because of the positive Z_{eff}. **6.56** The electron–electron repulsion is large and Z_{eff} is low. **6.58** $MgCl_2$ > LiCl > KCl > KBr **6.60** +195 kJ/mol **6.62** −325 kJ/mol **6.64** 808 kJ/mol **6.66** −537 kJ/mol **6.68** −176 kJ/mol

6.70

Na(g) → Na$^+$(g) + e$^-$ 495.8 kJ/mol	H(g) + e$^-$ → H$^-$ (g) − 72.8 kJ/mol
1/2 H$_2$ (g) → H(g) 218 kJ/mol	Na$^+$(g) + H$^-$ (g) → NaH(s) − 808 kJ/mol
Na(s) → Na(g) 107.3 kJ/mol	
Na(s) + 1/2 H$_2$(g) → NaH(s) − 60 kJ/mol	

6.72 (a) solid; (b) likely to react with Na, NaAt **6.74** Down each group, the valence electrons are farther from the nucleus and more easily removed. **6.76** (a) $2\,K(s) + 2\,H_2O(l) \rightarrow 2\,K^+(aq) + 2\,OH^-(aq) + H_2(g)$; (b) $2\,K(s) + 2\,NH_3(g) \rightarrow 2\,KNH_2(s) + H_2(g)$; (c) $2\,K(s) + Br_2(l) \rightarrow 2\,KBr(s)$; (d) $K(s) + O_2(g) \rightarrow KO_2(s)$ **6.78** (a) $Cl_2(g) + H_2(g) \rightarrow 2\,HCl(g)$; (b) $Cl_2(g) + Ar(g) \rightarrow$ N. R.; (c) $Cl_2(g) + 2\,Rb(s) \rightarrow 2\,RbCl(s)$ **6.80** $MnO_2(s) + 2\,Br^-(aq) + 4\,H^+(aq) \rightarrow Mn^{2+}(aq) + 2\,H_2O(l) + Br_2(aq)$ **6.82** $2\,Al_2O_3(soln) \rightarrow 4\,Al(l) + 3\,O_2(g)$ **6.84** (a) $TiCl_4$, titanium tetrachloride (b) $Ti(s) + 2\,Cl_2(g) \rightarrow TiCl_4(g)$; (c) $TiCl_4 + 2\,Mg(s) \rightarrow Ti(s) + 2\,MgCl_2(s)$ *Chapter Problems* **6.86** Cu^{2+} has fewer electrons and a larger effective nuclear charge. **6.88** MgF, −294 kJ/mol; MgF_2, −1114 kJ/mol; MgF_2 will form because the overall energy for the formation of MgF_2 is much more negative than for the formation of MgF. **6.90** Cl^+Na^-, +640 kJ/mol. Formation of Cl^+Na^- from its elements is not favored because the net energy change is positive whereas it is negative for the formation of Na^+Cl^-.
6.92 (a) $2\,Li(s) + 2\,H_2O(l) \rightarrow 2\,Li^+(aq) + 2\,OH^-(aq) + H_2(g)$; (b) $2\,Li(s) + 2\,NH_3(g) \rightarrow 2\,LiNH_2(s) + H_2(g)$; (c) $2\,Li(s) + Br_2(l) \rightarrow 2\,LiBr(s)$; (d) $6\,Li(s) + N_2(g) \rightarrow 2\,Li_3N(s)$; (e) $4\,Li(s) + O_2(g) \rightarrow 2\,Li_2O(s)$ **6.94** (a) $MgCl_2$, magnesium chloride; (b) CaO, calcium oxide; (c) Li_3N, lithium nitride; (d) Al_2O_3, aluminum oxide **6.96** When moving diagonally down and right on the periodic table, the increase in atomic radius caused by going to a larger shell is offset by a decrease caused by a higher Z_{eff}. **6.98** E_{ea2} = +744 kJ/mol. O^{2-} is not stable in the gas phase. It is stable in MgO because of the large lattice energy that results from the +2 and −2 charge of the ions and their small size. **6.100** (a) F; (b) Se^{2-} **6.102** 5295 kJ/mol *Multiconcept Problems* **6.104** (a) Fe: [Ar] $4s^2\,3d^6$; Fe^{2+}: [Ar] $3d^6$; Fe^{3+}: [Ar] $3d^5$; (b) n = 3, l = 2. (c) 40.6 nm; (d) The electron removed from Ru to go from Ru^{2+} to Ru^{3+} is a $4d$ electron. The electron with the higher principal quantum number, n = 4, is farther from the nucleus, less tightly held, and requires less energy to remove.

Chapter 7

7.1 (a) polar covalent; (b) ionic; (c) polar covalent; (d) polar covalent **7.2** $CCl_4 \sim ClO_2 < TiCl_3 < BaCl_2$ **7.3** H is positively polarized (blue). O is negatively polarized (red). This is consistent with the electronegativity values for O (3.5) and H (2.1).

7.4

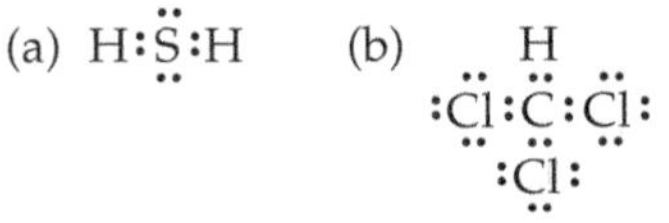

(a) H:S:H   (b)   :Cl:C:Cl: / :Cl:

7.5

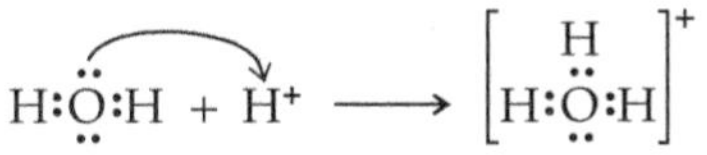

H:O:H + H⁺ ⟶ [H:O:H]⁺ (with H on top)

Hydronium ion

7.6

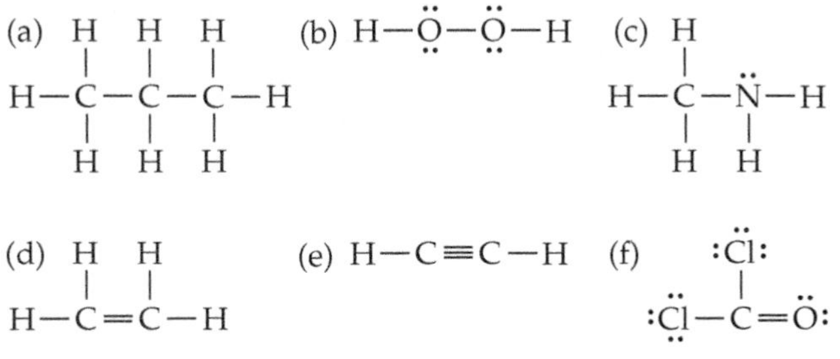

(a) H–C(H)(H)–C(H)(H)–C(H)(H)–H   (b) H–O–O–H   (c) H–C(H)(H)–N(H)–H

(d) H–C(H)=C(H)–H   (e) H–C≡C–H   (f) :Cl–C(Cl)=O:

7.7

H–C(H)(H)–C(H)(H)–O–H   and   H–C(H)(H)–O–C(H)(H)–H

7.8 $C_4H_5N_3O$

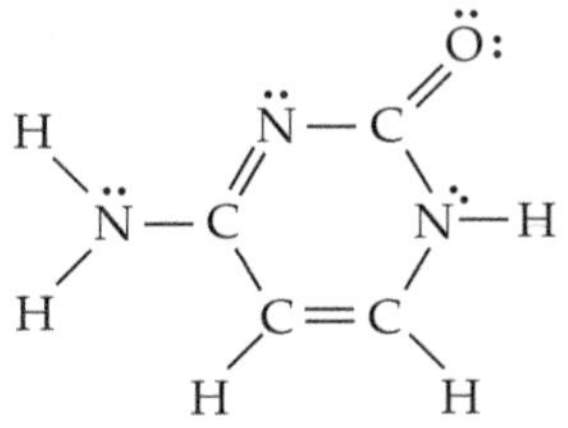

(heterocyclic ring structure)

7.9 :C≡O:

7.10

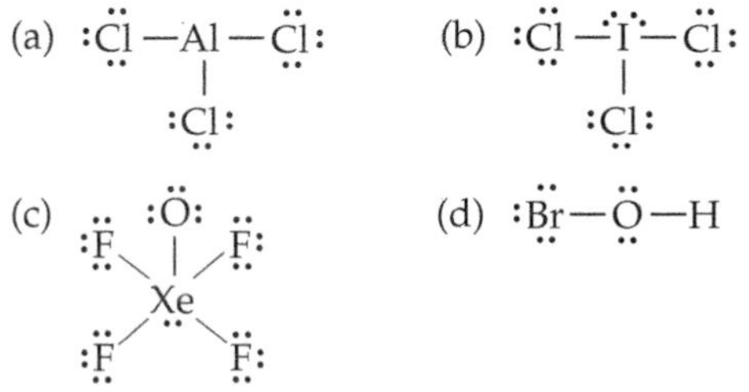

(a) :Cl–Al–Cl: with :Cl: below   (b) :Cl–I–Cl: with :Cl: below

(c) Xe with :O:, :F:, :F:, :F:, :F: (octahedral)   (d) :Br–O–H

7.11

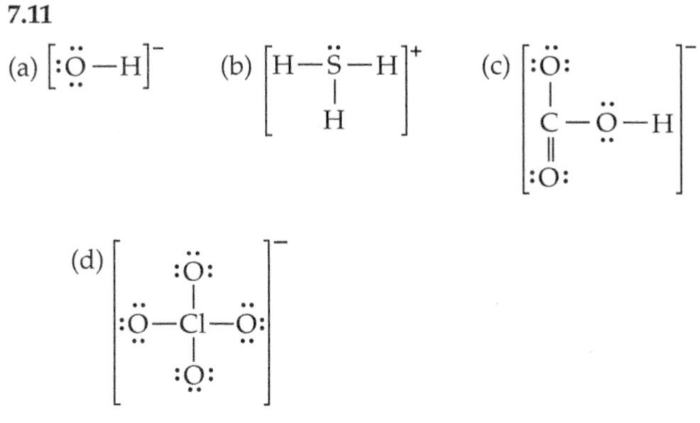

(a) [:O–H]⁻   (b) [H–S–H]⁺ with H below   (c) [:O: / C–O–H / :O:]⁻

(d) [:O: / :O–Cl–O: / :O:]⁻

7.12 :N=N=O: ⟷ :N≡N–O:

7.13

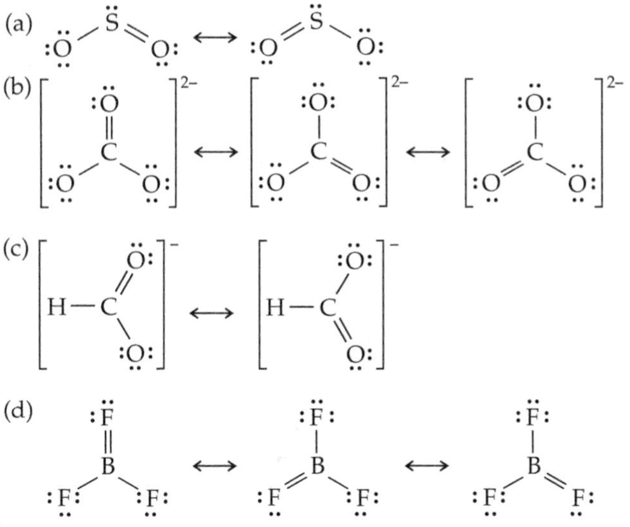

(a) :O–S=O: ⟷ :O=S–O:

(b) [:O: / :O–C=O:]²⁻ ⟷ [:O: / :O–C–O:]²⁻ ⟷ [:O: / :O=C–O:]²⁻

(c) [H–C(=O:)(–O:)]⁻ ⟷ [H–C(–O:)(=O:)]⁻

(d) :F=B(–F:)(–F:) ⟷ :F–B(=F:)(–F:) ⟷ :F–B(–F:)(=F:)

7.14

(benzene ring resonance structures with CH₃ and O substituents)

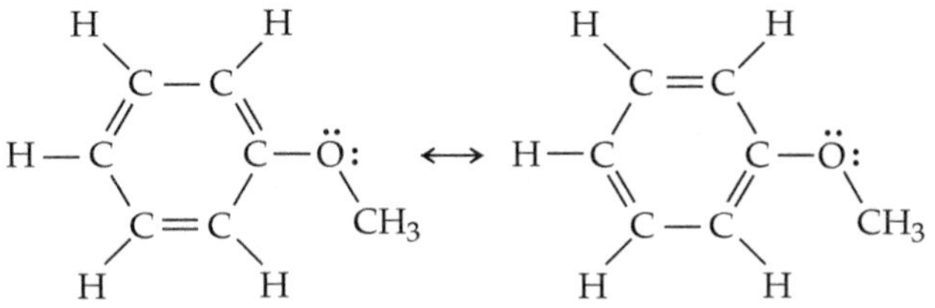

7.15 nitrogen +1; singly bound oxygen −1; doubly bound oxygen 0
7.16 (a) nitrogen −1; carbon 0; oxygen 0; (b) left oxygen −1; central oxygen +1; right oxygen 0 **7.17** (a) bent; (b) trigonal pyramidal; (c) linear; (d) octahedral;(e) square pyramidal; (f) tetrahedral; (g) tetrahedral; (h) tetrahedral; (i) square planar; (j) trigonal planar

7.18

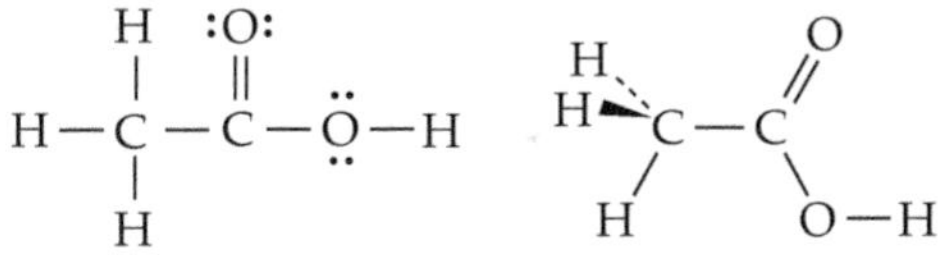

H–C(H)(H)–C(=O:)–O–H   and   H₂C–C(=O)–O–H (skeletal)

7.19 (a) tetrahedral; (b) seesaw **7.20** Each C is sp^3 hybridized. The C—C bond is formed by the overlap of one singly occupied sp^3 hybrid orbital from each C. The C—H bonds are formed by the overlap of one singly occupied sp^3 orbital on C with a singly occupied H 1s orbital.

7.21 The carbon in formaldehyde is sp^2 hybridized.

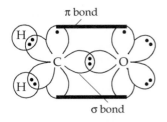

7.22 In HCN the carbon is sp hybridized.

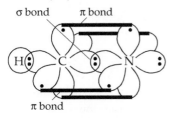

7.23 In CO_2 the carbon is sp hybridized.

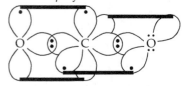

7.24 In Cl_2CO the carbon is sp^2 hybridized.

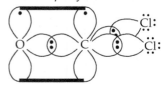

7.25 (a) sp^2 (b) sp (c) sp^3

7.26

For He_2^+ σ^*_{1s} ↑

   σ_{1s} ↑↓

He_2^+ should be stable with a bond order of $1/2$.

7.27

For B_2 σ^*_{2p} —

   π^*_{2p} — —

   σ_{2p} —

   π_{2p} ↑ ↑

   σ^*_{2s} ↑↓

   σ_{2s} ↑↓

B_2 Bond order = 1; paramagnetic

For C_2 σ^*_{2p} —

   π^*_{2p} — —

   σ_{2p} —

   π_{2p} ↑↓ ↑↓

   σ^*_{2s} ↑↓

   σ_{2s} ↑↓

C_2 Bond order = 2; diamagnetic

7.28

7.29 because a biologically active molecule is recognized and fits in a receptor molecule in the same way that a hand fits in a glove.
7.30 (a) has no handedness; (b) has handedness. *Conceptual Problems* **7.32** (a) square pyramidal; (b) trigonal pyramidal; (c) square planar; (d) trigonal planar **7.34** (c) does not have a tetrahedral central atom. **7.36** (a) $C_8H_9NO_2$; (b), (c), and (d)

All C's in ring, sp^2, trigonal planar

sp^3, tetrahedral

sp^2, trigonal planar

Section Problems **7.38** Electronegativity increases from left to right across a period and decreases down a group.

7.40 K < Li < Mg < Pb < C < Br **7.42** (a) polar covalent; (b) polar covalent; (c) polar covalent; (d) polar covalent; (e) Na^+–OH^- is ionic; OH^- is polar covalent; (f) polar covalent.
7.44

(a) $\overset{\delta-}{C}$–$\overset{\delta+}{H}$ $\overset{\delta+}{C}$–$\overset{\delta-}{Cl}$ (b) $\overset{\delta-}{Si}$–$\overset{\delta+}{Li}$ $\overset{\delta+}{Si}$–$\overset{\delta-}{Cl}$

(c) N–Cl $\overset{\delta-}{N}$–$\overset{\delta+}{Mg}$

7.46 (a) MgO, $BaCl_2$, LiBr; (b) P_4; (c) $CdBr_2$, BrF_3, NF_3, $POCl_3$
7.48 (a) $MgBr_2$; (b) PBr_3 **7.50** N_2H_2 **7.52** (a) Phosphorus trichloride; (b) Dinitrogen trioxide; (c) Tetraphosphorus heptoxide; (d) Bromine trifluoride; (e) Nitrogen trichloride; (f) Tetraphosphorus hexoxide; (g) Disulfur difluoride; (h) Selenium dioxide **7.54** The transition metals are characterized by partially filled d orbitals that can be used to expand their valence shell beyond the normal octet of electrons.

7.56

(a) :Br—C—Br: with Br above and below C

(b) :Cl—N—Cl: with Cl below N

(c) H H / H—C—C—Cl: with H above and below

(d) $\left[\begin{array}{c} :F: \\ | \\ :F—B—F: \\ | \\ :F: \end{array} \right]^-$ (e) $\left[:O—O: \right]^{2-}$ (f) $\left[:N≡O: \right]^+$

7.58

(a)   H—N≡N—N̈: ⟷ H—N̈=N=N̈: ⟷ H—N̈—N≡N:

(b)   resonance structures of SO_3

(c) $\left[:N≡C—S̈: \right]^- ⟷ \left[:N̈=C=S̈: \right]^- ⟷ \left[:N̈—C≡S: \right]^-$

7.60

H—Ö—C—C—Ö—H with two =O above the carbons

7.62 (a) yes; (b) yes; (c) yes; (d) yes **7.64** (a) A1; (b) P

7.66

(a)   :Cl—C—Ö—C—H with =O above first C and H's on second C

(b)   H—C—C≡C—H with H above and below first C

7.68 :C≡O: carbon −1; oxygen +1;

7.70

$:\ddot{O}^-—\overset{+}{Cl}—\ddot{O}:^- ⟷ :\ddot{O}^-—\overset{+}{Cl}=\ddot{O}$

7.72

(a) $\overset{H}{\underset{H}{}}C=\overset{+}{N}=\overset{-}{\ddot{N}}:$ (b) $\overset{H}{\underset{H}{}}C—\overset{+}{\ddot{N}}=\overset{-}{\ddot{N}}:$

Structure (a) is more important because of the octet of electrons around carbon.

7.74

$$:\ddot{C}l-\overset{\overset{\displaystyle :\ddot{C}l:\quad \overset{\displaystyle \ddot{O}:}{\|}}{}}{\underset{\underset{\displaystyle :\ddot{C}l:}{|}}{C}}-\overset{+}{N}-\ddot{\underset{..}{O}}:\quad \longleftrightarrow \quad :\ddot{C}l-\overset{\overset{\displaystyle :\ddot{C}l::\ddot{O}:}{}}{\underset{\underset{\displaystyle :\ddot{C}l:}{|}}{C}}-\overset{+}{N}=\ddot{O}:$$

7.76 (a) trigonal planar; (b) trigonal bipyramidal; (c) linear;
(d) octahedral **7.78** (a) tetrahedral, 4; (b) octahedral, 6; (c) bent, 3 or 4;
(d) linear, 2 or 5; (e) square pyramidal, 6; (f) trigonal pyramidal, 4
7.80 (a) bent; (b) tetrahedral; (c) bent; (d) trigonal planar
7.82 (a) trigonal bipyramidal; (b) see saw; (c) trigonal pyramidal;
(d) tetrahedral **7.84** (a) tetrahedral; (b) tetrahedral; (c) tetrahedral;
(d) trigonal pyramidal; (e) tetrahedral; (f) linear
7.86 (a) approximately 109°; (b) approximately 120°; (c) 90°;
(d) approximately 120°

7.88

$$\overset{H}{\underset{H}{}}C_a=\overset{H}{\underset{H}{}}C_b-C_c\equiv N$$

$H-C_a-H$, ~120°, C_b-C_c-N, 180°; $H-C_a-H_b$, ~120°;
C_a-C_b-H, ~120°; $C_a-C_b-C_c$, ~120°; $H-C_b-C_c$, ~120°

7.90

(Structure: central C bonded to four F atoms, and an S below bonded to six F atoms)

109.5° around carbon and 90° around S.

7.92 The geometry about each carbon is tetrahedral with a
C—C—C bond angle of approximately 109°. Because the
geometry about each carbon is tetrahedral, the cyclohexane ring
cannot be flat. **7.94** In a π bond, the shared electrons occupy a
region above and below a line connecting the two nuclei. A σ bond
has its shared electrons located along the axis between the two
nuclei. **7.96** (a) sp (b) sp^2 (c) sp^3 **7.98** (a) sp^2 (b) sp^2 (c) sp^3 (d) sp^2

7.100

$$H-O-\overset{\overset{\displaystyle O}{\|}}{C_a}-\overset{\overset{\displaystyle O}{\|}}{C_b}-\overset{\overset{\displaystyle H}{|}}{\underset{\underset{\displaystyle H}{|}}{C_c}}-\overset{\overset{\displaystyle O}{\|}}{C_d}-O-H$$

Carbon a, b, and d are sp^2 hybridized and carbon c is sp^3
hybridized. The bond angles around carbons a, b, and d are ~120°.
The bond angles around carbon c are ~109°. The terminal
H—O—C bond angles are ~109°.

7.102

	O_2^+	O_2	O_2^-
σ^*_{2p}	—	—	—
π^*_{2p}	↑ —	↑ ↑	↑↓ ↑
π_{2p}	↑↓ ↑↓	↑↓ ↑↓	↑↓ ↑↓
σ_{2p}	↑↓	↑↓	↑↓
σ^*_{2s}	↑↓	↑↓	↑↓
σ_{2s}	↑↓	↑↓	↑↓

Bond order: O_2^+, 2.5; O_2, 2; O_2^-, 1.5. All are stable. All have
unpaired electrons. **7.104** (a) C_2 bond order = 2;
(b) Add one electron; (c) C_2^- bond order = 2.5

7.106 (a) diamagnetic; (b) paramagnetic; (c) paramagnetic;
(d) diamagnetic; (e) paramagnetic

7.108

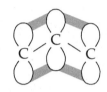

p orbitals in allyl cation

(Structure: three carbons with H atoms arranged)

allyl cation showing only
the σ bonds (each C is
sp^2 hybridized)

(Structure: delocalized MO representation with three carbons)

delocalized MO model for
π bonding in the allyl cation

Chapter Problems

7.110

(Lewis structure of a cyclic organic molecule with multiple O, H, and C atoms)

7.112

(Lewis structure with labeled sp^3 carbons)

All carbons except the two indicated are sp^2.
7.114 Every carbon is sp^2 hybridized. There are 18 σ bonds and
5 π bonds.

7.116

$$H-\overset{\overset{\displaystyle H}{|}}{\underset{\underset{\displaystyle H}{|}}{C}}-\ddot{N}=C=\ddot{O}:\quad \longleftrightarrow \quad H-\overset{\overset{\displaystyle H}{|}}{\underset{\underset{\displaystyle H}{|}}{C}}-\overset{+}{\ddot{N}}\equiv C-\ddot{\underset{..}{O}}:$$

7.118 (a) reactants: boron 0; oxygen 0; product: boron −1; oxygen
+1; (b) Reactants: B, sp^2, trigonal planar; O, sp^3, bent. Product: B,
sp^3, tetrahedral; O, sp^3, trigonal pyramidal. **7.120** The triply bonded
carbon atoms are sp hybridized. The theoretical bond angle for
C—C≡C is 180°. Benzyne is so reactive because the C—C≡C
bond angle is closer to 120° and is very strained.

7.122

7.124

C_2^{2-}

bond order = 3 **7.126** −109 kJ

7.128

Structures (a)–(d) make more important contributions to the resonance hybrid because of only −1 and 0 formal charges on the oxygens.

7.130

21 σ bonds
5 π bonds

Each C with a double bond is sp^2 hybridized. The —CH_3 is sp^3 hybridized.

7.132

(a)

(b) paramagnetic; (c) 2; (d) The two added electrons go into the antibonding π^*_{3p} MOs, and the bond length in S_2^{2-} should be longer.

7.134

(a)

left S: seesaw; right S: bent

(b)

left C: tetrahedral; right C: trigonal planar; central two C's: linear.

Multiconcept Problems

7.136 $\left[:\ddot{O}-H\right]^-$ $:\ddot{O}-H$

(b) The oxygen in OH has a half-filled $2p$ orbital that can accept the additional electron. $n = 2$ and $l = 1$; (c) When OH gains an additional electron, it achieves an octet configuration.

7.138

(a)

(b) Each Cr atom has 6 pairs of electrons around it. The likely geometry about each Cr atom is tetrahedral because each Cr has 4 charge clouds.

7.140 (a) Each carbon is sp^2 hybridized; (b) & (c);

(d) The cyclooctatetraene dianion has only paired electrons and is diamagnetic.

Chapter 8

8.1 (a) and (b) are state functions; (c) is not. **8.2** $+1.9 \times 10^4$ J flows into the system **8.3** −0.25 kJ; The expanding system loses work energy and does work on the surroundings. **8.4** (a) $P\Delta V$ is negative for this reaction because the system volume is decreased at constant pressure. (b) ΔH is negative. Its value is slightly more negative than ΔE. **8.5** $w = 0.57$ kJ; $\Delta E = -120$ kJ **8.6** −45.2 kJ **8.7** (a) 780 kJ evolved; (b) 1.24 kJ absorbed **8.8** 1.000×10^3 kJ **8.9** $q = -32$ kJ **8.10** 0.130 J/(g·°C) **8.11** -1.1×10^2 kJ **8.12** −202 kJ **8.13** (a) A + 2 B → D; $\Delta H° = -150$ kJ; (b) red arrow: step 1; green arrow: step 2; blue arrow: overall reaction; (c) top energy level represents A + 2 B, middle energy level represents C + B, bottom energy level represents D

8.14

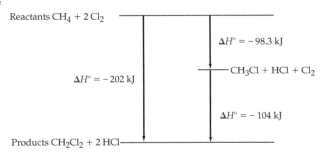

Reactants $CH_4 + 2 Cl_2$

$\Delta H° = -202$ kJ

$\Delta H° = -98.3$ kJ

$CH_3Cl + HCl + Cl_2$

$\Delta H° = -104$ kJ

Products $CH_2Cl_2 + 2 HCl$

8.15 −901.2 kJ **8.16** +2803 kJ **8.17** +78 kJ **8.18** −81 kJ
8.19 −2635.5 kJ/mol; −45.35 kJ/g **8.20** $\Delta S°$ is negative because
the reaction decreases the number of moles of gaseous molecules.
8.21 The reaction proceeds from a solid and a gas (reactants) to
all gas (product). Randomness increases, so $\Delta S°$ is positive.
8.22 (a) spontaneous; (b) nonspontaneous
8.23 $\Delta G° = -32.9$ kJ; reaction is spontaneous; $T = 190$ °C
8.24 (a) $2 A_2 + B_2 \rightarrow 2 A_2B$; (b) ΔH is negative; ΔS is negative;
(c) low temperatures only **8.25** $C_2H_6O + 3 O_2 \rightarrow 2 CO_2 + 3 H_2O$;
$2 C_{19}H_{38}O_2 + 55 O_2 \rightarrow 38 CO_2 + 38 H_2O$ **8.26** Because the
standard heat of formation of $CO_2(g)$ (−393.5 kJ/mol) is more
negative than that of $H_2O(g)$ (−241.8 kJ/mol), formation of CO_2
releases more heat than formation of H_2O. According to the
balanced equations, combustion of ethanol yields a 2:3 ratio of CO_2
to H_2O, whereas combustion of biodiesel yields a 1:1 ratio. Thus
biodiesel has a more favorable (more negative) combustion
enthalpy per gram *Conceptual Problems* **8.28** (a) yes; $w < 0$;
(b) yes; $\Delta H < 0$; exothermic
8.30

Reactants

Step 1

Net reaction

Step 2

$H°$

Products

8.32 The volume decreases from 5 L to 3 L.

1 atm

$V = 3.00$ L

8.34 $\Delta G < 0$; $\Delta H > 0$; $\Delta S > 0$ *Section Problems* **8.36** Heat is the
energy transferred from one object to another as the result of a
temperature difference between them. Temperature is a measure of
the kinetic energy of molecular motion. Energy is the capacity to do
work or supply heat. Work is defined as the distance moved times
the force that opposes the motion ($w = d \times F$). Kinetic energy is
the energy of motion. Potential energy is stored energy.
8.38 Car: 7.1×10^5 J; truck: 6.7×10^5 J **8.40** −70 J. The energy
change is negative. **8.42** (a) 35 min; (b) 150 min **8.44** (a) −593 J;
(b) 26.4 cm **8.46** $\Delta E = q_v$ is the heat of a reaction at constant
volume. $\Delta H = q_p$ is the heat of a reaction at constant pressure.
8.48 ΔH and ΔE are nearly equal when there are no gases involved
in a chemical reaction, or, if gases are involved, $\Delta V = 0$.
8.50 −0.30 kJ **8.52** 45.4 kJ **8.54** $\Delta E = -314$ kJ **8.56** 25.5 kJ **8.58** 131 kJ
8.60 0.388 kJ is evolved; exothermic. **8.62** Heat capacity is the
amount of heat required to raise the temperature of a substance a
given amount. Specific heat is the amount of heat necessary to raise
the temperature of exactly 1 g of a substance by exactly 1 °C.
8.64 1.23 J/(g•°C) **8.66** −83.7 kJ **8.68** $\Delta H = -56$ kJ/mol; same

temperature increase because NaOH is still the limiting reactant.
8.70 The standard state of an element is its most stable form at
1 atm and 25 °C. **8.72** The overall enthalpy change for a reaction is
equal to the sum of the enthalpy changes for the individual
steps in the reaction. Hess's Law works because of the law of
conservation of energy. **8.74** (a) gas; (b) liquid; (c) gas; (d) solid
8.76 (a) $2 Fe(s) + 3/2 O_2(g) \rightarrow Fe_2O_3(s)$;
(b) $12 C(s) + 11 H_2(g) + 11/2 O_2(g) \rightarrow C_{12}H_{22}O_{11}(s)$;
(c) $U(s) + 3 F_2(g) \rightarrow UF_6(s)$ **8.78** −395.7 kJ/mol **8.80** −909.3 kJ
8.82 +104 kJ/mol **8.84** −16.9 kJ/mol **8.86** +179.2 kJ
8.88 −6 kJ **8.90** −2645 kJ **8.92** Entropy is a measure of molecular
randomness. **8.94** A reaction can be spontaneous yet endothermic
if ΔS is positive (more randomness) and the $T\Delta S$ term is
larger than ΔH. **8.96** (a) positive; (b) negative **8.98** (a) zero;
(b) zero; (c) negative **8.100** ΔS is positive. The reaction increases
the total number of molecules. **8.102** (a) spontaneous; exothermic.
(b) nonspontaneous; exothermic. (c) spontaneous; endothermic.
(d) nonspontaneous; endothermic. **8.104** 570 K
8.106 (a) spontaneous at all temperatures; (b) has a crossover
temperature; (c) has a crossover temperature; (d) nonspontaneous
at all temperatures **8.108** 31.6 J/(K•mol) *Chapter Problems*
8.110 −468 kJ **8.112** −171.5 kJ **8.114** 279 K **8.116** (a) +34 kJ;
(b) −451 kJ; (c) −87 kJ **8.118** (a) $2 C_8H_{18}(l) + 25 O_2(g) \rightarrow$
$16 CO_2(g) + 18 H_2O(l)$; (b) −259 kJ/mol **8.120** (a) $\Delta G = -T\Delta S_{total}$;
(b) $\Delta S_{surr} = -9399$ J/(K•mol) **8.122** $\Delta H° = +201.9$ kJ **8.124** 311 g
8.126 −56 kJ **8.128** −1198.4 kJ *Multiconcept Problems*

8.130 (a)

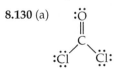

(b) −183 kJ/mol. The calculation of $\Delta H°_f$ from bond energies
is only an estimate because the bond energies are average
values derived from many different compounds.
8.132 (a) $2 K(s) + 2 H_2O(l) \rightarrow 2 KOH(aq) + H_2(g)$;
(b) −393.2 kJ; (c) 47.7 °C; (d) 0.483 M; 174 mL of 0.554 M H_2SO_4
8.134 (a) Y is ClF_3 and X is ClF;

(b) T-shaped

(c) −139.2 kJ/mol ClF_3; (d) 55.9 kJ is released.

Chapter 9

9.1 1.00 atm = 14.7 psi; 1.00 mm Hg = 1.93×10^{-2} psi
9.2 10.3 m **9.3** 0.650 atm **9.4** 1000 mm Hg

9.5   (a)   (b)

9.6 4.461×10^3 mol; 7.155×10^4 g **9.7** 5.0 atm **9.8** 267 mol **9.9** 28 °C
9.10 (a) The volume should increase by about 10%.

(b) the volume should decrease by half;

(c) the volume is unchanged.

9.11 14.8 g; 7.55 L **9.12** 190 L **9.13** 34.1 amu; H_2S, hydrogen sulfide **9.14** $X_{H_2} = 0.7281$; $X_{N_2} = 0.2554$; $X_{NH_3} = 0.0165$ **9.15** $P_{total} = 25.27$ atm; $P_{H_2} = 18.4$ atm; $P_{N_2} = 6.45$ atm; $P_{NH_3} = 0.417$ atm **9.16** 0.0280 atm **9.17** $P_{red} = 300$ mm Hg; $P_{yellow} = 100$ mm Hg; $P_{green} = 200$ mm Hg **9.18** at 37 °C, 525 m/s; at −25 °C, 470 m/s **9.19** −187.0 °C **9.20** (a) O_2, 1.62; (b) C_2H_2, 1.04 **9.21** $^{20}Ne(1.05) > {}^{21}Ne(1.02) > {}^{22}Ne(1.00)$ **9.22** ideal gas law: 20.5 atm; van der Waals equation: 20.3 atm **9.23** 3.8×10^{-5} m **9.24** 2.0% **9.25** (a) 5.9 mm Hg; (b) 0.41 g *Conceptual Problems* **9.26** The picture on the right will be the same as that on the left, apart from random scrambling of the He and Ar atoms. **9.28** (a) the volume will increase by a factor of 1.5; (b) the volume will decrease by a factor of 2; (c) there is no change in volume.

9.30 (c). **9.32** The gas pressure in the bulb in mm Hg is equal to the difference in the height of the Hg in the two arms of the manometer. **9.34** (a) yellow; (b) 36 amu *Section Problems* **9.36** Temperature is a measure of the average kinetic energy of gas particles. **9.38** 0.632 atm; 6.40×10^4 Pa **9.40** 930 mm Hg **9.42** 1.046×10^5 Pa **9.44** 28.96 amu **9.46** (a) P would triple; (b) P would be 1/3 the initial pressure. (c) P would increase by 1.8 times; (d) P would be 0.17 times the initial pressure. **9.48** They all contain the same number of gas molecules. **9.50** 7210 L; 51.5 L **9.52** 2.1×10^4 mm Hg **9.54** 1×10^{-17} mm Hg **9.56** 1.23×10^4 g **9.58** ice **9.60** Weigh the containers. The heavier container contains O_2. **9.62** 1.5×10^4 g O_2 **9.64** (a) 0.716 g/L; (b) 1.96 g/L; (c) 1.43 g/L **9.66** 34.0 amu **9.68** 0.5469 L **9.70** (a) 9.44 L; (b) 6.05 g Zn **9.72** (a) 380 g; (b) 5.4 days **9.74** $P_{N_2} = 0.7808$ atm; $P_{O_2} = 0.2095$ atm; $P_{Ar} = 0.0093$ atm; $P_{CO_2} = 0.000\ 38$ atm **9.76** $P_{O_2} = 0.970$ atm; $P_{CO_2} = 0.007\ 11$ atm; **9.78** $X_{HCl} = 0.026$; $X_{H_2} = 0.094$; $X_{Ne} = 0.88$ **9.80** (a) 1.68 atm; (b) 0.219 atm. **9.82** $P_{H_2} = 723$ mm Hg; 3.36 g Mg **9.84** See list in text Section 9.6. **9.86** Heat is the energy transferred from one object to another as the result of a temperature difference between them. Temperature is a measure of the kinetic energy of molecular motion. **9.88** $u = 443$ m/s **9.90** For H_2, $u = 1360$ m/s. For He, $u = 2010$ m/s **9.92** 17.2 amu **9.94** Relative rates of diffusion are HCl (1.05) > F_2 (1.02) > Ar (1.00). **9.96** −272.83 °C *Chapter Problems* **9.98** (a) ozone depletion; (b) acid rain; (c) global warming; (d) air pollution **9.100** Relative rates of diffusion are $^{35}Cl_2$ (1.03) > $^{35}Cl^{37}Cl$ (1.01) > $^{37}Cl_2$ (1.00). **9.102** 1.1 L **9.104** (a) ideal gas law: 1.79 atm; (b) van der Waals equation: 1.74 atm **9.106** (a) Kr < O_2; (b) O_2 < Kr; (c) Kr < O_2; (d) Both are the same. **9.108** (a) 372 mm Hg; (b) 222 mm Hg; (c) 46.5 mm Hg **9.110** 504.3 g **9.112** (a) Bulb A contains $CO_2(g)$ and $N_2(g)$; B contains $CO_2(g)$, $N_2(g)$, and $H_2O(s)$; (b) $n = 0.0013$ mol H_2O; (c) A contains $N_2(g)$; B contains $N_2(g)$ and $H_2O(s)$; C contains $N_2(g)$ and $CO_2(s)$; (d) 0.010 92 mol N_2; (e) 0.0181 mol CO_2 **9.114** ideal gas law: $P = 59.1$ atm at 0 °C; 70.0 atm at 50 °C; 80.8 atm at 100 °C. van der Waals equation: $P = 36.5$ atm at 0 °C; 48.5 atm at 50 °C; 60.5 atm at 100 °C **9.116** 816 atm **9.118** (a) 0.901 mol; (b) 1.44 atm; (c) $P_{CH_4} = 1.32$ atm; $P_{C_2H_6} = 0.12$ atm; (d) Heat liberated = −843 kJ **9.120** (a) 196 g/mol; XeO_4; (b) $P_{Xe} = 0.313$ atm; $P_{O_2} = 0.626$ atm; $P_{total} = 0.939$ atm **9.122** 1.43 atm **9.124** 12.7% **9.126** $X_{NO_2} = 0.380$;

$X_{N_2O_4} = 0.620$ *Multiconcept Problems* **9.128** (a) 3.75 g; (b) 310 °C; (c) 1.02 atm **9.130** (a) $2 C_8H_{18}(l) + 25 O_2(g) \rightarrow 16 CO_2(g) + 18 H_2O(g)$; (b) 1.1×10^{11} kg; (c) 5.7×10^{13} L; (d) 59.5 mol, 1.33×10^3 L **9.132** (a) 0.0290 mol; (b) 0.0100 mol A; A = H_2O; (c) 0.0120 mol B; B = CO_2; (d) 0.001 00 mol C; C = O_2; 0.006 00 mol D; 28.0 g/mol; D = N_2; (e) $4 C_3H_5N_3O_9(l) \rightarrow 10 H_2O(g) + 12 CO_2(g) + O_2(g) + 6 N_2(g)$

Chapter 10

10.1 41%; HF has more ionic character than HCl. **10.2** (a) SF_6 is symmetrical (octahedral) and has no dipole moment; (b) $H_2C{=}CH_2$ is symmetrical; no dipole moment.

(c)

The C–Cl bonds in $CHCl_3$ are polar covalent bonds, and the molecule is polar.

(d)

The C–Cl bonds in CH_2Cl_2 are polar covalent bonds, and the molecule is polar.

10.3
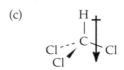

10.4 The N atom is electron rich (red) because of its high electronegativity. The C and H atoms are electron poor (blue) because they are less electronegative. **10.5** (a) HNO_3; (b) HNO_3; (c) Ar **10.6** H_2S, dipole–dipole, dispersion; CH_3OH, hydrogen bonding, dipole–dipole, dispersion; C_2H_6, dispersion; Ar, dispersion; Ar < C_2H_6 < H_2S < CH_3OH **10.7** (a) positive; (b) negative; (c) positive **10.8** 334 K **10.9** 47 °C **10.10** 31.4 kJ/mol **10.11** (a) 2 atoms; (b) 4 atoms **10.12** 167 pm **10.13** 9.31 g/cm^3 **10.14** There are several possibilities. Here's one.

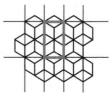

10.15 For CuCl: 4 minuses, 4 pluses. For $BaCl_2$: 8 pluses, 8 minuses **10.16** (a) 1 Re atom, 3 O atoms; (b) ReO_3; (c) +6; (d) linear; (e) octahedral **10.17** The triple point pressure of 5.11 atm **10.18** (a) $CO_2(s) \rightarrow CO_2(g)$; (b) $CO_2(l) \rightarrow CO_2(g)$; (c) $CO_2(g) \rightarrow CO_2(l) \rightarrow$ supercritical CO_2

10.19
(a)
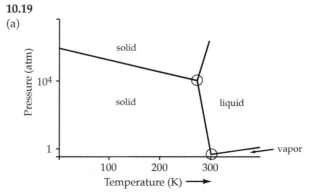

(b) two; (c) Increasing the pressure favors the liquid phase, giving the solid/liquid boundary a negative slope. At 1 atm pressure the liquid phase is more dense than the solid phase. **10.20** As the name implies, the constituent particles in an ionic liquid are cations and anions rather than molecules. **10.21** In ionic liquids the cation has an irregular shape and one or both of the ions are large and bulky to disperse charges over a large volume. Both factors minimize the crystal lattice energy, making the solid less stable and favoring the liquid. *Conceptual Problems* **10.22** The electronegative O atoms are electron rich (red), while the rest of the molecule is electron poor (blue). **10.24** (a) cubic closest-packed; (b) 4 S^{2-}; 4 Zn^{2+} **10.26** (a) normal boiling point $\approx$ 300 K, normal melting point $\approx$ 180 K; (b) (i) solid, (ii) gas, (iii) supercritical fluid

10.28 Here are two possibilities.

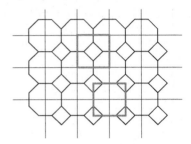

10.30

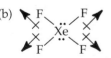

Section Problems **10.32** If a molecule has polar covalent bonds, the molecular shape (and location of lone pairs of electrons) determines whether the bond dipoles cancel and thus whether the molecule has a dipole moment. **10.34** (a) Dipole–dipole forces; dispersion forces are also present; (b) dispersion forces; (c) dispersion forces; (d) dipole–dipole forces and hydrogen bonding; dispersion forces are also present. **10.36** For CH_3OH and CH_4, dispersion forces are small. CH_3OH can hydrogen bond; CH_4 cannot. This accounts for the large difference in boiling points. For 1-decanol and decane, dispersion forces are comparable and relatively large along the C—H chain. 1-decanol can hydrogen bond; decane cannot. This accounts for the 57 °C higher boiling point for 1-decanol.

10.38

(a) [structure with Cl—O—Cl, Net]
(b) [XeF4 structure, Net dipole moment = 0]
(c) [CH3—C with Cl and H, Net]
(d) [BF3 structure, Net dipole moment = 0]

10.40 5.05%

10.42

[SO2 bent structure, Net] [O=C=O linear structure, Net dipole moment = 0]

SO_2 is bent and the individual bond dipole moments add to give a net dipole moment. CO_2 is linear and the individual bond dipole moments cancel.

10.44 (a) $\left[\begin{array}{c} Br \\ | \\ Cl-Pt-Cl \\ | \\ Br \end{array} \right]^{2-}$ (b) $\left[\begin{array}{c} Br \\ | \\ Cl-Pt-Br \\ | \\ Cl \end{array} \right]^{2-}$

10.46

[Hydrogen bond structure between two NH groups]
Hydrogen bond

10.48 surface tension **10.50** ΔH_{vap} is usually larger than ΔH_{fusion} because ΔH_{vap} is the heat required to overcome all intermolecular forces. **10.52** (a) $Hg(l) \rightarrow Hg(g)$; (b) no change of state, Hg remains a liquid; (c) $Hg(g) \rightarrow Hg(l) \rightarrow Hg(s)$ **10.54** As the pressure is lowered, more of the liquid H_2O is converted to H_2O vapor. This conversion is an endothermic process and the temperature decreases. The decrease in pressure and temperature takes the system across the liquid/solid boundary in the phase diagram so the H_2O that remains turns to ice. **10.56** 2.40 kJ **10.58** 3.73 kJ

10.60

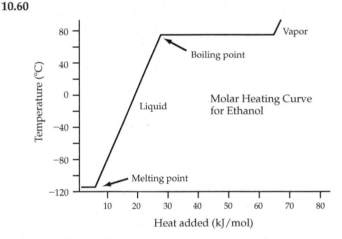

10.62 88.2 J/(K • mol) **10.64** 28.0 kJ/mol **10.66** 294 mm Hg
10.68

T(K)	P_{vap}(mm Hg)	ln P_{vap}	1/T
263	80.1	4.383	0.003 802
273	133.6	4.8949	0.003 663
283	213.3	5.3627	0.003 534
293	329.6	5.7979	0.003 413
303	495.4	6.2054	0.003 300
313	724.4	6.5853	0.003 195

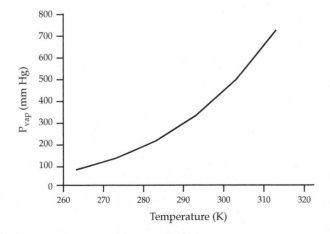

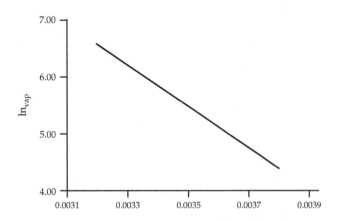

10.70 ΔH_{vap} = 30.1 kJ/mol **10.72** 30.1 kJ/mol. The calculated ΔH_{vap} and that obtained from the plot in Problem 10.68 are the same. **10.74** molecular solid, CO_2, I_2; metallic solid, any metallic element; covalent network solid, diamond; ionic solid, NaCl **10.76** (a) rubber; (b) Na_3PO_4; (c) CBr_4; (d) quartz; (e) Au **10.78** covalent network **10.80** 201 pm **10.82** The unit cell is the smallest repeating unit in a crystal. **10.84** 128 pm; 8.90 g/cm³ **10.86** 404.9 pm **10.88** 137 pm **10.90** face-centered cubic **10.92** Six Na^+ ions touch each H^- ion, and six H^- ions touch each Na^+ ion. **10.94** 244 pm **10.96** (a) gas; (b) liquid; (c) solid

10.98

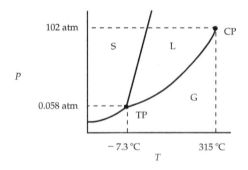

10.100 (a) $Br_2(s)$; (b) $Br_2(l)$ **10.102** Solid O_2 does not melt when pressure is applied because the solid is denser than the liquid, and the solid/liquid boundary in the phase diagram slopes to the right. **10.104** The starting phase is benzene as a solid, and the final phase is benzene as a gas.

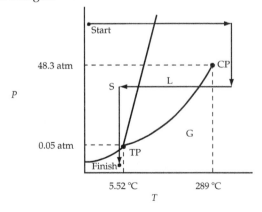

10.106 solid → liquid → supercritical fluid → liquid → solid → gas
***Chapter Problems* 10.108** Because chlorine is larger than fluorine, the charge separation is larger in CH_3Cl compared to CH_3F, resulting in CH_3Cl having a slightly larger dipole moment.

10.110 0.192 kJ **10.112** 0.837 atm **10.114** 60% **10.116** 650°C **10.118** −30.7 °C **10.120** 23.3 kJ/mol **10.122** Kr cannot be liquified at room temperature because room temperature is above T_c(−63 °C).

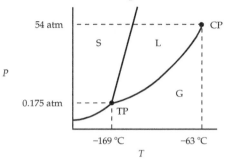

10.124 68% **10.126** 6.01 × 10²³ atoms/mol **10.128** (a) 556 pm; (b) 2.26 g/cm³ **10.130** Al_2O_3, ionic (greater lattice energy than NaCl because of higher ion charges); F_2, dispersion; H_2O, H–bonding, dipole–dipole; Br_2, dispersion (larger and more polarizable than F_2), ICl, dipole–dipole, NaCl, ionic; F_2 < Br_2 < ICl < H_2O < NaCl < Al_2O_3

10.132 (a)

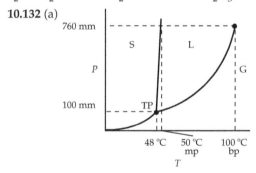

(b) (i) solid, (ii) gas, (iii) liquid, (iv) liquid, (v) solid
***Multiconcept Problems* 10.134** (a) 1.926 g; (b) Fe_3O_4; (c) 24 Fe atoms; 32 O atoms **10.136** (a) 231 pm; (b) K; (c) density of solid = 0.857 g/cm³; density of vapor = 7.29 × 10⁻⁶ g/cm³

Glossary

Absorption spectrum a plot of the amount of light absorbed versus wavelength (*Section 20.10*)

Accuracy how close to the true value a given measurement is (*Section 1.12*)

Achiral lacking handedness (*Section 20.9*)

Acid a substance that provides H^+ ions when dissolved in water (*Section 4.5*)

Acid–base indicator a substance that changes color in a specific pH range (*Section 14.6*)

Acid–base neutralization reaction a process in which an acid reacts with a base to yield water plus an ionic compound called a salt (*Sections 4.5, 15.1*)

Acid-dissociation constant (K_a) the equilibrium constant for the dissociation of an acid in water (*Section 14.8*)

Actinide one of the 14 inner-transition metals starting with actinium in the periodic table (*Section 1.3*)

Activation energy (E_a) the height of the energy barrier between reactants and products (*Section 12.12*)

Active site a small three-dimensional region of an enzyme with the specific shape necessary to bind the substrate and catalyze the appropriate reaction (*Chapter 12 Inquiry*)

Activity series a list of elements in order of their reducing ability in aqueous solution (*Section 4.8*)

Acyclic an open-chain compound; not containing a ring (*Section 23.5*)

Addition reaction an organic reaction in which a reagent adds to the multiple bond of the unsaturated reactant to yield a saturated product (*Section 23.4*)

Adenosine triphosphate (ATP) a molecule that is formed as the final result of food catabolism and plays a pivotal role in the production of biological energy (*Section 23.9*)

Advanced ceramic a ceramic material that has high-tech engineering, electronic, or biomedical applications (*Section 21.8*)

Alcohol an organic molecule that contains an —OH group (*Section 23.7*)

Aldehyde an organic molecule that contains one alkyl group and one hydrogen bonded to a $C{=}O$ carbon (*Section 23.8*)

Alkali metal an element in group 1A of the periodic table (*Sections 1.4, 6.9*)

Alkaline earth metal an element in group 2A of the periodic table (*Sections 1.4, 6.10*)

Alkane a compound that contains only carbon and hydrogen and has only single bonds (*Section 23.1*)

Alkene a hydrocarbon that has a carbon–carbon double bond (*Section 23.4*)

Alkyl group the part of an alkane that remains when a hydrogen is removed (*Section 23.3*)

Alkyne a hydrocarbon that has a carbon–carbon triple bond (*Section 23.4*)

Allotropes different structural forms of an element (*Section 10.10*)

Alloy a solid solution of two or more metals (*Section 21.2*)

Alpha (α) radiation a type of radioactive emission; a helium nucleus (*Section 2.8*)

Aluminosilicate a silicate mineral in which partial substitution of Si^{4+} by Al^{3+} has occurred (*Section 19.8*)

Amide an organic molecule that contains one alkyl group and one nitrogen bonded to a $C{=}O$ carbon (*Section 23.8*)

Amine an organic derivative of ammonia (*Section 23.7*)

Amino acid a molecule that contains both a basic amine group (—NH_2) and an acidic carboxyl group (—CO_2H); the building block from which proteins are made (*Section 23.10*)

Amorphous solid a solid whose constituent particles are randomly arranged and have no ordered, long-range structure (*Section 10.6*)

Amphoteric exhibiting both acidic and basic properties (*Sections 15.12, 18.9*)

Amplitude a wave's height measured from the midpoint between peak and trough (*Section 5.2*)

Anabolism metabolic reaction sequences that put building blocks together to assemble larger molecules (*Section 23.9*)

Angular-momentum quantum number (l) a variable in the solutions to the Schrödinger wave equation that gives the three-dimensional shape of an orbital (*Section 5.6*)

Anion a negatively charged atom or group of atoms (*Section 2.11*)

Anode the electrode at which oxidation takes place (*Section 17.1*)

Anodizing the oxidation of a metal anode to yield a protective metal oxide coat (*Chapter 17 Inquiry*)

Antibonding molecular orbital a molecular orbital that is higher in energy than the atomic orbitals it is derived from (*Section 7.13*)

Aqueous solution a solution with water as solvent (*Chapter 4 Introduction*)

Aromatic compound the class of compounds related to benzene (*Section 23.6*)

Arrhenius acid a substance that provides H^+ ions when dissolved in water (*Sections 4.5, 14.1*)

Arrhenius base a substance that provides OH^- ions when dissolved in water (*Sections 4.5, 14.1*)

Arrhenius equation an equation relating reaction rate constant, temperature, and activation energy; $k = Ae^{-E_a/RT}$ (*Section 12.12*)

Atmosphere (atm) a common unit of pressure measurement; standard atmospheric pressure at sea level is defined as exactly 760 mm Hg (*Section 9.1*)

Atom the smallest particle that retains the chemical properties of an element (*Section 2.2*)

Atomic mass the weighted average mass of an element's naturally occurring atoms (*Section 2.6*)

Atomic mass unit (amu) a convenient unit of mass; 1/12th the mass of a $^{12}_{6}C$ atom (*Section 2.6*)

Atomic number (Z) the number of protons in an atom's nucleus (*Section 2.5*)

Aufbau principle a set of rules that guides the electron filling order of orbitals in atoms (*Section 5.11*)

Avogadro's law The volume of a gas at a fixed pressure and temperature is proportional to its molar amount (*Section 9.2*).

Avogadro's number (N_A) the number of units in a mole; 6.022×10^{23} (*Section 2.6*)

Balanced a chemical equation in which the numbers and kinds of atoms are the same on both sides of the reaction arrow (*Section 3.1*)

Balmer–Rydberg equation an equation that accounts for the lines in the hydrogen spectrum (*Section 5.2*)

$$\frac{1}{\lambda} = R_\infty \left[\frac{1}{m^2} - \frac{1}{n^2} \right] \text{ or } \nu = R_\infty \cdot c \left[\frac{1}{m^2} - \frac{1}{n^2} \right]$$

Band gap the energy difference between the bonding MOs in the valence band and the antibonding MOs in the conduction band of a semiconductor (*Section 21.5*)

Band theory the molecular orbital theory for metals (*Section 21.4*)

Base a substance that provides OH^- ions when dissolved in water (*Sections 4.5, 14.1*)

Base-dissociation constant (K_b) the equilibrium constant for the reaction of a base with water (*Section 14.12*)

Basic oxygen process a method for purifying iron and converting it to steel (*Section 21.3*)

Battery *see* Galvanic cell (*Sections 17.1, 17.9*)

Bayer process purification of Al_2O_3 by treating bauxite with hot aqueous NaOH (*Sections 18.9, 21.2*)

Beta (β) radiation a type of radioactive emission consisting of electrons (*Section 2.8*)

Bidentate ligand a ligand that bonds to a metal using electron pairs on two donor atoms (*Section 20.6*)

Bimolecular reaction an elementary reaction that results from a collision between two reactant molecules (*Section 12.9*)

Binary hydride a compound that contains hydrogen and one other element (*Section 18.5*)

Binding energy the energy that holds nucleons together in the nucleus of an atom (*Section 22.1*)

Biochemistry the chemistry of living organisms (*Chapter 23 Introduction*)

Biofuel a fuel such as biodiesel, made from a renewable plant source (*Chapter 8 Inquiry*)

Blast furnace a huge reactor in which iron is produced by reduction of iron ore with carbon monoxide (*Section 21.3*)

Bleaching decolorizing a colored material (*Section 4.11*)

Body-centered cubic packing a packing arrangement of spheres into a body-centered cubic unit cell (*Section 10.8*)

Body-centered cubic unit cell a cubic unit cell with an atom at each of its eight corners and an additional atom in the center of the cube (*Section 10.8*)

Boiling point the temperature at which liquid and vapor coexist in equilibrium (*Section 10.4*)

Bond angle the angle at which two adjacent bonds intersect (*Section 7.9*)

Bond dissociation energy (D) the amount of energy necessary to break a chemical bond in an isolated molecule in the gaseous state (*Section 7.2*)

Bond length the minimum-energy distance between nuclei in a covalent bond (*Section 7.1*)

Bond order the number of electron pairs shared between two bonded atoms (*Section 7.5*)

Bonding electron pair a pair of valence electrons in a covalent bond (*Section 7.5*)

Bonding molecular orbital a molecular orbital that is lower in energy than the atomic orbitals it is derived from (*Section 7.13*)

Borane any compound of boron and hydrogen (*Section 19.4*)

Born–Haber cycle a pictorial way of viewing the energy changes in the various steps during formation of an ionic solid from its elements (*Section 6.7*)

Boyle's law The volume of a fixed amount of gas at a constant temperature varies inversely with its pressure (*Section 9.2*).

Bragg equation an equation used in X-ray crystallography for calculating the distance between atoms in a crystal (*Section 10.7*)

Branched-chain alkane an alkane with a branching connection of carbons (*Section 23.1*)

Brønsted–Lowry acid a substance that can transfer H^+ to a base in an acid–base reaction (*Section 14.1*)

Brønsted–Lowry base a substance that can accept H^+ from an acid in an acid–base reaction (*Section 14.1*)

Buffer capacity a measure of the amount of acid or base that a buffer can absorb without a significant change in pH (*Section 15.3*)

Buffer solution a solution of a weak acid and its conjugate base that resists drastic changes in pH (*Section 15.3*)

C-Terminal amino acid the amino acid with a free $-CO_2H$ group on the end of a protein chain (*Section 23.10*)

Carbide a carbon compound in which the carbon atom has a negative oxidation state (*Section 19.7*)

Carbohydrate a large class of organic molecules commonly called sugars and related to glucose (*Section 23.11*)

Carbonyl group the $C{=}O$ group (*Section 23.8*)

Carboxylate anion the anion $-CO_2^-$ that results from deprotonation of a carboxylic acid (*Section 23.8*)

Carboxylic acid an organic molecule that contains the $-CO_2H$ group (*Section 23.8*)

Catabolism metabolic reaction sequences that break molecules apart (*Section 23.9*)

Catalyst a substance that increases the rate of a reaction without itself being consumed (*Section 12.14*)

Cathode the electrode at which reduction takes place (*Section 17.1*)

Cathode ray the visible glow emitted when an electric potential is applied across two electrodes in an evacuated chamber (*Section 2.3*)

Cathodic protection a technique for protecting a metal from corrosion by connecting it to a second metal that is more easily oxidized (*Section 17.11*)

Cation a positively charged atom or group of atoms (*Section 2.11*)

Cell potential (E) *see* Electromotive force (*Section 17.3*)

Cell voltage *see* Electromotive force (*Section 17.3*)

Celsius degree (°C) a common unit of temperature; 0 °C = 273.15 K (*Section 1.8*)

Centimeter (cm) a common unit of length; 1 cm = 0.01 m (*Section 1.7*)

Ceramic an inorganic, nonmetallic, nonmolecular solid (*Section 21.8*)

Ceramic composite a hybrid material made of two ceramics (*Section 21.9*)

Ceramic–metal composite a hybrid material made of a metal reinforced with a ceramic (*Section 21.9*)

Ceramic–polymer composite a hybrid material made of a polymer reinforced with a ceramic (*Section 21.9*)

Chain reaction a self-sustaining reaction whose product initiates further reaction (*Section 22.2*)

Change of state *see* Phase change (*Section 10.4*)

Charles's law The volume of a fixed amount of gas at a constant pressure varies directly with its absolute temperature (*Section 9.2*).

Chelate the cyclic complex formed by a metal atom and a polydentate ligand (*Section 20.6*)

Chelating agent a polydentate ligand (*Section 20.6*)

Chemical bond the force that holds atoms together in chemical compounds (*Section 2.10*)

Chemical compound a chemical substance composed of atoms of more than one element (*Section 2.1*)

Chemical energy potential energy stored in chemical bonds (*Section 8.1*)

Chemical equation a format for writing a chemical reaction, listing reactants on the left, products on the right, and an arrow between them (*Section 2.1*)

Chemical equilibrium the state reached when the concentrations of reactants and products remain constant in time (*Section 13.1*)

Chemical formula a format for listing the number and kind of constituent elements in a compound (*Section 2.1*)

Chemical kinetics the area of chemistry concerned with reaction rates and the sequence of steps by which reactions occur (*Chapter 12*)

Chemical property a characteristic that results in a change in the chemical makeup of a sample (*Section 1.4*)

Chemical reaction the transformation of one substance into another (*Section 2.1*)

Chemistry the study of the composition, properties, and transformations of matter (*Chapter 1*)

Chiral having handedness (*Section 20.9*)

Chlor-alkali industry the commercial method of production for Cl_2 and NaOH by electrolysis of aqueous sodium chloride (*Section 17.13*)

Chromosome a threadlike strand of DNA in the nucleus of cells (*Section 23.13*)

Cis isomer the isomer of a metal complex or alkene in which identical ligands or groups are adjacent rather than opposite (*Sections 20.8, 23.4*)

Clausius–Clapeyron equation a mathematical relationship between vapor pressure and heat of vaporization for a substance (*Section 10.5*)

Coefficient a number placed before a formula in a chemical equation to indicate how many formula units are required to balance the equation (*Section 3.1*)

Colligative property a property that depends only on the amount of dissolved solute rather than on the chemical identity of the solute (*Section 11.5*)

Collision theory a model by which bimolecular reactions occur when two properly oriented reactant molecules come together in a sufficiently energetic collision (*Section 12.12*)

Colloid a homogeneous mixture containing particles with diameters in the range 2–500 nm (*Section 11.1*)

Combustion a chemical reaction that sustains a flame (*Sections 4.11, 8.7*)

Common-ion effect the shift in the position of an equilibrium on addition of a substance that provides an ion in common with one of the ions already involved in the equilibrium (*Section 15.2*)

Complex ion an ion that contains a metal cation bonded to one or more small molecules or ions (*Section 15.12*)

Condensation the change of a gas to a liquid (*Section 10.4*)

Condensed structure a shorthand method for drawing organic structures in which C—H and C—C single bonds are "understood" rather than shown (*Section 23.1*)

Conduction band the antibonding molecular orbitals in a semiconductor (*Section 21.5*)

Conjugate acid the species HA formed by addition of H^+ to a base A^- (*Section 14.1*)

Conjugate acid–base pair chemical species whose formulas differ only by one proton (*Section 14.1*)

Conjugate base the species A^- formed by loss of H^+ from an acid HA (*Section 14.1*)

Constitutional isomers isomers that have different connections among their constituent atoms (*Section 20.8*)

Contact process the commercial process for making sulfuric acid from sulfur (*Section 19.13*)

Conversion factor an expression that describes the relationship between different units (*Section 1.14*)

Coordinate covalent bond a bond formed when one atom donates two electrons to another atom that has a vacant valence orbital (*Section 7.5*)

Coordination compound a compound in which a central metal ion is attached to a group of surrounding molecules or ions by coordinate covalent bonds (*Section 20.5*)

Coordination number the number of nearest-neighbor atoms in a crystal (*Section 10.8*) or the number of ligand donor atoms that surround a central metal ion in a complex (*Section 20.5*)

Core electrons inner-shell electrons (*Section 6.3*)

Corrosion the oxidative deterioration of a metal, such as the conversion of iron to rust (*Sections 4.11, 17.11*)

Cosmic ray a stream of energetic particles, primarily protons, coming from interstellar space (*Section 22.4*)

Coulomb's law The force resulting from the interaction of two electric charges is equal to a constant k times the magnitude of the charges divided by the square of the distance between them (*Section 6.8*).

Covalent bond a bond that occurs when two atoms share several (usually two) electrons (*Section 2.10; Chapter 7*)

Covalent hydride a compound in which hydrogen is attached to another element by a covalent bond (*Section 18.5*)

Covalent network solid a solid whose atoms are linked together by covalent bonds into a giant three-dimensional array (*Sections 10.6, 10.10*)

Critical mass the amount of material necessary for a nuclear chain reaction to become self-sustaining (*Section 22.2*)

Critical point a combination of temperature and pressure beyond which a gas cannot be liquefied (*Section 10.11*)

Crystal field splitting the energy splitting between two sets of d orbitals in a metal complex (*Section 20.12*)

Crystal field theory a model that views the bonding in metal complexes as arising from electrostatic interactions and considers the effect of the ligand charges on the energies of the metal ion d orbitals (*Section 20.12*)

Crystalline solid a solid whose atoms, ions, or molecules have an ordered arrangement extending over a long range (*Section 10.6*)

Cubic centimeter (cm^3) a common unit of volume, equal in size to the milliliter; $1\ cm^3 = 10^{-6}\ m^3$ (*Section 1.9*)

Cubic closest-packed a packing arrangement of spheres into a face-centered cubic unit cell with three alternating layers (*Section 10.8*)

Cubic meter (m^3) the SI unit of volume (*Section 1.9*)

Cycloalkane an alkane that contains a ring of carbon atoms (*Section 23.5*)

***d*-Block element** a transition metal element in which d orbitals are filled (*Section 5.13; Chapter 20*)

Dalton (Da) an alternative name for the atomic mass unit, amu (*Section 2.6*)

Dalton's law of partial pressures The total pressure exerted by a mixture of gases in a container at constant V and T is equal to the sum of the pressures exerted by each individual gas in the container (*Section 9.5*).

de Broglie equation an equation that relates mass, wavelength, and velocity, $m = h/\lambda v$ (*Section 5.4*)

Decay constant the first-order rate constant for radioactive decay (*Section 12.6*)

Degenerate having the same energy level (*Section 5.11*)

Density an intensive physical property that relates the mass of an object to its volume (*Section 1.10*)

Deoxyribonucleic acid (DNA) an immense biological molecule, made up of deoxyribonucleotide units and containing an organism's genetic information (*Section 23.13*)

Deposition the change of a gas directly to a solid (*Section 10.4*)

Diamagnetic a substance that has no unpaired electrons and is weakly repelled by a magnetic field (*Section 7.14*)

Diastereoisomers non-mirror-image stereoisomers (*Section 20.8*)

Diffraction scattering of a light beam by an object containing regularly spaced lines or points (*Section 10.7*)

Diffusion the mixing of different gases by random molecular motion with frequent collisions (*Section 9.7*)

Dimensional-analysis a method of problem solving whereby problems are set up so that unwanted units cancel (*Section 1.14*)

Diode a semiconductor device that permits electric current to flow in one direction but is highly resistant to current flow in the opposite direction (*Section 21.6*)

Dipole a pair of separated electrical charges (*Section 10.1*)

Dipole–dipole force an intermolecular force resulting from electrical interactions among dipoles on neighboring molecules (*Section 10.2*)

Dipole moment (μ) the measure of net molecular polarity; $\mu = Q \times r$ (*Section 10.1*)

Diprotic acid an acid that has two dissociable protons (*Section 4.5*)

Disproportionation reaction a reaction in which a substance is both oxidized and reduced (*Section 18.10*)

Dissociate splitting apart to give ions when dissolved in water (*Section 4.2*)

Donor atom the atom attached directly to a metal in a coordination compound (*Section 20.6*)

Doping the addition of a small amount of an impurity to increase the conductivity of a semiconductor (*Section 21.5*)

Double bond a covalent bond formed by sharing four electrons between atoms (*Section 7.5*)

Effective nuclear charge (Z_{eff}) the net nuclear charge actually felt by an electron (*Sections 5.10, 5.14*)

Effusion the escape of gas molecules through a tiny hole in a membrane without molecular collisions (*Section 9.7*)

Electrochemical cell a device for interconverting chemical and electrical energy (*Section 17.1*)

Electrochemistry the area of chemistry concerned with the interconversion of chemical and electrical energy (*Chapter 17*)

Electrode a conductor through which electrical current enters or leaves a cell (*Section 17.1*)

Electrolysis the process of using an electric current to bring about chemical change (*Section 17.12*)

Electrolyte a substance that dissolves in water to produce ions (*Section 4.2*)

Electrolytic cell an electrochemical cell in which an electric current drives a nonspontaneous reaction (*Section 17.12*)

Electromagnetic radiation radiant energy (*Section 5.1*)

Electromagnetic spectrum the range of different kinds of electromagnetic radiation (*Section 5.1*)

Electromotive force (emf) the electrical potential that pushes electrons away from the anode and pulls them toward the cathode (*Section 17.3*)

Electron a negatively charged, fundamental atomic particle (*Section 2.3*)

Electron affinity (E_{ea}) the energy change that occurs when an electron is added to an isolated atom in the gaseous state (*Section 6.5*)

Electron capture a nuclear reaction in which a proton in the nucleus captures an inner-shell electron and is thereby converted into a neutron (*Section 2.8*)

Electron configuration a description of which orbitals in an atom are occupied by electrons (*Section 5.11*)

Electron-dot structure a representation of a molecule that shows valence electrons as dots; also called a Lewis structure (*Section 7.5*)

Electron-sea model a model that visualizes metals as a three-dimensional array of metal cations immersed in a sea of delocalized electrons that are free to move about (*Section 21.4*)

Electronegativity (EN) the ability of an atom in a molecule to attract the shared electrons in a covalent bond (*Section 7.4*)

Electroplating the coating of one metal on the surface of another using electrolysis (*Section 17.13*)

Electrorefining the purification of a metal by means of electrolysis (*Section 17.13*)

Element a fundamental substance that can't be chemically changed or broken down into anything simpler (*Section 1.2*)

Elemental analysis a technique for determining the identities and amounts of elements in a compound (*Section 3.11*)

Elementary reaction a single chemical step in a reaction mechanism (*Section 12.9*)

Elementary step *see* Elementary reaction (*Section 12.9*)

Empirical formula a formula that gives the ratios of atoms in a chemical compound but not necessarily the exact values (*Section 3.10*)

Enantiomers stereoisomers that are non-identical mirror images of each other (*Section 20.9*)

End point the point in a titration at which stoichiometrically equivalent quantities of reactants have been mixed together (*Sections 4.10, 15.5*)

Endothermic a reaction in which heat is absorbed and the temperature of the surroundings falls (*Section 8.6*)

Energy the capacity to do work or supply heat (*Sections 1.11, 8.1*)

Enthalpy (H) the quantity $E + PV$ (*Section 8.4*)

Enthalpy change (ΔH) the heat change in a reaction or process at constant pressure; $\Delta H = \Delta E + P\Delta V$ (*Section 8.4*)

Entropy (S) the amount of molecular randomness in a system (*Sections 8.12, 16.3*)

Entropy of solution (ΔS_{soln}) the entropy change during formation of a solution (*Section 11.2*)

Enzyme a large protein that acts as a catalyst for a biological reaction (*Chapter 12 Inquiry*)

Equilibrium constant (K_c) the constant in the equilibrium equation (*Section 13.2*)

Equilibrium constant (K_p) the equilibrium constant for reaction of gases, defined using partial pressures (*Section 13.3*)

Equilibrium equation an equation that relates the concentrations in an equilibrium mixture (*Section 13.2*)

Equilibrium mixture a mixture of reactants and products at equilibrium (*Section 13.1*)

Equivalence point the point in a titration at which stoichiometrically equivalent quantities of reactants have been mixed together (*Section 15.5*)

Ester an organic molecule that contains the —CO_2R group (*Section 23.8*)

Ether an organic molecule that contains two alkyl groups bonded to the same oxygen atom (*Section 23.7*)

Exothermic a reaction in which heat is evolved and the temperature of the surroundings rises (*Section 8.6*)

Extensive property a property whose value depends on the sample size (*Section 1.4*)

f-Block element a lanthanide or actinide element, in which f orbitals are filled (*Section 5.13*)

Face-centered cubic unit cell a cubic unit cell with an atom at each of its eight corners and an additional atom on each of its six faces (*Section 10.8*)

Faraday the electrical charge on 1 mol of electrons (96,485 C/mol e$^-$) (*Section 17.3*)

Fatty acid a long-chain carboxylic acid found as a constituent of fats and oils (*Section 23.12*)

First law of thermodynamics The total internal energy of an isolated system is constant (*Sections 8.1, 8.2*).

First-order reaction a reaction whose rate depends on the concentration of a single reactant raised to the first power (*Section 12.4*)

Flotation a metallurgical process that exploits differences in the ability of water and oil to wet the surfaces of mineral and gangue (*Section 21.2*)

Formal charge an electron bookkeeping device that tells whether an atom in a molecule has gained or lost electrons compared to an isolated atom (*Section 7.8*)

Formation constant (K_f) the equilibrium constant for formation of a complex ion (*Section 15.12*)

Formula mass the sum of atomic masses of all atoms in one formula unit of a substance (*Section 3.3*)

Formula unit one unit (atom, ion, or molecule) corresponding to a given formula (*Section 3.1*)

Fractional distillation the separation of volatile liquids on the basis of boiling point (*Section 11.10*)

Free-energy change (ΔG) $\Delta G = \Delta H - T\Delta S$ (*Sections 8.13, 16.7*)

Freezing the change of a liquid to a solid (*Section 10.4*)

Frequency (ν) the number of wave maxima that pass by a fixed point per unit time (*Section 5.1*)

Frequency factor the parameter A ($= pZ$) in the Arrhenius equation (*Section 12.12*)

Fuel cell a galvanic cell in which one of the reactants is a traditional fuel such as methane or hydrogen (*Section 17.10*)

Functional group a part of a larger molecule; composed of an atom or group of atoms that has characteristic chemical behavior (*Section 23.2*)

Fusion melting, or the change of a solid to a liquid (*Section 10.4*); also, the joining together of two nuclei in a nuclear reaction, accompanied by release of an enormous amount of energy (*Section 22.2*)

Galvanic cell an electrochemical cell in which a spontaneous chemical reaction generates an electric current (*Section 17.1*)

Galvanizing a process for protecting steel from corrosion by coating it with zinc (*Section 17.11*)

Gamma (γ) radiation a type of radioactive emission consisting of a stream of high-energy photons (*Section 2.8*)

Gangue the economically worthless material consisting of sand, clay, and other impurities that accompanies an ore (*Section 21.2*)

Gas constant (R) the constant in the ideal gas law $PV = nRT$ (*Section 9.3*)

Gas laws relationships among the variables P, V, n, and T for a gas sample (*Section 9.2*)

Gene a segment of a DNA chain that contains the instructions necessary to make a specific protein (*Section 23.13*)

Geometric isomers *see* Diastereoisomers (*Section 20.8*)

Gibbs free-energy change (ΔG) $\Delta G = \Delta H - T\Delta S$ (*Sections 8.13, 16.7*)

Graham's law The rate of effusion of a gas is inversely proportional to the square root of its molar mass (*Section 9.7*).

Gram (g) a common unit of mass; 1 g = 0.001 kg (*Section 1.6*)

Green chemistry a set of guidelines describing environmentally benign chemical reactions and practices (*Chapter 4 Inquiry*)

Ground-state electron configuration the lowest-energy electron configuration of an atom (*Section 5.11*)

Group a column of elements in the periodic table (*Section 1.3*)

Half-life ($t_{1/2}$) the time required for a reactant concentration to drop to one-half its initial value (*Section 12.5*)

Half-reaction the oxidation or reduction part of a redox reaction (*Sections 4.9, 17.1*)

Half-reaction method a method for balancing redox equations (*Section 4.9*)

Hall–Heroult process the commercial method for producing aluminum by electrolysis of a molten mixture of aluminum oxide and cryolite (*Section 17.13*)

Halogen an element in group 7A of the periodic table (*Sections 1.4, 6.11*)

Hard water water that contains appreciable concentrations of Ca^{2+}, Mg^{2+}, or Fe^{2+} cations (*Section 18.13*)

Heat the energy transferred from one object to another as the result of a temperature difference between them (*Section 8.1*)

Heat capacity (C) the amount of heat required to raise the temperature of an object or substance a given amount (*Section 8.7*)

Heat of combustion the amount of energy released on burning a substance (*Section 8.11*)

Heat of formation (ΔH°_f) *see* Standard heat of formation (*Section 8.9*)

Heat of fusion (ΔH_{fusion}) the amount of heat required for melting a solid to a liquid (*Section 10.4*)

Heat of reaction (ΔH) the enthalpy change for a reaction (*Section 8.4*)

Heat of solution (ΔH_{soln}) the enthalpy change during formation of a solution (*Section 11.2*)

Heat of sublimation (ΔH_{subl}) the amount of heat required for sublimation of a solid to a gas (*Section 8.6*)

Heat of vaporization (ΔH_{vap}) the amount of heat required for vaporization of a liquid to a gas (*Section 10.4*)

Heisenberg uncertainty principle The position and the velocity of an electron can never both be known beyond a certain level of precision (*Section 5.5*).

Henderson–Hasselbalch equation an equation relating the pH of a solution to the pK_a of the weak acid; pH = pK_a + log ([base]/[acid]) (*Section 15.4*)

Henry's law The solubility of a gas in a liquid at a given temperature is directly proportional to the partial pressure of the gas over the solution (*Section 11.4*).

Hertz (Hz) a unit of frequency; 1 Hz = 1 s^{-1} (*Section 5.1*)

Hess's law The overall enthalpy change for a reaction is equal to the sum of the enthalpy changes for the individual steps in the reaction (*Section 8.8*).

Heterogeneous catalyst a catalyst that exists in a different phase than the reactants (*Section 12.15*)

Heterogeneous equilibria equilibria in which reactants and products are present in more than one phase (*Section 13.4*)

Hexadentate ligand a ligand with six donor atoms that bonds to a metal (*Section 20.6*)

Hexagonal closest-packed a packing arrangement of spheres into a noncubic unit cell with two alternating layers (*Section 10.8*)

High-spin complex a metal complex in which the *d* electrons are arranged to give the maximum number of unpaired electrons (*Section 20.11*)

Homogeneous catalyst a catalyst that exists in the same phase as the reactants (*Section 12.15*)

Homogeneous equilibria equilibria in which all reactants and products are in a single phase, usually either gaseous or solution (*Section 13.4*)

Hund's rule If two or more degenerate orbitals are available, one electron goes in each until all are half full (*Section 5.11*).

Hybrid atomic orbital a wave function derived by combination of atomic wave functions (*Section 7.11*)

Hydrate a solid compound that contains water molecules (*Section 18.14*)

Hydration the addition of water to an alkene (*Section 23.4*)

Hydrocarbon a compound that contains only carbon and hydrogen (*Section 23.1*)

Hydrogen bond an attractive intermolecular force between a hydrogen atom bonded to an electronegative O, N, or F atom and an unshared electron pair on a nearby electronegative atom (*Section 10.2*)

Hydrogenation the addition of H_2 to an alkene to yield an alkane (*Section 23.4*)

Hydronium ion the protonated water molecule, H_3O^+ (*Sections 4.5, 14.3*)

Hygroscopic absorbing water from the air (*Section 18.14*)

Ideal gas a gas whose behavior exactly follows the ideal gas law (*Section 9.2*)

Ideal gas law a description of how the volume of a gas is affected by changes in pressure, temperature, and amount; $PV = nRT$ (*Section 9.3*)

Infrared radiation electromagnetic radiation with wavelengths in the range 750 nm to 0.1 mm (*Section 5.1*)

Initial rate the instantaneous rate at the beginning of a reaction (*Section 12.1*)

Inner transition metal element an element in the 14 groups shown separately at the bottom of the periodic table (*Section 1.3*)

Instantaneous rate the rate of a reaction at a particular time (*Section 12.1*)

Integrated rate law the integrated form of a rate law (*Section 12.4*)

Intensive property a property whose value does not depend on the sample size (*Section 1.4*)

Intermolecular force an attractive interaction between molecules (*Section 10.2*)

Internal energy (E) the sum of kinetic and potential energies for each particle in a system (*Section 8.2*)

International System of Units (SI) the seven base units, along with others derived from them, used for all scientific measurements (*Section 1.5*)

Interstitial hydride a metallic hydride that consists of a crystal lattice of metal atoms with the smaller hydrogen atoms occupying holes between the larger metal atoms (*Section 18.5*)

Ion a charged atom or group of atoms (*Section 2.11*)

Ion–dipole force an intermolecular force resulting from electrical interactions between an ion and the partial charges on a polar molecule (*Section 10.2*)

Ion exchange a process for softening hard water in which the Ca^{2+} and Mg^{2+} ions are replaced by Na^+ (*Section 18.13*)

Ion product (IP) a number defined in the same way as K_{sp}, except that the concentrations in the expression for IP are not necessarily equilibrium values (*Section 15.13*)

Ion-product constant for water (K_w) $[H_3O^+][OH^-] = 1.0 \times 10^{-14}$ (*Section 14.4*)

Ionic bond a bond that results from a transfer of one or more electrons between atoms (*Sections 2.11, 6.7*)

Ionic equation a chemical equation written so that ions are explicitly shown (*Section 4.3*)

Ionic hydride a saltlike, high-melting, white, crystalline compound formed by the alkali metals and the heavier alkaline earth metals (*Section 18.5*)

Ionic liquid a liquid whose constituent particles are ions rather than molecules (*Chapter 10 Inquiry*)

Ionic solid a solid whose constituent particles are ions ordered into a regular three–dimensional arrangement held together by ionic bonds (*Sections 2.11, 6.7*)

Ionization energy (E_i) the amount of energy necessary to remove the outermost electron from an isolated neutral atom in the gaseous state (*Section 6.3*)

Ionization isomers isomers that differ in the anion bonded to the metal ion (*Section 20.8*)

Isomers compounds that have the same formula but a different bonding arrangement of their constituent atoms (*Section 20.8*)

Isotope effect differences in properties that arise from differences in isotopic mass (*Section 18.2*)

Isotopes atoms with identical atomic numbers but different mass numbers (*Section 2.5*)

Joule (J) the SI unit of energy, equal to 1 (kg · m^2)/s^2 (*Section 1.11*)

K_a acid-dissociation constant; the equilibrium constant for dissociation of an acid in water (*Section 14.8*)

K_b base-dissociation constant; the equilibrium constant for the reaction of a base with water (*Section 14.12*)

K_b molal boiling-point-elevation constant; the amount by which the boiling point of a solvent is raised by dissolved substances (*Section 11.7*)

K_c equilibrium constant; the constant in the equilibrium equation (*Section 13.2*)

K_f formation constant; the equilibrium constant for formation of a complex ion (*Section 15.12*)

K_f molal freezing-point-depression constant; the amount by which the melting point of a solvent is lowered by dissolved substances (*Section 11.7*)

K_p equilibrium constant; the equilibrium constant for reaction of gases, defined using partial pressures (*Section 13.3*)

K_{sp} solubility-product constant; the equilibrium constant for a dissolution reaction (*Section 15.10*)

K_{spa} solubility-product constant in acid; the equilibrium constant for a dissolution reaction in acid (*Section 15.14*)

K_w ion-product constant for water; $[H_3O^+][OH^-] = 1.0 \times 10^{-14}$ (*Section 14.4*)

Kelvin (K) the SI unit of temperature; $0\ K = $ absolute zero (*Section 1.8*)

Ketone an organic molecule that contains two alkyl groups bonded to a $C=O$ carbon (*Section 23.8*)

kilogram (kg) the SI unit of mass; 1 kg = 2.205 U.S. lb (*Section 1.6*)

Kinetic energy (E_K) the energy of motion; $E_K = (1/2)mv^2$ (*Section 1.11*)

Kinetic–molecular theory a theory describing the quantitative behavior of gases (*Section 9.6*)

Lanthanide one of the 14 inner transition metals starting with lanthanum in the periodic table (*Section 1.3*)

Lanthanide contraction the decrease in atomic radii across the *f*-block lanthanide elements (*Section 20.2*)

Lattice energy (U) the sum of the electrostatic interactions between ions in a solid that must be overcome to break a crystal into individual ions (*Section 6.8*)

Law of conservation of energy Energy can be neither created nor destroyed (*Section 8.1*).

Law of definite proportions Different samples of a pure chemical substance always contain the same proportion of elements by mass (*Section 2.1*).

Law of mass conservation Mass is neither created nor destroyed in chemical reactions (*Section 2.1*).

Law of multiple proportions When two elements combine in different ways to form different substances, the mass ratios are small, whole-number multiples of one another (*Section 2.2*).

LD$_{50}$ the amount of a substance that is lethal to 50% of test animals (*Chapter 1 Inquiry*)

Le Châtelier's principle If a stress is applied to a reaction mixture at equilibrium, reaction occurs in the direction that relieves the stress (*Section 13.6*).

Lewis acid an electron-pair acceptor (*Section 14.16*)

Lewis base an electron-pair donor (*Section 14.16*)

Lewis structure an electron-dot structure, or representation of a molecule that shows valence electrons as dots (*Section 7.5*)

Ligand a molecule or ion that bonds to the central metal ion in a complex (*Sections 20.5, 20.6*)

Ligand donor atom an atom attached directly to the metal ion in a metal complex (*Section 20.5*)

Light-emitting diode (LED) a semiconductor device that converts electrical energy into light (*Section 21.6*)

Limiting reactant the reactant present in limiting amount that controls the extent to which a reaction occurs (*Section 3.5*)

Line spectrum the wavelengths of light emitted by an energetically excited atom (*Section 5.2*)

Linkage isomers isomers that arise when a ligand bonds to a metal through either of two different donor atoms (*Section 20.8*)

Lipid a naturally occurring organic molecule that dissolves in nonpolar organic solvents when a sample of plant or animal tissue is crushed or ground (*Section 23.12*)

Liter (L) a common unit of volume; $1\ L = 10^{-3}\ m^3$ (*Section 1.9*)

Lock-and-key model a model that pictures an enzyme as a large, irregularly shaped molecule with a cleft into which substrate can fit (*Chapter 12 Inquiry*)

London dispersion force an intermolecular force resulting from the presence of temporary dipoles in atoms or molecules (*Section 10.2*)

Lone pair electrons a pair of valence electrons not used for bonding (*Section 7.5*)

Low-spin complex a metal complex in which the d electrons are paired up to give a maximum number of doubly occupied d orbitals and a minimum number of unpaired electrons (*Section 20.11*)

Magnetic quantum number (m_l) a variable in the solutions to the Schrödinger wave equation that defines the spatial orientation of an orbital (*Section 5.6*)

Main-group element an element in the two groups on the left and the six groups on the right of the periodic table (*Section 1.3; Chapters 6, 19*)

Manometer a simple instrument for measuring gas pressure; similar in principle to the mercury barometer (*Section 9.1*)

Mass the amount of matter in an object (*Section 1.6*)

Mass defect the loss in mass that occurs when protons and neutrons combine to form a nucleus (*Section 22.1*)

Mass number (A) the total number of protons and neutrons in an atom (*Section 2.5*)

Mass percent a unit of concentration; the mass of one component divided by the total mass of the solution times 100% (*Section 11.3*)

Mass spectrometry a technique for determining molecular mass by passing ionized molecules through a magnetic field (*Section 3.12*)

Matter a term used to describe anything that has mass (*Section 1.6*)

Melting point the temperature at which solid and liquid coexist in equilibrium (*Section 10.4*)

Mesosphere the region of the atmosphere from 50–85 km above the Earth's surface (*Section 9.9*)

Metabolism the sum of the many organic reactions that go on in cells (*Section 23.9*)

Metal complex see Coordination compound (*Section 20.5*)

Metal an element on the left side of the periodic table, bounded on the right by a zigzag line running from boron to astatine (*Section 1.4; Chapter 21*)

Metallic hydride a compound formed by reaction of lanthanide, actinide, or some *d*-block transition metals with variable amounts of hydrogen (*Section 18.5*)

Metallic solid a solid consisting of metal atoms, whose crystals have metallic properties such as electrical conductivity (*Section 10.6*)

Metalloid *see* Semimetal (*Section 1.4*)

Metallurgy the science and technology of extracting metals from their ores (*Section 21.2*)

Meter (m) the SI unit of length (*Section 1.7*)

Microgram (μg) a common unit of mass; $1\ \mu g = 0.001\ mg = 10^{-6}\ g$ (*Section 1.6*)

Micrometer (μm) a common unit of length; $1\ \mu m = 0.001\ mm = 10^{-6}\ m$ (*Section 1.7*)

Milligram (mg) a common unit of mass; $1\ mg = 0.001\ g = 10^{-6}\ kg$ (*Section 1.6*)

Milliliter (mL) a common unit of volume; $1\ mL = 1\ cm^3$ (*Section 1.9*)

Millimeter (mm)   a common unit of length; 1 mm = 0.001 m (*Section 1.7*)

Millimeter of mercury (mm Hg)   a common unit of pressure; the millimeter of mercury, also called a *torr*, is based on atmospheric pressure measurements using a mercury barometer (*Section 9.1*)

Mineral   a crystalline, inorganic constituent of the rocks that make up the Earth's crust (*Section 21.1*)

Miscible   mutually soluble in all proportions (*Section 11.4*)

Mixture   a blend of two or more substances in some arbitrary proportion (*Section 2.10*)

Molal boiling-point-elevation constant (K_b)   the amount by which the boiling point of a solvent is raised by dissolved substances (*Section 11.7*)

Molal freezing-point-depression constant (K_f)   the amount by which the melting point of a solvent is lowered by dissolved substances (*Section 11.7*)

Molality (m)   a unit of concentration; the number of moles of solute per kilogram of solvent (mol/kg) (*Section 11.3*)

Molar heat capacity (C_m)   the amount of heat necessary to raise the temperature of 1 mol of a substance 1 °C (*Section 8.7*)

Molar mass   the mass of 1 mol of substance; equal to the molecular or formula mass of the substance in grams (*Section 2.6*)

Molarity (M)   a common unit of concentration; the number of moles of solute per liter of solution (*Sections 3.6, 11.3*)

Mole (mol)   the SI unit for amount of substance; the quantity of a substance that contains as many molecules or formula units as there are atoms in exactly 12 g of carbon-12 (*Section 2.6*)

Mole fraction (X)   a unit of concentration; the number of moles of a component divided by the total number of moles in the mixture (*Sections 9.5, 11.3*)

Molecular equation   a chemical equation written using the complete formulas of reactants and products (*Section 4.3*)

Molecular formula   a formula that tells the identity and numbers of atoms in a molecule (*Section 3.10*)

Molecular mass   the sum of atomic masses of the atoms in a molecule (*Section 3.3*)

Molecular orbital theory   a quantum mechanical description of bonding in which electrons occupy molecular orbitals that belong to the entire molecule rather than to an individual atom (*Section 7.13*)

Molecular solid   a solid whose constituent particles are molecules held together by intermolecular forces (*Section 10.6*)

Molecularity   the number of molecules on the reactant side of the chemical equation for an elementary reaction (*Section 12.9*)

Molecule   the unit of matter that results when two or more atoms are joined by covalent bonds (*Section 2.10*)

Mond process   a chemical method for purification of nickel from its ore (*Section 21.2*)

Monodentate ligand   a ligand that bonds to a metal using the electron pair of a single donor atom (*Section 20.6*)

Monoprotic acid   an acid that has a single dissociable proton (*Section 4.5*)

Monosaccharide   a carbohydrate such as glucose that can't be broken down into smaller molecules by hydrolysis (*Section 23.11*)

N-Terminal amino acid   the amino acid with a free —NH_2 group on the end of a protein chain (*Section 23.10*)

n-Type semiconductor   a semiconductor doped with an impurity that has more electrons than necessary for bonding (*Section 21.5*)

Nanometer (nm)   a common unit of length; 1 nm = 10^{-9} m (*Section 1.7*)

Nanotechnology   the study and production of materials and structures that have at least one dimension between 1 nm and 100 nm (*Chapter 21 Inquiry*)

Nernst equation   an equation for calculating cell potentials under non-standard-state conditions; $E = E° - (RT \ln Q)/(nF)$ (*Section 17.6*)

Net ionic equation   a chemical equation written so that spectator ions are removed (*Section 4.3*)

Neutralization reaction   *see* Acid–base neutralization reaction (*Sections 4.5, 15.1*)

Neutron   a neutral, fundamental atomic particle in the nucleus of atoms (*Section 2.4*)

Newton (N)   the SI unit for force (*Section 9.1*)

Noble gas   an element in group 8A of the periodic table (*Sections 1.4, 6.12*)

Node   a region where a wave has zero amplitude (*Section 5.7*)

Nonelectrolyte   a substance that does not produce ions when dissolved in water (*Section 4.2*)

Nonmetal   hydrogen plus elements on the right side of the periodic table, bounded on the left by a zigzag line running from boron to astatine (*Section 1.4*)

Nonspontaneous process   a process that requires a continuous input of energy to proceed (*Section 8.13*)

Nonstoichiometric compound   a compound whose atomic composition can't be expressed as a ratio of small whole numbers (*Section 18.5*)

Normal boiling point   the temperature at which boiling occurs when there is exactly 1 atm of external pressure (*Sections 10.5, 10.11*)

Normal melting point   the temperature at which melting occurs when there is exactly 1 atm of external pressure (*Section 10.11*)

Nuclear chemistry   the study of the properties and reactions of atomic nuclei (*Section 2.7*)

Nuclear equation   an equation for a nuclear reaction in which the sums of the nucleons are the same on both sides and the sums of the charges on the nuclei and any elementary particles are the same on both sides (*Section 2.7*)

Nuclear fission   the fragmenting of heavy nuclei (*Section 22.2*)

Nuclear fusion   the joining together of light nuclei (*Section 22.2*)

Nuclear reaction   a reaction that changes an atomic nucleus (*Section 2.7*)

Nuclear transmutation   the change of one element into another by a nuclear reaction (*Section 22.3*)

Nucleic acid   a biological molecule made up of nucleotide units linked together to form a long chain (*Section 23.13*)

Nucleon   a general term for nuclear particles, both protons and neutrons (*Section 2.8*)

Nucleoside   a constituent of nucleotides; composed of an aldopentose sugar plus an amine base (*Section 23.13*)

Nucleotide   a building block from which nucleic acids are made; composed of a nucleoside plus phosphoric acid (*Section 23.13*)

Nucleus   the central core of an atom consisting of protons and neutrons (*Section 2.4*)

Octet rule   the statement that main-group elements tend to undergo reactions that leave them with eight valence electrons (*Section 6.6*)

Orbital   a solution to the Schrödinger wave equation, describing a region of space where an electron is likely to be found (*Section 5.6*)

Ore   a mineral deposit from which a metal can be produced economically (*Section 21.1*)

Organic chemistry   the study of carbon compounds (*Chapter 23*)

Osmosis   the passage of solvent through a membrane from the less concentrated side to the more concentrated side (*Section 11.8*)

Osmotic pressure   the amount of pressure necessary to cause osmosis to stop (*Section 11.8*)

Ostwald process   the commercial process for making nitric acid from ammonia (*Section 19.10*)

Overvoltage   the additional voltage required above that calculated for an electrolysis reaction (*Section 17.12*)

Oxidation   the loss of one or more electrons by a substance (*Section 4.6*)

Oxidation number   a value that measures whether an atom in a compound is neutral, electron-rich, or electron-poor compared to an isolated atom (*Section 4.6*)

Oxidation–reduction (redox) reaction   a process in which one or more electrons are transferred between reaction partners (*Section 4.6*)

Oxide   a binary compound with oxygen in the −2 oxidation state (*Section 18.9*)

Oxidizing agent   a substance that causes an oxidation by accepting an electron (*Section 4.7*)

Oxoacid   an acid that contains oxygen in addition to hydrogen and another element (*Section 4.5*)

Oxoanion   an anion of an oxoacid (*Section 2.12*)

Ozone layer   an atmospheric band stretching from about 20 to 40 km above the Earth's surface (*Section 9.9*)

p-Block element   an element in groups 3A–8A, in which *p* orbitals are filled (*Section 5.13*)

p-Type semiconductor   a semiconductor doped with an impurity that has fewer electrons than necessary for bonding (*Section 21.5*)

Paramagnetic   a substance that contains unpaired electrons and is attracted by a magnetic field (*Section 7.14*)

Parts per billion (ppb)   a concentration unit for very dilute solutions; a concentration of 1 ppb means that each kilogram of solution contains 1 μg of solute (*Section 11.3*)

Parts per million (ppm)   a concentration unit for very dilute solutions; a concentration of 1 ppm means that each kilogram of solution contains 1 mg of solute (*Section 11.3*)

Pascal (Pa)   the SI unit for pressure (*Section 9.1*)

Pauli exclusion principle   No two electrons in an atom can have the same four quantum numbers (*Section 5.9*).

Peptide bond   the amide bond linking two amino acids in a protein (*Section 23.10*)

Percent composition   a list of elements present in a compound and the mass percent of each (*Section 3.10*)

Percent dissociation   the concentration of the acid that dissociates divided by the initial concentration of the acid times 100% (*Section 14.10*)

Percent yield   the amount of product actually formed in a reaction divided by the amount theoretically possible and multiplied by 100% (*Section 3.4*)

Period   a row of elements in the periodic table (*Section 1.3*)

Periodic table   a chart of the elements arranged by increasing atomic number so that elements in a given group have similar chemical properties (*Section 1.3*)

Peroxide   a binary compound with oxygen in the −1 oxidation state (*Section 18.10*)

Petroleum   a complex mixture of organic substances, primarily hydrocarbons (*Section 8.11*)

pH   the negative base-10 logarithm of the molar hydronium ion concentration (*Section 14.5*)

pH titration curve   a plot of the pH of a solution as a function of the volume of added base or acid (*Section 15.5*)

Phase   a state of matter (*Section 10.4*)

Phase change   a process in which the physical form but not the chemical identity of a substance changes (*Section 10.4*)

Phase diagram   a plot showing the effects of pressure and temperature on the physical state of a substance (*Section 10.11*)

Photoelectric effect   the ejection of electrons from a metal on exposure to radiant energy (*Section 5.3*)

Photon   the smallest possible amount of radiant energy; a quantum (*Section 5.3*)

Photovoltaic cell   a semiconductor device that converts light into electrical energy (*Section 21.6*)

Physical property   a characteristic that can be determined without changing the chemical makeup of a sample (*Section 1.4*)

Pi (π) bond   a covalent bond formed by sideways overlap of orbitals in which shared electrons occupy a region above and below a line connecting the two nuclei (*Section 7.12*)

Picometer (pm)   a common unit of length; 1 pm = 10^{-12} m (*Section 1.7*)

Planck's constant (*h*) 6.626×10^{-34} J $\cdot$ s; a fundamental physical constant that relates energy and frequency, $E = h\nu$ (*Section 5.3*)

Polar covalent bond   a bond in which the bonding electrons are attracted somewhat more strongly by one atom than by the other (*Section 7.4*)

Polarizability   the ease with which a molecule's electron cloud can be distorted by a nearby electric field (*Section 10.2*)

Polyatomic ion   a charged, covalently bonded group of atoms (*Section 2.11*)

Polydentate ligand   a ligand that bonds to a metal through electron pairs on more than one donor atom (*Section 20.6*)

Polyprotic acid   an acid that contains more than one dissociable proton (*Section 14.11*)

Polysaccharide   a compound such as cellulose that is made of many simple sugars linked together (*Section 23.11*)

Positron emission   a nuclear reaction that converts a proton into a neutron plus an ejected positron (*Section 2.8*)

Potential energy (E_P)   energy that is stored, either in an object because of its position or in a molecule because of its chemical composition (*Section 1.11*)

Precipitation reaction   a reaction in which an insoluble solid precipitate forms and drops out of solution (*Section 4.4*)

Precision   how well a number of independent measurements agree with one another (*Section 1.12*)

Primitive-cubic unit cell   a cubic unit cell with an atom at each of its eight corners (*Section 10.8*)

Principal quantum number (*n*)   a variable in the solutions to the Schrödinger wave equation on which the size and energy level of an orbital primarily depends (*Section 5.6*)

Principal reaction   the proton-transfer reaction that proceeds farther to the right when calculating equilibrium concentrations in solutions of weak acids (*Section 14.9*)

Property   any characteristic that can be used to describe or identify matter (*Section 1.4*)

Protein a biological molecule made up of many amino acids linked together to form a long chain (*Section 23.10*)

Proton a positively charged, fundamental atomic particle in the nucleus of atoms (*Section 2.4*)

Pseudohalide an ion such as cyanide ion that behaves chemically like a halide ion (*Section 19.7*)

Qualitative analysis a procedure for identifying the ions present in an unknown solution (*Section 15.15*)

Quantized changing only in discrete amounts (*Section 5.3*)

Quantum the smallest possible amount of radiant energy (*Section 5.3*)

Quantum mechanical model a model of atomic structure that concentrates on an electron's wavelike properties (*Section 5.5*)

Quantum number a variable in solutions to the Schrödinger wave equation that describes the energy level and position in space where an electron is most likely to be found (*Section 5.6*)

Racemic mixture a 1:1 mixture of enantiomers (*Section 20.9*)

Radioactivity the spontaneous emission of radiation accompanying a nuclear reaction (*Section 2.8*)

Radiocarbon dating a technique for dating archaeological artifacts by measuring the amount of ^{14}C in the sample (*Section 22.5*)

Radioisotope a radioactive isotope (*Section 2.8*)

Raoult's law The vapor pressure of a solution containing a nonvolatile solute is equal to the vapor pressure of pure solvent times the mole fraction of the solvent (*Section 11.6*).

Rate constant the proportionality constant in a rate law (*Section 12.2*)

Rate-determining step the slowest step in a reaction mechanism (*Section 12.11*)

Rate law an equation that tells how reaction rate depends on the concentration of each reactant (*Section 12.2*)

Reaction intermediate a species that is formed in one step of a reaction mechanism and consumed in a subsequent step (*Section 12.9*)

Reaction mechanism the sequence of molecular events that defines the pathway from reactants to products (*Section 12.9*)

Reaction order the value of the exponents of concentration terms in the rate law (*Section 12.2*)

Reaction quotient (Q_c) similar to the equilibrium constant K_c except that the concentrations in the equilibrium constant expression are not necessarily equilibrium values (*Section 13.5*)

Reaction rate the increase in the concentration of a product per unit time or the decrease in the concentration of a reactant per unit time (*Section 12.1*)

Redox reaction an oxidation–reduction reaction (*Section 4.6*)

Redox titration a procedure for determining the concentration of a redox agent (*Section 4.10*)

Reducing agent a substance that causes a reduction by donating an electron (*Section 4.7*)

Reduction the gain of one or more electrons by a substance (*Section 4.6*)

Replication the process by which identical copies of DNA are made (*Section 23.13*)

Resonance hybrid an average of several valid electron-dot structures for a molecule (*Section 7.7*)

Respiration the process of breathing and using oxygen for biological redox reactions (*Section 4.11*)

Reverse osmosis the passage of solvent through a membrane from the more concentrated side to the less concentrated side (*Section 11.9*)

Ribonucleic acid (RNA) a biological polymer of ribonucleotide units that serves to transcribe the genetic information in DNA and uses that information to direct the synthesis of proteins (*Section 23.13*)

Roasting a metallurgical process that involves heating a mineral in air (*Section 21.2*)

Rounding off deleting digits to keep only the correct number of significant figures in a calculation (*Section 1.13*)

s-Block element an element in groups 1A or 2A, in which s orbitals are filled (*Section 5.13*)

Sacrificial anode an easily oxidized metal that corrodes instead of a less reactive metal to which it is connected (*Section 17.11*)

Salt an ionic compound formed in an acid–base neutralization reaction (*Section 4.1*)

Salt bridge a tube that contains a gel permeated with a solution of an inert electrolyte connecting the two sides of an electrochemical cell (*Section 17.1*)

Saponification the base-catalyzed hydrolysis of an ester to yield a carboxylic acid and an alcohol (*Section 23.8*)

Saturated hydrocarbon a hydrocarbon that contains only single bonds (*Section 23.4*)

Saturated solution a solution containing the maximum possible amount of dissolved solute at equilibrium (*Section 11.4*)

Schrödinger wave equation an equation describing the behavior of an electron in an atom (*Section 5.6*)

Scientific notation a system in which a large or small number is written as a number between 1 and 10 times a power of 10 (*Section 1.5*)

Second Law of thermodynamics In any spontaneous process, the total entropy of a system and its surroundings always increases (*Section 16.6*).

Second-order reaction a reaction whose rate depends on the concentration of a single reactant raised to the second power or on the concentrations of two different reactants, each raised to the first power (*Section 12.7*)

Semiconductor a material that has an electrical conductivity intermediate between that of a metal and that of an insulator (*Section 21.5*)

Semimetal an element adjacent to the zigzag boundary between metals and nonmetals (*Section 1.4*)

Semipermeable membrane a membrane that allows passage of water or other small molecules but not the passage of large solute molecules or ions (*Section 11.8*)

Shell a grouping of orbitals according to principal quantum number (*Section 5.6*)

Side chain the group attached to the α carbon of an amino acid (*Section 23.10*)

Sigma (σ) bond a covalent bond formed by head-on overlap of orbitals in which the shared electrons are centered about the axis between the two nuclei (*Section 7.10*)

Significant figures the total number of digits in a measurement (*Section 1.12*)

Silicate an ionic compound that contains silicon oxoanions along with cations, such as Na^+, K^+, Mg^{2+}, or Ca^{2+} (*Section 19.8*)

Simple cubic packing a packing arrangement of spheres into a primitive-cubic unit cell (*Section 10.8*)

Single bond a covalent bond formed by sharing two electrons between atoms (*Section 7.5*)

Sintering a process in which the particles of a powder are "welded" together without completely melting (*Section 21.8*)

Slag a byproduct of iron production, consisting mainly of calcium silicate (*Section 21.3*)

Solubility the amount of a substance that dissolves in a given volume of solvent at a given temperature (*Sections 4.4, 11.4*)

Solubility product (K_{sp}) the equilibrium constant for a dissolution reaction (*Section 15.10*)

Solute the dissolved substance in a solution (*Section 11.1*)

Solution a homogeneous mixture containing particles the size of a typical ion or covalent molecule (*Section 11.1*)

Solvent the major component in a solution (*Section 11.1*)

Sol–gel method a method of preparing ceramics, involving synthesis of a metal oxide powder from a metal alkoxide (*Section 21.8*)

sp Hybrid orbital a hybrid orbital formed by combination of one atomic s orbital with one p orbital (*Section 7.12*)

sp^2 Hybrid orbital a hybrid orbital formed by combination of one s and two p atomic orbitals (*Section 7.12*)

sp^3 Hybrid orbital a hybrid orbital formed by combination of one s and three p atomic orbitals (*Section 7.11*)

sp^3d^2 Hybrid orbital a hybrid orbital formed by combination of one s, three p, and two d atomic orbitals (*Section 20.11*)

Specific heat the amount of heat necessary to raise the temperature of 1 gram of a substance 1 °C (*Section 8.7*)

Spectator ion an ion that appears on both sides of the reaction arrow (*Section 4.3*)

Spectrochemical series an ordered list of ligands in which crystal field splitting increases (*Section 20.12*)

Spin quantum number (m_s) a variable that describes the spin of an electron, either +1/2 or −1/2 (*Section 5.9*)

Spontaneous process one that proceeds on its own without any continuous external influence (*Section 8.13*)

Standard cell potential ($E°$) the cell potential when both reactants and products are in their standard states (*Section 17.3*)

Standard electrode potential *see* Standard reduction potential (*Section 17.4*)

Standard enthalpy of reaction ($\Delta H°$) enthalpy change under standard-state conditions (*Section 8.6*)

Standard entropy of reaction ($\Delta S°$) the entropy change for a chemical reaction under standard-state conditions (*Section 16.5*)

Standard free-energy change ($\Delta G°$) the free-energy change that occurs when reactants in their standard states are converted to products in their standard states (*Section 16.8*)

Standard free energy of formation ($\Delta G°_f$) the free-energy change for formation of 1 mol of a substance in its standard state from the most stable form of the constituent elements in their standard states (*Section 16.9*)

Standard heat of formation ($\Delta H°_f$) the enthalpy change $\Delta H°_f$ for the hypothetical formation of 1 mol of a substance in its standard state from the most stable forms of its constituent elements in their standard states (*Section 8.9*)

Standard hydrogen electrode (S.H.E.) a reference half-cell consisting of a platinum electrode in contact with H_2 gas and aqueous H^+ ions at standard-state conditions (*Section 17.4*)

Standard molar entropy ($S°$) the entropy of 1 mol of a pure substance at 1 atm pressure and a specified temperature, usually 25 °C (*Section 16.5*)

Standard molar volume the volume of 1 mol of a gas at 0 °C and 1 atm pressure; 22.414 L (*Section 9.2*)

Standard reduction potential the standard potential for a reduction half-cell (*Section 17.4*)

Standard temperature and pressure (STP) $T = 273.15$ K; $P = 1$ atm (*Section 9.3*)

State function a function or property whose value depends only on the present condition of the system, not on the path used to arrive at that condition (*Section 8.2*)

Steam–hydrocarbon re-forming process an important industrial method for producing hydrogen from methane (*Section 18.3*)

Stereoisomers isomers that have the same connections among atoms but have a different arrangement of the atoms in space (*Section 20.8*)

Steric factor the fraction of collisions with the proper orientation for converting reactants to products (*Section 12.12*)

Stoichiometry mole/mass relationships between reactants and products (*Section 3.3*)

Straight-chain alkane an alkane that has all its carbons connected in a row (*Section 23.1*)

Stratosphere the region of the atmosphere from 20–50 km above the Earth's surface (*Section 9.9*)

Strong acid an acid that dissociates completely in water to give H^+ ions and is a strong electrolyte (*Sections 4.5, 14.2*)

Strong base a base that dissociates or reacts completely with water to give OH^- ions and is a strong electrolyte (*Sections 4.5, 14.2*)

Strong electrolyte a compound that dissociates completely into ions when dissolved in water (*Section 4.2*)

Strong-field ligand a ligand that has a large crystal field splitting (*Section 20.12*)

Structural formula a representation that shows the specific connections between atoms in a molecule (*Section 2.10*)

Sublimation the direct conversion of a solid to a vapor without going through a liquid state (*Sections 8.6, 10.4*)

Subshell a grouping of orbitals by angular-momentum quantum number (*Section 5.6*)

Subsidiary reaction any proton-transfer process other than the principal one in an acid–base reaction (*Section 14.9*)

Substitution reaction an organic reaction in which one group substitutes for another, particularly on aromatic rings (*Section 23.6*)

Substrate the compound acted on by an enzyme (*Chapter 12 Inquiry*)

Superconducting transition temperature (T_c) the temperature below which a superconductor loses all electrical resistance (*Section 21.7*)

Superconductor a material that loses all electrical resistance below a certain temperature (*Section 21.7*)

Supercritical fluid a state of matter beyond the critical point that is neither liquid nor gas (*Section 10.11*)

Superoxide a binary compound with oxygen in the −1/2 oxidation state (*Section 18.10*)

Supersaturated solution a solution containing a greater-than-equilibrium amount of solute (*Section 11.4*)

Surface tension the resistance of a liquid to spreading out and increasing its surface area (*Section 10.3*)

Suspension a homogeneous mixture containing particles greater than about 1000 nm in diameter that are visible with a low-power microscope (*Section 11.1*)

Symmetry plane a plane that cuts through an object so that one half of the object is a mirror image of the other half (*Section 20.9*)

Temperature a measure of the kinetic energy of molecular motion (*Section 8.1*)

Termolecular reaction an elementary reaction that results from collisions between three reactant molecules (*Section 12.9*)

Theory a consistent explanation of known observations (*Section 1.1*)

Thermochemistry a study of the heat changes that take place during reactions (*Chapter 8*)

Thermodynamic standard state conditions under which thermodynamic measurements are reported; 298.15 K (25 °C), 1 atm pressure for each gas, 1 M concentration for solutions (*Section 8.5*)

Thermodynamics the study of the interconversion of heat and other forms of energy (*Chapter 16*)

Thermosphere the region of the atmosphere from 85–120 km above the Earth's surface (*Section 9.9*)

Third law of thermodynamics The entropy of a perfectly ordered crystalline substance at 0 K is zero (*Section 16.4*).

Three-center, two-electron bond a covalent bond in which three atoms share two electrons (*Section 19.4*)

Titration a procedure for determining the concentration of a solution (*Section 3.9*)

Torr an alternative name for the pressure unit, millimeter of mercury (*Section 9.1*)

Trans isomer the isomer of a metal complex or alkene in which identical ligands or groups are opposite one another rather than adjacent (*Sections 20.8, 23.4*)

Transcription the process by which information in DNA is transferred to and decoded by RNA (*Section 23.13*)

Transistor a semiconductor device that controls and amplifies electrical signals (*Section 21.6*)

Transition metal element an element in the 10 groups in the middle of the periodic table (*Section 1.3; Chapter 20*)

Transition state the configuration of atoms at the maximum in the potential energy profile for a reaction (*Section 12.12*)

Translation the process by which RNA builds proteins (*Section 23.13*)

Transuranium elements the 26 artificially produced elements beyond uranium in the periodic table (*Section 22.3*)

Triacylglycerol a triester of glycerol (1,2,3-propanetriol) with three long-chain carboxylic acids (*Section 23.12*)

Triple bond a covalent bond formed by sharing six electrons between atoms (*Section 7.5*)

Triple point a unique combination of pressure and temperature at which gas, liquid, and solid phases coexist in equilibrium (*Section 10.11*)

Triprotic acid an acid that can provide three H^+ ions (*Section 4.5*)

Troposphere the region of the atmosphere from 0–20 km above the Earth's surface (*Section 9.9*)

Turnover number the number of substrate molecules acted on by one molecule of enzyme per unit time (*Chapter 12 Inquiry*)

Ultraviolet radiation electromagnetic radiation with wavelengths in the range 10–400 nm (*Section 5.1*)

Unimolecular reaction an elementary reaction that involves a single reactant molecule (*Section 12.9*)

Unit cell a small repeating unit that makes up a crystal (*Section 10.8*)

Unsaturated an organic molecule that contains a double or triple bond (*Section 23.4*)

Valence band the bonding molecular orbitals in a semiconductor (*Section 21.5*)

Valence bond theory a quantum mechanical description of bonding that pictures covalent bond formation as the overlap of two singly occupied atomic orbitals (*Section 7.10*)

Valence shell the outermost electron shell (*Section 5.13*)

Valence-shell electron-pair repulsion (VSEPR) model a model for predicting the approximate shape of a molecule (*Section 7.9*)

van der Waals equation a modification of the ideal gas law that introduces correction factors to account for the behavior of real gases (*Section 9.8*)

van der Waals forces an alternative name for intermolecular forces (*Section 10.2*)

van't Hoff factor (*i*) a measure of the extent of dissociation of a substance, used in interpreting colligative property measurements (*Section 11.6*)

Vapor pressure (P_{vap}) the partial pressure of a gas in equilibrium with liquid (*Section 10.5*)

Vaporization the change of a liquid to a gas (*Section 10.4*)

Viscosity the measure of a liquid's resistance to flow (*Section 10.3*)

Visible light electromagnetic radiation with wavelengths in the range 400–780 nm (*Section 5.1*)

Voltaic cell *see* Galvanic cell (*Section 17.1*)

Volume the amount of space occupied by an object (*Section 1.9*)

Water-gas shift reaction a method for the industrial preparation of H_2 by reaction of CO with H_2O (*Section 18.3*)

Watson–Crick model a model of DNA structure, consisting of two polynucleotide strands coiled around each other in a double helix (*Section 23.13*)

Wave function a solution to the Schrödinger wave equation (*Section 5.6*)

Wavelength (λ) the length of a wave from one maximum to the next (*Section 5.1*)

Weak acid an acid that dissociates incompletely in water and is a weak electrolyte (*Sections 4.5, 14.2*)

Weak base a base that dissociates or reacts incompletely with water and is a weak electrolyte (*Sections 4.5, 14.2*)

Weak electrolyte a compound that dissociates incompletely when dissolved in water (*Section 4.2*)

Weak-field ligand a ligand that has a small crystal field splitting (*Section 20.12*)

Work (*w*) the distance (*d*) moved times the force (*F*) that opposes the motion (*Section 8.3*)

X ray electromagnetic radiation with wavelengths in the range 0.01–10 nm (*Section 5.1*)

X-ray crystallography a technique for determining molecular structure by analysis of the diffraction pattern produced when a crystal is struck by X rays (*Section 10.7*)

Yield the amount of product formed in a reaction (*Section 3.4*)

Zeroth-order reaction one whose rate remains constant, independent of reactant concentrations (*Section 12.8*)

Zone refining a purification technique in which a heater melts a narrow zone at the top of a rod of some material and then sweeps slowly down the rod bringing impurities with it (*Section 19.8*)

Index

Photo Credits

(T) = (top); (C) = (center); (L) = (left); (R) = (right); (B) = (bottom)

Chapter 1: 1, Austin Evan, used under a Creative Commons license. *http://www.flickr.com/photos/austinevan/3316195479/*; **1 (T)**, US Department of Energy Joint Genome Institute; **1 (L)**, Sylvain Grandadam/AGE Fotostock; **1 (R)**, Holger Mette/iStockphoto; **2**, McCracken Photographer, Pearson Education; **4**, Sciencephotos/Alamy; **5 (L-R)**, Richard Megna/Fundamental Photographs; **7**, McCracken Photographers, Pearson Education; **8 (L-R)**, Richard Megna/Fundamental Photographs; **9 (TL)**, McCracken Photographers, Pearson Education; **9 (TR)**, REUTERS/China Newsphoto HAN/JJ; **9 (BL-BR)**, Richard Megna/Fundamental Photographs; **11**, Tom Krueger/iStockphoto; **12 (L)**, Mettler Toledo; **12 (R)**, OHAUS Corporation.; **12 (B)**, Dr. Tony Brain/Science Photo Library/Photo Researchers, Inc.; **14**, Richard Megna/Fundamental Photographs; **15 (L-R)**, McCracken Photographers, Pearson Education; **16 (T)**, Richard Megna/Fundamental Photographs; **16 (B)**, Christian Wilkinson /Shutterstock; **17**, iStockphoto; **18**, Dex Images/Corbis; **19**, McCracken Photographers, Pearson Education; **21**, Texas Instruments Inc.; **22**, Andy Lyons / Getty Images; **23**, Susumu Nishinaga/Photo Researchers, Inc.; **24**, Jeff Richt/Koenigsegg; **26**, Cephalon Corp.

Chapter 2: 34, Armand Photo CGI/Alamy; **35**, Richard Megna/Fundamental Photographs; **36 (L-R)**, Richard Megna/Fundamental Photographs; **37**, Richard Megna/Fundamental Photographs; **38 (T-B)**, Richard Megna/Fundamental Photographs; **39 (L-R)**, Richard Megna/Fundamental Photographs; **42**, James Montgomery/JAI/AGE Fotostock; **45**, Vladimir Chistyakov/AP Wide World Photos; **47**, Richard Megna/Fundamental Photographs; **51**, National Cancer Institute; **55 (T)**, Tom Till/Alamy; **55 (B)**, Bettmann/Corbis; **59 (T)**, Richard Megna/Fundamental Photographs; **59 (B)**, Eric Schrader, Pearson Science; **60**, Karel Gallas/Shutterstock; **62**, Richard Megna/Fundamental Photographs; **67 (T)**, NASA/Marshall Space Flight Center; **67 (B)**, NASA/Space Telescope Science Institute/ESA.

Chapter 3: 74, John Gillmoure/Corbis; **76**, Gregg Adams Photography; **77**, Corbis Royalty Free; **79**, AP Photo/Anja Niedringhaus; **82**, Sergio Piumatti; **88 (L-R)**, Richard Megna/Fundamental Photographs; **90**, Paul Silverman/Fundamental Photographs; **91 (L-R)**, Richard Megna/Fundamental Photographs; **92**, Paul Silverman/Fundamental Photographs; **93 (L-R)**, Richard Megna/Fundamental Photographs; **102 (T)**, Library of Congress; **102 (B)**, Science Photo Library/Photo Researchers, Inc.

Chapter 4: 112, Bildagentur RM/Tips Italia/Photolibrary; **113**, McCracken Photographers, Pearson Education; **114 (L-R)**, Richard Megna/Fundamental Photographs; **117**, Richard Megna/Fundamental Photographs; **118**, McCracken Photographers, Pearson Education; **121**, McCracken Photographers, Pearson Education; **124 (L)**, McCracken Photographers, Pearson Education; **124 (C)**, Richard Megna/Fundamental Photographs; **124 (R)**, McCracken Photographers, Pearson Education; **127**, Picture Desk, Inc./Kobal Collection; **129 (L-R)**, McCracken Photographers, Pearson Education; **131 (L-R)**, Kip Peticolas & Richard Megna/Fundamental Photographs; **133 (L-R)**, Richard Megna/Fundamental Photographs; **137 (L-R)**, McCracken Photographers, Pearson Education; **138**, Paul Silverman/Fundamental Photographs; **139**, Jeff Gentner/Stringer/Getty Images; **141**, iStockphoto.

Chapter 5: 150, Pfeiffer; J/ARCO/AGE Fotostock; **152**, Phillip Long/Getty Images - Stone Allstock; **153**, Richard Cummins/Corbis; **154 (CL)**, Pictor/ ImageState Media Partners Limited; **154 (CR)**, Karin Lau/Shutterstock; **154 (BL-BR)**, Debra Crowe; **157**, Jens Johnson; **158**, iStockphoto; **161**, Alan Sailer/Flickr RM/Getty Images; **165**, Richard Megna/Fundamental Photographs; **179 (T)**, Andre Thijssen/Photolibrary; **179 (B)**, General Electric Corporate Research & Development Center.

Chapter 6: 186, Travel Ink/Getty Images; **203**, Richard Megna/Fundamental Photographs; **204 (L-R)**, Richard Megna/Fundamental Photographs; **205 (L-R)**, Richard Megna/Fundamental Photographs; **206**, Richard Megna/ Fundamental Photographs; **207**, iStockphoto; **208**, Llinos Mair Pritchard/ Alamy; **209**, AP Photo/Sakchai Lalit.

Chapter 7: 216, FA/COLOR CHINA PHOTO/SIPA Press; **219**, McCracken Photographers, Pearson Education; **253**, McCracken Photographers, Pearson Education; **256**, Jaimie D. Travis/iStockphoto; **257 (L)**, iStockphoto; **257 (R)**, pixelman/Shutterstock.

Chapter 8: 266, Frank Lane Picture Agency; **270**, iStockphoto; **270**, Dorian Hanner; **273**, mtr/Shutterstock; **276 (T)**, Mikko Pitkanen/Shutterstock; **276 (C)**, luchschen/Shutterstock; **276 (B)**, Ezio Geneletti/Stone/Getty Images; **277**, Richard Megna/Fundamental Photographs; **280**, John McMurry; **281**, McCracken Photographers, Pearson Education; **285**, Fred Lyon/Fred Lyon Pictures; **287**, iStockphoto; **289**, Rob Belknap/iStockphoto; **290**, iStockphoto; **291**, World Pictures/Alamy; **292 (L)**, Mikko Pitkanen/Shutterstock; **292 (C)**, luchschen/Shutterstock; **292 (R)**, Ezio Geneletti/ Stone/Getty Images; **294 (L-R)**, iStockphoto; **297**, iStockphoto.

Chapter 9: 308, Chuck Pelfley/Photolibrary; **309**, Shutterstock; **310**, NASA; **312**, Pichugin Dmitry/Shutterstock; **314**, Leapingllamas via Flickr, used under a Creative Commons license *http://creativecommons.org/licenses/by/2.0/ deed.en*; **316**, iStockphoto; **320**, Paulo Resende/Shutterstock; **321**, Donald Johnston/Getty Images - Stone Allstock; **323**, Eric Schrader, Pearson Science; **325**, David B. Fleetman/SeaPics.com; **330**, U.S. Department of Energy/Photo Researchers, Inc.; **333 (T)**, Niilo Tippler/iStockphoto; **333 (B)**, Richard Megna/Fundamental Photographs; **334 (B)**, NASA; **336**, Charlotte Zeepvat.

Chapter 10: 346, Jeff Foott/Discovery Channel Images/Getty Images; **351**, David Taylor/Science Photo Library/Photo Researchers, Inc.; **355**, Bronwyn Photo/Shutterstock; **357 (R)**, Alexel Zaycev/iStockphoto; **357 (L)**, Harry Taylor, © Dorling Kindersley, Natural History Museum, London; **359**, Alamy Images Royalty Free; **360**, AP Photo; **362**, Richard Megna/Fundamental Photographs; **364**, Richard Megna/Fundamental Photographs; **366 (L)**, Jeffrey A. Scovil Photography; **366 (R)**, Ryan McVay/Getty Images - Photodisc./Royalty Free; **368**, Pearson Education/PH College; **371**, Yenwen Lu/iStockphoto; **372**, iStockphoto; **378**, General Electric Corporate Research & Development Center; **380 (T)**, Linda Whitwam, © Dorling Kindersley; **380 (B)**, Richard Megna/Fundamental Photographs; **382**, Paul Silverman/Fundamental Photographs; **383**, BASF/Fundamental Photographs.

Useful Conversion Factors and Relationships

Length

SI unit: meter (m)

$1 \text{ km} = 10^3 \text{ m} = 0.621\,37 \text{ mi}$

$1 \text{ mi} = 5280 \text{ ft} = 1760 \text{ yd} = 1.6093 \text{ km}$

$1 \text{ m} = 10^2 \text{ cm} = 1.0936 \text{ yd}$

$1 \text{ in.} = 2.54 \text{ cm (exactly)}$

$1 \text{ cm} = 0.393\,70 \text{ in.}$

$1 \text{ Å} = 10^{-10} \text{ m} = 100 \text{ pm}$

Mass

SI unit: kilogram (kg)

$1 \text{ kg} = 10^3 \text{ g} = 2.2046 \text{ lb}$

$1 \text{ lb} = 16 \text{ oz} = 453.59 \text{ g}$

$1 \text{ oz} = 28.35 \text{ g}$

$1 \text{ ton} = 2000 \text{ lb} = 907.185 \text{ kg}$

$1 \text{ metric ton} = 10^3 \text{ kg} = 1.102 \text{ tons}$

$1 \text{ amu} = 1.660\,54 \times 10^{-27} \text{ kg}$

Temperature

SI unit: kelvin (K)

$0 \text{ K} = -273.15 \text{ °C} = -459.67 \text{ °F}$

$\text{K} = \text{°C} + 273.15$

$\text{°C} = \dfrac{5}{9}(\text{°F} - 32)$

$\text{°F} = \dfrac{9}{5}(\text{°C}) + 32$

Energy (derived)

SI unit: joule (J)

$1 \text{ J} = 1 \text{ (kg} \cdot \text{m}^2)/\text{s}^2 = 0.239\,01 \text{ cal}$

$\quad = 1 \text{ C} \times 1 \text{ V}$

$1 \text{ cal} = 4.184 \text{ J (exactly)}$

$1 \text{ eV} = 1.602\,176 \times 10^{-19} \text{ J}$

$1 \text{ MeV} = 1.602\,176 \times 10^{-13} \text{ J}$

$1 \text{ kWh} = 3.600 \times 10^6 \text{ J}$

$1 \text{ Btu} = 1055 \text{ J}$

Pressure (derived)

SI unit: pascal (Pa)

$1 \text{ Pa} = 1 \text{ N/m}^2 = 1 \text{ kg}/(\text{m} \cdot \text{s}^2)$

$1 \text{ atm} = 101{,}325 \text{ Pa} = 1.013\,25 \text{ bar}$

$\quad = 760 \text{ mm Hg (torr)}$

$\quad = 14.70 \text{ lb/in.}^2$

$1 \text{ bar} = 10^5 \text{ Pa}$

Volume (derived)

SI unit: cubic meter (m³)

$1 \text{ L} = 10^{-3} \text{ m}^3 = 1 \text{ dm}^3 = 10^3 \text{ cm}^3$

$\quad = 1.0567 \text{ qt}$

$1 \text{ gal} = 4 \text{ qt} = 3.7854 \text{ L}$

$1 \text{ cm}^3 = 1 \text{ mL}$

$1 \text{ in.}^3 = 16.4 \text{ cm}^3$

Fundamental Constants

Atomic mass unit	1 amu	$= 1.660\,539 \times 10^{-27} \text{ kg}$
	1 g	$= 6.022\,142 \times 10^{23} \text{ amu}$
Avogadro's number	N_A	$= 6.022\,142 \times 10^{23}/\text{mol}$
Boltzmann's constant	k	$= 1.380\,650 \times 10^{-23} \text{ J/K}$
Electron charge	$-e$	$= -1.602\,176 \times 10^{-19} \text{ C}$
Electron charge-to-mass ratio	$-e/m_e$	$= -1.758\,820 \times 10^{11} \text{ C/kg}$
Electron mass	m_e	$= 5.485\,799 \times 10^{-4} \text{ amu}$
		$= 9.109\,382 \times 10^{-31} \text{ kg}$
Elementary charge	e	$= 1.602\,176 \times 10^{-19} \text{ C}$
Faraday's constant	F	$= 9.648\,534 \times 10^4 \text{ C/mol}$
Gas constant	R	$= 8.314\,472 \text{ J/(mol} \cdot \text{K)}$
		$= 0.082\,0582 \text{ (L} \cdot \text{atm)/(mol} \cdot \text{K)}$
Neutron mass	m_n	$= 1.008\,665 \text{ amu}$
		$= 1.674\,927 \times 10^{-27} \text{ kg}$
Pi	π	$= 3.141\,592\,6536$
Planck's constant	h	$= 6.626\,069 \times 10^{-34} \text{ J} \cdot \text{s}$
Proton mass	m_p	$= 1.007\,276 \text{ amu}$
		$= 1.672\,622 \times 10^{-27} \text{ kg}$
Rydberg constant	R_∞	$= 1.097\,373 \times 10^7/\text{m}$
Speed of light	c	$= 2.997\,924\,58 \times 10^8 \text{ m/s}$